Robert Lee Marlin Jr.

HA232
Math Dept NCSU

Real and Complex Analysis

McGRAW-HILL SERIES IN HIGHER MATHEMATICS

E. H. Spanier | ***Consulting Editor***

Auslander and MacKenzie | Introduction to Differentiable Manifolds
Curry | Foundations of Mathematical Logic
Goldberg | Unbounded Linear Operators
Guggenheimer | Differential Geometry
Rogers | Theory of Recursive Functions and Effective Computability
Rudin | Real and Complex Analysis
Spanier | Algebraic Topology
Valentine | Convex Sets

Real and Complex Analysis

Walter Rudin

Professor of Mathematics
University of Wisconsin

McGraw-Hill Book Company

New York St. Louis
San Francisco Toronto
London Sydney

Real and Complex Analysis

 Library of Congress Catalog Card Number 65-27982

54232

7 8 9 10 11 12 – MAMM – 7 5 4 3 2 1 0

Preface

In this book I present an analysis course which I have taught to first-year graduate students at the University of Wisconsin since 1962.

The course was developed for two reasons. The first was a belief that one could present the basic techniques and theorems of analysis in one year, with enough applications to make the subject interesting, in such a way that students could then specialize in any direction they choose.

The second and perhaps even more important one was the desire to do away with the outmoded and misleading idea that analysis consists of two distinct halves, "real variables" and "complex variables." Traditionally (with some oversimplification) the first of these deals with Lebesgue integration, with various types of convergence, and with the pathologies exhibited by very discontinuous functions; whereas the second one concerns itself only with those functions that are as smooth as can be, namely, the holomorphic ones. That these two areas interact most intimately has of course been well known for at least 60 years and is evident to anyone who is acquainted with current research. Nevertheless, the standard curriculum in most American universities still contains a year course in complex variables, followed by a year course in real variables, and usually neither of these courses acknowledges the existence of the subject matter of the other.

I have made an effort to demonstrate the interplay among the various parts of analysis, including some of the basic ideas from functional analysis. Here are a few examples. The Riesz representation theorem and the Hahn-Banach theorem allow one to "guess" the Poisson integral formula. They team up in the proof of Runge's theorem, from which the homology version of Cauchy's theorem follows easily. They combine with Blaschke's theorem on the zeros of bounded holomorphic functions to give a proof of the Müntz-Szasz theorem, which concerns approximation on an interval. The fact that L^2 is a Hilbert space is used in the proof of the Radon-Nikodym theorem, which leads to the theorem about differentiation of indefinite integrals (incidentally, differentiation seems to be unduly slighted in most modern texts), which in turn yields the existence of radial limits of bounded harmonic functions. The theorems of Plancherel and Cauchy combined give a theorem of Paley and Wiener which, in turn, is used in the Denjoy-Carleman theorem about infinitely differentiable functions on the real line. The maximum modulus theorem gives information about linear transformations on L^p-spaces.

Since most of the results presented here are quite classical (the novelty lies in the arrangement, and some of the proofs are new), I have not attempted to document the source of every item. References are gathered at the end, in Notes and Comments. They are not always to the original sources, but more often to more recent works where further references can be found. In no case does the absence of a reference imply any claim to originality on my part.

The prerequisite for this book is a good course in advanced calculus (set-theoretic manipulations, metric spaces, uniform continuity, and uniform convergence). The first seven chapters of my earlier book "Principles of Mathematical Analysis" furnish sufficient preparation.

Chapters 1 to 8 and 10 to 15 should be taken up in the order in which they are presented. Chapter 9 is not referred to again until Chapter 19. The last five chapters are quite independent of each other, and probably not all of them should be taken up in any one year. There are over 350 problems, some quite easy, some more challenging. About half of these have been assigned to my classes at various times.

The students' response to this course has been most gratifying, and I have profited much from some of their comments. Notes taken by Aaron Strauss and Stephen Fisher helped me greatly in the writing of the final manuscript. The text contains a number of improvements which were suggested by Howard Conner, Simon Hellerstein, Marvin Knopp, and E. L. Stout. It is a pleasure to express my sincere thanks to them for their generous assistance.

Walter Rudin

Contents

Chapter 14 | Conformal Mapping, 268

Chapter 15 | Zeros of Holomorphic Functions, 290

Chapter 16 | Analytic Continuation, 312

Chapter 17 | H^p-Spaces, 328

Chapter 18 | Elementary Theory of Banach Algebras, 351

Prologue

The Exponential Function

This is undoubtedly the most important function in mathematics. It is defined, for every complex number z, by the formula

$$\text{(1)} \qquad \exp(z) = \sum_{n=0}^{\infty} \frac{z^n}{n!}.$$

The series (1) converges absolutely for every z and converges uniformly on every bounded subset of the complex plane. Thus exp is a continuous function. The absolute convergence of (1) shows that the computation

$$\sum_{k=0}^{\infty} \frac{a^k}{k!} \sum_{m=0}^{\infty} \frac{b^m}{m!} = \sum_{n=0}^{\infty} \frac{1}{n!} \sum_{k=0}^{n} \frac{n!}{k!(n-k)!} a^k b^{n-k} = \sum_{n=0}^{\infty} \frac{(a+b)^n}{n!}$$

is correct. It gives the important addition formula

$$\text{(2)} \qquad \exp(a) \exp(b) = \exp(a+b),$$

valid for all complex numbers a and b.

We define the number e to be exp (1), and shall usually replace exp (z) by the customary shorter expression e^z. Note that $e^0 = \exp(0) = 1$, by (1).

Theorem

(*a*) *For every complex z we have $e^z \neq 0$.*
(*b*) exp *is its own derivative:* $\exp'(z) = \exp(z)$.
(*c*) *The restriction of* exp *to the real axis is a monotonically increasing positive function, and*

$$e^x \to \infty \textit{ as } x \to \infty, \qquad e^x \to 0 \textit{ as } x \to -\infty.$$

(*d*) *There exists a positive number* π *such that* $e^{\pi i/2} = i$ *and such that* $e^z = 1$ *if and only if* $z/(2\pi i)$ *is an integer.*
(*e*) exp *is a periodic function, with period* $2\pi i$.
(*f*) *The mapping* $t \to e^{it}$ *maps the real axis onto the unit circle.*
(*g*) *If* w *is a complex number and* $w \neq 0$, *then* $w = e^z$ *for some* z.

PROOF By (2), $e^z \cdot e^{-z} = e^{z-z} = e^0 = 1$. This implies (*a*). Next,

$$\exp'(z) = \lim_{h\to 0} \frac{\exp(z+h) - \exp(z)}{h} = \exp(z) \lim_{h\to 0} \frac{\exp(h) - 1}{h} = \exp(z).$$

The first of the above equalities is a matter of definition, the second follows from (2), and the third from (1), and (*b*) is proved.

That exp is monotonically increasing on the positive real axis, and that $e^x \to \infty$ as $x \to \infty$, is clear from (1). The other assertions of (*c*) are consequences of $e^x \cdot e^{-x} = 1$.

For any real number t, (1) shows that e^{-it} is the complex conjugate of e^{it}. Thus

$$|e^{it}|^2 = e^{it} \cdot \overline{e^{it}} = e^{it} \cdot e^{-it} = e^{it-it} = e^0 = 1,$$

or

(3) $$|e^{it}| = 1 \qquad (t \text{ real}).$$

In other words, if t is real, e^{it} lies on the unit circle. We define $\cos t$, $\sin t$ to be the real and imaginary parts of e^{it}:

(4) $$\cos t = \operatorname{Re}[e^{it}], \qquad \sin t = \operatorname{Im}[e^{it}] \qquad (t \text{ real}).$$

If we differentiate both sides of Euler's identity

(5) $$e^{it} = \cos t + i \sin t,$$

which is equivalent to (4), and if we apply (*b*), we obtain

$$\cos' t + i \sin' t = ie^{it} = -\sin t + i \cos t,$$

so that

(6) $$\cos' = -\sin, \qquad \sin' = \cos.$$

The power series (1) yields the representation

(7) $$\cos t = 1 - \frac{t^2}{2!} + \frac{t^4}{4!} - \frac{t^6}{6!} + \cdots.$$

Take $t = 2$. The terms of the series (7) then decrease in absolute value (except for the first one) and their signs alternate. Hence $\cos 2$ is less than the sum of the first three terms of (7), with $t = 2$; thus $\cos 2 < -\frac{1}{3}$. Since $\cos 0 = 1$ and cos is a continuous real function on the real axis, we conclude that there is a smallest positive number t_0 for which $\cos t_0 = 0$. We define

$$\pi = 2t_0. \tag{8}$$

It follows from (3) and (5) that $\sin t_0 = \pm 1$. Since

$$\sin' (t) = \cos t > 0$$

on the segment $(0,t_0)$ and since $\sin 0 = 0$, we have $\sin t_0 > 0$, hence $\sin t_0 = 1$, and therefore

$$e^{\pi i/2} = i. \tag{9}$$

It follows that $e^{\pi i} = i^2 = -1$, $e^{2\pi i} = (-1)^2 = 1$, and then $e^{2\pi i n} = 1$ for every integer n. Also, (*e*) follows immediately:

$$e^{z+2\pi i} = e^z e^{2\pi i} = e^z. \tag{10}$$

If $z = x + iy$, x and y real, then $e^z = e^x e^{iy}$; hence $|e^z| = e^x$. If $e^z = 1$, we therefore must have $e^x = 1$, so that $x = 0$; to prove that $y/2\pi$ must be an integer, it is enough to show that $e^{iy} \neq 1$ if $0 < y < 2\pi$, by (10).

Suppose $0 < y < 2\pi$, and

$$e^{iy/4} = u + iv \qquad (u \text{ and } v \text{ real}). \tag{11}$$

Since $0 < y/4 < \pi/2$, we have $u > 0$ and $v > 0$. Also

$$e^{iy} = (u + iv)^4 = u^4 - 6u^2v^2 + v^4 + 4iuv(u^2 - v^2). \tag{12}$$

The right side of (12) is real only if $u^2 = v^2$; since $u^2 + v^2 = 1$, this happens only when $u^2 = v^2 = \frac{1}{2}$, and then (12) shows that

$$e^{iy} = -1 \neq 1.$$

This completes the proof of (*d*).

We already know that $t \to e^{it}$ maps the real axis *into* the unit circle. To prove (*f*), fix w so that $|w| = 1$; we shall show that $w = e^{it}$ for some real t. Write $w = u + iv$, u and v real, and suppose first that $u \geq 0$ and $v \geq 0$. Since $u \leq 1$, the definition of π shows that there exists a t, $0 \leq t \leq \pi/2$, such that $\cos t = u$; then $\sin^2 t = 1 - u^2 = v^2$, and since $\sin t \geq 0$ if $0 \leq t \leq \pi/2$, we have $\sin t = v$. Thus $w = e^{it}$.

If $u < 0$ and $v \geq 0$, the preceding conditions are satisfied by $-iw$. Hence $-iw = e^{it}$ for some real t, and $w = e^{i(t+\pi/2)}$. Finally, if $v < 0$, the preceding two cases show that $-w = e^{it}$ for some real t, hence $w = e^{i(t+\pi)}$. This completes the proof of (*f*).

If $w \neq 0$, put $\alpha = w/|w|$. Then $w = |w|\alpha$. By (*c*), there is a real x such that $|w| = e^x$. Since $|\alpha| = 1$, (*f*) shows that $\alpha = e^{iy}$ for some real y. Hence $w = e^{x+iy}$. This proves (g) and completes the theorem.

We shall encounter the integral of $(1 + x^2)^{-1}$ over the real line. To evaluate it, put $\varphi(t) = \sin t/\cos t$ in $(-\pi/2,\pi/2)$. By (6), $\varphi' = 1 + \varphi^2$. Hence φ is a monotonically increasing mapping of $(-\pi/2,\pi/2)$ onto $(-\infty,\infty)$, and we obtain

$$\int_{-\infty}^{\infty} \frac{dx}{1 + x^2} = \int_{-\pi/2}^{\pi/2} \frac{\varphi'(t)\, dt}{1 + \varphi^2(t)} = \int_{-\pi/2}^{\pi/2} dt = \pi.$$

1

Abstract Integration

Toward the end of the nineteenth century it became clear to many mathematicians that the Riemann integral (about which one learns in calculus courses) should be replaced by some other type of integral, more general and more flexible, better suited for dealing with limit processes. Among the attempts made in this direction, the most notable ones were due to Jordan, Borel, W. H. Young, and Lebesgue. It was Lebesgue's construction which turned out to be the most successful.

In brief outline, here is the main idea: The Riemann integral of a function f over an interval $[a,b]$ can be approximated by sums of the form

$$\sum_{i=1}^{n} f(t_i)m(E_i)$$

where $E_1, \ldots, E_n$ are disjoint intervals whose union is $[a,b]$, $m(E_i)$ denotes the length of E_i, and $t_i \in E_i$ for $n = 1, \ldots, n$. Lebesgue discovered that a completely satisfactory theory of integration results if the sets E_i in the above sum are allowed to belong to a larger class of subsets of the line, the so-called "measurable sets," and if the class of functions under consideration is enlarged to what he called "measurable functions." The crucial set-theoretic properties involved are the following: The union and the intersection of any countable family of measurable sets are measurable; so is the complement of every measurable set; and, most important, the notion of "length" (now called "measure") can be extended to them in such a way that

$$m(E_1 \cup E_2 \cup E_3 \cup \cdots) = m(E_1) + m(E_2) + m(E_3) + \cdots$$

for every countable collection $\{E_i\}$ of pairwise disjoint measurable sets. This property of m is called *countable additivity.*

The passage from Riemann's theory of integration to that of Lebesgue is a process of completion (in a sense which will appear more precisely later). It is of the same fundamental importance in analysis as is the construction of the real number system from the rationals.

The above-mentioned measure m is of course intimately related to the geometry of the real line. In this chapter we shall present an abstract (axiomatic) version of the Lebesgue integral, relative to *any* countably additive measure on *any* set. (The precise definitions follow.) This abstract theory is not in any way more difficult than the special case of the real line; it shows that a large part of integration theory is independent of any geometry (or topology) of the underlying space; and, of course, it gives us a tool of much wider applicability. The existence of a large class of measures, among them that of Lebesgue, will be established in Chap. 2.

Set-theoretic Notations and Terminology

1.1 Some sets can be described by listing their members. Thus $\{x_1, \ldots, x_n\}$ is the set whose members are $x_1, \ldots, x_n$; and $\{x\}$ is the set whose only member is x. More often, sets are described by properties. We write

$$\{x: P\}$$

for the set of all elements x which have the property P. The symbol $\varnothing$ denotes the empty set. The words *collection, family,* and *class* will be used synonymously with *set.*

We write $x \in A$ if x is a member of the set A; otherwise $x \notin A$. If B is a subset of A, i.e., if $x \in B$ implies $x \in A$, we write $B \subset A$. If $B \subset A$ and $A \subset B$, then $A = B$. If $B \subset A$ and $A \neq B$, B is a *proper* subset of A. Note that $\varnothing \subset A$ for every set A.

$A \cup B$ and $A \cap B$ are the union and intersection of A and B, respectively. If $\{A_\alpha\}$ is a collection of sets, where α runs through some index set I, we write

$$\bigcup_{\alpha \in I} A_\alpha \quad \text{and} \quad \bigcap_{\alpha \in I} A_\alpha$$

for the union and intersection of $\{A_\alpha\}$:

$$\bigcup_{\alpha \in I} A_\alpha = \{x: x \in A_\alpha \text{ for at least one } \alpha \in I\}$$

$$\bigcap_{\alpha \in I} A_\alpha = \{x: x \in A_\alpha \text{ for every } \alpha \in I\}.$$

If I is the set of all positive integers, the customary notations are

$$\bigcup_{n=1}^{\infty} A_n \quad \text{and} \quad \bigcap_{n=1}^{\infty} A_n.$$

If no two members of $\{A_\alpha\}$ have an element in common, then $\{A_\alpha\}$ is a *disjoint collection* of sets.

We write $A - B = \{x: x \in A, x \notin B\}$, and denote the complement of A by A^c whenever it is clear from the context with respect to which larger set the complement is taken.

The *cartesian product* $A_1 \times \cdots \times A_n$ of the sets $A_1, \ldots, A_n$ is the set of all ordered n-tuples $(a_1, \ldots, a_n)$ where $a_i \in A_i$ for $1 = 1, \ldots, n$.

The *real line* (or real number system) is R^1, and

$$R^k = R^1 \times \cdots \times R^1 \qquad (k \text{ factors}).$$

The *extended real number system* is R^1 with two symbols, ∞ and $-\infty$, adjoined, and with the obvious ordering. If $-\infty \leq a \leq b \leq \infty$, the *interval* $[a,b]$ and the *segment* (a,b) are defined to be

$$[a,b] = \{x: a \leq x \leq b\}, \qquad (a,b) = \{x: a < x < b\}.$$

We also write

$$[a,b) = \{x: a \leq x < b\}, \qquad (a,b] = \{x: a < x \leq b\}.$$

If $E \subset [-\infty, \infty]$ and $E \neq \emptyset$, the least upper bound (supremum) and greatest lower bound (infimum) of E exist in $[-\infty, \infty]$ and are denoted by $\sup E$ and $\inf E$.

Sometimes (but only when $\sup E \in E$) we write $\max E$ for $\sup E$.

The symbol

$$f: X \to Y$$

means that f is a *function* (or *mapping* or *transformation*) of the set X into the set Y; i.e., f assigns to each $x \in X$ an element $f(x) \in Y$. If $A \subset X$ and $B \subset Y$, the *image* of A and the *inverse image* (or pre-image) of B are

$$f(A) = \{y: y = f(x) \text{ for some } x \in A\},$$

$$f^{-1}(B) = \{x: f(x) \in B\}.$$

Note that $f^{-1}(B)$ may be empty although $B \neq \emptyset$.

The *domain* of f is X. The *range* of f is $f(X)$.

If $f(X) = Y$, f is said to map X *onto* Y.

We write $f^{-1}(y)$, instead of $f^{-1}(\{y\})$, for every $y \in Y$. If $f^{-1}(y)$ consists of at most one point, for each $y \in Y$, f is said to be *one-to-one*. If f is one-to-one, then f^{-1} is a function with domain $f(X)$ and range X.

If $f: X \to [-\infty, \infty]$ and $E \subset X$, it is customary to write $\sup_{x \in E} f(x)$ rather than $\sup f(E)$.

If $f: X \to Y$ and $g: Y \to Z$, the composite function $g \circ f: X \to Z$ is defined by the formula

$$(g \circ f)(x) = g(f(x)) \qquad (x \in X).$$

The Concept of Measurability

The class of measurable functions plays a fundamental role in integration theory. It has some basic properties in common with another most important class of functions, namely, the continuous ones. It is helpful to keep these similarities in mind. Our presentation is therefore organized in such a way that the analogies between the concepts *topological space, open set,* and *continuous function,* on the one hand, and *measurable space, measurable set,* and *measurable function,* on the other, are strongly emphasized. It seems that the relations between these concepts emerge most clearly when the setting is quite abstract, and this (rather than a desire for mere generality) motivates our approach to the subject.

1.2 Definition

(*a*) A collection τ of subsets of a set X is said to be a *topology in X* if τ has the following three properties:

(i) $\varnothing \in \tau$ and $X \in \tau$.
(ii) If $V_i \in \tau$ for $i = 1, \ldots, n$, then $V_1 \cap V_2 \cap \cdots \cap V_n \in \tau$.
(iii) If $\{V_\alpha\}$ is an arbitrary collection of members of τ (finite, countable, or uncountable), then $\bigcup_\alpha V_\alpha \in \tau$.

(*b*) If τ is a topology in X, then X is called a *topological space,* and the members of τ are called the *open sets* in X.

(*c*) If X and Y are topological spaces and if f is a mapping of X into Y, then f is said to be *continuous* provided that $f^{-1}(V)$ is an open set in X for every open set V in Y.

1.3 Definition

(*a*) A collection $\mathfrak{M}$ of subsets of a set X is said to be a *σ-algebra in X* if $\mathfrak{M}$ has the following three properties:

(i) $X \in \mathfrak{M}$.
(ii) If $A \in \mathfrak{M}$, then $A^c \in \mathfrak{M}$, where A^c is the complement of A relative to X.
(iii) If $A = \bigcup_{n=1}^{\infty} A_n$ and if $A_n \in \mathfrak{M}$ for $n = 1, 2, 3, \ldots$, then $A \in \mathfrak{M}$.

(*b*) If $\mathfrak{M}$ is a σ-algebra in X, then X is called a *measurable space,* and the members of $\mathfrak{M}$ are called the *measurable sets* in X.

(*c*) If X is a measurable space, Y is a topological space, and f is a mapping of X into Y, then f is said to be *measurable* provided that $f^{-1}(V)$ is a measurable set in X for every open set V in Y.

It would perhaps be more satisfactory to apply the term "measurable space" to the ordered pair $(X,\mathfrak{M})$, rather than to X. After all, X is a set, and X has not been changed in any way by the fact that we now also have a σ-algebra of its subsets in mind. Similarly, a topological space is an ordered pair (X,τ). But if this sort of thing were systematically done in all mathematics, the terminology would become awfully cumbersome. We shall discuss this again at somewhat greater length in Sec. 1.21.

1.4 Comments on Definition 1.2 The most familiar topological spaces are the *metric spaces*. We shall assume some familiarity with metric spaces but shall give the basic definitions, for the sake of completeness.

A *metric space* is a set X in which a *distance function* (or *metric*) ρ is defined, with the following properties:

(*a*) $0 \leq \rho(x,y) < \infty$ for all x and $y \in X$.
(*b*) $\rho(x,y) = 0$ if and only if $x = y$.
(*c*) $\rho(x,y) = \rho(y,x)$ for all x and $y \in X$.
(*d*) $\rho(x,y) \leq \rho(x,z) + \rho(z,y)$ for all x, y, and $z \in X$.

Property (*d*) is called the *triangle inequality*.

If $x \in X$ and $r \geq 0$, the *open ball* with center at x and radius r is the set $\{y \in X : \rho(x,y) < r\}$.

If X is a metric space and if τ is the collection of all sets $E \subset X$ which are arbitrary unions of open balls, then τ is a topology in X. This is not hard to verify; the intersection property depends on the fact that if $x \in B_1 \cap B_2$, where B_1 and B_2 are open balls, then x is the center of an open ball $B \subset B_1 \cap B_2$. We leave this as an exercise.

For instance, in the real line R^1 a set is open if and only if it is a union of open segments (a,b). In the plane R^2, the open sets are those which are unions of open circular discs.

Another topological space, which we shall encounter frequently, is the extended real line $[-\infty,\infty]$; its topology is defined by declaring the following sets to be open: (a,b), $[-\infty,a)$, $(a,\infty]$, and any union of segments of this type.

The definition of continuity given in Sec. 1.2(*c*) is a global one. Frequently it is desirable to define continuity locally: A mapping f of X into Y is said to be *continuous at the point* $x_0 \in X$ if to every neighborhood V of $f(x_0)$ there corresponds a neighborhood W of x_0 such that $f(W) \subset V$.

(A *neighborhood* of a point x is, by definition, an open set which contains x.)

For metric spaces, this local definition is of course the same as the usual epsilon-delta definition.

The following easy proposition relates the two definitions of continuity in the expected manner:

1.5 Proposition *Let X and Y be topological spaces. A mapping f of X into Y is continuous if and only if f is continuous at every point of X.*

PROOF If f is continuous and $x_0 \in X$, then $f^{-1}(V)$ is a neighborhood of x_0, for every neighborhood V of $f(x_0)$. Since $f(f^{-1}(V)) \subset V$, it follows that f is continuous at x_0.

If f is continuous at every point of X and if V is open in Y, every point $x \in f^{-1}(V)$ has a neighborhood W_x such that $f(W_x) \subset V$. Hence $W_x \subset f^{-1}(V)$. It follows that $f^{-1}(V)$ is the union of the open sets W_x, so $f^{-1}(V)$ is itself open. Thus f is continuous.

1.6 Comments on Definition 1.3 Let $\mathfrak{M}$ be a σ-algebra in a set X. Referring to Properties (i) to (iii) of Definition 1.3(a), we immediately derive the following:

(a) Since $\varnothing = X^c$, (i) and (ii) imply that $\varnothing \in \mathfrak{M}$.

(b) Taking $A_{n+1} = A_{n+2} = \cdots = \varnothing$ in (iii), we see that $A_1 \cup A_2 \cup \cdots \cup A_n \in \mathfrak{M}$ if $A_i \in \mathfrak{M}$ for $i = 1, \ldots, n$.

(c) Since

$$\bigcap_{n=1}^{\infty} A_n = \left(\bigcup_{n=1}^{\infty} A_n^c\right)^c,$$

$\mathfrak{M}$ is closed under the formation of countable (and also finite) intersections.

(d) Since $A - B = B^c \cap A$, we have $A - B \in \mathfrak{M}$ if $A \in \mathfrak{M}$ and $B \in \mathfrak{M}$.

The prefix σ refers to the fact that (iii) is required to hold for all *countable* unions of members of $\mathfrak{M}$. If (iii) is required for finite unions only, then $\mathfrak{M}$ is called an *algebra* of sets.

1.7 Theorem *Let Y and Z be topological spaces, and let $g: Y \to Z$ be continuous.*

(a) *If X is a topological space, if $f: X \to Y$ is continuous, and if $h = g \circ f$, then $h: X \to Z$ is continuous.*

(b) *If X is a measurable space, if $f: X \to Y$ is measurable, and if $h = g \circ f$, then $h: X \to Z$ is measurable.*

Stated informally, continuous functions of continuous functions are continuous; continuous functions of measurable functions are measurable.

PROOF If V is open in Z, then $g^{-1}(V)$ is open in Y, and

$$h^{-1}(V) = f^{-1}(g^{-1}(V)).$$

If f is continuous, it follows that $h^{-1}(V)$ is open, proving (a).

If f is measurable, it follows that $h^{-1}(V)$ is measurable, proving (b).

1.8 Theorem *Let u and v be real measurable functions on a measurable space X, let Φ be a continuous mapping of the plane into a topological space Y, and define*

$$h(x) = \Phi(u(x),v(x))$$

for $x \in X$. Then $h: X \to Y$ is measurable.

PROOF Put $f(x) = (u(x),v(x))$. Then f maps X into the plane. Since $h = \Phi \circ f$, Theorem 1.7 shows that it is enough to prove the measurability of f.

If R is any open rectangle in the plane, with sides parallel to the axes, then R is the cartesian product of two segments I_1 and I_2, and

$$f^{-1}(R) = u^{-1}(I_1) \cap v^{-1}(I_2),$$

which is measurable, by our assumption on u and v. Every open set V in the plane is a countable union of such rectangles R_i, and since

$$f^{-1}(V) = f^{-1}\left(\bigcup_{i=1}^{\infty} R_i\right) = \bigcup_{i=1}^{\infty} f^{-1}(R_i),$$

$f^{-1}(V)$ is measurable.

1.9 Let X be a measurable space. The following propositions are corollaries of Theorems 1.7 and 1.8:

(*a*) *If $f = u + iv$, where u and v are real measurable functions on X, then f is a complex measurable function on X.*
This follows from Theorem 1.8, with $\Phi(z) = z$.

(*b*) *If $f = u + iv$ is a complex measurable function on X, then u, v, and $|f|$ are real measurable functions on X.*
This follows from Theorem 1.7, with $g(z) = \mathrm{Re}\,(z)$, $\mathrm{Im}\,(z)$, and $|z|$.

(*c*) *If f and g are complex measurable functions on X, then so are $f + g$ and fg.*
For real f and g this follows from Theorem 1.8, with

$$\Phi(s,t) = s + t$$

and $\Phi(s,t) = st$. The complex case then follows from (*a*) and (*b*).

(*d*) *If E is a measurable set in X and if*

$$\chi_E(x) = \begin{cases} 1 & \text{if } x \in E \\ 0 & \text{if } x \notin E \end{cases}$$

then χ_E is a measurable function.
This is obvious. We call χ_E the *characteristic function* of the set E. The letter χ will be reserved for characteristic functions throughout this book.

(*e*) *If f is a complex measurable function on X, there is a complex measurable function α on X such that $|\alpha| = 1$ and $f = \alpha|f|$.*

PROOF Let $E = \{x: f(x) = 0\}$, let Y be the complex plane with the origin removed, define $\varphi(z) = z/|z|$ for $z \in Y$, and put

$$\alpha(x) = \varphi(f(x) + \chi_E(x)) \qquad (x \in X).$$

If $x \in E$, $\alpha(x) = 1$; if $x \notin E$, $\alpha(x) = f(x)/|f(x)|$. Since φ is continuous on Y and since E is measurable (why?), the measurability of α follows from (*c*), (*d*), and Theorem 1.7.

We now show that σ-algebras exist in great profusion.

1.10 Theorem *If $\mathfrak{F}$ is any collection of subsets of X, there exists a smallest σ-algebra $\mathfrak{M}^*$ in X such that $\mathfrak{F} \subset \mathfrak{M}^*$.*

This $\mathfrak{M}^*$ is sometimes called the σ-algebra generated by $\mathfrak{F}$.

PROOF Let Ω be the family of all σ-algebras $\mathfrak{M}$ in X which contain $\mathfrak{F}$. Since the collection of all subsets of X is such a σ-algebra, Ω is not empty. Let $\mathfrak{M}^*$ be the intersection of all $\mathfrak{M} \in \Omega$. It is clear that $\mathfrak{F} \subset \mathfrak{M}^*$ and that $\mathfrak{M}^*$ lies in every σ-algebra in X which contains $\mathfrak{F}$. To complete the proof, we have to show that $\mathfrak{M}^*$ is itself a σ-algebra.

If $A_n \in \mathfrak{M}^*$ for $n = 1, 2, 3, \ldots$, and if $\mathfrak{M} \in \Omega$, then $A_n \in \mathfrak{M}$, so $\bigcup A_n \in \mathfrak{M}$, since $\mathfrak{M}$ is a σ-algebra. Since $\bigcup A_n \in \mathfrak{M}$ for *every* $\mathfrak{M} \in \Omega$, we conclude that $\bigcup A_n \in \mathfrak{M}^*$. The other two defining properties of a σ-algebra are verified in the same manner.

1.11 Borel Sets Let X be a topological space. By Theorem 1.10, there exists a smallest σ-algebra $\mathfrak{B}$ in X such that every open set in X belongs to $\mathfrak{B}$. The members of $\mathfrak{B}$ are called the *Borel sets* of X.

In particular, closed sets are Borel sets (being, by definition, the complements of open sets), and so are all countable unions of closed sets and all countable intersections of open sets. These last two are called F_σ's and G_δ's, respectively, and play a considerable role. The notation is due to Hausdorff. The letters F and G were used for closed and open sets, respectively, and σ refers to union (Summe), δ to intersection (Durchschnitt). For example, every half-open interval $[a,b)$ is a G_δ and an F_σ in R^1.

Since $\mathfrak{B}$ is a σ-algebra, we may now regard X as a measurable space, with the Borel sets playing the role of the measurable sets; more concisely, we consider the measurable space $(X,\mathfrak{B})$. If $f: X \to Y$ is a continuous mapping of X, where Y is any topological space, then it is evident from the definitions that $f^{-1}(V) \in \mathfrak{B}$ for every open set V in Y. In other words, *every continuous mapping of X is Borel measurable.*

If Y is the real line or the complex plane, the Borel measurable mappings will be called *Borel functions.*

1.12 Theorem *Suppose $\mathfrak{M}$ is a σ-algebra in X and Y is a topological space. Let f map X into Y.*

(a) *If Ω is the collection of all sets $E \subset Y$ such that $f^{-1}(E) \in \mathfrak{M}$, then Ω is a σ-algebra in Y.*
(b) *If f is measurable and E is a Borel set in Y, then $f^{-1}(E) \in \mathfrak{M}$.*
(c) *If $Y = [-\infty, \infty]$ and $f^{-1}((\alpha, \infty]) \in \mathfrak{M}$ for every real α, then f is measurable.*

PROOF (a) follows from the relations

$$f^{-1}(Y) = X, \qquad f^{-1}(Y - A) = X - f^{-1}(A),$$

and $$f^{-1}(A_1 \cup A_2 \cup \cdots) = f^{-1}(A_1) \cup f^{-1}(A_2) \cup \cdots.$$

To prove (b), let Ω be as in (a); the measurability of f implies that Ω contains all open sets in Y, and since Ω is a σ-algebra, Ω contains all Borel sets in Y.

To prove (c), let Ω be the collection of all $E \subset [-\infty, \infty]$ such that $f^{-1}(E) \in \mathfrak{M}$. Since Ω is a σ-algebra in $[-\infty, \infty]$, and since $(\alpha, \infty] \in \Omega$ for all real α, the same is true of the sets

$$[-\infty,\alpha) = \bigcup_{n=1}^{\infty} \left[-\infty, \alpha - \frac{1}{n}\right] = \bigcup_{n=1}^{\infty} \left(\alpha - \frac{1}{n}, \infty\right]^c$$

and $$(\alpha,\beta) = [-\infty,\beta) \cap (\alpha, \infty].$$

Since every open set in $[-\infty, \infty]$ is a countable union of segments of the above types, Ω contains every open set, so f is measurable.

1.13 Definition Let $\{a_n\}$ be a sequence in $[-\infty, \infty]$, and put

(1) $$b_k = \sup \{a_k, a_{k+1}, a_{k+2}, \ldots\} \qquad (k = 1, 2, 3, \ldots)$$

and

(2) $$\beta = \inf \{b_1, b_2, b_3, \ldots\}.$$

We call β the *upper limit* of $\{a_n\}$, and write

(3) $$\beta = \limsup_{n\to\infty} a_n.$$

The following properties are easily verified: First, $b_1 \geq b_2 \geq b_3 \geq \cdots$, so that $b_k \to \beta$ as $k \to \infty$; secondly, there is a subsequence $\{a_{n_i}\}$ of $\{a_n\}$ such that $a_{n_i} \to \beta$ as $i \to \infty$, and β is the largest number with this property.

The *lower limit* is defined analogously: simply interchange sup and inf in (1) and (2). Note that

$$\liminf_{n\to\infty} a_n = -\limsup_{n\to\infty} (-a_n). \tag{4}$$

If $\{a_n\}$ converges, then evidently

$$\limsup_{n\to\infty} a_n = \liminf_{n\to\infty} a_n = \lim_{n\to\infty} a_n. \tag{5}$$

Suppose $\{f_n\}$ is a sequence of extended-real functions on a set X. Then $\sup_n f_n$ and $\limsup_{n\to\infty} f_n$ are the functions defined on X by

$$(\sup_n f_n)(x) = \sup_n (f_n(x)), \tag{6}$$

$$(\limsup_{n\to\infty} f_n)(x) = \limsup_{n\to\infty} (f_n(x)). \tag{7}$$

If

$$f(x) = \lim_{n\to\infty} f_n(x), \tag{8}$$

the limit being assumed to exist at every $x \in X$, then we call f the *pointwise limit* of the sequence $\{f_n\}$.

1.14 Theorem *If $f_n: X \to [-\infty, \infty]$ is measurable, for $n = 1, 2, 3, \ldots,$ and*

$$g = \sup_{n\geq 1} f_n, \qquad h = \limsup_{n\to\infty} f_n,$$

then g and h are measurable.

PROOF $g^{-1}((\alpha, \infty]) = \bigcup_{n=1}^{\infty} f_n^{-1}((\alpha, \infty])$. Hence Theorem 1.12(*c*) implies that g is measurable. The same result holds of course with inf in place of sup, and since

$$h = \inf_{k\geq 1} \{\sup_{i\geq k} f_i\},$$

it follows that h is measurable.

Corollaries

(*a*) *The limit of every pointwise convergent sequence of complex measurable functions is measurable.*

(*b*) *If f and g are measurable (with range in $[-\infty, \infty]$), then so are* $\max\{f,g\}$ *and* $\min\{f,g\}$. *In particular, this is true of the functions*

$$f^+ = \max\{f,0\} \quad \textit{and} \quad f^- = -\min\{f,0\}.$$

1.15 The above functions f^+ and f^- are called the *positive* and *negative parts* of f. We have $|f| = f^+ + f^-$ and $f = f^+ - f^-$, a standard representation of f as a difference of two nonnegative functions, with a certain minimum property:

Proposition *If $f = g - h$, $g \geq 0$, and $h \geq 0$, then $f^+ \leq g$ and $f^- \leq h$.*

PROOF $f \leq g$ and $0 \leq g$ clearly implies $\max \{f,0\} \leq g$.

Simple Functions

1.16 Definition A function s on a measurable space X whose range consists of only finitely many points in $[0, \infty)$ will be called a *simple function.*

(Sometimes it is convenient to call *any* function with finite range simple. The above situation is, however, the one we shall be mainly interested in. Note that we explicitly exclude ∞ from the values of a simple function.)

If $\alpha_1, \ldots, \alpha_n$ are the distinct values of a simple function s, and if $A_i = \{x: s(x) = \alpha_i\}$, then clearly

$$s = \sum_{i=1}^{n} \alpha_i \chi_{A_i},$$

where χ_{A_i} is the characteristic function of A_i, as defined in Sec. 1.9(d).

It is also clear that s is measurable if and only if each of the sets A_i is measurable.

1.17 Theorem *Let $f: X \to [0, \infty]$ be measurable. There exist simple measurable functions s_n on X such that*

(*a*) $0 \leq s_1 \leq s_2 \leq \cdots \leq f$.
(*b*) $s_n(x) \to f(x)$ *as* $n \to \infty$, *for every* $x \in X$.

PROOF For $n = 1, 2, 3, \ldots$, and for $1 \leq i \leq n2^n$, define

$$(1) \quad E_{n,i} = f^{-1}\left(\left[\frac{i-1}{2^n}, \frac{i}{2^n}\right)\right) \quad \text{and} \quad F_n = f^{-1}([n, \infty])$$

and put

$$(2) \quad s_n = \sum_{i=1}^{n2^n} \frac{i-1}{2^n} \chi_{E_{n,i}} + n\chi_{F_n}.$$

Theorem 1.12(b) shows that $E_{n,i}$ and F_n are measurable sets. It is easily seen that the functions (2) satisfy (a). If x is such that $f(x) < \infty$, then $s_n(x) \geq f(x) - 2^{-n}$ as soon as n is large enough; if $f(x) = \infty$, then $s_n(x) = n$; this proves (b).

It should be observed that the preceding construction yields a uniformly convergent sequence $\{s_n\}$ if f is bounded.

Elementary Properties of Measures

1.18 Definition

(a) A *positive measure* is a function μ, defined on a σ-algebra $\mathfrak{M}$, whose range is in $[0, \infty]$ and which is *countably additive.* This means that if $\{A_i\}$ is a *disjoint* countable collection of members of $\mathfrak{M}$, then

$$\mu\left(\bigcup_{i=1}^{\infty} A_i\right) = \sum_{i=1}^{\infty} \mu(A_i). \tag{1}$$

To avoid trivialities, we shall also assume that $\mu(A) < \infty$ for at least one $A \in \mathfrak{M}$.

(b) A *measure space* is a measurable space which has a positive measure defined on the σ-algebra of its measurable sets.

(c) A *complex measure* is a complex-valued countably additive function defined on a σ-algebra.

Note: What we have called a *positive measure* is frequently just called a *measure;* we add the word "positive" for emphasis. If $\mu(E) = 0$ for every $E \in \mathfrak{M}$, then μ is a positive measure, by our definition. The value ∞ is admissible for a positive measure; but when we talk of a complex measure μ, it is understood that $\mu(E)$ is a complex number, for every $E \in \mathfrak{M}$. The *real measures* form a subclass of the complex ones, of course.

1.19 Theorem *Let μ be a positive measure on a σ-algebra $\mathfrak{M}$. Then*

(a) $\mu(\varnothing) = 0$.

(b) $\mu(A_1 \cup \cdots \cup A_n) = \mu(A_1) + \cdots + \mu(A_n)$ *if* $A_1, \ldots, A_n$ *are pairwise disjoint members of* $\mathfrak{M}$.

(c) $A \subset B$ *implies* $\mu(A) \leq \mu(B)$ *if* $A \in \mathfrak{M}$, $B \in \mathfrak{M}$.

(d) $\mu(A_n) \to \mu(A)$ *as* $n \to \infty$ *if* $A = \bigcup_{n=1}^{\infty} A_n$, $A_n \in \mathfrak{M}$, *and*

$$A_1 \subset A_2 \subset A_3 \subset \cdots.$$

(e) $\mu(A_n) \to \mu(A)$ *as* $n \to \infty$ *if* $A = \bigcap_{n=1}^{\infty} A_n$, $A_n \in \mathfrak{M}$,

$$A_1 \supset A_2 \supset A_3 \supset \cdots,$$

and $\mu(A_1)$ *is finite.*

As the proof will show, these properties, with the exception of (*c*), also hold for complex measures; (*b*) is called *finite additivity;* (*c*) is called *monotonicity.*

PROOF

(*a*) Take $A \in \mathfrak{M}$ so that $\mu(A) < \infty$, and take $A_1 = A$ and $A_2 = A_3 = \cdots = \emptyset$ in 1.18(1).

(*b*) Take $A_{n+1} = A_{n+2} = \cdots = \emptyset$ in 1.18(1).

(*c*) Since $B = A \cup (B - A)$ and $A \cap (B - A) = \emptyset$, (*b*) gives $\mu(B) = \mu(A) + \mu(B - A) \geq \mu(A)$.

(*d*) Put $B_1 = A_1$, $B_n = A_n - A_{n-1}$ for $n = 2, 3, 4, \ldots$. Then $B_n \in \mathfrak{M}$, $B_i \cap B_j = \emptyset$ if $i \neq j$, $A_n = B_1 \cup \cdots \cup B_n$, and $A = \bigcup_{i=1}^{\infty} B_i$. Hence

$$\mu(A_n) = \sum_{i=1}^{n} \mu(B_i) \quad \text{and} \quad \mu(A) = \sum_{i=1}^{\infty} \mu(B_i).$$

Now (*d*) follows, by the definition of the sum of an infinite series.

(*e*) Put $C_n = A_1 - A_n$. Then $C_1 \subset C_2 \subset C_3 \subset \cdots$,

$$\mu(C_n) = \mu(A_1) - \mu(A_n),$$

$A_1 - A = \bigcup C_n$, and so (*d*) shows that

$$\mu(A_1) - \mu(A) = \mu(A_1 - A) = \lim_{n\to\infty} \mu(C_n) = \mu(A_1) - \lim_{n\to\infty} \mu(A_n).$$

This implies (*e*).

1.20 Examples The construction of interesting measure spaces requires some labor, as we shall see. However, a few simple-minded examples can be given immediately:

(*a*) For any $E \subset X$, where X is any set, define $\mu(E) = \infty$ if E is an infinite set, and let $\mu(E)$ be the number of points in E if E is finite. This μ is called the *counting measure* on X.

(*b*) Fix $x_0 \in X$, define $\mu(E) = 1$ if $x_0 \in E$ and $\mu(E) = 0$ if $x_0 \notin E$, for any $E \subset X$. This μ may be called the *unit mass* concentrated at x_0.

(*c*) Let μ be the counting measure on the set $\{1,2,3, \ldots\}$, let $A_n = \{n, n+1, n+2, \ldots\}$. Then $\bigcap A_n = \emptyset$ but $\mu(A_n) = \infty$ for $n = 1, 2, 3, \ldots$. This shows that the hypothesis

$$\text{“}\mu(A_1) < \infty\text{”}$$

is not superfluous in Theorem 1.19(*e*).

1.21 A Comment on Terminology One frequently sees measure spaces referred to as "ordered triples" $(X,\mathfrak{M},\mu)$ where X is a set, $\mathfrak{M}$ is a σ-algebra in X, and μ is a measure defined on $\mathfrak{M}$. Similarly, measurable spaces are "ordered pairs" $(X,\mathfrak{M})$. This is logically all right, and often convenient, though somewhat redundant. For instance, in $(X,\mathfrak{M})$ the set X is merely the largest member of $\mathfrak{M}$, so if we know $\mathfrak{M}$ we also know X. Similarly, every measure has a σ-algebra for its domain, by definition, so if we know a measure μ we also know the σ-algebra $\mathfrak{M}$ on which μ is defined and we know the set X in which $\mathfrak{M}$ is a σ-algebra.

It is therefore perfectly legitimate to use expressions like "Let μ be a measure" or, if we wish to emphasize the σ-algebra or the set in question, to say "Let μ be a measure on $\mathfrak{M}$" or "Let μ be a measure on X."

What is logically rather meaningless but customary (and we shall often follow mathematical custom rather than logic) is to say "Let X be a measure space"; the emphasis should not be on the set, but on the measure. Of course, when this wording is used, it is tacitly understood that there is a measure defined on some σ-algebra in X and that it is this measure which is really under discussion.

Similarly, a topological space is an ordered pair (X,τ), where τ is a topology in the set X, and the significant data are contained in τ, not in X, but "the topological space X" is what one talks about.

This sort of tacit convention is used throughout mathematics. Most mathematical systems are sets with some class of distinguished subsets or some binary operations or some relations (which are required to have certain properties), and one can list these and then describe the system as an ordered pair, triple, etc., depending on what is needed. For instance, the real line may be described as a quadruple $(R^1,+,\cdot,<)$, where $+$, $\cdot$, and $<$ satisfy the axioms of a complete archimedean ordered field. But it is a safe bet that very few mathematicians think of the real field as an ordered quadruple.

Arithmetic in $[0,\infty]$

1.22 Throughout integration theory, one inevitably encounters ∞. One reason is that one wants to be able to integrate over sets of infinite measure; after all, the real line has infinite length. Another reason is that even if one is primarily interested in real-valued functions, the lim sup of a sequence of positive real functions or the sum of a sequence of positive real functions may well be ∞ at some points, and much of the elegance of theorems like 1.26 and 1.27 would be lost if one had to make some special provisions whenever this occurs.

Let us define $a + \infty = \infty + a = \infty$ if $0 \le a \le \infty$, and

$$a \cdot \infty = \infty \cdot a = \begin{cases} \infty & \text{if } 0 < a \le \infty \\ 0 & \text{if } a = 0; \end{cases}$$

sums and products of real numbers are of course defined in the usual way.

It may seem strange to define $0 \cdot \infty = 0$. However, one verifies without difficulty that with this definition the *commutative, associative, and distributive laws hold in* $[0, \infty]$ *without any restriction.*

The cancellation laws have to be treated with some care: $a + b = a + c$ implies $b = c$ only when $a < \infty$, and $ab = ac$ implies $b = c$ only when $0 < a < \infty$.

Observe that the following useful proposition holds:

If $0 \leq a_1 \leq a_2 \leq \cdots$, $0 \leq b_1 \leq b_2 \leq \cdots$, $a_n \to a$, *and* $b_n \to b$, *then* $a_n b_n \to ab$.

If we combine this with Theorems 1.17 and 1.14, we see that *sums and products of measurable functions into* $[0, \infty]$ *are measurable.*

Integration of Positive Functions

In this section, $\mathfrak{M}$ will be a σ-algebra in a set X and μ will be a positive measure on $\mathfrak{M}$.

1.23 Definition If s is a measurable simple function on X, of the form

$$s = \sum_{i=1}^{n} \alpha_i \chi_{A_i}, \tag{1}$$

where $\alpha_1, \ldots, \alpha_n$ are the distinct values of s (compare Definition 1.16), and if $E \in \mathfrak{M}$, we define

$$\int_E s \, d\mu = \sum_{i=1}^{n} \alpha_i \mu(A_i \cap E). \tag{2}$$

The convention $0 \cdot \infty = 0$ is used here; it may happen that $\alpha_i = 0$ for some i and that $\mu(A_i \cap E) = \infty$.

If $f: X \to [0, \infty]$ is measurable, and $E \in \mathfrak{M}$, we define

$$\int_E f \, d\mu = \sup \int_E s \, d\mu, \tag{3}$$

the supremum being taken over all simple measurable functions s such that $0 \leq s \leq f$.

The left member of (3) is called the *Lebesgue integral* of f over E, with respect to the measure μ. It is a number in $[0, \infty]$.

Observe that we apparently have two definitions for $\int_E f \, d\mu$ if f is simple, namely, (2) and (3). However, these assign the same value to the integral, since f is, in this case, the largest of the functions s which occur on the right of (3).

1.24 The following propositions are immediate consequences of the definitions. The functions and sets occurring in them are assumed to be measurable:

(a) If $0 \le f \le g$, then $\int_E f\,d\mu \le \int_E g\,d\mu$.
(b) If $A \subset B$ and $f \ge 0$, then $\int_A f\,d\mu \le \int_B f\,d\mu$.
(c) If $f \ge 0$ and c is a constant, $0 \le c < \infty$, then

$$\int_E cf\,d\mu = c\int_E f\,d\mu.$$

(d) If $f(x) = 0$ for all $x \in E$, then $\int_E f\,d\mu = 0$, even if $\mu(E) = \infty$.
(e) If $\mu(E) = 0$, then $\int_E f\,d\mu = 0$, even if $f(x) = \infty$ for every $x \in E$.
(f) If $f \ge 0$, then $\int_E f\,d\mu = \int_X \chi_E f\,d\mu$.

This last result shows that we could have restricted our definition of integration to integrals over all of X, without losing any generality. If we wanted to integrate over subsets, we could then use *(f)* as the definition. It is purely a matter of taste which definition is preferred.

One may also remark here that every measurable subset E of a measure space X is again a measure space, in a perfectly natural way: The new measurable sets are simply those measurable subsets of X which lie in E, and the measure is unchanged, except that its domain is restricted. This shows again that as soon as we have integration defined over every measure space, we automatically have it defined over every measurable subset of every measure space.

1.25 Proposition *Let s and t be measurable simple functions on X. For $E \in \mathfrak{M}$, define*

(1)
$$\varphi(E) = \int_E s\,d\mu.$$

Then φ is a measure on $\mathfrak{M}$. Also

(2)
$$\int_X (s+t)\,d\mu = \int_X s\,d\mu + \int_X t\,d\mu.$$

(This proposition contains provisional forms of Theorems 1.27 and 1.29.)

PROOF If s is as in Definition 1.23, and if $E_1, E_2, \ldots$ are disjoint members of $\mathfrak{M}$ whose union is E, the countable additivity of μ shows that

$$\varphi(E) = \sum_{i=1}^{n} \alpha_i \mu(A_i \cap E) = \sum_{i=1}^{n} \alpha_i \sum_{r=1}^{\infty} \mu(A_i \cap E_r)$$

$$= \sum_{r=1}^{\infty} \sum_{i=1}^{n} \alpha_i \mu(A_i \cap E_r) = \sum_{r=1}^{\infty} \varphi(E_r).$$

Also, $\varphi(\varnothing) = 0$, so that φ is not identically ∞.

Next, let s be as before, let $\beta_1, \ldots, \beta_m$ be the distinct values of

t, and let $B_j = \{x : t(x) = \beta_j\}$. If $E_{ij} = A_i \cap B_j$, then

$$\int_{E_{ij}} (s + t)\, d\mu = (\alpha_i + \beta_j)\mu(E_{ij})$$

and
$$\int_{E_{ij}} s\, d\mu + \int_{E_{ij}} t\, d\mu = \alpha_i\mu(E_{ij}) + \beta_j\mu(E_{ij}).$$

Thus (2) holds with E_{ij} in place of X. Since X is the disjoint union of the sets E_{ij} ($1 \le i \le n$, $1 \le j \le m$), the first half of our proposition implies that (2) holds.

We now come to the interesting part of the theory. One of its most remarkable features is the ease with which it handles limit operations.

1.26 Lebesgue's Monotone Convergence Theorem *Let $\{f_n\}$ be a sequence of measurable functions on X and suppose that*

(a) $0 \le f_1(x) \le f_2(x) \le \cdots \le \infty$ for every $x \in X$,
(b) $f_n(x) \to f(x)$ as $n \to \infty$, for every $x \in X$.

Then f is measurable, and

$$\int_X f_n\, d\mu \to \int_X f\, d\mu \qquad \text{as } n \to \infty.$$

PROOF Since $\int f_n \le \int f_{n+1}$, there exists an $\alpha \in [0, \infty]$ such that

$$\int_X f_n\, d\mu \to \alpha \qquad \text{as } n \to \infty. \tag{1}$$

By Theorem 1.14, f is measurable. Since $f_n \le f$, we have $\int f_n \le \int f$ for every n, so (1) implies

$$\alpha \le \int_X f\, d\mu. \tag{2}$$

Let s be any simple measurable function such that $0 \le s \le f$, let c be a constant, $0 < c < 1$, and define

$$E_n = \{x : f_n(x) \ge cs(x)\} \qquad (n = 1, 2, 3, \ldots). \tag{3}$$

Each E_n is measurable, $E_1 \subset E_2 \subset E_3 \subset \cdots$, and $X = \bigcup E_n$. For if $f(x) = 0$, then $x \in E_1$; and if $f(x) > 0$, then $cs(x) < f(x)$, since $c < 1$; hence $x \in E_n$ for some n. Also

$$\int_X f_n\, d\mu \ge \int_{E_n} f_n\, d\mu \ge c \int_{E_n} s\, d\mu \qquad (n = 1, 2, 3, \ldots). \tag{4}$$

Let $n \to \infty$, applying Proposition 1.25 and Theorem 1.19(d) to the last integral in (4). The result is

$$\alpha \ge c \int_X s\, d\mu. \tag{5}$$

Since (5) holds for every $c < 1$, we have

(6) $$\alpha \geq \int_X s\,d\mu$$

for every simple measurable s satisfying $0 \leq s \leq f$, so that

(7) $$\alpha \geq \int_X f\,d\mu.$$

The theorem follows from (1), (2), and (7).

1.27 Theorem *If $f_n: X \to [0, \infty]$ is measurable, for $n = 1, 2, 3, \ldots$, and*

(1) $$f(x) = \sum_{n=1}^{\infty} f_n(x) \qquad (x \in X),$$

then

(2) $$\int_X f\,d\mu = \sum_{n=1}^{\infty} \int_X f_n\,d\mu.$$

PROOF First, there are sequences $\{s_i'\}$, $\{s_i''\}$ of simple measurable functions such that $s_i' \to f_1$ and $s_i'' \to f_2$, as in Theorem 1.17. If $s_i = s_i' + s_i''$, then $s_i \to f_1 + f_2$, and the monotone convergence theorem, combined with Proposition 1.25, shows that

(3) $$\int_X (f_1 + f_2)\,d\mu = \int_X f_1\,d\mu + \int_X f_2\,d\mu.$$

Next, put $g_N = f_1 + \cdots + f_N$. The sequence $\{g_N\}$ converges monotonically to f, and if we apply induction to (3) we see that

(4) $$\int_X g_N\,d\mu = \sum_{n=1}^{N} \int_X f_n\,d\mu.$$

Applying the monotone convergence theorem once more, we obtain (2), and the proof is complete.

If we let μ be the counting measure on a countable set, Theorem 1.27 is a statement about double series of nonnegative real numbers (which can of course be proved by elementary means):

Corollary *If $a_{ij} \geq 0$ for i and $j = 1, 2, 3, \ldots$, then*

$$\sum_{i=1}^{\infty} \sum_{j=1}^{\infty} a_{ij} = \sum_{j=1}^{\infty} \sum_{i=1}^{\infty} a_{ij}.$$

1.28 Fatou's Lemma *If $f_n: X \to [0, \infty]$ is measurable, for each positive integer n, then*

(1) $$\int_X \left(\liminf_{n \to \infty} f_n\right) d\mu \leq \liminf_{n \to \infty} \int_X f_n\,d\mu.$$

Strict inequality can occur in (1); see Exercise 2.

PROOF Put

(2) $$g_k(x) = \inf_{i\geq k} f_i(x) \qquad (k = 1, 2, 3, \ldots; x \in X).$$

Then $g_k \leq f_k$, so that

(3) $$\int_X g_k \, d\mu \leq \int_X f_k \, d\mu \qquad (k = 1, 2, 3, \ldots).$$

Also, $0 \leq g_1 \leq g_2 \leq \cdots$, and g_k is measurable, by Theorem 1.14, and $g_k(x) \to \liminf f_n(x)$ as $k \to \infty$, by Definition 1.13. The monotone convergence theorem therefore shows that the left side of (3) tends to the left side of (1), as $k \to \infty$. Hence (1) follows from (3).

1.29 Theorem *Suppose $f: X \to [0, \infty]$ is measurable, and*

(1) $$\varphi(E) = \int_E f \, d\mu \qquad (E \in \mathfrak{M}).$$

Then φ is a measure on $\mathfrak{M}$, and

(2) $$\int_X g \, d\varphi = \int_X gf \, d\mu$$

for every measurable g on X with range in $[0, \infty]$.

PROOF Let $E_1, E_2, E_3, \ldots$ be disjoint members of $\mathfrak{M}$ whose union is E. Observe that

(3) $$\chi_E f = \sum_{j=1}^{\infty} \chi_{E_j} f$$

and that

(4) $$\varphi(E) = \int_X \chi_E f \, d\mu, \qquad \varphi(E_j) = \int_X \chi_{E_j} f \, d\mu.$$

It now follows from Theorem 1.27 that

(5) $$\varphi(E) = \sum_{j=1}^{\infty} \varphi(E_j).$$

Since $\varphi(\varnothing) = 0$, (5) proves that φ is a measure.

Next, (1) shows that (2) holds whenever $g = \chi_E$ for some $E \in \mathfrak{M}$. Hence (2) holds for every simple measurable function g, and the general case follows from the monotone convergence theorem.

Remark The second assertion of Theorem 1.29 is sometimes written in the form

(6) $$d\varphi = f \, d\mu.$$

We assign no independent meaning to the symbols $d\varphi$ and $d\mu$; (6) merely means that (2) holds for every measurable $g \geq 0$.

Theorem 1.29 has a very important converse, the Radon-Nikodym theorem, which will be proved in Chap. 6.

Integration of Complex Functions

As before, μ will in this section be a positive measure on an arbitrary measurable space X.

1.30 Definition We define $L^1(\mu)$ to be the collection of all complex measurable functions f on X for which

$$\int_X |f| \, d\mu < \infty.$$

Note that the measurability of f implies that of $|f|$, as we saw in Proposition 1.9(*b*); hence the above integral is defined.

The members of $L^1(\mu)$ are called *Lebesgue integrable* functions (with respect to μ) or *summable functions.* The significance of the exponent 1 will become clear in Chap. 3.

1.31 Definition If $f = u + iv$, where u and v are real measurable functions on X, and if $f \in L^1(\mu)$, we define

$$(1) \qquad \int_E f \, d\mu = \int_E u^+ \, d\mu - \int_E u^- \, d\mu + i \int_E v^+ \, d\mu - i \int_E v^- \, d\mu$$

for every measurable set E.

Here u^+ and u^- are the positive and negative parts of u, as defined in Sec. 1.15; v^+ and v^- are similarly obtained from v. These four functions are measurable, real, and nonnegative; hence the four integrals on the right of (1) exist, by Definition 1.23. Furthermore, we have $u^+ \leq |u| \leq |f|$, etc., so that each of these four integrals is finite. Thus (1) defines the integral on the left as a complex number.

Occasionally it is desirable to define the integral of a measurable function f with range in $[-\infty, \infty]$ to be

$$(2) \qquad \int_E f \, d\mu = \int_E f^+ \, d\mu - \int_E f^- \, d\mu,$$

provided that at least one of the integrals on the right of (2) is finite. The left side of (2) is then a number in $[-\infty, \infty]$.

1.32 Theorem *Suppose f and $g \in L^1(\mu)$ and α and β are complex numbers. Then $\alpha f + \beta g \in L^1(\mu)$, and*

$$(1) \qquad \int_X (\alpha f + \beta g) \, d\mu = \alpha \int_X f \, d\mu + \beta \int_X g \, d\mu.$$

PROOF The measurability of $\alpha f + \beta g$ follows from Proposition 1.9(*c*). By Sec. 1.24 and Theorem 1.27,

$$\int_X |\alpha f + \beta g| \, d\mu \leq \int_X (|\alpha| \, |f| + |\beta| \, |g|) \, d\mu$$

$$= |\alpha| \int_X |f| \, d\mu + |\beta| \int_X |g| \, d\mu < \infty.$$

Thus $\alpha f + \beta g \in L^1(\mu)$.

To prove (1), it is clearly sufficient to prove

$$\int_X (f + g) \, d\mu = \int_X f \, d\mu + \int_X g \, d\mu \tag{2}$$

and

$$\int_X (\alpha f) \, d\mu = \alpha \int_X f \, d\mu, \tag{3}$$

and the general case of (2) will follow if we prove (2) for real f and g in $L^1(\mu)$.

Assuming this, and setting $h = f + g$, we have

$$h^+ - h^- = f^+ - f^- + g^+ - g^-$$

or

$$h^+ + f^- + g^- = f^+ + g^+ + h^-. \tag{4}$$

By Theorem 1.27,

$$\int h^+ + \int f^- + \int g^- = \int f^+ + \int g^+ + \int h^-, \tag{5}$$

and since each of these integrals is finite, we may transpose and obtain (2).

That (3) holds if $\alpha \geq 0$ follows from Proposition 1.24(*c*). It is easy to verify that (3) holds if $\alpha = -1$, using relations like $(-u)^+ = u^-$. The case $\alpha = i$ is also easy: If $f = u + iv$, then

$$\int (if) = \int (iu - v) = \int (-v) + i \int u = -\int v + i \int u = i\left(\int u + i \int v\right) = i \int f.$$

Combining these cases with (2), we obtain (3) for any complex α.

1.33 Theorem *If $f \in L^1(\mu)$, then*

$$\left| \int_X f \, d\mu \right| \leq \int_X |f| \, d\mu.$$

PROOF Put $z = \int_X f \, d\mu$. Since z is a complex number, there is a complex number α, with $|\alpha| = 1$, such that $\alpha z = |z|$. Let u be the real part of αf. Then $u \leq |\alpha f| = |f|$. Hence

$$\left| \int_X f \, d\mu \right| = \alpha \int_X f \, d\mu = \int_X \alpha f \, d\mu = \int_X u \, d\mu \leq \int_X |f| \, d\mu.$$

The third of the above equalities holds since the preceding ones show that $\int \alpha f\,d\mu$ is real.

We conclude this section with another important convergence theorem.

1.34 Lebesgue's Dominated Convergence Theorem *Suppose $\{f_n\}$ is a sequence of complex measurable functions on X such that*

(1) $$f(x) = \lim_{n\to\infty} f_n(x)$$

exists for every $x \in X$. If there is a function $g \in L^1(\mu)$ such that

(2) $$|f_n(x)| \le g(x) \qquad (n = 1, 2, 3, \ldots ; x \in X),$$

then $f \in L^1(\mu)$,

(3) $$\lim_{n\to\infty} \int_X |f_n - f|\,d\mu = 0,$$

and

(4) $$\lim_{n\to\infty} \int_X f_n\,d\mu = \int_X f\,d\mu.$$

PROOF Since $|f| \le g$ and f is measurable, $f \in L^1(\mu)$. Since $|f_n - f| \le 2g$, Fatou's lemma applies to the functions $2g - |f_n - f|$ and yields

$$\begin{aligned}\int_X 2g\,d\mu &\le \liminf_{n\to\infty} \int_X (2g - |f_n - f|)\,d\mu \\ &= \int_X 2g\,d\mu + \liminf_{n\to\infty} \left(-\int_X |f_n - f|\,d\mu\right) \\ &= \int_X 2g\,d\mu - \limsup_{n\to\infty} \int_X |f_n - f|\,d\mu.\end{aligned}$$

Since $\int 2g\,d\mu$ is finite, we may subtract it and obtain

(5) $$\limsup_{n\to\infty} \int_X |f_n - f|\,d\mu \le 0.$$

If a sequence of nonnegative real numbers fails to converge to 0, then its upper limit is positive. Thus (5) implies (3). By Theorem 1.33, applied to $f_n - f$, (3) implies (4).

The Role Played by Sets of Measure Zero

1.35 Definition Let P be a property which a point x may or may not have. For instance, P might be the property "$f(x) > 0$" if f is a given function, or it might be "$\{f_n(x)\}$ converges" if $\{f_n\}$ is a given sequence of functions.

If μ is a measure on a σ-algebra $\mathfrak{M}$ and if $E \in \mathfrak{M}$, the statement "P holds almost everywhere on E" (abbreviated to "P holds a.e. on E") means that there exists an $N \in \mathfrak{M}$ such that $\mu(N) = 0$, $N \subset E$, and P holds at every point of $E - N$. This concept of a.e. depends of course very strongly on the given measure, and we shall write "a.e. $[\mu]$" whenever clarity requires that the measure be indicated.

For example, if f and g are measurable functions and if

$$\mu(\{x: f(x) \neq g(x)\}) = 0, \tag{1}$$

we say that $f = g$ a.e. $[\mu]$ on X, and we may write $f \sim g$. This is easily seen to be an equivalence relation. The transitivity ($f \sim g$ and $g \sim h$ implies $f \sim h$) is a consequence of the fact that the union of two sets of measure 0 has measure 0.

Note that if $f \sim g$, then, for every $E \in \mathfrak{M}$,

$$\int_E f\, d\mu = \int_E g\, d\mu. \tag{2}$$

To see this, let N be the set which appears in (1); then E is the union of the disjoint sets $E - N$ and $E \cap N$; on $E - N$, $f = g$, and $\mu(E \cap N) = 0$.

Thus, generally speaking, sets of measure 0 are negligible in integration. It ought to be true that every subset of a negligible set is negligible. But it may happen that some set $N \in \mathfrak{M}$ with $\mu(N) = 0$ has a subset E which is not a member of $\mathfrak{M}$. Of course we can *define* $\mu(E) = 0$ in this case. But will this extension of μ still be a measure, i.e., will it still be defined on a σ-algebra? It is a pleasant fact that the answer is affirmative:

1.36 Theorem *Let $(X,\mathfrak{M},\mu)$ be a measure space, let $\mathfrak{M}^*$ be the collection of all $E \subset X$ for which there exist sets A and $B \in \mathfrak{M}$ such that $A \subset E \subset B$ and $\mu(B - A) = 0$, and define $\mu(E) = \mu(A)$ in this situation. Then $\mathfrak{M}^*$ is a σ-algebra, and μ is a measure on $\mathfrak{M}^*$.*

This extended measure μ is called *complete* since all subsets of sets of measure 0 are now measurable; the σ-algebra $\mathfrak{M}^*$ is called the *μ-completion* of $\mathfrak{M}$. The theorem says that every measure can be completed, so, whenever it is convenient, we may assume that any given measure is complete; this just gives us more measurable sets, hence more measurable functions. Most measures that one meets in the ordinary course of events are already complete, but there are exceptions; one of these will occur in the proof of Fubini's theorem in Chap. 7.

PROOF We verify the three defining properties of a σ-algebra. (i) $X \in \mathfrak{M}$, hence $X \in \mathfrak{M}^*$. (ii) If $A \subset E \subset B$, then $B^c \subset E^c \subset A^c$, and $A^c - B^c = B - A$. (iii) If $A_i \subset E_i \subset B_i$, $A = \bigcup A_i$, $E = \bigcup E_i$, and $B = \bigcup B_i$, then $A \subset E \subset B$ and

$$B - A \subset \bigcup_1^\infty (B_i - A_i),$$

so that $\mu(B - A) = 0$ if $\mu(B_i - A_i) = 0$ for $i = 1, 2, 3, \ldots$.

Next, we check that μ is well defined on $\mathfrak{M}^*$. Suppose $A \subset E \subset B$, $A_1 \subset E \subset B_1$, and $\mu(B - A) = \mu(B_1 - A_1) = 0$. Then

$$A - A_1 \subset B_1 - A_1,$$

so $\mu(A - A_1) = 0$. Similarly, $\mu(A_1 - A) = 0$. Hence

$$\mu(A) = \mu(A_1 \cap A) = \mu(A_1).$$

The countable additivity of μ on $\mathfrak{M}^*$ is obvious.

1.37 The fact that functions which are equal a.e. are indistinguishable as far as integration is concerned suggests that our definition of measurable function might profitably be enlarged. Let us call a function f defined on a set $E \in \mathfrak{M}$ *measurable on* X if $\mu(E^c) = 0$ and if $f^{-1}(V) \cap E$ is measurable for every open set V. If we define $f(x) = 0$ for $x \in E^c$, we obtain a measurable function on X, in the old sense. If our measure happens to be complete, we can define f on E^c in a perfectly arbitrary manner, and we still get a measurable function. The integral of f over any set $A \in \mathfrak{M}$ is independent of the definition of f on E^c; therefore this definition need not even be specified at all.

There are many situations where this occurs naturally. For instance, a function f on the real line may be differentiable only almost everywhere (with respect to Lebesgue measure), but under certain conditions it is still true that f is the integral of its derivative; this will be discussed in Chap. 8. Or a sequence $\{f_n\}$ of measurable functions on X may converge only almost everywhere; with our new definition of measurability, the limit is still a measurable function on X, and we do not have to cut down to the set on which convergence actually occurs.

To illustrate, let us state a corollary of Lebesgue's dominated convergence theorem in a form in which exceptional sets of measure zero are admitted:

1.38 Theorem *Suppose $\{f_n\}$ is a sequence of complex measurable functions defined a.e. on X such that*

(1)
$$\sum_{n=1}^\infty \int_X |f_n| \, d\mu < \infty.$$

Then the series

(2)
$$f(x) = \sum_{n=1}^\infty f_n(x)$$

converges for almost all x, $f \in L^1(\mu)$, and

$$\int_X f\,d\mu = \sum_{n=1}^{\infty} \int_X f_n\,d\mu. \tag{3}$$

PROOF Let S_n be the set on which f_n is defined, so that $\mu(S_n{}^c) = 0$. Put $\varphi(x) = \Sigma|f_n(x)|$, for $x \in S = \bigcap S_n$. Then $\mu(S^c) = 0$. By (1) and Theorem 1.27,

$$\int_S \varphi\,d\mu < \infty. \tag{4}$$

If $E = \{x \in S: \varphi(X) < \infty\}$, it follows from (4) that $\mu(E^c) = 0$. The series (2) converges absolutely for every $x \in E$, and if $f(x)$ is defined by (2) for $x \in E$, then $|f(x)| \le \varphi(x)$ on E, so that $f \in L^1(\mu)$ on E, by (4). If $g_n = f_1 + \cdots + f_n$, then $|g_n| \le \varphi$, $g_n(x) \to f(x)$ for all $x \in E$, and Theorem 1.34 gives (3) with E in place of X. This is equivalent to (3), since $\mu(E^c) = 0$.

Note that even if the f_n were defined at *every* point of X, (1) would only imply that (2) converges *almost everywhere.* Here are some other situations in which we can draw conclusions only almost everywhere:

1.39 Theorem

(*a*) *Suppose $f: X \to [0, \infty]$ is measurable, $E \in \mathfrak{M}$, and $\int_E f\,d\mu = 0$. Then $f = 0$ a.e. on E.*

(*b*) *Suppose $f \in L^1(\mu)$ and $\int_E f\,d\mu = 0$ for every $E \in \mathfrak{M}$. Then $f = 0$ a.e. on X.*

(*c*) *Suppose $f \in L^1(\mu)$ and*

$$\left|\int_X f\,d\mu\right| = \int_X |f|\,d\mu.$$

Then there is a constant α such that $\alpha f = |f|$ a.e. on X.

Note that (*c*) describes the condition under which equality holds in Theorem 1.33.

PROOF

(*a*) If $A_n = \{x \in E: f(x) > 1/n\}$, $n = 1, 2, 3, \ldots$, then

$$\frac{1}{n}\mu(A_n) \le \int_{A_n} f\,d\mu \le \int_E f\,d\mu = 0,$$

so that $\mu(A_n) = 0$. Since $\{x \in E: f(x) > 0\} = \bigcup A_n$, (*a*) follows.

(*b*) Put $f = u + iv$, let $E = \{x\colon u(x) \geq 0\}$. The real part of $\int_E f\,d\mu$ is then $\int_E u^+\,d\mu$. Hence $\int_E u^+\,d\mu = 0$, and (*a*) implies that $u^+ = 0$ a.e. We conclude similarly that

$$u^- = v^+ = v^- = 0 \text{ a.e.}$$

(*c*) Examine the proof of Theorem 1.33. Our present assumption implies that the last inequality in the proof of Theorem 1.33 must actually be an equality. Hence $\int(|f| - u)\,d\mu = 0$. Since $|f| - u \geq 0$, (*a*) shows that $|f| = u$ a.e. This says that the real part of αf is equal to $|\alpha f|$ a.e., hence $\alpha f = |\alpha f| = |f|$ a.e., which is the desired conclusion.

1.40 Theorem *Suppose $\mu(X) < \infty$, $f \in L^1(\mu)$, S is a closed set in the complex plane, and the averages*

$$A_E(f) = \frac{1}{\mu(E)} \int_E f\,d\mu$$

lie in S for every $E \in \mathfrak{M}$ with $\mu(E) > 0$. Then $f(x) \in S$ for almost all $x \in X$.

PROOF Let Δ be a closed circular disc (with center at α and radius $r > 0$, say) in the complement of S. Since S^c is the union of countably many such discs, it is enough to prove that $\mu(E) = 0$, where $E = f^{-1}(\Delta)$.

If we had $\mu(E) > 0$, then

$$|A_E(f) - \alpha| = \frac{1}{\mu(E)} \left| \int_E (f - \alpha)\,d\mu \right| \leq \frac{1}{\mu(E)} \int_E |f - \alpha|\,d\mu \leq r,$$

which is impossible, since $A_E(f) \in S$. Hence $\mu(E) = 0$.

1.41 Theorem *Let $\{E_k\}$ be a sequence of measurable sets in X, such that*

$$\sum_{k=1}^{\infty} \mu(E_k) < \infty. \tag{1}$$

Then almost all $x \in X$ lie in at most finitely many of the sets E_k.

PROOF If A is the set of all x which lie in infinitely many E_k, we have to prove that $\mu(A) = 0$. Put

$$g(x) = \sum_{k=1}^{\infty} \chi_{E_k}(x) \qquad (x \in X). \tag{2}$$

For each x, each term in this series is either 0 or 1. Hence $x \in A$ if and only if $g(x) = \infty$. By Theorem 1.27, the integral of g over X is equal to the sum in (1). Thus $g \in L^1(\mu)$ and so $g(x) < \infty$ a.e.

Exercises

1 Let $\{a_n\}$ and $\{b_n\}$ be sequences in $[-\infty, \infty]$, and prove the following assertions:

(a) $$\limsup_{n\to\infty} (-a_n) = -\liminf_{n\to\infty} a_n.$$

(b) $$\limsup_{n\to\infty} (a_n + b_n) \le \limsup_{n\to\infty} a_n + \limsup_{n\to\infty} b_n$$

provided none of the sums is of the form $\infty - \infty$.

(c) If $a_n \le b_n$ for all n, then

$$\liminf_{n\to\infty} a_n \le \liminf_{n\to\infty} b_n.$$

Show by an example that strict inequality can hold in (b).

2 Put $f_n = \chi_E$ if n is odd, $f_n = 1 - \chi_E$ if n is even. What is the relevance of this example to Fatou's lemma?

3 Suppose $f_n\colon X \to [0, \infty]$ is measurable for $n = 1, 2, 3, \ldots,$ $f_1 \ge f_2 \ge f_3 \ge \cdots \ge 0$, $f_n(x) \to f(x)$ as $n \to \infty$, for every $x \in X$, and $f_1 \in L^1(\mu)$. Prove that then

$$\lim_{n\to\infty} \int_X f_n \, d\mu = \int_X f \, d\mu$$

and show that this conclusion does *not* follow if the condition "$f_1 \in L^1(\mu)$" is omitted.

4 Prove that if f is a real function on a measurable space X such that $\{x\colon f(x) \ge r\}$ is measurable for every rational r, then f is measurable.

5 Prove that the set of points at which a sequence of measurable real functions converges is a measurable set.

6 Let X be an uncountable set, let $\mathfrak{M}$ be the collection of all sets $E \subset X$ such that either E or E^c is at most countable, and define $\mu(E) = 0$ in the first case, $\mu(E) = 1$ in the second. Prove that $\mathfrak{M}$ is a σ-algebra in X and that μ is a measure on $\mathfrak{M}$.

7 Does there exist an infinite σ-algebra which has only countably many members?

8 Prove an analogue of Theorem 1.8 for n functions.

9 Prove the conclusion of Theorem 1.7(b) under the weaker hypothesis that g is Borel measurable; i.e., prove that Borel measurable functions of measurable functions are measurable.

10 Suppose $\mu(X) < \infty$, $\{f_n\}$ is a sequence of bounded complex measurable functions on X, and $f_n \to f$ uniformly on X. Prove that

$$\lim_{n\to\infty} \int_X f_n \, d\mu = \int_X f \, d\mu,$$

and show that the hypothesis "$\mu(X) < \infty$" cannot be omitted.

11 Show that

$$A = \bigcap_{n=1}^{\infty} \bigcup_{k=n}^{\infty} E_k$$

in Theorem 1.41, and hence prove the theorem without any reference to integration.

12 Suppose $f \in L^1(\mu)$. Prove that to each $\epsilon > 0$ there exists a $\delta > 0$ such that $\int_E |f| \, d\mu < \epsilon$ whenever $\mu(E) < \delta$.

13 Show that proposition 1.24(*c*) is also true for $c = \infty$.

2

Positive Borel Measures

Vector Spaces

2.1 Definition A *complex vector space* (or a vector space over the complex field) is a set V, whose elements are called *vectors* and in which two operations, called *addition* and *scalar multiplication*, are defined, with the following familiar algebraic properties:

To every pair of vectors x and y there corresponds a vector $x + y$, in such a way that $x + y = y + x$ and $x + (y + z) = (x + y) + z$; V contains a unique vector 0 (the *zero vector* or *origin* of V) such that $x + 0 = x$ for every $x \in V$; and to each $x \in V$ there corresponds a unique vector $-x$ such that $x + (-x) = 0$.

To each pair (α,x), where $x \in V$ and α is a scalar (in this context, the word *scalar* means *complex number*), there is associated a vector $\alpha x \in V$, in such a way that $1x = x$, $\alpha(\beta x) = (\alpha\beta)x$, and such that the two distributive laws

$$(1) \qquad \alpha(x + y) = \alpha x + \alpha y, \qquad (\alpha + \beta)x = \alpha x + \beta x$$

hold.

A *linear transformation* of a vector space V into a vector space V_1 is a mapping Λ of V into V_1 such that

$$(2) \qquad \Lambda(\alpha x + \beta y) = \alpha\Lambda x + \beta\Lambda y$$

for all x and $y \in V$ and for all scalars α and β. In the special case in which V_1 is the field of scalars (this is the simplest example of a vector space, except for the trivial one consisting of 0 alone), Λ is called a *linear functional*. A linear functional is thus a complex function on V which satisfies (2).

Note that one often writes Λx, rather than $\Lambda(x)$, if Λ is linear.

The preceding definitions can of course be made equally well with any field whatsoever in place of the complex field. Unless the contrary is explicitly stated, however, all vector spaces occurring in this book will be complex, with one notable exception: the euclidean spaces R^k are vector spaces over the *real* field.

2.2 Integration as a Linear Functional Analysis is full of vector spaces and linear transformations, and there is an especially close relationship between integration on the one hand and linear functionals on the other.

For instance, Theorem 1.32 shows that $L^1(\mu)$ is a vector space, for any positive measure μ, and that the mapping

$$f \to \int_X f\,d\mu \tag{1}$$

is a linear functional on $L^1(\mu)$. Similarly, if g is any bounded measurable function, the mapping

$$f \to \int_X fg\,d\mu \tag{2}$$

is a linear functional on $L^1(\mu)$; we shall see in Chap. 6 that the functionals (2) are, in a sense, the only interesting ones on $L^1(\mu)$.

For another example, let C be the set of all continuous complex functions on the unit interval $I = [0,1]$. The sum of two continuous functions is continuous, and so is any scalar multiple of a continuous function. Hence C is a vector space, and if

$$\Lambda f = \int_0^1 f(x)\,dx \qquad (f \in C), \tag{3}$$

the integral being the ordinary Riemann integral, then Λ is clearly a linear functional on C; Λ has an additional interesting property: it is a *positive linear functional.* This means that $\Lambda f \geq 0$ whenever $f \geq 0$.

One of the tasks which is still ahead of us is the construction of the Lebesgue measure. The construction can be based on the linear functional (3), by the following observation: Consider a segment $(a,b) \subset I$ and consider the class of all $f \in C$ such that $0 \leq f \leq 1$ on I and $f(x) = 0$ for all x not in (a,b). We have $\Lambda f < b - a$ for all such f, but we can choose f so that Λf is as close to $b - a$ as desired. Thus the length (or measure) of (a,b) is intimately related to the values of the functional Λ.

The preceding observation, when looked at from a more general point of view, leads to a remarkable and extremely important theorem of F. Riesz:

To every positive linear functional Λ on C there corresponds a finite positive Borel measure μ on I such that

$$\Lambda f = \int_I f\,d\mu \qquad (f \in C). \tag{4}$$

[The converse is obvious: if μ is a finite positive Borel measure on I and if Λ is defined by (4), then Λ is a positive linear functional on C.]

It is clearly of interest to replace the bounded interval I by R^1. We can do this by restricting attention to those continuous functions on R^1 which vanish outside some bounded interval. (These functions are Riemann integrable, for instance.) Next, functions of several variables occur frequently in analysis. Thus we ought to move from R^1 to R^n. It turns out that the proof of the Riesz theorem still goes through, with hardly any changes. Moreover, it turns out that the euclidean properties of R^n (coordinates, orthogonality, etc.) play no role in the proof; in fact, if one thinks of them too much they just get in the way. Essential to the proof are certain *topological* properties of R^n. (Naturally. We are now dealing with *continuous* functions.) The crucial property is that of *local compactness:* each point of R^n has a neighborhood whose closure is compact.

We shall therefore establish the Riesz theorem in a very general setting (Theorem 2.14). The existence of Lebesgue measure then follows as a special case. Those who wish to concentrate on a more concrete situation may skip lightly over the following section on topological preliminaries (Urysohn's lemma is the item of greatest interest there; see Exercise 14) and may replace X by R^1 in the remainder of this chapter, at least for a first reading.

Topological Preliminaries

2.3 Definitions Let X be a topological space, as defined in Sec. 1.2.

(*a*) A set $E \subset X$ is *closed* if its complement E^c is open. (Hence $\varnothing$ and X are closed, finite unions of closed sets are closed, and arbitrary intersections of closed sets are closed.)

(*b*) The *closure* $\bar{E}$ of a set $E \subset X$ is the smallest closed set in X which contains E. (The following argument proves the existence of $\bar{E}$: The collection Ω of all closed subsets of X which contain E is not empty, since $X \in \Omega$; let $\bar{E}$ be the intersection of all members of Ω.)

(*c*) A set $K \subset X$ is *compact* if every open cover of K contains a finite subcover. More explicitly, the requirement is that if $\{V_\alpha\}$ is a collection of open sets whose union contains K, then the union of some finite subcollection of $\{V_\alpha\}$ also contains K.

In particular, if X is itself compact, then X is called a *compact space.*

(*d*) A *neighborhood* of a point $p \in X$ is any open subset of X which contains p. (The use of this term is not quite standardized; some use "neighborhood of p" for any set which contains an open set containing p.)

(*e*) X is a *Hausdorff space* if the following is true: If $p \in X$, $q \in X$, and $p \neq q$, then p has a neighborhood U and q has a neighborhood V such that $U \cap V = \emptyset$.

(*f*) X is *locally compact* if every point of X has a neighborhood whose closure is compact.

Obviously, every compact space is locally compact.

We recall the Heine-Borel theorem: *The compact subsets of a euclidean space R^n are precisely those that are closed and bounded* ([26],† Theorem 2.41). From this it follows easily that R^n is a locally compact Hausdorff space. Also, every metric space is a Hausdorff space.

2.4 Theorem *Suppose K is compact and F is closed, in a topological space X. If $F \subset K$, then F is compact.*

PROOF If $\{V_\alpha\}$ is an open cover of F and $W = F^c$, then $W \cup \bigcup_\alpha V_\alpha$ covers X; hence there is a finite collection $\{V_{\alpha_i}\}$ such that

$$K \subset W \cup V_{\alpha_1} \cup \cdots \cup V_{\alpha_n}.$$

Then $F \subset V_{\alpha_1} \cup \cdots \cup V_{\alpha_n}$.

Corollary *If $A \subset B$ and if B has compact closure, so does A.*

2.5 Theorem *Suppose X is a Hausdorff space, $K \subset X$, K is compact, and $p \in K^c$. Then there are open sets U and W such that $p \in U$, $K \subset W$, and $U \cap W = \emptyset$.*

PROOF If $q \in K$, the Hausdorff separation axiom implies the existence of disjoint open sets U_q and V_q, such that $p \in U_q$ and $q \in V_q$. Since K is compact, there are points $q_1, \ldots, q_n \in K$ such that

$$K \subset V_{q_1} \cup \cdots \cup V_{q_n}.$$

Our requirements are then satisfied by the sets

$$U = U_{q_1} \cap \cdots \cap U_{q_n} \quad \text{and} \quad W = V_{q_1} \cup \cdots \cup V_{q_n}.$$

Corollaries

(*a*) *Compact subsets of Hausdorff spaces are closed.*

(*b*) *If F is closed and K is compact in a Hausdorff space, then $F \cap K$ is compact.*

Corollary (*b*) follows from (*a*) and Theorem 2.4.

† Numbers in brackets refer to the Bibliography.

2.6 Theorem *If $\{K_\alpha\}$ is a collection of compact subsets of a Hausdorff space and if $\bigcap_\alpha K_\alpha = \emptyset$, then some finite subcollection of $\{K_\alpha\}$ also has empty intersection.*

PROOF Put $V_\alpha = K_\alpha^c$. Fix a member K_1 of $\{K_\alpha\}$. Since no point of K_1 belongs to every K_α, $\{V_\alpha\}$ is an open cover of K_1. Hence $K_1 \subset V_{\alpha_1} \cup \cdots \cup V_{\alpha_n}$ for some finite collection $\{V_{\alpha_i}\}$. This implies that

$$K_1 \cap K_{\alpha_1} \cap \cdots \cap K_{\alpha_n} = \emptyset.$$

2.7 Theorem *Suppose U is open in a locally compact Hausdorff space X, $K \subset U$, and K is compact. Then there is an open set V with compact closure such that*

$$K \subset V \subset \bar{V} \subset U.$$

PROOF Since every point of K has a neighborhood with compact closure, and since K is covered by the union of finitely many of these neighborhoods, K lies in an open set G with compact closure. If $U = X$, take $V = G$.

Otherwise, let C be the complement of U. Theorem 2.5 shows that to each $p \in C$ there corresponds an open set W_p such that $K \subset W_p$ and $p \notin \bar{W}_p$. Hence $\{C \cap \bar{G} \cap \bar{W}_p\}$, where p ranges over C, is a collection of compact sets with empty intersection. By Theorem 2.6 there are points $p_1, \ldots, p_n \in C$ such that

$$C \cap \bar{G} \cap \bar{W}_{p_1} \cap \cdots \cap \bar{W}_{p_n} = \emptyset.$$

The set

$$V = G \cap W_{p_1} \cap \cdots \cap W_{p_n}$$

then has the required properties, since

$$\bar{V} \subset \bar{G} \cap \bar{W}_{p_1} \cap \cdots \cap \bar{W}_{p_n}.$$

2.8 Definition Let f be a real (or extended-real) function on a topological space. If

$$\{x: f(x) > \alpha\}$$

is open for every real α, f is said to be *lower semicontinuous*. If

$$\{x: f(x) < \alpha\}$$

is open for every real α, f is said to be *upper semicontinuous*.

The following properties of semicontinuous functions are almost immediate consequences of this definition:

(a) *A real function is continuous if and only if it is both upper semicontinuous and lower semicontinuous.*

(*b*) *Characteristic functions of open sets are lower semicontinuous; characteristic functions of closed sets are upper semicontinuous.*
(*c*) *The supremum of any collection of lower semicontinuous functions is lower semicontinuous. The infimum of any collection of upper semicontinuous functions is upper semicontinuous.*

2.9 Definition The *support* of a complex function f on a topological space X is the closure of the set

$$\{x: f(x) \neq 0\}.$$

The collection of all continuous complex functions on X whose support is compact is denoted by $C_c(X)$.

Observe that $C_c(X)$ is a vector space. This is due to two facts:

(*a*) The support of $f + g$ lies in the union of the support of f and the support of g, and any finite union of compact sets is compact.
(*b*) The sum of two continuous complex functions is continuous as are scalar multiples of continuous functions.

(Statement and proof of Theorem 1.8 hold verbatim if "measurable function" is replaced by "continuous function," "measurable space" by "topological space"; take $\Phi(s,t) = s + t$, or $\Phi(s,t) = st$, to prove that sums and products of continuous functions are continuous.)

2.10 Theorem *Let X and Y be topological spaces, and let $f: X \to Y$ be continuous. If K is a compact subset of X, then $f(K)$ is compact.*

PROOF If $\{V_\alpha\}$ is an open cover of $f(K)$, then $\{f^{-1}(V_\alpha)\}$ is an open cover of K, hence $K \subset f^{-1}(V_{\alpha_1}) \cup \cdots \cup f^{-1}(V_{\alpha_n})$ for some $\alpha_1, \ldots,$ α_n, hence $f(K) \subset V_{\alpha_1} \cup \cdots \cup V_{\alpha_n}$.

Corollary *The range of any $f \in C_c(X)$ is a compact subset of the complex plane.*

In fact, if K is the support of $f \in C_c(X)$, then $f(X) \subset f(K) \cup \{0\}$. If X is not compact, then $0 \in f(X)$, but 0 need not lie in $f(K)$, as is seen by easy examples.

2.11 Notation In this chapter the following conventions will be used. The notation

$$K \prec f \tag{1}$$

will mean that K is a compact subset of X, that $f \in C_c(X)$, that $0 \leq f(x) \leq 1$ for all $x \in X$, and that $f(x) = 1$ for all $x \in K$. The notation

$$f \prec V \tag{2}$$

will mean that V is open, that $f \in C_c(X)$, $0 \le f \le 1$, and that the support of f lies in V. The notation

$$(3) \qquad K \prec f \prec V$$

will be used to indicate that both (1) and (2) hold.

2.12 Urysohn's Lemma *Suppose X is a locally compact Hausdorff space, V is open in X, $K \subset V$, and K is compact. Then there exists an $f \in C_c(X)$, such that*

$$(1) \qquad K \prec f \prec V.$$

In terms of characteristic functions, the conclusion asserts the existence of a *continuous function* f which satisfies the inequalities $\chi_K \le f \le \chi_V$. Note that it is easy to find *semicontinuous* functions which do this; examples are χ_K and χ_V.

PROOF Put $r_1 = 0$, $r_2 = 1$, and let $r_3, r_4, r_5, \ldots$ be an enumeration of the rationals in (0,1). By Theorem 2.7, we can find open sets V_0 and then V_1 such that $\bar{V}_0$ is compact and

$$(2) \qquad K \subset V_1 \subset \bar{V}_1 \subset V_0 \subset \bar{V}_0 \subset V.$$

Suppose $n \ge 2$ and $V_{r_1}, \ldots, V_{r_n}$ have been chosen in such a manner that $r_i < r_j$ implies $\bar{V}_{r_j} \subset V_{r_i}$. Then one of the numbers $r_1, \ldots, r_n$, say r_i, will be the largest one which is smaller than r_{n+1}, and another, say r_j, will be the smallest one larger than r_{n+1}. Using Theorem 2.7 again, we can find $V_{r_{n+1}}$ so that

$$\bar{V}_{r_j} \subset V_{r_{n+1}} \subset \bar{V}_{r_{n+1}} \subset V_{r_i}.$$

Continuing, we obtain a collection $\{V_r\}$ of open sets, one for every rational $r \in [0,1]$, with the following properties: $K \subset V_1$, $\bar{V}_0 \subset V$, *each $\bar{V}_r$ is compact, and*

$$(3) \qquad s > r \quad \textit{implies} \quad \bar{V}_s \subset V_r.$$

Define

$$(4) \quad f_r(x) = \begin{cases} r & \text{if } x \in V_r, \\ 0 & \text{otherwise,} \end{cases} \qquad g_s(x) = \begin{cases} 1 & \text{if } x \in \bar{V}_s, \\ s & \text{otherwise,} \end{cases}$$

and

$$(5) \qquad f = \sup_r f_r, \qquad g = \inf_s g_s.$$

The remarks following Definition 2.8 show that f is lower semicontinuous and that g is upper semicontinuous. It is clear that $0 \le f \le 1$, that $f(x) = 1$ if $x \in K$, and that f has its support in $\bar{V}_0$. The proof will be completed by showing that $f = g$.

The inequality $f_r(x) > g_s(x)$ is possible only if $r > s$, $x \in V_r$, and $x \notin \bar{V}_s$. But $r > s$ implies $V_r \subset V_s$. Hence $f_r \leq g_s$ for all r and s, so $f \leq g$.

Suppose $f(x) < g(x)$ for some x. Then there are rationals r and s such that $f(x) < r < s < g(x)$. Since $f(x) < r$, we have $x \notin V_r$; since $g(x) > s$, we have $x \in \bar{V}_s$. By (3), this is a contradiction. Hence $f = g$.

2.13 Theorem *Suppose $V_1, \ldots, V_n$ are open subsets of a locally compact Hausdorff space X, K is compact, and*

$$K \subset V_1 \cup \cdots \cup V_n.$$

Then there exist functions $h_i \prec V_i$ $(i = 1, \ldots, n)$ such that

$$h_1(x) + \cdots + h_n(x) = 1 \qquad (x \in K). \tag{1}$$

Because of (1), the collection $\{h_1, \ldots, h_n\}$ is called a *partition of unity on K*, subordinate to the cover $\{V_1, \ldots, V_n\}$.

PROOF By Theorem 2.7, each $x \in K$ has a neighborhood W_x with compact closure $\bar{W}_x \subset V_i$ for some i (depending on x). There are points $x_1, \ldots, x_m$ such that $W_{x_1} \cup \cdots \cup W_{x_m} \supset K$. If $1 \leq i \leq n$, let H_i be the union of those $\bar{W}_{x_j}$ which lie in V_i. By Urysohn's lemma, there are functions g_i such that $H_i \prec g_i \prec V_i$. Define

$$\begin{aligned} h_1 &= g_1 \\ h_2 &= (1 - g_1)g_2 \\ &\cdots\cdots \\ h_n &= (1 - g_1)(1 - g_2) \cdots (1 - g_{n-1})g_n. \end{aligned} \tag{2}$$

Then $h_i \prec V_i$. It is easily verified, by induction, that

$$h_1 + h_2 + \cdots + h_n = 1 - (1 - g_1)(1 - g_2) \cdots (1 - g_n). \tag{3}$$

Since $K \subset H_1 \cup \cdots \cup H_n$, at least one $g_i(x) = 1$ at each point $x \in K$; hence (3) shows that (1) holds.

The Riesz Representation Theorem

2.14 Theorem *Let X be a locally compact Hausdorff space, and let Λ be a positive linear functional on $C_c(X)$. Then there exists a σ-algebra $\mathfrak{M}$ in X which contains all Borel sets in X, and there exists a unique positive measure μ on $\mathfrak{M}$ which represents Λ in the sense that*

$$\Lambda f = \int_X f \, d\mu \tag{a}$$

for every $f \in C_c(X)$ *and which has the following additional properties:*

(*b*) $\mu(K) < \infty$ *for every compact set* $K \subset X$.

(*c*) *For every* $E \in \mathfrak{M}$, *we have*

$$\mu(E) = \inf \{\mu(V): E \subset V, V \text{ open}\}.$$

(*d*) *The relation*

$$\mu(E) = \sup \{\mu(K): K \subset E, K \text{ compact}\}$$

holds for every open set E, *and for every* $E \in \mathfrak{M}$ *with* $\mu(E) < \infty$.

(*e*) *If* $E \in \mathfrak{M}$, $A \subset E$, *and* $\mu(E) = 0$, *then* $A \in \mathfrak{M}$.

Property (*a*) is of course the one of greatest interest. After we define $\mathfrak{M}$ and μ, (*b*) to (*d*) will be established in the course of proving that $\mathfrak{M}$ is a σ-algebra and that μ is countably additive. We shall see later (Theorem 2.18) that in "reasonable" spaces X *every* Borel measure which satisfies (*b*) also satisfies (*c*) and (*d*) and that (*d*) actually holds for every $E \in \mathfrak{M}$, in those cases. Property (*e*) merely says that $(X,\mathfrak{M},\mu)$ is a complete measure space, in the sense of Theorem 1.36.

Throughout the proof of this theorem, the letter K will stand for a compact subset of X, and V will denote an open set in X.

Let us begin by proving the uniqueness of μ. If μ satisfies (*c*) and (*d*), it is clear that μ is determined on $\mathfrak{M}$ by its values on compact sets. Hence it suffices to prove that $\mu_1(K) = \mu_2(K)$ for all K, whenever μ_1 and μ_2 are measures for which the theorem holds. So, fix K and $\epsilon > 0$. By (*b*) and (*c*), there exists a $V \supset K$ with $\mu_2(V) < \mu_2(K) + \epsilon$; by Urysohn's lemma, there exists an f so that $K \prec f \prec V$; hence

$$\mu_1(K) = \int_X \chi_K \, d\mu_1 \leq \int_X f \, d\mu_1 = \Lambda f = \int_X f \, d\mu_2$$

$$\leq \int_X \chi_V \, d\mu_2 = \mu_2(V) < \mu_2(K) + \epsilon.$$

Thus $\mu_1(K) \leq \mu_2(K)$. If we interchange the roles of μ_1 and μ_2, the opposite inequality is obtained, and the uniqueness of μ is proved.

Incidentally, the above computation shows that (*a*) forces (*b*).

Construction of μ *and* $\mathfrak{M}$

For every open set V in X, define

(1) $$\mu(V) = \sup \{\Lambda f: f \prec V\}.$$

If $V_1 \subset V_2$, it is clear that (1) implies $\mu(V_1) \leq \mu(V_2)$. Hence

(2) $$\mu(E) = \inf \{\mu(V): E \subset V, V \text{ open}\}$$

if E is an open set, and it is consistent with (1) to *define* $\mu(E)$ by (2), for *every* $E \subset X$.

Note that although we have defined $\mu(E)$ for every $E \subset X$, the countable additivity of μ will be proved only on a certain σ-algebra $\mathfrak{M}$ in X.

Let $\mathfrak{M}_F$ be the class of all $E \subset X$ which satisfy two conditions: $\mu(E) < \infty$, and

$$\mu(E) = \sup \{\mu(K) : K \subset E,\ K \text{ compact}\}. \tag{3}$$

Finally, let $\mathfrak{M}$ be the class of all $E \subset X$ such that $E \cap K \in \mathfrak{M}_F$ for every compact K.

Proof that μ and $\mathfrak{M}$ have the required properties

It is evident that μ is *monotone*, i.e., that $\mu(A) \leq \mu(B)$ if $A \subset B$ and that $\mu(E) = 0$ implies $E \in \mathfrak{M}_F$ and $E \in \mathfrak{M}$. Thus (*e*) holds, and so does (*c*), by definition.

Since the proof of the other assertions is rather long, it will be convenient to divide it into several steps.

Observe that the positivity of Λ implies that Λ is *monotone:* $f \leq g$ implies $\Lambda f \leq \Lambda g$. This is clear, since $\Lambda g = \Lambda f + \Lambda(g - f)$ and $g - f \geq 0$. This monotonicity will be used in Steps II and X.

STEP I *If $E_1, E_2, E_3, \ldots$ are arbitrary subsets of X, then*

$$\mu\left(\bigcup_{i=1}^{\infty} E_i\right) \leq \sum_{i=1}^{\infty} \mu(E_i). \tag{4}$$

PROOF We first show that

$$\mu(V_1 \cup V_2) \leq \mu(V_1) + \mu(V_2) \tag{5}$$

if V_1 and V_2 are open. Choose $g \prec V_1 \cup V_2$. By Theorem 2.13 there are functions h_1 and h_2 such that $h_i \prec V_i$ and $h_1(x) + h_2(x) = 1$ for all x in the support of g. Hence $h_ig \prec V_i$, $g = h_1g + h_2g$, and so

$$\Lambda g = \Lambda(h_1g) + \Lambda(h_2g) \leq \mu(V_1) + \mu(V_2). \tag{6}$$

Since (6) holds for *every* $g \prec V_1 \cup V_2$, (5) follows.

If $\mu(E_i) = \infty$ for some i, then (4) is trivially true. Suppose therefore that $\mu(E_i) < \infty$ for every i. Choose $\epsilon > 0$. By (2) there are open sets $V_i \supset E_i$ such that

$$\mu(V_i) < \mu(E_i) + 2^{-i}\epsilon \qquad (i = 1, 2, 3, \ldots). \tag{7}$$

Put $V = \bigcup_1^{\infty} V_i$, and choose $f \prec V$. Since f has compact support, $f \prec V_1 \cup \cdots \cup V_n$ for some n. Applying induction to (5), we therefore obtain

$$\Lambda f \le \mu(V_1 \cup \cdots \cup V_n) \le \mu(V_1) + \cdots + \mu(V_n) \le \sum_{i=1}^{\infty} \mu(E_i) + \epsilon.$$

Since this holds for every $f \prec V$, and since $\bigcup E_i \subset V$, it follows that

$$\mu(\bigcup_{i=1}^{\infty} E_i) \le \mu(V) \le \sum_{i=1}^{\infty} \mu(E_i) + \epsilon, \tag{8}$$

which proves (4), since ϵ was arbitrary.

STEP II $\mathfrak{M}_F$ *contains every compact set.*

This implies assertion (*b*) of the theorem.

PROOF If $K \prec f$, let $V = \{x: f(x) > \frac{1}{2}\}$. Then $K \subset V$, and $g \le 2f$ whenever $g \prec V$. Hence

$$\mu(K) \le \mu(V) = \sup \{\Lambda g: g \prec V\} \le \Lambda(2f) < \infty.$$

Since K evidently satisfies (3), $K \in \mathfrak{M}_F$.

STEP III *Every open set satisfies* (3). *Hence* $\mathfrak{M}_F$ *contains every open set* V *with* $\mu(V) < \infty$.

PROOF Let α be a real number such that $\alpha < \mu(V)$. There exists an $f \prec V$ with $\alpha < \Lambda f$. If W is *any* open set which contains the support K of f, then $f \prec W$, hence $\Lambda f \le \mu(W)$. Thus $\Lambda f \le \mu(K)$. This exhibits a compact $K \subset V$ with $\alpha < \mu(K)$, so that (3) holds for V.

STEP IV *Suppose* $E = \bigcup_{i=1}^{\infty} E_i$, *where* $E_1, E_2, E_3, \ldots$ *are pairwise disjoint members of* $\mathfrak{M}_F$. *Then*

$$\mu(E) = \sum_{i=1}^{\infty} \mu(E_i). \tag{9}$$

If, in addition, $\mu(E) < \infty$, *then also* $E \in \mathfrak{M}_F$.

PROOF We first show that

$$\mu(K_1 \cup K_2) = \mu(K_1) + \mu(K_2) \tag{10}$$

if K_1 and K_2 are disjoint compact sets. Choose $\epsilon > 0$. By Theorem 2.7 (with K_1 in place of K and K_2^c in place of U) there are disjoint open sets V_1 and V_2 such that $K_i \subset V_i$. By Step II, there is an open set $W \supset K_1 \cup K_2$ such that $\mu(W) < \mu(K_1 \cup K_2) + \epsilon$, and there are functions $f_i \prec W \cap V_i$ such that $\Lambda f_i > \mu(W \cap V_i) - \epsilon$, for $i = 1, 2$.

Since $K_i \subset W \cap V_i$ and $f_1 + f_2 \prec W$ (it is here that $V_1 \cap V_2 = \emptyset$ is used!), we obtain

$$\mu(K_1) + \mu(K_2) \leq \mu(W \cap V_1) + \mu(W \cap V_2) < \Lambda f_1 + \Lambda f_2 + 2\epsilon$$
$$\leq \mu(W) + 2\epsilon < \mu(K_1 \cup K_2) + 3\epsilon.$$

Since ϵ was arbitrary, (10) follows from Step I.

If $\mu(E) = \infty$, (9) follows from Step I. Assume therefore that $\mu(E) < \infty$, and choose $\epsilon > 0$. Since $E_i \in \mathfrak{M}_F$, there are compact sets $H_i \subset E_i$ with

$$\mu(H_i) > \mu(E_i) - 2^{-i}\epsilon \qquad (i = 1, 2, 3, \ldots). \tag{11}$$

Putting $K_n = H_1 \cup \cdots \cup H_n$ and using induction on (10), we obtain

$$\mu(E) \geq \mu(K_n) = \sum_{i=1}^{n} \mu(H_i) > \sum_{i=1}^{n} \mu(E_i) - \epsilon. \tag{12}$$

Since (12) holds for every n and every $\epsilon > 0$, the left side of (9) is not smaller than the right side, and so (9) follows from Step I.

But if $\mu(E) < \infty$ and $\epsilon > 0$, (9) shows that

$$\mu(E) \leq \sum_{i=1}^{N} \mu(E_i) + \epsilon \tag{13}$$

for some N. By (12), it follows that $\mu(E) \leq \mu(K_N) + 2\epsilon$, and this shows that E satisfies (3); hence $E \in \mathfrak{M}_F$.

STEP V *If $E \in \mathfrak{M}_F$ and $\epsilon > 0$, there is a compact K and an open V such that $K \subset E \subset V$ and $\mu(V - K) < \epsilon$.*

PROOF Our definitions show that there exist K and V so that

$$\mu(V) - \frac{\epsilon}{2} < \mu(E) < \mu(K) + \frac{\epsilon}{2}.$$

Since $V - K$ is open, $V - K \in \mathfrak{M}_F$, by Step III. Hence Step IV implies that

$$\mu(K) + \mu(V - K) = \mu(V) < \mu(K) + \epsilon.$$

STEP VI *If $A \in \mathfrak{M}_F$ and $B \in \mathfrak{M}_F$, then $A - B$, $A \cup B$, and $A \cap B$ belong to $\mathfrak{M}_F$.*

PROOF If $\epsilon > 0$, Step V shows that there are sets K_i and V_i such that $K_1 \subset A \subset V_1$, $K_2 \subset B \subset V_2$, and $\mu(V_i - K_i) < \epsilon$, for $i = 1, 2$. Since

$$A - B \subset V_1 - K_2 \subset (V_1 - K_1) \cup (K_1 - V_2) \cup (V_2 - K_2),$$

Step I shows that

$$\mu(A - B) \leq \epsilon + \mu(K_1 - V_2) + \epsilon. \tag{14}$$

Since $K_1 - V_2$ is a compact subset of $A - B$, (14) shows that $A - B$ satisfies (3), so that $A - B \in \mathfrak{M}_F$.

Since $A \cup B = (A - B) \cup B$, it follows (by Step IV) that $A \cup B \in \mathfrak{M}_F$. Since $A \cap B = A - (A - B)$, we also have $A \cap B \in \mathfrak{M}_F$.

STEP VII *$\mathfrak{M}$ is a σ-algebra in X which contains all Borel sets.*

PROOF Let K be an arbitrary compact set in X.

If $A \in \mathfrak{M}$, then $A^c \cap K = K - (A \cap K)$, so that $A^c \cap K$ is a difference of two members of $\mathfrak{M}_F$. Hence $A^c \cap K \in \mathfrak{M}_F$, and we conclude: $A \in \mathfrak{M}$ implies $A^c \in \mathfrak{M}$.

Next, suppose $A = \bigcup_1^\infty A_i$, where each $A_i \in \mathfrak{M}$. Put $B_1 = A_1 \cap K$, and

(15) $$B_n = (A_n \cap K) - (B_1 \cup \cdots \cup B_{n-1}) \qquad (n = 2, 3, 4, \ldots).$$

Then $\{B_n\}$ is a disjoint sequence of members of $\mathfrak{M}_F$, by Step VI, and $A \cap K = \bigcup_1^\infty B_n$. It follows from Step IV that $A \cap K \in \mathfrak{M}_F$. Hence $A \in \mathfrak{M}$.

Finally, if C is closed, then $C \cap K$ is compact, hence $C \cap K \in \mathfrak{M}_F$, so $C \in \mathfrak{M}$. In particular, $X \in \mathfrak{M}$.

We have thus proved that $\mathfrak{M}$ is a σ-algebra in X which contains all closed subsets of X. Hence $\mathfrak{M}$ contains all Borel sets in X.

STEP VIII *$\mathfrak{M}_F$ consists of precisely those sets $E \in \mathfrak{M}$ for which $\mu(E) < \infty$.*

This implies assertion (*d*) of the theorem.

PROOF If $E \in \mathfrak{M}_F$, Steps II and VI imply that $E \cap K \in \mathfrak{M}_F$ for every compact K, hence $E \in \mathfrak{M}$.

Conversely, suppose $E \in \mathfrak{M}$ and $\mu(E) < \infty$, and choose $\epsilon > 0$. There is an open set $V \supset E$ with $\mu(V) < \infty$; by III and V, there is a compact $K \subset V$ with $\mu(V - K) < \epsilon$. Since $E \cap K \in \mathfrak{M}_F$, there is a compact $H \subset E \cap K$ with

$$\mu(E \cap K) < \mu(H) + \epsilon.$$

Since $E \subset (E \cap K) \cup (V - K)$, it follows that

$$\mu(E) \leq \mu(E \cap K) + \mu(V - K) < \mu(H) + 2\epsilon,$$

which implies that $E \in \mathfrak{M}_F$.

STEP IX *μ is a measure on $\mathfrak{M}$.*

PROOF The countable additivity of μ on $\mathfrak{M}$ follows immediately from Steps IV and VIII.

STEP X *For every $f \in C_c(X)$, $\Lambda f = \int_X f\,d\mu$.*

This proves (*a*), and completes the theorem.

PROOF Clearly, it is enough to prove this for real f. Also, it is enough to prove the *inequality*

$$\Lambda f \leq \int_X f\,d\mu \tag{16}$$

for every real $f \in C_c(X)$. For once (16) is established, the linearity of Λ shows that

$$-\Lambda f = \Lambda(-f) \leq \int_X (-f)\,d\mu = -\int_X f\,d\mu,$$

which, together with (16), shows that equality holds in (16).

Let K be the support of a real $f \in C_c(X)$, let $[a,b]$ be an interval which contains the range of f (note the Corollary to Theorem 2.10), choose $\epsilon > 0$, and choose y_i, for $i = 0, 1, \ldots, n$, so that $y_i - y_{i-1} < \epsilon$ and

$$y_0 < a < y_1 < \cdots < y_n = b. \tag{17}$$

Put

$$E_i = \{x \colon y_{i-1} < f(x) \leq y_i\} \cap K \qquad (i = 1, \ldots, n). \tag{18}$$

Since f is continuous, f is Borel measurable, and the sets E_i are therefore disjoint Borel sets whose union is K. There are open sets $V_i \supset E_i$ such that

$$\mu(V_i) < \mu(E_i) + \frac{\epsilon}{n} \qquad (i = 1, \ldots, n) \tag{19}$$

and such that $f(x) < y_i + \epsilon$ for all $x \in V_i$. By Theorem 2.13, there are functions $h_i \prec V_i$ such that $\Sigma h_i = 1$ on K. Hence $f = \Sigma h_i f$. Since $h_i f \leq (y_i + \epsilon)h_i$, and since $y_i - \epsilon < f(x)$ on E_i, we have

$$\begin{aligned}
\Lambda f &= \sum_{i=1}^{n} \Lambda(h_i f) \leq \sum_{i=1}^{n} (y_i + \epsilon)\Lambda h_i \leq \sum_{i=1}^{n} (y_i + \epsilon)\mu(V_i) \\
&\leq \sum_{i=1}^{n} (y_i + \epsilon)\mu(E_i) + \sum_{i=1}^{n} (y_i + \epsilon)\frac{\epsilon}{n} \\
&\leq \sum_{i=1}^{n} (y_i - \epsilon)\mu(E_i) + 2\epsilon\mu(K) + (b + \epsilon)\epsilon \\
&\leq \sum_{i=1}^{n} \int_{E_i} f\,d\mu + \epsilon[2\mu(K) + b + \epsilon] \\
&= \int_X f\,d\mu + \epsilon[2\mu(K) + b + \epsilon].
\end{aligned}$$

Since ϵ was arbitrary, (16) is established, and the proof of the theorem is complete.

Regularity Properties of Borel Measures

2.15 Definition A measure μ defined on the σ-algebra of all Borel sets in a locally compact Hausdorff space X is called a *Borel measure on* X. If μ is positive, a Borel set $E \subset X$ is *outer regular* or *inner regular*, respectively, if E has property (*c*) or (*d*) of Theorem 2.14. If every Borel set in X is both outer and inner regular, μ is called *regular*.

In our proof of the Riesz theorem, outer regularity of every set E was built into the construction, but inner regularity was proved only for the open sets and for those $E \in \mathfrak{M}$ for which $\mu(E) < \infty$. It turns out that this flaw is in the nature of things. One cannot prove regularity of μ under the hypothesis of Theorem 2.14; an example is described in Exercise 16.

However, a slight strengthening of the hypotheses does give us a regular measure. Theorem 2.17 shows this. And if we specialize a little more, Theorem 2.18 shows that all regularity problems neatly disappear.

2.16 Definition A set E in a topological space is called *σ-compact* if E is a countable union of compact sets.

A set E in a measure space (with measure μ) is said to have *σ-finite measure* if E is a countable union of sets E_i with $\mu(E_i) < \infty$.

For example, in the situation described in Theorem 2.14, every σ-compact set has σ-finite measure. Also, it is easy to see that if $E \in \mathfrak{M}$ and E has σ-finite measure, then E is inner regular.

2.17 Theorem *Suppose X is a locally compact, σ-compact Hausdorff space. If $\mathfrak{M}$ and μ are as described in the statement of Theorem* 2.14, *then $\mathfrak{M}$ and μ have the following properties:*

(*a*) *If $E \in \mathfrak{M}$ and $\epsilon > 0$, there is a closed set F and an open set V such that $F \subset E \subset V$ and $\mu(V - F) < \epsilon$.*
(*b*) *μ is a regular Borel measure on X.*
(*c*) *If $E \in \mathfrak{M}$, there are sets A and B such that A is an F_σ, B is a G_δ, $A \subset E \subset B$, and $\mu(B - A) = 0$.*

As a corollary of (*c*) we see that every $E \in \mathfrak{M}$ is the union of an F_σ and a set of measure 0.

PROOF Let $X = K_1 \cup K_2 \cup K_3 \cup \cdots$, where each K_n is compact. If $E \in \mathfrak{M}$ and $\epsilon > 0$, then $\mu(K_n \cap E) < \infty$, and there are open sets

$V_n \supset K_n \cap E$ such that

$$(1) \qquad \mu(V_n - (K_n \cap E)) < \frac{\epsilon}{2^{n+1}} \qquad (n = 1, 2, 3, \ldots).$$

If $V = \bigcup V_n$, then $V - E \subset \bigcup(V_n - (K_n \cap E))$, so that

$$\mu(V - E) < \frac{\epsilon}{2}.$$

Apply this to E^c in place of E: There is an open set $W \supset E^c$ such that $\mu(W - E^c) < \epsilon/2$. If $F = W^c$, then $F \subset E$, and $E - F = W - E^c$. Now (a) follows.

If F is closed, then $F = \bigcup(K_n \cap F)$, each $K_n \cap F$ is compact, and

$$\mu((K_1 \cup \cdots \cup K_n) \cap F) \to \mu(F)$$

as $n \to \infty$. Hence (b) follows from (a).

If we apply (a) with $\epsilon = 1/j$ $(j = 1, 2, 3, \ldots)$, we obtain closed sets F_j and open sets V_j such that $F_j \subset E \subset V_j$ and $\mu(V_j - F_j) < 1/j$. Put $A = \bigcup F_j$ and $B = \bigcap V_j$. Then $A \subset E \subset B$, A is an F_σ, B is a G_δ, and $\mu(B - A) = 0$ since $B - A \subset V_j - F_j$ for $j = 1, 2, 3, \ldots$. This proves (c).

2.18 Theorem *Let X be a locally compact Hausdorff space in which every open set is σ-compact. Let λ be any positive Borel measure on X such that $\lambda(K) < \infty$ for every compact set K. Then λ is regular.*

Note that every euclidean space R^k satisfies the present hypothesis, since every open set in R^k is a countable union of closed balls.

PROOF Put $\Lambda f = \int_X f\, d\lambda$, for $f \in C_c(X)$. Since $\lambda(K) < \infty$ for every compact K, Λ is a positive linear functional on $C_c(X)$, and there is a measure μ, satisfying the conclusions of Theorem 2.17, such that

$$(1) \qquad \int_X f\, d\lambda = \int_X f\, d\mu \qquad (f \in C_c(X)).$$

Let V be open in X. Then $V = \bigcup H_i$, where H_i is compact for $i = 1, 2, 3, \ldots$. Choose f_1 so that $H_1 \prec f_1 \prec V$. Having chosen $f_1, \ldots, f_n$, with supports $K_1, \ldots, K_n$, choose f_{n+1} so that

$$(2) \qquad H_1 \cup \cdots \cup H_n \cup K_1 \cup \cdots \cup K_n \prec f_{n+1} \prec V.$$

The sequence $\{f_n\}$ increases monotonically to χ_V at every point of X. Hence (1) implies

$$(3) \qquad \lambda(V) = \lim_{n\to\infty} \int_X f_n\, d\lambda = \lim_{n\to\infty} \int_X f_n\, d\mu = \mu(V).$$

Let E be a Borel set in X, and choose $\epsilon > 0$. Since μ satisfies Theorem 2.17, there is a closed set F and an open set V such that

$F \subset E \subset V$ and $\mu(V - F) < \epsilon$. But $V - F$ is open. Hence (3) shows that $\lambda(V - F) < \epsilon$, and this proves the regularity of λ, as in Theorem 2.17.

Note: It also follows easily that $\lambda(E) = \mu(E)$ for every Borel set E in X. In Exercise 17 a compact Hausdorff space is described which contains an open set which is not σ-compact and in which the preceding theorem fails.

Lebesgue Measure

2.19 Euclidean Spaces Euclidean k-dimensional space R^k is the set of all points $x = (\xi_1, \ldots, \xi_k)$ whose coordinates ξ_i are real numbers, with the following algebraic and topological structure:

If $x = (\xi_1, \ldots, \xi_k)$, $y = (\eta_1, \ldots, \eta_k)$, and α is a real number, $x + y$ and αx are defined by

(1) $$x + y = (\xi_1 + \eta_1, \ldots, \xi_k + \eta_k), \qquad \alpha x = (\alpha\xi_1, \ldots, \alpha\xi_k).$$

This makes R^k into a real vector space. If $x \cdot y = \Sigma \xi_i \eta_i$ and $|x| = (x \cdot x)^{\frac{1}{2}}$, the Schwarz inequality $|x \cdot y| \le |x|\,|y|$ leads to the triangle inequality

(2) $$|x - y| \le |x - z| + |z - y|;$$

hence we obtain a metric by setting $\rho(x,y) = |x - y|$. We assume that these facts are familiar to the reader, and shall prove them in greater generality in Chap. 4.

If $E \subset R^k$ and $x \in R^k$, the *translate of E by x* is the set

(3) $$E + x = \{y + x : y \in E\}.$$

A set of the form

(4) $$W = \{x : \alpha_i < \xi_i < \beta_i,\ 1 \le i \le k\},$$

or any set obtained by replacing any or all of the $<$ signs in (4) by $\le$, is called a *k-cell;* its volume is defined to be

(5) $$\text{vol}\,(W) = \prod_{i=1}^{k} (\beta_i - \alpha_i).$$

If $a \in R^k$ and $\delta > 0$, we shall call the set

(6) $$Q(a;\delta) = \{x : \alpha_i \le \xi_i < \alpha_i + \delta,\ 1 \le i \le k\}$$

the *δ-box with corner at a.* Here $a = (\alpha_1, \ldots, \alpha_k)$.

For $n = 1, 2, 3, \ldots$, we let P_n be the set of all $x \in R^k$ whose coordinates are integral multiples of 2^{-n}, and we let Ω_n be the collection of all

2^{-n}-boxes with corners at points of P_n. We shall need the following four properties of $\{\Omega_n\}$. The first three are obvious by inspection.

(a) *If n is fixed, each $x \in R^k$ lies in one and only one member of Ω_n.*
(b) *If $Q' \in \Omega_n$, $Q'' \in \Omega_r$, and $r < n$, then either $Q' \subset Q''$ or $Q' \cap Q'' = \varnothing$.*
(c) *If $Q \in \Omega_r$, then* vol $(Q) = 2^{-rk}$; *and if $n > r$, the set P_n has exactly $2^{(n-r)k}$ points in Q.*
(d) *Every nonempty open set in R^k is a countable union of disjoint boxes belonging to $\Omega_1 \cup \Omega_2 \cup \Omega_3 \cup \cdots$.*

PROOF OF (*d*) If V is open, every $x \in V$ lies in an open ball which lies in V; hence $x \in Q \subset V$ for some Q belonging to some Ω_n. In other words, V is the union of all boxes which lie in V and which belong to some Ω_n. From this collection of boxes, select those which belong to Ω_1, and remove those in $\Omega_2, \Omega_3, \ldots$ which lie in any of the selected boxes. From the remaining collection, select those boxes of Ω_2 which lie in V, and remove those in $\Omega_3, \Omega_4, \ldots$ which lie in any of the selected boxes. If we proceed in this way, (*a*) and (*b*) show that (*d*) holds.

2.20 Theorem *There exists a positive complete measure m defined on a σ-algebra $\mathfrak{M}$ in R^k, with the following properties:*

(a) $m(W) =$ vol (W) *for every k-cell W.*
(b) *$\mathfrak{M}$ contains all Borel sets in R^k; more precisely, $E \in \mathfrak{M}$ if and only if there are sets A and $B \subset R^k$ such that $A \subset E \subset B$, A is an F_σ, B is a G_δ, and $m(B - A) = 0$. Also, m is regular.*
(c) *m is translation invariant, i.e.,*

$$m(E + x) = m(E)$$

for every $E \in \mathfrak{M}$ and every $x \in R^k$.
(d) *If μ is any positive translation invariant Borel measure on R^k such that $\mu(K) < \infty$ for every compact set K, then there is a constant c such that $\mu(E) = cm(E)$ for all Borel sets $E \subset R^k$.*

The members of $\mathfrak{M}$ are the *Lebesgue measurable* sets in R^k; m is the *Lebesgue measure* on R^k. When clarity requires it, we shall write m_k in place of m. For a description of other measures on R^1, see Theorem 8.14.

PROOF If f is any complex function on R^k, with compact support, define

$$\Lambda_n f = 2^{-nk} \sum_{x \in P_n} f(x) \qquad (n = 1, 2, 3, \ldots), \tag{1}$$

where P_n is as in Sec. 2.19.

Now suppose $f \in C_c(R^k)$, f is real, W is an open k-cell which contains the support of f, and $\epsilon > 0$. The uniform continuity of f ([26], Theorem 4.19) shows that there is an integer N and that there are functions g and h with support in W, such that (i) g and h are constant on each box belonging to Ω_N, (ii) $g \leq f \leq h$, and (iii) $h - g < \epsilon$. If $n > N$, Property 2.19(c) shows that

$$\Lambda_N g = \Lambda_n g \leq \Lambda_n f \leq \Lambda_n h = \Lambda_N h. \tag{2}$$

Thus the upper and lower limits of $\{\Lambda_n f\}$ differ by at most ϵ vol (W), and since ϵ was arbitrary, we have proved the existence of

$$\Lambda f = \lim_{n \to \infty} \Lambda_n f \qquad (f \in C_c(R^k)). \tag{3}$$

It is immediate that Λ is a positive linear functional on $C_c(R^k)$. (In fact, Λf is precisely the Riemann integral of f over R^k. We went through the preceding construction in order not to have to rely on any theorems about Riemann integrals in several variables.) *We define m and $\mathfrak{M}$ to be the measure and σ-algebra associated with this Λ as in Theorem* 2.14.

Since Theorem 2.14 gives us a complete measure and since R^k is σ-compact, Theorem 2.17 implies assertion (b) of Theorem 2.20.

To prove (a), let W be the open cell 2.19(4), let E_r be the union of those boxes belonging to Ω_r whose closure lies in W, and choose f so that $\bar{E}_r \prec f \prec W$. Our construction of Λf then shows that

$$\Lambda f \geq \prod_{i=1}^{k} (\beta_i - \alpha_i - 2^{1-r}). \tag{4}$$

Let $r \to \infty$, and recall that

$$m(W) = \sup \{\Lambda f : f \prec W\}, \tag{5}$$

by the construction in Theorem 2.14. Thus $m(W) = \text{vol}\,(W)$ for every open cell W, and since every cell is the intersection of a decreasing sequence of open cells, we obtain (a).

Since vol $(W + x) = $ vol (W), it follows that

$$m(E + x) = m(E) \qquad (x \in R^k) \tag{6}$$

holds for every cell E; in particular, (6) holds for every box E; Property 2.19(d) therefore implies that (6) holds for every open set E; and now (6) follows for every $E \in \mathfrak{M}$, since

$$m(E) = \inf \{m(V) : E \subset V,\ V \text{ open}\}.$$

This proves (c).

Finally, suppose μ is a translation invariant Borel measure on R^k.

Put $c = \mu(Q_0)$, where Q_0 is a 1-box. Since Q_0 is the union of 2^{nk} disjoint 2^{-n}-boxes, since these are translates of each other, and since $m(Q_0) = 1$, we have

$$(7) \qquad 2^{nk}\mu(Q) = \mu(Q_0) = cm(Q_0) = 2^{nk}cm(Q)$$

for every 2^{-n}-box Q. Property 2.19(d) now implies that $\mu(E) = cm(E)$ for every open set E, and the regularity of m and μ (Theorem 2.18) shows that this last equation holds for every Borel set E.

This completes the proof.

2.21 Remarks If m is the Lebesgue measure on R^k, it is customary to write $L^1(R^k)$ in place of $L^1(m)$. If E is a Lebesgue measurable subset of R^k, and if m is restricted to the measurable subsets of E, a new measure space is obtained in an obvious fashion. The phrase "$f \varepsilon L^1$ on E" or "$f \varepsilon L^1(E)$" is used to indicate that f is integrable on this measure space.

If $k = 1$, if I is any of the sets (a,b), $(a,b]$, $[a,b)$, $[a,b]$, and if $f \varepsilon L^1(I)$, it is customary to write

$$\int_a^b f(x)\,dx \qquad \text{in place of} \qquad \int_I f\,dm.$$

Since the Lebesgue measure of any single point is 0, it makes no difference over which of these four sets the integral is extended.

If f is a continuous complex function on $[a,b]$, then the Riemann integral of f and the Lebesgue integral of f over $[a,b]$ coincide. This is obvious from our construction if $f(a) = f(b) = 0$ and if $f(x)$ is defined to be 0 for $x < a$ and for $x > b$. The general case follows without difficulty. Actually the same thing is true for every Riemann integrable f on $[a,b]$. Since we shall have no occasion to discuss Riemann integrable functions in the sequel, we omit the proof and refer to Theorem 10.33 of [26].

A natural question, which may have occurred to some readers, is whether *every* subset of R^k is Lebesgue measurable. It is a consequence of the axiom of choice that the answer is negative, even for $k = 1$.

2.22 Example For real numbers x and y, write $x \sim y$ if and only if $x - y$ is rational. It is clear that $x \sim x$, that $x \sim y$ implies $y \sim x$, and that $x \sim y$, $y \sim z$ implies $x \sim z$. Thus $\sim$ is an equivalence relation. (In algebraic terminology, letting Q be the additive group of the rational numbers, each equivalence class is a coset of Q in R^1.) Let E be a set in $(0,1)$ which contains exactly one point in every equivalence class. (The assertion that there is such a set E is a direct application of the axiom of choice.) *We claim that E is not Lebesgue measurable.*

As in Sec. 2.19, let $E + r = \{x + r : x \varepsilon E\}$. We need two properties of E:

(*a*) *If* $x \in (0,1)$, *then* $x \in E + r$ *for some rational* $r \in (-1,1)$.
(*b*) *If* r *and* s *are distinct rationals, then* $(E + r) \cap (E + s) = \emptyset$.

To prove (*a*), note that to every $x \in (0,1)$ there corresponds a $y \in E$ such that $x \sim y$. If $r = x - y$, then $x = y + r \in E + r$.

To prove (*b*), suppose $x \in (E + r) \cap (E + s)$. Then $x = y + r = z + s$ for some $y \in E$, $z \in E$. Since $y - z = s - r \neq 0$, we have $y \sim z$, and E contains two equivalent points, in contradiction to our choice of E.

Now assume that E is Lebesgue measurable, and put $\alpha = m(E)$. Define $S = \bigcup(E + r)$, the union being extended over all rational $r \in (-1,1)$. By (*b*), the sets $E + r$ are pairwise disjoint; since m is translation invariant, $m(E + r) = \alpha$ for every r; since $S \subset (-1,2)$, $m(S) \leq 3$. The countable additivity of m now forces $\alpha = 0$, and hence $m(S) = 0$. But (*a*) implies that $(0,1) \subset S$, hence $1 \leq m(S)$, and we have a contradiction.

Continuity Properties of Measurable Functions

Since the continuous functions played such a prominent role in our construction of Borel measures, and of Lebesgue measure in particular, it seems reasonable to expect that there are some interesting relations between continuous functions and measurable functions. In this section we shall give two theorems of this kind.

We shall assume, in both of them, *that* μ *is a measure on a locally compact Hausdorff space* X *which has the properties stated in Theorem* 2.14. In particular, μ could be Lebesgue measure on some R^k.

2.23 Lusin's Theorem *Suppose* f *is a complex measurable function on* X, $\mu(A) < \infty$, $f(x) = 0$ *if* $x \notin A$, *and* $\epsilon > 0$. *Then there exists a* $g \in C_c(X)$ *such that*

$$\mu(\{x: f(x) \neq g(x)\}) < \epsilon. \tag{1}$$

Furthermore, we may arrange it so that

$$\sup_{x \in X} |g(x)| \leq \sup_{x \in X} |f(x)|. \tag{2}$$

PROOF Assume first that $0 \leq f < 1$ and that A is compact. Attach a sequence $\{s_n\}$ to f, as in the proof of Theorem 1.17, and put $t_1 = s_1$ and $t_n = s_n - s_{n-1}$ for $n = 2, 3, 4, \ldots$. Then $2^n t_n$ is the characteristic function of a set $T_n \subset A$, and

$$f(x) = \sum_{n=1}^{\infty} t_n(x) \qquad (x \in X). \tag{3}$$

Fix an open set V such that $A \subset V$ and $\bar{V}$ is compact. There are compact sets K_n and open sets V_n such that $K_n \subset T_n \subset V_n \subset V$ and

$\mu(V_n - K_n) < 2^{-n}\epsilon$. By Urysohn's lemma, there are functions h_n such that $K_n \prec h_n \prec V_n$. Define

(4) $$g(x) = \sum_{n=1}^{\infty} 2^{-n}h_n(x) \qquad (x \in X).$$

This series converges uniformly on X, so g is continuous. Also, the support of g lies in $\bar{V}$. Since $2^{-n}h_n(x) = t_n(x)$ except in $V_n - K_n$, we have $g(x) = f(x)$ except in $\bigcup(V_n - K_n)$, and this latter set has measure less than ϵ. Thus (1) holds if A is compact and $0 \leq f < 1$.

It follows that (1) holds if A is compact and f is a bounded measurable function. The compactness of A is easily removed, for if $\mu(A) < \infty$ then A contains a compact set K with $\mu(A - K)$ smaller than any preassigned positive number. Next, if f is a complex measurable function and if $B_n = \{x: |f(x)| > n\}$, then $\bigcap B_n = \varnothing$, so $\mu(B_n) \to 0$, by Theorem 1.19(*e*). Since f coincides with the bounded function $(1 - \chi_{B_n}) \cdot f$ except on B_n, (1) follows in the general case.

Finally, let $R = \sup \{|f(x)|: x \in X\}$, and put $\varphi(z) = z$ if $|z| \leq R$, $\varphi(z) = Rz/|z|$ if $|z| > R$. Then φ is a continuous mapping of the complex plane onto the disc of radius R. If g satisfies (1) and $g_1 = \varphi \circ g$, then g_1 satisfies (1) and (2).

Corollary *Assume that the hypotheses of Lusin's theorem are satisfied and that* $|f| \leq 1$. *Then there is a sequence* $\{g_n\}$ *such that* $g_n \in C_c(X)$, $|g_n| \leq 1$, *and*

(5) $$f(x) = \lim_{n\to\infty} g_n(x) \qquad \text{a.e.}$$

PROOF The theorem implies that to each n there corresponds a $g_n \in C_c(X)$, with $|g_n| \leq 1$, such that $\mu(E_n) < 2^{-n}$, where E_n is the set of all x at which $f(x) \neq g_n(x)$. For almost every x it is then true that x lies in at most finitely many of the sets E_n (Theorem 1.41). For any such x, it follows that $f(x) = g_n(x)$ for all large enough n. This gives (5).

2.24 The Vitali-Carathéodory Theorem *Suppose* $f \in L^1(\mu)$, f *is real-valued, and* $\epsilon > 0$. *Then there exist functions* u *and* v *on* X *such that* $u \leq f \leq v$, u *is upper semicontinuous and bounded above,* v *is lower semicontinuous and bounded below, and*

(1) $$\int_X (v - u)\, d\mu < \epsilon.$$

PROOF Assume first that $f \geq 0$ and that f is not identically 0. Since f is the pointwise limit of an increasing sequence of simple functions s_n, f is the sum of the simple functions $t_n = s_n - s_{n-1}$ (taking $s_0 = 0$), and since t_n is a linear combination of characteristic functions, we see that there are measurable sets E_i (not necessarily disjoint) and constants $c_i > 0$ such that

$$f(x) = \sum_{i=1}^{\infty} c_i \chi_{E_i}(x) \qquad (x \in X). \tag{2}$$

Since

$$\int_X f\, d\mu = \sum_{i=1}^{\infty} c_i \mu(E_i), \tag{3}$$

the series in (3) converges. There are compact sets K_i and open sets V_i such that $K_i \subset E_i \subset V_i$ and

$$c_i \mu(V_i - K_i) < 2^{-i-1}\epsilon \qquad (i = 1, 2, 3, \ldots). \tag{4}$$

Put

$$v = \sum_{i=1}^{\infty} c_i \chi_{V_i}, \qquad u = \sum_{i=1}^{N} c_i \chi_{K_i}, \tag{5}$$

where N is chosen so that

$$\sum_{N+1}^{\infty} c_i \mu(E_i) < \frac{\epsilon}{2}. \tag{6}$$

Then v is lower semicontinuous, u is upper semicontinuous, $u \leq f \leq v$, and

$$\begin{aligned} v - u &= \sum_{i=1}^{N} c_i(\chi_{V_i} - \chi_{K_i}) + \sum_{N+1}^{\infty} c_i \chi_{V_i} \\ &\leq \sum_{i=1}^{\infty} c_i(\chi_{V_i} - \chi_{K_i}) + \sum_{N+1}^{\infty} c_i \chi_{E_i} \end{aligned}$$

so that (4) and (6) imply (1).

In the general case, write $f = f^+ - f^-$, attach u_1 and v_1 to f^+, attach u_2 and v_2 to f^-, as above, and put $u = u_1 - v_2$, $v = v_1 - u_2$. Since $-v_2$ is upper semicontinuous and since the sum of two upper semicontinuous functions is upper semicontinuous (similarly for lower semicontinuous; we leave the proof of this as an exercise), u and v have the desired properties.

Exercises

In Exercises 1 to 5, m stands for Lebesgue measure on R^1.

1 Given $\epsilon > 0$, construct an open set $E \subset [0,1]$ which is dense in $[0,1]$, such that $m(E) = \epsilon$. (To say that A is dense in B means that the closure of A contains B.)

2 Construct a totally disconnected compact set $K \subset R^1$ such that $m(K) > 0$. (K is to have no connected subset consisting of more than one point.)

If v is lower semicontinuous and $v \leq \chi_K$, show that actually $v \leq 0$. Hence χ_K cannot be approximated from below by lower semicontinuous functions, in the sense of the Vitali-Carathéodory theorem.

3 Construct a Borel set $E \subset R^1$ such that

$$0 < m(E \cap I) < m(I)$$

for every nonempty segment I. Is it possible to have $m(E) < \infty$ for such a set?

4 Show that there are uncountable sets $E \subset R^1$ with $m(E) = 0$.

5 If f is a Lebesgue measurable complex function on R^1, prove that there is a Borel function g on R^1 such that $f = g$ a.e. $[m]$.

6 Construct a sequence of continuous functions f_n on $[0,1]$ such that $0 \leq f_n \leq 1$, such that

$$\lim_{n\to\infty} \int_0^1 f_n(x)\, dx = 0,$$

but such that the sequence $\{f_n(x)\}$ converges for no $x \in [0,1]$.

7 If $\{f_n\}$ is a sequence of continuous functions on $[0,1]$ such that $0 \leq f_n \leq 1$ and such that $f_n(x) \to 0$ as $n \to \infty$, for every $x \in [0,1]$, then

$$\lim_{n\to\infty} \int_0^1 f_n(x)\, dx = 0.$$

Try to prove this without using any measure theory or any theorems about Lebesgue integration. (This is to impress you with the power of the Lebesgue integral. A nice proof was given by W. F. Eberlein in *Communications on Pure and Applied Mathematics*, vol. X, pp. 357–360, 1957.)

8 If μ is an arbitrary positive measure and if $f \in L^1(\mu)$, prove that $\{x: f(x) \neq 0\}$ has σ-finite measure.

9 Let f be an arbitrary complex function on R^1, and define

$$\varphi(x,\delta) = \sup \{|f(s) - f(t)|: s, t \in (x - \delta, x + \delta)\},$$

$$\varphi(x) = \inf \{\varphi(x,\delta): \delta > 0\}.$$

Prove that φ is upper semicontinuous, that f is continuous at a point x if and only if $\varphi(x) = 0$, and hence that the set of points of continuity of an arbitrary complex function is a G_δ.

Formulate and prove an analogous statement for general topological spaces in place of R^1.

10 Let $\{f_n\}$ be a sequence of real nonnegative functions on R^1, and consider the following four statements:

(*a*) If f_1 and f_2 are upper semicontinuous, then $f_1 + f_2$ is upper semicontinuous.

(*b*) If f_1 and f_2 are lower semicontinuous, then $f_1 + f_2$ is lower semicontinuous.

(*c*) If each f_n is upper semicontinuous, then $\sum_1^\infty f_n$ is upper semicontinuous.

(*d*) If each f_n is lower semicontinuous, then $\sum_1^\infty f_n$ is lower semicontinuous.

Show that three of these are true and that one is false. What happens if the word "nonnegative" is omitted? Is the truth of the statements affected if R^1 is replaced by a general topological space?

11 Let μ be a regular Borel measure on a compact Hausdorff space X; assume $\mu(X) = 1$. Prove that there is a compact set $K \subset X$ (the *carrier* or *support* of μ) such that $\mu(K) = 1$ but $\mu(H) < 1$ for every proper compact subset H of K. *Hint:* Let K be the intersection of all compact K_α with $\mu(K_\alpha) = 1$; show that every open set V which contains K also contains some K_α. Regularity of μ is needed; compare Exercise 17. Show that K^c is the largest open set in X whose measure is 0.

12 Show that every compact subset of R^1 is the support of a Borel measure.

13 Is it true that every compact subset of R^1 is the support of a continuous function? If not, can you describe the class of all compact sets in R^1 which are supports of continuous functions? Is your description valid in other topological spaces?

14 Let X be a metric space, with metric ρ. For any nonempty $E \subset X$, define

$$\rho_E(x) = \inf \{\rho(x,y) : y \in E\}.$$

Show that ρ_E is a uniformly continuous function on X. If A and B are disjoint nonempty closed subsets of X, examine the relevance of the function

$$f(x) = \frac{\rho_A(x)}{\rho_A(x) + \rho_B(x)}$$

to Urysohn's lemma.

15 Examine the proof of the Riesz theorem and prove the following two statements:

(*a*) If $E_1 \subset V_1$ and $E_2 \subset V_2$, where V_1 and V_2 are disjoint open sets, then $\mu(E_1 \cup E_2) = \mu(E_1) + \mu(E_2)$, even if E_1 and E_2 are not in $\mathfrak{M}$.

(*b*) If $E \in \mathfrak{M}_F$, then $E = N \cup K_1 \cup K_2 \cup \cdots$, where $\{K_i\}$ is a disjoint countable collection of compact sets and $\mu(N) = 0$.

16 Let X be the plane, with the following topology: A set is open if and only if its intersection with every vertical line is an open subset of that line, with respect to the usual topology of R^1. Show that this X is a locally compact Hausdorff space. If $f \in C_c(X)$, let $x_1, \ldots, x_n$ be those values of x for which $f(x,y) \neq 0$ for at least one y (there are only finitely many such x!), and define

$$\Lambda f = \sum_{j=1}^{n} \int_{-\infty}^{\infty} f(x_j,y)\, dy.$$

Let μ be the measure associated with this Λ by Theorem 2.14. If E is the x-axis, show that $\mu(E) = \infty$ although $\mu(K) = 0$ for every compact $K \subset E$.

17 This exercise requires more set-theoretic skill than the preceding ones. Let X be a well-ordered uncountable set which has a last element ω_1, such that every predecessor of ω_1 has at most countably many predecessors. ("Construction": take any well-ordered set which has elements with uncountably many predecessors, and let ω_1 be the first of these; ω_1 is called the first uncountable ordinal.) For $\alpha \in X$, let $P_\alpha[S_\alpha]$ be the set of all predecessors (successors) of α, and call a subset of X open if it is a P_α or an S_β or a $P_\alpha \cap S_\beta$ or a union of such sets. Prove that X is then a compact Hausdorff space. (*Hint:* No well-ordered set contains an infinite decreasing sequence.)

Prove that the complement of the point ω_1 is an open set which is not σ-compact.

Prove that to every $f \in C(X)$ there corresponds an $\alpha \neq \omega_1$ such that f is constant on S_α.

Prove that the intersection of every countable collection $\{K_n\}$ of uncountable compact subsets of X is uncountable. (*Hint:* Consider limits of increasing countable sequences in X which intersect each K_n in infinitely many points.)

Let $\mathfrak{M}$ be the collection of all $E \subset X$ such that either $E \cup \{\omega_1\}$ or $E^c \cup \{\omega_1\}$ contains an uncountable compact set; in the first case, define $\lambda(E) = 1$; in the second case, define $\lambda(E) = 0$. Prove that $\mathfrak{M}$ is a σ-algebra which contains all Borel sets in X, that λ is a measure on $\mathfrak{M}$ which is *not* regular (every neighborhood of ω_1 has measure 1), and that

$$f(\omega_1) = \int_X f\,d\lambda$$

for every $f \in C(X)$. Describe the regular μ which Theorem 2.14 associates with this linear functional.

18 Does there exist a sequence of continuous real functions f_n on R^1 such that $f_n(x) \to \infty$ if and only if x is rational? What if "rational" is replaced by "irrational"?

19 It is easy to guess the limits of

$$\int_0^n \left(1 - \frac{x}{n}\right)^n e^{x/2}\,dx \qquad \text{and} \qquad \int_0^n \left(1 + \frac{x}{n}\right)^n e^{-2x}\,dx,$$

as $n \to \infty$. Prove that your guesses are correct.

20 If m is Lebesgue measure on R^k, prove that $m(-E) = m(E)$, where $-E = \{-x : x \in E\}$, and hence that

$$\int_{R^k} f(x)\,dx = \int_{R^k} f(-x)\,dx$$

for all $f \in L^1(R^k)$.

21 There is an error in the final computation on p. 46. Find it. Show that $\mu(K) \le \Lambda(\Sigma h_i)$ by a variation of the argument used in Step II (replace $\frac{1}{2}$ by $\alpha < 1$, let $\alpha \to 1$) and check that the following computation is correct:

$$\begin{aligned}
\Lambda f &= \sum_{i=1}^n \Lambda(h_i f) \le \sum_{i=1}^n (y_i + \epsilon)\Lambda h_i \\
&= \sum_{i=1}^n (|a| + y_i + \epsilon)\Lambda h_i - |a| \sum_{i=1}^n \Lambda h_i \\
&\le \sum_{i=1}^n (|a| + y_i + \epsilon)[\mu(E_i) + \epsilon/n] - |a|\mu(K) \\
&= \sum_{i=1}^n (y_i - \epsilon)\mu(E_i) + 2\epsilon\mu(K) + \frac{\epsilon}{n} \sum_{i=1}^n (|a| + y_i + \epsilon) \\
&\le \int_X f\,d\mu + \epsilon[2\mu(K) + |a| + b + \epsilon].
\end{aligned}$$

3

L^p-spaces

Convex Functions and Inequalities

Many of the most common inequalities in analysis have their origin in the notion of convexity.

3.1 Definition A real function φ defined on a segment (a,b), where $-\infty \le a < b \le \infty$, is called *convex* if the inequality

$$\varphi((1-\lambda)x + \lambda y) \le (1-\lambda)\varphi(x) + \lambda\varphi(y) \tag{1}$$

holds whenever $a < x < b$, $a < y < b$, and $0 \le \lambda \le 1$.

Graphically, the condition is that if $x < t < y$, then the point $(t,\varphi(t))$ should lie below or on the line connecting the points $(x,\varphi(x))$ and $(y,\varphi(y))$ in the plane. Also, (1) is equivalent to the requirement that

$$\frac{\varphi(t) - \varphi(s)}{t - s} \le \frac{\varphi(u) - \varphi(t)}{u - t} \tag{2}$$

whenever $a < s < t < u < b$.

The mean value theorem for differentiation, combined with (2), shows immediately that a real differentiable function φ is convex in (a,b) if and only if $a < s < t < b$ implies $\varphi'(s) \le \varphi'(t)$, i.e., if and only if the derivative φ' is a monotonically increasing function.

For example, the exponential function is convex on $(-\infty, \infty)$.

3.2 Theorem *If φ is convex on (a,b), then φ is continuous on (a,b).*

PROOF The idea of the proof is most easily conveyed in geometric language. Those who may worry that this is not "rigorous" are invited to transcribe it in terms of epsilons and deltas.

Suppose $a < s < x < y < t < b$. Write S for the point $(s,\varphi(s))$ in the plane, and deal similarly with x, y, and t. Then X is on or below the line SY, hence Y is on or above the line through S and X; also, Y is on or below XT. As $y \to x$, it follows that $Y \to X$, i.e.,

$\varphi(y) \to \varphi(x)$. Left-hand limits are handled in the same manner, and the continuity of φ follows.

Note that this theorem depends on the fact that we are working on an *open* segment. For instance, if $\varphi(x) = 0$ on $[0,1)$ and $\varphi(1) = 1$, then φ satisfies 3.1(1) on $[0,1]$ without being continuous.

3.3 Theorem (Jensen's Inequality) *Let μ be a positive measure on a σ-algebra $\mathfrak{M}$ in a set Ω, so that $\mu(\Omega) = 1$. If f is a real function in $L^1(\mu)$, if $a < f(x) < b$ for all $x \in \Omega$, and if φ is convex on (a,b), then*

$$\varphi\left(\int_\Omega f\,d\mu\right) \le \int_\Omega (\varphi \circ f)\,d\mu. \tag{1}$$

Note: The cases $a = -\infty$ and $b = \infty$ are not excluded.

PROOF Put $t = \int_\Omega f\,d\mu$. Then $a < t < b$. If β is the supremum of the quotients on the left of 3.1(2), where $a < s < t$, then β is no larger than any of the quotients on the right of 3.1(2), for any $u \in (t,b)$. It follows that

$$\varphi(s) \ge \varphi(t) + \beta(s - t) \qquad (a < s < b). \tag{2}$$

Hence

$$\varphi(f(x)) - \varphi(t) - \beta(f(x) - t) \ge 0 \tag{3}$$

for every $x \in \Omega$. Since φ is continuous, $\varphi \circ f$ is measurable. If we integrate both sides of (3) with respect to μ, (1) follows from our choice of t and the assumption $\mu(\Omega) = 1$.

To give an example, take $\varphi(x) = e^x$. Then (1) becomes

$$\exp\left\{\int_\Omega f\,d\mu\right\} \le \int_\Omega e^f\,d\mu. \tag{4}$$

If Ω is a finite set, consisting of points $p_1, \ldots, p_n$, say, and if

$$\mu(\{p_i\}) = 1/n, \qquad f(p_i) = x_i,$$

(4) becomes

$$\exp\left\{\frac{1}{n}(x_1 + \cdots + x_n)\right\} \le \frac{1}{n}(e^{x_1} + \cdots + e^{x_n}), \tag{5}$$

for real x_i. Putting $y_i = e^{x_i}$, we obtain the familiar inequality between the arithmetic and geometric means of n positive numbers:

$$(y_1 y_2 \cdots y_n)^{1/n} \le \frac{1}{n}(y_1 + y_2 + \cdots + y_n). \tag{6}$$

Going back from this to (4), it should become clear why the left and right sides of

$$\exp\left\{\int_\Omega \log g\,d\mu\right\} \le \int_\Omega g\,d\mu \tag{7}$$

are often called the geometric and arithmetic means, respectively, of the positive function g.

If we take $\mu(\{p_i\}) = \alpha_i > 0$, where $\Sigma\alpha_i = 1$, then we obtain

(8) $$y_1^{\alpha_1} y_2^{\alpha_2} \cdots y_n^{\alpha_n} \le \alpha_1 y_1 + \alpha_2 y_2 + \cdots + \alpha_n y_n$$

in place of (6). These are just a few samples of what is contained in Theorem 3.3.

For a converse, see Exercise 20.

3.4 Definition If p and q are positive real numbers such that $p + q = pq$, or equivalently

(1) $$\frac{1}{p} + \frac{1}{q} = 1,$$

then we call p and q a pair of *conjugate exponents*. It is clear that (1) implies $1 < p < \infty$ and $1 < q < \infty$. An important special case is $p = q = 2$.

As $p \to 1$, (1) forces $q \to \infty$. Consequently 1 and ∞ are also regarded as a pair of conjugate exponents.

3.5 Theorem *Let p and q be conjugate exponents, $1 < p < \infty$. Let X be a measure space, with measure μ. Let f and g be measurable functions on X, with range in $[0, \infty]$. Then*

(1) $$\int_X fg \, d\mu \le \left\{\int_X f^p \, d\mu\right\}^{1/p} \left\{\int_X g^q \, d\mu\right\}^{1/q}$$

and

(2) $$\left\{\int_X (f + g)^p \, d\mu\right\}^{1/p} \le \left\{\int_X f^p \, d\mu\right\}^{1/p} + \left\{\int_X g^p \, d\mu\right\}^{1/p}.$$

The inequality (1) is Hölder's, (2) is Minkowski's. If $p = q = 2$, (1) is known as the Schwarz inequality.

PROOF Let A and B be the two factors on the right of (1). If $A = 0$, then $f = 0$ a.e. (by Theorem 1.39); hence $fg = 0$ a.e., so (1) holds. If $A > 0$ and $B = \infty$, (1) is again trivial. So we need consider only the case $0 < A < \infty$, $0 < B < \infty$. Put

(3) $$F = \frac{f}{A}, \qquad G = \frac{g}{B}.$$

This gives

(4) $$\int_X F^p \, d\mu = \int_X G^q \, d\mu = 1.$$

If $x \in X$ is such that $0 < F(x) < \infty$ and $0 < G(x) < \infty$, there are real numbers s and t such that $F(x) = e^{s/p}$, $G(x) = e^{t/q}$. Since

$1/p + 1/q = 1$, the convexity of the exponential function implies that

$$e^{s/p+t/q} \le p^{-1}e^s + q^{-1}e^t. \tag{5}$$

It follows that

$$F(x)G(x) \le p^{-1}F(x)^p + q^{-1}G(x)^q \tag{6}$$

for every $x \in X$. Integration of (6) yields

$$\int_X FG\,d\mu \le p^{-1} + q^{-1} = 1, \tag{7}$$

by (4); inserting (3) into (7), we obtain (1).

To prove (2), we write

$$(f+g)^p = f\cdot(f+g)^{p-1} + g\cdot(f+g)^{p-1}. \tag{8}$$

Hölder's inequality gives

$$\int f\cdot(f+g)^{p-1} \le \left\{\int f^p\right\}^{1/p}\left\{\int (f+g)^{(p-1)q}\right\}^{1/q}. \tag{9}$$

Let (9′) be the inequality (9) with f and g interchanged. Since $(p-1)q = p$, addition of (9) and (9′) gives

$$\int (f+g)^p \le \left\{\int (f+g)^p\right\}^{1/q}\left[\left\{\int f^p\right\}^{1/p} + \left\{\int g^p\right\}^{1/p}\right]. \tag{10}$$

Clearly, it is enough to prove (2) in the case that the left side is greater than 0 and the right side is less than ∞. The convexity of the function t^p for $0 < t < \infty$ shows that

$$\left(\frac{f+g}{2}\right)^p \le \frac{1}{2}(f^p + g^p).$$

Hence the left side of (2) is less than ∞, and (2) follows from (10) if we divide by the first factor on the right of (10), bearing in mind that $1 - 1/q = 1/p$. This completes the proof.

It is sometimes useful to know the conditions under which equality can hold in an inequality. In many cases this information may be obtained by examining the proof of the inequality.

For instance, equality holds in (7) if and only if equality holds in (6) for almost every x. In (5), equality holds if and only if $s = t$. Hence "$F^p = G^q$ a.e." is a necessary and sufficient condition for equality in (7), if (4) is assumed. In terms of the original functions f and g, the following result is then obtained:

Assuming $A < \infty$ and $B < \infty$, equality holds in (1) *if and only if there are constants α and β, not both* 0, *such that $\alpha f^p = \beta g^q$* a.e.

We leave the analogous discussion of equality in (2) as an exercise.

The L^p-spaces

In this section, X will be an arbitrary measure space with a positive measure μ.

3.6 Definition If $0 < p < \infty$ and if f is a complex measurable function on X, define

(1) $$\|f\|_p = \left\{\int_X |f|^p \, d\mu\right\}^{1/p}$$

and let $L^p(\mu)$ consist of all f for which

(2) $$\|f\|_p < \infty.$$

We call $\|f\|_p$ the L^p-norm of f.

If μ is Lebesgue measure on R^k, we write $L^p(R^k)$ instead of $L^p(\mu)$, as in Sec. 2.21. If μ is the counting measure on a set A, it is customary to denote the corresponding L^p-space by $\ell^p(A)$, or simply by ℓ^p, if A is countable. An element of ℓ^p may be regarded as a complex sequence $x = \{\xi_n\}$, and

$$\|x\|_p = \left\{\sum_{n=1}^{\infty} |\xi_n|^p\right\}^{1/p}.$$

3.7 Definition Suppose $g: X \to [0, \infty]$ is measurable. Let S be the set of all real α such that

(1) $$\mu(g^{-1}((\alpha, \infty])) = 0.$$

If $S = \varnothing$, put $\beta = \infty$. If $S \neq \varnothing$, put $\beta = \inf S$. Since

(2) $$g^{-1}((\beta, \infty]) = \bigcup_{n=1}^{\infty} g^{-1}\left(\left(\beta + \frac{1}{n}, \infty\right]\right),$$

and since the union of a countable collection of sets of measure 0 has measure 0, we see that $\beta \in S$. We call β the *essential supremum* of g.

If f is a complex measurable function on X, we define $\|f\|_\infty$ to be the essential supremum of $|f|$, and we let $L^\infty(\mu)$ consist of all f for which $\|f\|_\infty < \infty$. The members of $L^\infty(\mu)$ are sometimes called the *essentially bounded* measurable functions on X.

It follows from this definition that the inequality $|f(x)| \leq \lambda$ *holds for almost all* x *if and only if* $\lambda \geq \|f\|_\infty$.

As in Definition 3.6, $L^\infty(R^k)$ denotes the class of all essentially bounded (with respect to Lebesgue measure) functions on R^k, and $\ell^\infty(A)$ is the class of all bounded functions on A. (Here bounded means the same as essentially bounded, since every nonempty set has positive measure!)

3.8 Theorem *If p and q are conjugate exponents, $1 \le p \le \infty$, and if $f \in L^p(\mu)$ and $g \in L^q(\mu)$, then $fg \in L^1(\mu)$, and*

(1) $$\|fg\|_1 \le \|f\|_p\|g\|_q.$$

PROOF For $1 < p < \infty$, (1) is simply Hölder's inequality, applied to $|f|$ and $|g|$. If $p = \infty$, note that

(2) $$|f(x)g(x)| \le \|f\|_\infty|g(x)|$$

for almost all x; integrating (2), we obtain (1). If $p = 1$, then $q = \infty$, and the same argument applies.

3.9 Theorem *Suppose $1 \le p \le \infty$, and $f \in L^p(\mu)$, $g \in L^p(\mu)$. Then $f + g \in L^p(\mu)$, and*

(1) $$\|f + g\|_p \le \|f\|_p + \|g\|_p.$$

PROOF For $1 < p < \infty$, this follows from Minkowski's inequality, since

$$\int_X |f + g|^p \, d\mu \le \int_X (|f| + |g|)^p \, d\mu.$$

For $p = 1$ or $p = \infty$, (1) is a trivial consequence of the inequality $|f + g| \le |f| + |g|$.

3.10 Remarks Fix p, $1 \le p \le \infty$. If $f \in L^p(\mu)$ and α is a complex number, it is clear that $\alpha f \in L^p(\mu)$. In fact,

(1) $$\|\alpha f\|_p = |\alpha| \, \|f\|_p.$$

In conjunction with Theorem 3.9, this shows that $L^p(\mu)$ is a *complex vector space.*

Suppose f, g, and h are in $L^p(\mu)$. Replacing f by $f - g$ and g by $g - h$ in Theorem 3.9, we obtain

(2) $$\|f - h\|_p \le \|f - g\|_p + \|g - h\|_p.$$

This suggests that a metric may be introduced in $L^p(\mu)$ by defining the distance between f and g to be $\|f - g\|_p$. Call this distance $d(f,g)$ for the moment. Then $0 \le d(f,g) < \infty$, $d(f,f) = 0$, $d(f,g) = d(g,f)$, and (2) shows that the triangle inequality $d(f,h) \le d(f,g) + d(g,h)$ is satisfied. The only other property which d should have to define a metric space is that $d(f,g) = 0$ should imply that $f = g$. In our present situation this need not be so; we have *$d(f,g) = 0$ precisely when $f(x) = g(x)$ for almost all x.*

Let us write $f \sim g$ if and only if $d(f,g) = 0$. It is clear that this is an equivalence relation in $L^p(\mu)$ which partitions $L^p(\mu)$ into equivalence classes; each class consists of all functions which are equivalent to a given one. If F and G are two equivalence classes, choose $f \in F$ and $g \in G$, and define $d(F,G) = d(f,g)$; note that $f \sim f_1$ and $g \sim g_1$ implies

$$d(f,g) = d(f_1,g_1),$$

so that $d(F,G)$ is well defined.

With this definition, the set of equivalence classes is now a metric space. Note that it is also a vector space, since $f \sim f_1$ and $g \sim g_1$ implies $f + g \sim f_1 + g_1$ and $\alpha f \sim \alpha f_1$.

When $L^p(\mu)$ is regarded as a metric space, then the space which is really under consideration is therefore *not a space whose elements are functions, but a space whose elements are equivalence classes of functions.* For the sake of simplicity of language, it is, however, customary to relegate this distinction to the status of a tacit understanding and to continue to speak of $L^p(\mu)$ as a space of functions. We shall follow this custom.

If $\{f_n\}$ is a sequence in $L^p(\mu)$, if $f \in L^p(\mu)$, and if $\lim_{n\to\infty} \|f_n - f\|_p = 0$, we say that $\{f_n\}$ *converges to f in $L^p(\mu)$* (or that $\{f_n\}$ converges to f in the mean of order p, or that $\{f_n\}$ is L^p-convergent to f). If to every $\epsilon > 0$ there corresponds an integer N such that $\|f_n - f_m\|_p < \epsilon$ as soon as $n > N$ and $m > N$, we call $\{f_n\}$ a *Cauchy sequence* in $L^p(\mu)$. These definitions are exactly as in any metric space.

It is a very important fact that $L^p(\mu)$ is a *complete* metric space, i.e., that every Cauchy sequence in $L^p(\mu)$ converges to an element of $L^p(\mu)$:

3.11 Theorem *$L^p(\mu)$ is a complete metric space, for $1 \le p \le \infty$ and for every positive measure μ.*

PROOF Assume first that $1 \le p < \infty$. Let $\{f_n\}$ be a Cauchy sequence in $L^p(\mu)$. There is a subsequence $\{f_{n_i}\}$, $n_1 < n_2 < \cdots$, such that

$$(1) \qquad \|f_{n_{i+1}} - f_{n_i}\| < 2^{-i} \qquad (i = 1, 2, 3, \ldots).$$

Put

$$(2) \qquad g_k = \sum_{i=1}^{k} |f_{n_{i+1}} - f_{n_i}|, \qquad g = \sum_{i=1}^{\infty} |f_{n_{i+1}} - f_{n_i}|.$$

Since (1) holds, the Minkowski inequality shows that $\|g_k\|_p < 1$ for $k = 1, 2, 3, \ldots$. Hence an application of Fatou's lemma to $\{g_k^p\}$ gives $\|g\|_p \le 1$. In particular, $g(x) < \infty$ a.e., so that the series

$$(3) \qquad f_{n_1}(x) + \sum_{i=1}^{\infty} (f_{n_{i+1}}(x) - f_{n_i}(x))$$

converges absolutely for almost every $x \in X$. Denote the sum of (3) by $f(x)$, for those x at which (3) converges; put $f(x) = 0$ on the remaining set of measure zero. Since

(4) $$f_{n_i} + \sum_{i=1}^{k-1} (f_{n_{i+1}} - f_{n_i}) = f_{n_k},$$

we see that

(5) $$f(x) = \lim_{i\to\infty} f_{n_i}(x) \qquad \text{a.e.}$$

Having found a function f which is the pointwise limit a.e. of $\{f_{n_i}\}$, we now have to prove that this f is the L^p-limit of $\{f_n\}$. Choose $\epsilon > 0$. There exists an N such that $\|f_n - f_m\|_p < \epsilon$ if $n > N$ and $m > N$. For every $m > N$, Fatou's lemma therefore shows that

(6) $$\int_X |f - f_m|^p \, d\mu \le \liminf_{i\to\infty} \int_X |f_{n_i} - f_m|^p \, d\mu \le \epsilon^p.$$

We conclude from (6) that $f - f_m \in L^p(\mu)$, hence that $f \in L^p(\mu)$ [since $f = (f - f_m) + f_m$], and finally that $\|f - f_m\|_p \to 0$ as $m \to \infty$. This completes the proof for the case $1 \le p < \infty$.

In $L^\infty(\mu)$ the proof is much easier. Suppose $\{f_n\}$ is a Cauchy sequence in $L^\infty(\mu)$, let A_k and $B_{m,n}$ be the sets where $|f_k(x)| > \|f_k\|_\infty$ and $|f_n(x) - f_m(x)| > \|f_n - f_m\|_\infty$, and let E be the union of these sets, for $k, m, n = 1, 2, 3, \ldots$. Then $\mu(E) = 0$, and on the complement of E the sequence $\{f_n\}$ converges uniformly to a bounded function f. Define $f(x) = 0$ for $x \in E$. Then $f \in L^\infty(\mu)$, and $\|f_n - f\|_\infty \to 0$ as $n \to \infty$.

The preceding proof contains a result which is interesting enough to be stated separately:

3.12 Theorem *If $1 \le p \le \infty$ and if $\{f_n\}$ is a Cauchy sequence in $L^p(\mu)$, with limit f, then $\{f_n\}$ has a subsequence which converges pointwise almost everywhere to $f(x)$.*

The simple functions play an interesting role in $L^p(\mu)$:

3.13 Theorem *Let S be the class of all complex, measurable, simple functions on X such that*

(1) $$\mu(\{x\colon s(x) \ne 0\}) < \infty.$$

If $1 \le p < \infty$, then S is dense in $L^p(\mu)$.

PROOF First, it is clear that $S \subset L^p(\mu)$. Suppose $f \ge 0$, $f \in L^p(\mu)$, and let $\{s_n\}$ be as in Theorem 1.17. Since $0 \le s_n \le f$, we have $s_n \in L^p(\mu)$, hence $s_n \in S$. Since $|f - s_n|^p \le f^p$, the dominated convergence theorem shows that $\|f - s_n\|_p \to 0$ as $n \to \infty$. Thus f is in the L^p-closure of S. The general case (f complex) follows from this.

Approximation by Continuous Functions

So far we have considered $L^p(\mu)$ on any measure space. Now let X be a locally compact Hausdorff space, and let μ be a measure on a σ-algebra $\mathfrak{M}$ in X, with the properties stated in Theorem 2.14. For example, X might be R^k, and μ might be Lebesgue measure on R^k.

Under these circumstances, we have the following analogue of Theorem 3.13:

3.14 Theorem *For* $1 \leq p < \infty$, $C_c(X)$ *is dense in* $L^p(\mu)$.

PROOF Define S as in Theorem 3.13. If $s \in S$ and $\epsilon > 0$, there exists a $g \in C_c(X)$ such that $g(x) = s(x)$ except on a set of measure $< \epsilon$, and $|g| \leq \|s\|_\infty$ (Lusin's theorem). Hence

(1) $$\|g - s\|_p \leq 2\epsilon^{1/p}\|s\|_\infty.$$

Since S is dense in $L^p(\mu)$, this completes the proof.

3.15 Remarks Let us discuss the relations between the spaces $L^p(R^k)$ (the L^p-spaces in which the underlying measure is Lebesgue measure on R^k) and the space $C_c(R^k)$ in some detail. We consider a fixed dimension k.

For every $p \in [1, \infty]$ we have a metric on $C_c(R^k)$; the distance between f and g is $\|f - g\|_p$. Note that this is a genuine metric and that we do not have to pass to equivalence classes. The point is that if two continuous functions on R^k are not identical, then they differ on some nonempty open set V, and $m(V) > 0$, since V contains a k-cell. Thus if two members of $C_c(R^k)$ are equal a.e., they are equal. It is also of interest to note that in $C_c(R^k)$ the essential supremum is the same as the actual supremum: for $f \in C_c(R^k)$

(1) $$\|f\|_\infty = \sup_{x \in R^k} |f(x)|.$$

If $1 \leq p < \infty$, Theorem 3.14 says that $C_c(R^k)$ is dense in $L^p(R^k)$, and Theorem 3.11 shows that $L^p(R^k)$ is complete. Thus $L^p(R^k)$ *is the completion of the metric space which is obtained by endowing* $C_c(R^k)$ *with the* L^p*-metric.*

The cases $p = 1$ and $p = 2$ are the ones of greatest interest. Let us state once more, in different words, what the preceding result says if $p = 1$ and $k = 1$; the statement shows that the Lebesgue integral is indeed the "right" generalization of the Riemann integral:

If the distance between two continuous functions f and g, with compact supports in R^1, is defined to be

(2) $$\int_{-\infty}^{\infty} |f(t) - g(t)|\, dt,$$

the completion of the resulting metric space consists precisely of the Lebesgue integrable functions on R^1, provided we identify any two that are equal almost everywhere.

Of course, *every* metric space S has a completion S^* whose elements may be viewed abstractly as equivalence classes of Cauchy sequences in S (see [26], p. 71). The important point in the present situation is that the various L^p-completions of $C_c(R^k)$ again turn out to be spaces of functions on R^k.

The case $p = \infty$ differs from the cases $p < \infty$. *The L^∞-completion of $C_c(R^k)$ is not $L^\infty(R^k)$, but is $C_0(R^k)$, the space of all continuous functions on R^k which "vanish at infinity,"* a concept which will be defined in Sec. 3.16. Since (1) shows that the L^∞-norm coincides with the supremum norm on $C_c(R^k)$, the above assertion about $C_0(R^k)$ is a special case of Theorem 3.17.

3.16 Definition A complex function f on a locally compact Hausdorff space X is said to *vanish at infinity* if to every $\epsilon > 0$ there exists a compact set $K \subset X$ such that $|f(x)| < \epsilon$ for all x not in K.

The class of all continuous f on X which vanish at infinity is called $C_0(X)$.

It is clear that $C_c(X) \subset C_0(X)$, and that the two classes coincide if X is compact. In that case we write $C(X)$ for either of them.

3.17 Theorem *If X is a locally compact Hausdorff space, then $C_0(X)$ is the completion of $C_c(X)$, relative to the metric defined by the supremum norm*

$$\|f\| = \sup_{x \in X} |f(x)|. \tag{1}$$

PROOF An elementary verification shows that $C_0(X)$ satisfies the axioms of a metric space if the distance between f and g is taken to be $\|f - g\|$. We have to show that (*a*) $C_c(X)$ is dense in $C_0(X)$ and (*b*) $C_0(X)$ is a complete metric space.

Given $f \in C_0(X)$ and $\epsilon > 0$, there is a compact set K so that $|f(x)| < \epsilon$ outside K. Urysohn's lemma gives us a function $g \in C_c(X)$ such that $0 \leq g \leq 1$ and $g(x) = 1$ on K. Put $h = fg$. Then $h \in C_c(X)$ and $\|f - h\| < \epsilon$. This proves (*a*).

To prove (*b*), let $\{f_n\}$ be a Cauchy sequence in $C_0(X)$, i.e., assume that $\{f_n\}$ converges uniformly. Then its pointwise limit function f is continuous. Given $\epsilon > 0$, there exists an n so that $\|f_n - f\| < \epsilon/2$ and there is a compact set K so that $|f_n(x)| < \epsilon/2$ outside K. Hence $|f(x)| < \epsilon$ outside K, and we have proved that f vanishes at infinity. Thus $C_0(X)$ is complete.

Exercises

1 Prove that the supremum of any collection of convex functions on (a,b) is convex on (a,b) and that pointwise limits of sequences of convex functions are convex. What can you say about upper and lower limits of sequences of convex functions?

2 If φ is convex on (a,b) and if ψ is convex and nondecreasing on the range of φ, prove that $\psi \circ \varphi$ is convex on (a,b). For $\varphi > 0$, show that the convexity of $\log \varphi$ implies the convexity of φ, but not vice versa.

3 Assume that φ is a continuous real function on (a,b) such that

$$\varphi\left(\frac{x+y}{2}\right) \leq \frac{1}{2}\varphi(x) + \frac{1}{2}\varphi(y)$$

for all x and $y \in (a,b)$. Prove that φ is convex. (The conclusion does *not* follow if continuity is omitted from the hypotheses.)

4 Suppose f is a complex measurable function on X, μ is a positive measure on X, and

$$\varphi(p) = \int_X |f|^p \, d\mu = \|f\|_p^p \qquad (0 < p < \infty).$$

Let $E = \{p\colon \varphi(p) < \infty\}$. Assume $\|f\|_\infty > 0$.

(*a*) If $r < p < s$, $r \in E$, and $s \in E$, prove that $p \in E$.

(*b*) Prove that $\log \varphi$ is convex in the interior of E and that φ is continuous on E.

(*c*) By (*a*), E is connected. Is E necessarily open? Closed? Can E consist of a single point? Can E be any connected subset of $(0, \infty)$?

(*d*) If $r < p < s$, prove that $\|f\|_p \leq \max(\|f\|_r, \|f\|_s)$. Hence $L^r(\mu) \cap L^s(\mu) \subset L^p(\mu)$.

(*e*) Assume that $\|f\|_r < \infty$ for some $r < \infty$ and prove that

$$\|f\|_p \to \|f\|_\infty \qquad \text{as } p \to \infty.$$

5 Assume, in addition to the hypotheses of Exercise 4, that

$$\mu(X) = 1.$$

(*a*) Prove that $\|f\|_r \leq \|f\|_s$ if $0 < r < s \leq \infty$.

(*b*) Under what conditions does it happen that $0 < r < s \leq \infty$ and $\|f\|_r = \|f\|_s < \infty$?

(*c*) Prove that $L^r(\mu) \supset L^s(\mu)$ if $0 < r < s$. Under what conditions do these two spaces contain the same functions?

(*d*) Assume that $\|f\|_r < \infty$ for some $r > 0$, and prove that

$$\lim_{p\to 0} \|f\|_p = \exp\left\{\int_X \log |f|\, d\mu\right\}$$

if $\exp\{-\infty\}$ is defined to be 0.

6 Let m be Lebesgue measure on [0,1], and define $\|f\|_p$ with respect to m. Find all functions Φ on $[0, \infty)$ such that the relation

$$\Phi(\lim_{p\to 0} \|f\|_p) = \int_0^1 (\Phi \circ f)\, dm$$

holds for every bounded, measurable, positive f. Show first that

$$c\Phi(x) + (1 - c)\Phi(1) = \Phi(x^c) \qquad (x > 0,\ 0 \leq c \leq 1).$$

Compare with Exercise 5(*d*).

7 For some measures, the relation $r < s$ implies $L^r(\mu) \subset L^s(\mu)$; for others, the inclusion is reversed; and there are some for which $L^r(\mu)$ does not contain $L^s(\mu)$ if $r \neq s$. Give examples of these situations, and find conditions on μ under which these situations will occur.

8 If g is a positive function on (0,1) such that $g(x) \to \infty$ as $x \to 0$, then there is a convex function h on (0,1) such that $h \leq g$ and $h(x) \to \infty$ as $x \to 0$. True or false? Is the problem changed if (0,1) is replaced by $(0, \infty)$ and $x \to 0$ is replaced by $x \to \infty$?

9 Suppose f is Lebesgue measurable on (0,1), and not essentially bounded. By Exercise 4(*e*), $\|f\|_p \to \infty$ as $p \to \infty$. Can $\|f\|_p$ tend to ∞ arbitrarily slowly? More precisely, is it true that to every positive function Φ on $(0, \infty)$ such that $\Phi(p) \to \infty$ as $p \to \infty$ one can find an f such that $\|f\|_p \to \infty$ as $p \to \infty$, but $\|f\|_p \leq \Phi(p)$ for all sufficiently large p?

10 Suppose $f_n \in L^p(\mu)$, for $n = 1, 2, 3, \ldots$, and $\|f_n - f\|_p \to 0$ and $f_n \to g$ a.e., as $n \to \infty$. What relation exists between f and g?

11 Suppose $\mu(\Omega) = 1$, and suppose f and g are positive measurable functions on Ω such that $fg \geq 1$. Prove that

$$\int_\Omega f\, d\mu \cdot \int_\Omega g\, d\mu \geq 1.$$

12 Suppose $\mu(\Omega) = 1$ and $h: \Omega \to [0, \infty]$ is measurable. If

$$A = \int_\Omega h\, d\mu,$$

prove that

$$\sqrt{1 + A^2} \leq \int_\Omega \sqrt{1 + h^2}\, d\mu \leq 1 + A.$$

If μ is Lebesgue measure on [0,1] and if h is continuous, $h = f'$, the above inequalities have a simple geometric interpretation.

From this, conjecture (for general Ω) under what conditions on h equality can hold in either of the above inequalities, and prove your conjecture.

13 Under what conditions on f and g does equality hold in the conclusions of Theorems 3.8 and 3.9? You may have to treat the cases $p = 1$ and $p = \infty$ separately.

14 Suppose $1 < p < \infty$, $f \in L^p = L^p((0, \infty))$, relative to Lebesgue measure, and

$$F(x) = \frac{1}{x} \int_0^x f(t)\, dt \qquad (0 < x < \infty).$$

(*a*) Prove Hardy's inequality

$$\|F\|_p \le \frac{p}{p-1} \|f\|_p$$

which shows that the mapping $f \rightarrow F$ carries L^p into L^p.

(*b*) Prove that equality holds only if $f = 0$ a.e.

(*c*) Prove that the constant $p/(p-1)$ cannot be replaced by a smaller one.

(*d*) If $f > 0$ and $f \in L^1$, prove that $F \notin L^1$.

Suggestions: (*a*) Assume first that $f \ge 0$ and $f \in C_c((0, \infty))$. Integration by parts gives

$$\int_0^\infty F^p(x)\, dx = -p \int_0^\infty F^{p-1}(x) x F'(x)\, dx.$$

Note that $xF' = f - F$, and apply Hölder's inequality to $\int F^{p-1} f$. Then derive the general case. (*c*) Take $f(x) = x^{-1/p}$ on $[1, A]$, $f(x) = 0$ elsewhere, for large A.

15 Suppose $\{a_n\}$ is a sequence of positive numbers. Prove that

$$\sum_{N=1}^{\infty} \left(\frac{1}{N} \sum_{n=1}^{N} a_n \right)^p \le \left(\frac{p}{p-1} \right)^p \sum_{n=1}^{\infty} a_n{}^p$$

if $1 < p < \infty$. *Hint:* If $a_n \ge a_{n+1}$, the result can be made to follow from Exercise 14. This special case implies the general one.

16 Prove Egoroff's theorem: If $\mu(X) < \infty$, if $\{f_n\}$ is a sequence of complex measurable functions which converges pointwise at every point of X, and if $\epsilon > 0$, there is a measurable set $E \subset X$, with $\mu(X - E) < \epsilon$, such that $\{f_n\}$ converges uniformly on E.

(The conclusion is that by redefining the f_n on a set of arbitrarily small measure we can convert a pointwise convergent sequence to a uniformly convergent one; note the similarity with Lusin's theorem.)

Hint: Put

$$S(n,k) = \bigcap_{i,j>n} \left\{ x \colon |f_i(x) - f_j(x)| < \frac{1}{k} \right\}$$

and show that there is a suitably increasing sequence $\{n_k\}$ such that $E = \bigcap S(n_k,k)$ has the desired property.

Does the result extend to σ-finite spaces?

17 Suppose μ is a positive measure on X, $1 \le p < \infty$, $f \in L^p(\mu)$, $f_n \in L^p(\mu)$, $f_n(x) \to f(x)$ a.e., and $\|f_n\|_p \to \|f\|_p$, as $n \to \infty$. Prove that then $\|f - f_n\|_p \to 0$ as $n \to \infty$.

Hint: Assume $\|f_n\|_p = \|f\|_p = 1$ for all n. Put $X = A \cup B$, where $\int_A |f|^p < \epsilon$. Apply Fatou's lemma to $\int_B |f_n|^p$ and conclude that the upper limit of $\int_A |f_n|^p$ is at most ϵ. Show that matters can be so arranged (by Egoroff's theorem) that $\{f_n\}$ converges to f uniformly on B.

Show that the conclusion is false if the hypothesis $\|f_n\|_p \to \|f\|_p$ is omitted, even if $\mu(X) < \infty$.

18 Let μ be a positive measure on X. A sequence $\{f_n\}$ of complex measurable functions on X is said to *converge in measure* to the measurable function f if to every $\epsilon > 0$ there corresponds an N such that

$$\mu(\{x: |f_n(x) - f(x)| > \epsilon\}) < \epsilon$$

for all $n > N$. (This notion is of importance in probability theory.) Assume $\mu(X) < \infty$ and prove the following statements:

(*a*) If $f_n(x) \to f(x)$ a.e., then $f_n \to f$ in measure.

(*b*) If $f_n \in L^p(\mu)$ and $\|f_n - f\|_p \to 0$, then $f_n \to f$ in measure; here $1 \le p \le \infty$.

(*c*) If $f_n \to f$ in measure, then $\{f_n\}$ has a subsequence which converges to f a.e.

Investigate the converses of (*a*) and (*b*). What happens to (*a*), (*b*), and (*c*) if $\mu(X) = \infty$, for instance, if μ is Lebesgue measure on R^1?

19 Define the *essential range* of a function $f \in L^\infty(\mu)$ to be the set R_f consisting of all complex numbers w such that

$$\mu(\{x: |f(x) - w| < \epsilon\}) > 0$$

for every $\epsilon > 0$. Prove that R_f is compact. What relation exists between the set R_f and the number $\|f\|_\infty$?

Let A_f be the set of all averages

$$\frac{1}{\mu(E)} \int_E f\, d\mu$$

where $E \in \mathfrak{M}$ and $\mu(E) > 0$. What relations exist between A_f and R_f? Is A_f always closed? Are there measures μ such that A_f is convex for every $f \in L^\infty(\mu)$? Are there measures μ such that A_f fails to be convex for some $f \in L^\infty(\mu)$?

How are these results affected if $L^\infty(\mu)$ is replaced by $L^1(\mu)$, for instance?

20 Suppose φ is a real function on R^1 such that

$$\varphi\left(\int_0^1 f(x)\,dx\right) \le \int_0^1 \varphi(f)\,dx$$

for every real bounded measurable f. Prove that φ is then convex.

21 Call a metric space Y a *completion* of a metric space X if X is dense in Y and Y is complete. In Sec. 3.15 reference was made to "the" completion of a metric space. State and prove a uniqueness theorem which justifies this terminology.

4

Elementary Hilbert Space Theory

Inner Products and Linear Functionals

4.1 Definition A complex vector space H is called an *inner product space* (or *unitary space*) if to each ordered pair of vectors x and $y \in H$ there is associated a complex number (x,y), the so-called "inner product" (or "scalar product") of x and y, such that the following rules hold:

(*a*) $(y,x) = \overline{(x,y)}$. (The bar denotes complex conjugation.)
(*b*) $(x + y, z) = (x,z) + (y,z)$ if x, y, and $z \in H$.
(*c*) $(\alpha x,y) = \alpha(x,y)$ if x and $y \in H$ and α is a scalar.
(*d*) $(x,x) \geq 0$ for all $x \in H$.
(*e*) $(x,x) = 0$ only if $x = 0$.

Let us list some immediate consequences of these axioms:

(*c*) implies that $(0,y) = 0$ for all $y \in H$.
(*b*) and (*c*) may be combined into the statement: *For every $y \in H$, the mapping $x \rightarrow (x,y)$ is a linear functional on H.*
(*a*) and (*c*) show that $(x,\alpha y) = \bar{\alpha}(x,y)$.
(*a*) and (*b*) imply the second distributive law:

$$(z, x + y) = (z,x) + (z,y).$$

By (*d*), we may define $\|x\|$, the *norm* of the vector $x \in H$, to be the nonnegative square root of (x,x). Thus

$$\|x\|^2 = (x,x). \qquad (f)$$

4.2 The Schwarz Inequality *The properties* 4.1(*a*) *to* (*d*) *imply that*

$$|(x,y)| \leq \|x\| \, \|y\|$$

for all x and $y \in H$.

PROOF Put $A = \|x\|^2$, $B = |(x,y)|$, and $C = \|y\|^2$. There is a complex number α such that $|\alpha| = 1$ and $\alpha(y,x) = B$. For any real r, we then have

$$(1) \quad (x - r\alpha y,\ x - r\alpha y) = (x,x) - r\alpha(y,x) - r\bar{\alpha}(x,y) + r^2(y,y).$$

The expression on the left is real and not negative. Hence

$$(2) \qquad A - 2Br + Cr^2 \geq 0$$

for every real r. If $C = 0$, we must have $B = 0$, otherwise (2) is false for large positive r. If $C > 0$, take $r = B/C$ in (2), and obtain $B^2 \leq AC$.

4.3 The Triangle Inequality For x and $y \in H$, we have

$$\|x + y\| \leq \|x\| + \|y\|.$$

PROOF By the Schwarz inequality,

$$\begin{aligned}\|x + y\|^2 &= (x + y,\ x + y) = (x,x) + (x,y) + (y,x) + (y,y) \\ &\leq \|x\|^2 + 2\|x\|\,\|y\| + \|y\|^2 = (\|x\| + \|y\|)^2.\end{aligned}$$

4.4 Definition It follows from the triangle inequality that

$$(1) \qquad \|x - z\| \leq \|x - y\| + \|y - z\| \qquad (x, y, z \in H).$$

If we define the distance between x and y to be $\|x - y\|$, all the axioms for a metric space are satisfied; here, for the first time, we use part (*e*) of Definition 4.1.

Thus H is now a metric space. If this metric space is *complete*, i.e., if every Cauchy sequence converges in H, then H is called a *Hilbert space*.

Throughout the rest of this chapter, the letter H will denote a Hilbert space.

4.5 Examples

(*a*) For any fixed n, the set C^n of all n-tuples

$$x = (\xi_1, \ldots, \xi_n),$$

where $\xi_1, \ldots, \xi_n$ are complex numbers, is a Hilbert space if addition and scalar multiplication are defined componentwise, as usual, and if

$$(x,y) = \sum_{j=1}^{n} \xi_j \bar{\eta}_j \qquad (y = (\eta_1, \ldots, \eta_n)).$$

(*b*) If μ is any positive measure, $L^2(\mu)$ is a Hilbert space, with inner product

$$(f,g) = \int_X f\bar{g}\, d\mu.$$

The integrand on the right is in $L^1(\mu)$, by Theorem 3.8, so that (f,g) is well defined. Note that

$$\|f\| = (f,f)^{\frac{1}{2}} = \left\{\int_X |f|^2 \, d\mu\right\}^{\frac{1}{2}} = \|f\|_2.$$

The completeness of $L^2(\mu)$ (Theorem 3.11) shows that $L^2(\mu)$ is indeed a Hilbert space. [We recall that $L^2(\mu)$ should be regarded as a space of *equivalence classes* of functions; compare the discussion in Sec. 3.10.]

For $H = L^2(\mu)$, the inequalities 4.2 and 4.3 turn out to be special cases of the inequalities of Hölder and Minkowski.

Note that Example (*a*) is a special case of (*b*). What is the measure in (*a*)?

(*c*) The vector space of all continuous complex functions on [0,1] is an inner product space if

$$(f,g) = \int_0^1 f(t)\overline{g(t)} \, dt$$

but is not a Hilbert space.

4.6 Theorem *For any fixed $y \in H$, the mappings*

$$x \to (x,y), \qquad x \to (y,x), \qquad x \to \|x\|$$

are continuous functions on H.

PROOF The Schwarz inequality implies that

$$|(x_1,y) - (x_2,y)| = |(x_1 - x_2, \, y)| \leq \|x_1 - x_2\| \, \|y\|,$$

which proves that $x \to (x,y)$ is, in fact, uniformly continuous, and the same is true for $x \to (y,x)$. The triangle inequality $\|x_1\| \leq \|x_1 - x_2\| + \|x_2\|$ yields

$$\|x_1\| - \|x_2\| \leq \|x_1 - x_2\|,$$

and if we interchange x_1 and x_2 we see that

$$|\|x_1\| - \|x_2\|| \leq \|x_1 - x_2\|$$

for all x_1 and $x_2 \in H$. Thus $x \to \|x\|$ is also uniformly continuous.

4.7 Subspaces A subset M of a vector space V is called a *subspace* of V if M is itself a vector space, relative to the addition and scalar multiplication which are defined in V. A necessary and sufficient condition for a set $M \subset V$ to be a subspace is that $x + y \in M$ and $\alpha x \in M$ whenever x and $y \in M$ and α is a scalar.

In the vector space context, the word "subspace" will always have this meaning. Sometimes, for emphasis, we may use the term "linear subspace" in place of subspace.

For example, if V is the vector space of all complex functions on a set S, the set of all bounded complex functions on S is a subspace of V, but the set of all $f \in V$ with $|f(x)| \leq 1$ for all $x \in S$ is not. The real vector space R^3 has the following subspaces, and no others: (*a*) R^3, (*b*) all planes through the origin 0, (*c*) all straight lines through 0, and (*d*) $\{0\}$.

A *closed subspace* M of H is a subspace which is a closed set relative to the topology induced by the metric of H.

4.8 Convex Sets A set E in a vector space V is said to be *convex* if it has the following geometric property: Whenever $x \in E$, $y \in E$, and $0 < t < 1$, the point

$$z_t = (1 - t)x + ty$$

also lies in E. As t runs from 0 to 1, one may visualize z_t as describing a straight line segment in V, from x to y. Convexity requires that E contain the segments between any two of its points.

It is clear that every subspace of V is convex.

Also, if E is convex, so is each of its translates

$$E + x = \{y + x : y \in E\}.$$

4.9 Orthogonality If $(x,y) = 0$ for some x and $y \in H$, we say that x is orthogonal to y, and sometimes write $x \perp y$. Since $(x,y) = 0$ implies $(y,x) = 0$, the relation $\perp$ is symmetric.

Let $x^\perp$ denote the set of all $y \in H$ which are orthogonal to x; and if M is a subspace of H, let $M^\perp$ be the set of all $y \in H$ which are orthogonal to every $x \in M$.

Note that $x^\perp$ is a subspace of H, since $x \perp y$ and $x \perp y'$ implies $x \perp (y + y')$ and $x \perp \alpha y$. Also, $x^\perp$ is precisely the set of points where the continuous function $y \to (x,y)$ is 0. Hence $x^\perp$ is a *closed* subspace of H. Since

$$M^\perp = \bigcap_{x \in M} x^\perp,$$

$M^\perp$ is an intersection of closed subspaces, and it follows that *$M^\perp$ is a closed subspace of H.*

4.10 Theorem *Every nonempty, closed, convex set E in a Hilbert space H contains a unique element of smallest norm.*

In other words, there is one and only one $x_0 \in E$ such that $\|x_0\| \leq \|x\|$ for every $x \in E$.

PROOF An easy computation, using only the properties listed in Definition 4.1, establishes the identity

$$(1) \quad \|x + y\|^2 + \|x - y\|^2 = 2\|x\|^2 + 2\|y\|^2 \qquad (x \text{ and } y \in H).$$

This is known as the *parallelogram law:* If we interpret $\|x\|$ to be the length of the vector x, (1) says that the sum of the squares of the diagonals of a parallelogram is equal to the sum of the squares of its sides, a familiar proposition in plane geometry.

Let $\delta = \inf \{\|x\|: x \in E\}$. For any x and $y \in E$, we apply (1) to $\frac{1}{2}x$ and $\frac{1}{2}y$ and obtain

$$(2) \qquad \tfrac{1}{4}\|x - y\|^2 = \tfrac{1}{2}\|x\|^2 + \tfrac{1}{2}\|y\|^2 - \left\|\frac{x + y}{2}\right\|^2.$$

Since E is convex, $(x + y)/2 \in E$. Hence

$$(3) \qquad \|x - y\|^2 \leq 2\|x\|^2 + 2\|y\|^2 - 4\delta^2 \qquad (x \text{ and } y \in E).$$

If also $\|x\| = \|y\| = \delta$, then (3) implies $x = y$, and we have proved the uniqueness assertion of the theorem.

The definition of δ shows that there is a sequence $\{y_n\}$ in E so that $\|y_n\| \to \delta$ as $n \to \infty$. Replace x and y in (3) by y_n and y_m. Then, as $n \to \infty$ and $m \to \infty$, the right side of (3) will tend to 0. This shows that $\{y_n\}$ is a Cauchy sequence. Since H is complete, there exists an $x_0 \in H$ so that $y_n \to x_0$, i.e., $\|y_n - x_0\| \to 0$, as $n \to \infty$. Since $y_n \in E$ and E is closed, $x_0 \in E$. Since the norm is a continuous function on H (Theorem 4.6), it follows that

$$\|x_0\| = \lim_{n \to \infty} \|y_n\| = \delta.$$

4.11 Theorem *Let M be a closed subspace of H. There exists a unique pair of mappings P and Q such that P maps H into M, Q maps H into $M^\perp$, and*

$$(1) \qquad x = Px + Qx$$

for all $x \in H$. These mappings have the following further properties:

$$(2) \qquad \text{If } x \in M, \text{ then } Px = x,\ Qx = 0; \text{ if } x \in M^\perp, \text{ then } Px = 0,\ Qx = x.$$

$$(3) \qquad \|x - Px\| = \inf \{\|x - y\|: y \in M\} \text{ if } x \in H.$$

$$(4) \qquad \|x\|^2 = \|Px\|^2 + \|Qx\|^2.$$

(5) *P and Q are linear mappings.*

Corollary *If $M \neq H$, there exists a $y \in H$, $y \neq 0$, such that $y \perp M$.*

P and Q are called the *orthogonal projections* of H onto M and $M^\perp$.

PROOF For any $x \in H$, the set $x + M = \{x + y: y \in M\}$ is closed and convex. Define Qx to be the unique element of smallest norm in $x + M$; this exists, by Theorem 4.10. Define $Px = x - Qx$. Then

(1) holds. Since $Qx \in x + M$, it is clear that $Px \in M$. Thus P maps H into M.

We next have to show that $(Qx,y) = 0$ for all $y \in M$. Assume $\|y\| = 1$, without loss of generality, and put $z = Qx$. The minimal property of Qx shows that

$$(z,z) = \|z\|^2 \leq \|z - \alpha y\|^2 = (z - \alpha y, z - \alpha y)$$

for every scalar α. This simplifies to

$$0 \leq -\alpha(y,z) - \bar{\alpha}(z,y) + |\alpha|^2.$$

With $\alpha = (z,y)$, this gives $0 \leq -|(z,y)|^2$, so that $(z,y) = 0$. Thus Q maps H into $M^\perp$.

Now if $x = x_0 + x_1$, with $x_0 \in M$, $x_1 \in M^\perp$, then

$$x_0 - Px = Qx - x_1.$$

Since $x_0 - Px \in M$, $Qx - x_1 \in M^\perp$, and $M \cap M^\perp = \{0\}$ [an immediate consequence of the fact that $(x,x) = 0$ implies $x = 0$], we have $x_0 = Px$, $x_1 = Qx$, which proves the uniqueness assertion.

The linearity of P and Q is proved similarly: applying (1) to x, to y, and to $\alpha x + \beta y$, we obtain

$$P(\alpha x + \beta y) - \alpha Px - \beta Py = \alpha Qx + \beta Qy - Q(\alpha x + \beta y).$$

The left side is in M, the right side in $M^\perp$; hence both are 0, so P and Q are linear.

Property (2) follows from (1); (3) was used to define P; and (4) follows from (1), since $(Px,Qx) = 0$. To prove the corollary, take $x \in H$, $x \notin M$, and put $y = Qx$; since $x \neq Px$, $y \neq 0$.

We have already observed that $x \to (x,y)$ is, for each $y \in H$, a continuous linear functional on H. It is a very important fact that *all* continuous linear functionals on H are of this type.

4.12 Theorem *If L is a continuous linear functional on H, then there is a unique $y \in H$ such that*

$$Lx = (x,y) \qquad (x \in H). \tag{1}$$

PROOF If $Lx = 0$ for all x, take $y = 0$. Otherwise, define

$$M = \{x: Lx = 0\}. \tag{2}$$

The linearity of L shows that M is a subspace. The continuity of L shows that M is closed. Since $Lx \neq 0$ for some $x \in H$, Theorem 4.11 shows that $M^\perp$ does not consist of 0 alone.

It is clear that we must look for our desired y in $M^\perp$, and that we must have $Ly = (y,y)$.

Choose $z \in M^\perp$, $z \neq 0$. Then $z \notin M$, hence $Lz \neq 0$. Put $y = \alpha z$, where $\bar{\alpha} = (Lz)/(z,z)$. Then $y \in M^\perp$, $Ly = (y,y)$, and $y \neq 0$. For any $x \in H$, put

(3) $$x' = x - \frac{Lx}{(y,y)}\,y \qquad \text{and} \qquad x'' = \frac{Lx}{(y,y)}\,y.$$

Then $Lx' = 0$, hence $x' \in M$, hence $(x',y) = 0$, hence

(4) $$(x,y) = (x'',y) = Lx,$$

which gives the desired representation of Lx.

The uniqueness of y is easily proved, for if $(x,y) = (x,y')$ for all $x \in H$, set $z = y - y'$; then $(x,z) = 0$ for all $x \in H$; in particular, $(z,z) = 0$, hence $z = 0$.

Orthonormal Sets

4.13 Definitions If V is a vector space, if $x_1, \ldots, x_k \in V$, and if $c_1, \ldots, c_k$ are scalars, then $c_1x_1 + \cdots + c_kx_k$ is called a *linear combination* of $x_1, \ldots, x_k$. The set $\{x_1, \ldots, x_k\}$ is called *independent* if $c_1x_1 + \cdots + c_kx_k = 0$ implies that $c_1 = \cdots = c_k = 0$. A set $S \subset V$ is independent if every finite subset of S is independent. The set $[S]$ of all linear combinations of all finite subsets of S (also called the set of all *finite linear combinations* of members of S) is clearly a vector space; $[S]$ is the smallest subspace of V which contains S; $[S]$ is called the *span* of S, or the space spanned by S.

A set of vectors u_α in a Hilbert space H, where α runs through some index set A, is called *orthonormal* if it satisfies the orthogonality relations $(u_\alpha,u_\beta) = 0$ for all $\alpha \neq \beta$, $\alpha \in A$, and $\beta \in A$, and if it is normalized so that $\|u_\alpha\| = 1$ for each $\alpha \in A$. In other words, $\{u_\alpha\}$ is orthonormal provided that

(1) $$(u_\alpha,u_\beta) = \begin{cases} 1 & \text{if } \alpha = \beta, \\ 0 & \text{if } \alpha \neq \beta. \end{cases}$$

If $\{u_\alpha: \alpha \in A\}$ is orthonormal, we associate with each $x \in H$ a complex function $\hat{x}$ on the index set A, defined by

(2) $$\hat{x}(\alpha) = (x,u_\alpha) \qquad (\alpha \in A).$$

One sometimes calls the numbers $\hat{x}(\alpha)$ the *Fourier coefficients* of x, relative to the set $\{u_\alpha\}$.

4.14 Theorem *If $u_1, \ldots, u_k$ is an orthonormal set, and if $x = \sum_1^k c_n u_n$, then*

$$c_n = (x,u_n), \qquad \textit{for } 1 \le n \le k, \tag{1}$$

$$\|x\|^2 = \sum_1^k |c_n|^2. \tag{2}$$

PROOF Apply the relations 4.13(1).

Corollary *Every orthonormal set is independent.*

PROOF This follows from (2).

4.15 An Approximation Problem Let $v_1, \ldots, v_k$ be a set of independent vectors in H, and suppose $x \in H$. The problem is to *find a method of computing the minimum value of*

$$\left\| x - \sum_{j=1}^k c_j v_j \right\|, \tag{1}$$

where $c_1, \ldots, c_k$ range over all scalars, and to find the corresponding values of $c_1, \ldots, c_k$.

Let M be the span of $v_1, \ldots, v_k$. If we knew that M is closed, we could apply Theorem 4.11 and deduce the existence of a unique minimizing element $x_0 = Px$, where

$$x_0 = \sum_{j=1}^k c_j v_j, \tag{2}$$

which also has the property that $x - x_0 \in M^\perp$. These facts could then be used to obtain information about the coefficients $c_1, \ldots, c_k$ in (2).

Since M is the span of a finite set of vectors, it may seem obvious that M is closed. One may prove it by induction, observing that $\{0\}$ is certainly closed and proceeding with the aid of the following lemma:

If V is a closed subspace of H, if $y \in H$, $y \notin V$, and V^* is the space spanned by V and y, then V^* is closed.

To prove this, suppose z is a limit point of V^*. Then

$$z = \lim_{n \to \infty} (x_n + \lambda_n y),$$

where $x_n \in V$, and λ_n are scalars. Since convergent sequences in metric spaces are bounded, there exists an $\eta < \infty$ such that $\|x_n + \lambda_n y\| < \eta$ for $n = 1, 2, 3, \ldots$. If it were true that $|\lambda_n| \to \infty$, we should have

$$\|\lambda_n^{-1} x_n + y\| < \frac{\eta}{|\lambda_n|} \to 0$$

so that $-y \in V$, since V is closed. But $y \notin V$. Hence $\{\lambda_n\}$ has a Cauchy subsequence $\{\lambda_{n_i}\}$ converging to some λ, and so $\{x_{n_i}\}$, being a difference of two Cauchy sequences, is itself a Cauchy sequence in H and converges to some $x \in V$. Then $z = x + \lambda y$. This proves that V^* contains all its limit points.

We now return to our problem. Put

$$a_{ij} = (v_j, v_i), \qquad b_i = (x, v_i). \tag{3}$$

Then if x_0, given by (2), is the minimizing element, we must have

$$(x - x_0,\, v_i) = 0$$

for $i = 1, \ldots, k$, which leads to a set of k linear equations in the unknowns $c_1, \ldots, c_k$:

$$\sum_{j=1}^{k} a_{ij} c_j = b_i \qquad (1 \leq i \leq k). \tag{4}$$

We know from Theorem 4.11 that x_0 exists and is unique. Hence the determinant of the a_{ij} is not 0, and the c_j can be computed from (4).

Next, let δ be the minimum value of (1). Since $(x - x_0,\, v_i) = 0$, we have $(x - x_0,\, x_0) = 0$; hence

$$\delta^2 = (x - x_0,\, x - x_0) = (x,\, x - x_0) = \Big(x,\, x - \sum_{j=1}^{k} c_j v_j\Big),$$

so that

$$\delta^2 = \|x\|^2 - \sum_{j=1}^{k} \bar{c}_j b_j. \tag{5}$$

This solves our problem, in terms of the quantities (3).

Let us now turn to a special case: Replace $v_1, \ldots, v_k$ by an orthonormal set $u_1, \ldots, u_k$. Then $a_{ij} = 1$ if $i = j$, $a_{ij} = 0$ if $i \neq j$, hence (4) gives $c_i = b_i$, and (5) becomes

$$\delta^2 = \|x\|^2 - \sum_{j=1}^{k} |b_j|^2. \tag{6}$$

We may summarize as follows:

4.16 Theorem *Let $u_1, \ldots, u_k$ be an orthonormal set in H, and let $x \in H$. Then*

$$\Big\| x - \sum_{j=1}^{k} (x, u_j) u_j \Big\| \leq \Big\| x - \sum_{j=1}^{k} \lambda_j u_j \Big\| \tag{1}$$

for all scalars $\lambda_1, \ldots, \lambda_k$. *Equality holds in* (1) *if and only if* $\lambda_j = (x,u_j)$ *for* $1 \le j \le k$. *The vector*

(2) $$\sum_{j=1}^{k} (x,u_j)u_j$$

is the orthogonal projection of x *into the subspace* $[u_1, \ldots, u_k]$, *and if* δ *is the distance from* x *to this subspace, then*

(3) $$\sum_{j=1}^{k} |(x,u_j)|^2 = \|x\|^2 - \delta^2.$$

Corollary (Bessel's Inequality) *If* $\{u_\alpha : \alpha \in A\}$ *is any orthonormal set in* H, *if* $x \in H$, *and if* $\hat{x}(\alpha) = (x,u_\alpha)$, *then*

(4) $$\sum_{\alpha \in A} |\hat{x}(\alpha)|^2 \le \|x\|^2.$$

This corollary calls for some explanation and comment. The set A is any index set, possibly even uncountable, and not ordered in any way. Under those conditions, what does the sum on the left side of (4) signify? We define it as follows: If $0 \le \varphi(\alpha) \le \infty$ for each $\alpha \in A$, the symbol

(5) $$\sum_{\alpha \in A} \varphi(\alpha)$$

denotes the supremum of the set of all finite sums $\varphi(\alpha_1) + \varphi(\alpha_2) + \cdots + \varphi(\alpha_k)$, where $\alpha_1, \ldots, \alpha_k$ are distinct members of A. With this agreement, it is clear that (4) follows from (3).

A moment's consideration will show that *the sum* (5) *is precisely the Lebesgue integral of* φ *relative to the counting measure on* A. Let $\ell^2(A)$ be the L^2-space relative to this counting measure. Then (4) asserts that $\hat{x} \in \ell^2(A)$ and that $\|\hat{x}\|_2 \le \|x\|$.

One immediate consequence of (4) should be mentioned explicitly:

For any $x \in H$ *and any orthonormal set* $\{u_\alpha\}$ *in* H, *the set of all* α *such that* $\hat{x}(\alpha) \neq 0$ *is at most countable.*

Let F be the mapping which assigns to each $x \in H$ the function $\hat{x}$ on A. For each $\alpha \in A$, $x \to (x,u_\alpha)$ is a linear functional. Hence F is a linear transformation of H into $\ell^2(A)$ (see Definition 2.1). Also, F does not increase distances, since $\|\hat{x} - \hat{y}\|_2 \le \|x - y\|$. In particular, F is continuous.

We shall now see that the completeness of H implies that F maps H *onto* $\ell^2(A)$ and that under certain conditions on $\{u_\alpha\}$, F is actually an isometry, i.e., that $\|\hat{x}\|_2 = \|x\|$ for all $x \in H$. Then, of course, F will be one-to-one.

4.17 The Riesz-Fischer Theorem *Let $\{u_\alpha: \alpha \in A\}$ be an orthonormal set in H. Suppose $\varphi \in \ell^2(A)$.* Then $\varphi = \hat{x}$ *for some* $x \in H$.

PROOF For $n = 1, 2, 3, \ldots$, let $A_n = \{\alpha: |\varphi(\alpha)| > 1/n\}$. Each A_n is a finite set. (In fact, one checks easily that A_n has at most $n^2\|\varphi\|_2^2$ elements.) Put

$$x_n = \sum_{\alpha \in A_n} \varphi(\alpha) u_\alpha \qquad (n = 1, 2, 3, \ldots). \tag{1}$$

Then $\hat{x}_n = \varphi \cdot \chi_{A_n}$, so that $\hat{x}_n(\alpha) \to \varphi(\alpha)$ for every $\alpha \in A$, and $|\varphi - \hat{x}_n|^2 \leq |\varphi|^2$. Hence, by an elementary case of the dominated convergence theorem, $\|\varphi - \hat{x}_n\|_2 \to 0$. It follows that $\{\hat{x}_n\}$ is a Cauchy sequence in $\ell^2(A)$. Since the sets A_n are finite, Theorem 4.14 shows that $\|x_n - x_m\| = \|\hat{x}_n - \hat{x}_m\|_2$. Thus $\{x_n\}$ is a Cauchy sequence in H, and since H is complete, there exists an $x = \lim_{n\to\infty} x_n$ in H. For any $\alpha \in A$ we then have

$$\hat{x}(\alpha) = (x,u_\alpha) = \lim_{n\to\infty} (x_n,u_\alpha) = \lim_{n\to\infty} \hat{x}_n(\alpha) = \varphi(\alpha),$$

which completes the proof.

4.18 Theorem *Let $\{u_\alpha: \alpha \in A\}$ be an orthonormal set in H. Each of the following four conditions on $\{u_\alpha\}$ implies the other three:*

(*a*) *$\{u_\alpha\}$ is a maximal orthonormal set in H.*
(*b*) *The set S of all finite linear combinations of members of $\{u_\alpha\}$ is dense in H.*
(*c*) *For every $x \in H$, we have* $\|x\|^2 = \sum_{\alpha \in A} |\hat{x}(\alpha)|^2$.
(*d*) *If $x \in H$ and $y \in H$, then* $(x,y) = \sum_{\alpha \in A} \hat{x}(\alpha)\overline{\hat{y}(\alpha)}$.

This last formula is known as *Parseval's identity.* Observe that $\hat{x} \in \ell^2(A)$ and $\hat{y} \in \ell^2(A)$, hence $\hat{x}\overline{\hat{y}} \in \ell^1(A)$, so that the summation in (*d*) is well defined. Of course, (*c*) is the special case $x = y$ of (*d*). Maximal orthonormal sets are frequently called *complete orthonormal sets* or *orthonormal bases.*

PROOF To say that $\{u_\alpha\}$ is maximal means simply that no vector of H can be adjoined to $\{u_\alpha\}$ in such a way that the resulting set is still orthonormal. This happens precisely when there is no $x \neq 0$ in H which is orthogonal to every u_α.

We shall prove that (*a*) → (*b*) → (*c*) → (*d*) → (*a*).

Let M be the closure of S. Since S is a subspace, so is M ($x_n \to x$ and $y_n \to y$ implies $x_n + y_n \to x + y$, $\lambda x_n \to \lambda x$); and if S is not dense in H, then $M \neq H$, so that $M^\perp$ contains a nonzero vector, by Theorem 4.11. Thus $\{u_\alpha\}$ is not maximal if S is not dense, and (*a*) implies (*b*).

Suppose (*b*) holds. Fix $x \in H$, $\epsilon > 0$. Since S is dense, there is a finite set $u_{\alpha_1}, \ldots, u_{\alpha_n}$ such that some linear combination of these vectors has distance less than ϵ from x. By Theorem 4.16, this approximation can only be improved if we take $\hat{x}(\alpha_j)$ for the coefficient of u_{α_j}. Thus if

$$(1) \qquad z = \hat{x}(\alpha_1)u_{\alpha_1} + \cdots + \hat{x}(\alpha_k)u_{\alpha_k},$$

we have $\|x - z\| < \epsilon$, hence $\|x\| < \|z\| + \epsilon$, and Theorem 4.14 gives

$$(2) \quad (\|x\| - \epsilon)^2 < \|z\|^2 = |\hat{x}(\alpha_1)|^2 + \cdots + |\hat{x}(\alpha_k)|^2 \le \sum_{\alpha \in A} |\hat{x}(\alpha)|^2.$$

Since ϵ was arbitrary, (*c*) follows from (2) and the Bessel inequality.

The equation in (*c*) can also be written in the form

$$(3) \qquad (x,x) = (\hat{x},\hat{x}),$$

the inner product on the right being the one in the Hilbert space $\ell^2(A)$, as in Example 4.5(*b*). Fix $x \in H$, $y \in H$. If (*c*) holds, then

$$(4) \qquad (x + \lambda y,\, x + \lambda y) = (\hat{x} + \lambda\hat{y},\, \hat{x} + \lambda\hat{y})$$

for every scalar λ; hence

$$(5) \qquad \bar{\lambda}(x,y) + \lambda(y,x) = \bar{\lambda}(\hat{x},\hat{y}) + \lambda(\hat{y},\hat{x}).$$

Take $\lambda = 1$ and $\lambda = i$. Then (5) shows that (x,y) and $(\hat{x},\hat{y})$ have the same real and imaginary parts, hence are equal. Thus (*c*) implies (*d*).

Finally, if (*a*) is false, there exists a $u \neq 0$ in H so that $(u,u_\alpha) = 0$ for all $\alpha \in A$. If $x = y = u$, then $(x,y) = \|u\|^2 \neq 0$, but $\hat{x}(\alpha) = 0$ for all $\alpha \in A$, hence (*d*) fails. Thus (*d*) implies (*a*), and the proof is complete.

4.19 Isomorphisms Speaking informally, two algebraic systems of the same nature are said to be isomorphic if there is a one-to-one mapping of one onto the other which preserves all relevant properties. For instance, we may ask whether two groups are isomorphic or whether two fields are isomorphic. Two vector spaces are isomorphic if there is a one-to-one *linear* mapping of one onto the other. The linear mappings are the ones which preserve the relevant concepts in a vector space, namely, addition and scalar multiplication.

In the same way, two Hilbert spaces H_1 and H_2 are isomorphic if there is a one-to-one linear mapping Λ of H_1 onto H_2 which also preserves inner products: $(\Lambda x,\Lambda y) = (x,y)$ for all x and $y \in H_1$. Such a Λ is an isomorphism (or, more specifically, a *Hilbert space isomorphism*) of H_1 onto H_2. Using this terminology, Theorems 4.17 and 4.18 yield the following statement:

If $\{u_\alpha: \alpha \in A\}$ *is a maximal orthonormal set in a Hilbert space* H, *and if* $\hat{x}(\alpha) = (x,u_\alpha)$, *then the mapping* $x \to \hat{x}$ *is a Hilbert space isomorphism of* H *onto* $\ell^2(A)$.

One can prove (we shall omit this) that $\ell^2(A)$ and $\ell^2(B)$ are isomorphic if and only if the sets A and B have the same cardinal number. But we shall prove that every nontrivial Hilbert space (this means that the space does not consist of 0 alone) is isomorphic to some $\ell^2(A)$, by proving that every such space contains a maximal orthonormal set (Theorem 4.22). The proof will depend on a property of partially ordered sets which is equivalent to the axiom of choice.

4.20 Partially Ordered Sets A set $\mathcal{P}$ is said to be *partially ordered* by a binary relation $\leq$ if

(*a*) $a \leq b$ and $b \leq c$ implies $a \leq c$.
(*b*) $a \leq a$ for every $a \in \mathcal{P}$.
(*c*) $a \leq b$ and $b \leq a$ implies $a = b$.

A subset $\mathcal{Q}$ of a partially ordered set $\mathcal{P}$ is said to be *totally ordered* (or *linearly ordered*) if every pair a, $b \in \mathcal{Q}$ satisfies either $a \leq b$ or $b \leq a$.

For example, every collection of subsets of a given set is partially ordered by the inclusion relation $\subset$.

To give a more specific example, let $\mathcal{P}$ be the collection of all open subsets of the plane, partially ordered by set inclusion, and let $\mathcal{Q}$ be the collection of all open circular discs with center at the origin. Then $\mathcal{Q} \subset \mathcal{P}$, $\mathcal{Q}$ is totally ordered by $\subset$, and $\mathcal{Q}$ is a *maximal* totally ordered subset of $\mathcal{P}$. This means that if any member of $\mathcal{P}$ not in $\mathcal{Q}$ is adjoined to $\mathcal{Q}$, the resulting collection of sets is no longer totally ordered by $\subset$.

4.21 The Hausdorff Maximality Theorem *Every nonempty partially ordered set contains a maximal totally ordered subset.*

This is a consequence of the axiom of choice and is, in fact, equivalent to it; another (very similar) form of it is known as Zorn's lemma. We give the proof in the Appendix.

If now H is a nontrivial Hilbert space, then there exists a $u \in H$ with $\|u\| = 1$, so that there is a nonempty orthonormal set in H. The existence of a maximal orthonormal set is therefore a consequence of the following theorem:

4.22 Theorem *Every orthonormal set* B *in a Hilbert space* H *is contained in a maximal orthonormal set in* H.

PROOF Let $\mathcal{P}$ be the class of all orthonormal sets in H which contain the given set B. Partially order $\mathcal{P}$ by set inclusion. Since $B \in \mathcal{P}$,

$\mathcal{P} \neq \emptyset$. Hence $\mathcal{P}$ contains a maximal totally ordered class Ω. Let S be the union of all members of Ω. It is clear that $B \subset S$. We claim that S is a maximal orthonormal set:

If u_1 and $u_2 \in S$, then $u_1 \in A_1$ and $u_2 \in A_2$ for some A_1 and $A_2 \in \Omega$. Since Ω is totally ordered, $A_1 \subset A_2$ (or $A_2 \subset A_1$), so that $u_1 \in A_2$ and $u_2 \in A_2$. Since A_2 is orthonormal, $(u_1,u_2) = 0$ if $u_1 \neq u_2$, $(u_1,u_2) = 1$ if $u_1 = u_2$. Thus S is an orthonormal set.

Suppose S is not maximal. Then S is a proper subset of an orthonormal set S^*. Clearly, $S^* \notin \Omega$, and S^* contains every member of Ω. Hence we may adjoin S^* to Ω and still have a total order. This contradicts the maximality of Ω.

Trigonometric Series

4.23 Definitions Let T be the unit circle in the complex plane, i.e., the set of all complex numbers of absolute value 1. If F is any function on T and if f is defined on R^1 by

$$f(t) = F(e^{it}), \tag{1}$$

then f is a periodic function of period 2π. This means that $f(t + 2\pi) = f(t)$ for all real t. Conversely, if f is a function on R^1, with period 2π, then there is a function F on T such that (1) holds. Thus we may identify functions on T with 2π-periodic functions on R^1; and, for simplicity of notation, we shall sometimes write $f(t)$ rather than $f(e^{it})$, even if we think of f as being defined on T.

With these conventions in mind, we define $L^p(T)$, for $1 \leq p < \infty$, to be the class of all complex, Lebesgue measurable, 2π-periodic functions on R^1 for which the norm

$$\|f\|_p = \left\{\frac{1}{2\pi}\int_{-\pi}^{\pi} |f(t)|^p\,dt\right\}^{1/p} \tag{2}$$

is finite.

In other words, we are looking at $L^p(\mu)$, where μ is Lebesgue measure on $[0,2\pi)$ (or on T), divided by 2π. $L^\infty(T)$ will be the class of all 2π-periodic members of $L^\infty(R^1)$, with the essential supremum norm, and $C(T)$ consists of all continuous complex functions on T (or, equivalently, of all continuous, complex, 2π-periodic functions on R^1), with norm

$$\|f\|_\infty = \sup_t |f(t)|. \tag{3}$$

The factor $1/(2\pi)$ in (2) simplifies the formalism we are about to develop. For instance, the L^p-norm of the constant function 1 is 1.

A *trigonometric polynomial* is a finite sum of the form

$$f(t) = a_0 + \sum_{n=1}^{N} (a_n \cos nt + b_n \sin nt) \qquad (t \in R^1) \tag{4}$$

where $a_0, a_1, \ldots, a_N$ and $b_1, \ldots, b_N$ are complex numbers. On account of the Euler identities, (4) can also be written in the form

$$f(t) = \sum_{n=-N}^{N} c_n e^{int} \tag{5}$$

which is more convenient for most purposes. It is clear that every trigonometric polynomial has period 2π.

We shall denote the set of all integers (positive, zero, and negative) by Z, and put

$$u_n(t) = e^{int} \qquad (n \in Z). \tag{6}$$

If we define the inner product in $L^2(T)$ by

$$(f,g) = \frac{1}{2\pi}\int_{-\pi}^{\pi} f(t)\overline{g(t)}\,dt \tag{7}$$

[note that this is in agreement with (2)], an easy computation shows that

$$(u_n,u_m) = \frac{1}{2\pi}\int_{-\pi}^{\pi} e^{i(n-m)t}\,dt = \begin{cases} 1 & \text{if } n = m, \\ 0 & \text{if } n \neq m. \end{cases} \tag{8}$$

Thus $\{u_n : n \in Z\}$ is an orthonormal set in $L^2(T)$, usually called the *trigonometric system.* We shall now prove that this system is maximal, and shall then derive concrete versions of the abstract theorems previously obtained in the Hilbert space context.

4.24 The Completeness of the Trigonometric System Theorem 4.18 shows that the maximality (or completeness) of the trigonometric system will be proved as soon as we can show that the set of all trigonometric polynomials is dense in $L^2(T)$. Since $C(T)$ is dense in $L^2(T)$, by Theorem 3.14 (note that T is compact), it suffices to show that to every $f \in C(T)$ and to every $\epsilon > 0$ there is a trigonometric polynomial P such that $\|f - P\|_2 < \epsilon$. Since $\|g\|_2 \leq \|g\|_\infty$ for every $g \in C(T)$, the estimate $\|f - P\|_2 < \epsilon$ will follow from $\|f - P\|_\infty < \epsilon$, and it is this estimate which we shall prove.

Suppose we had trigonometric polynomials $Q_1, Q_2, Q_3, \ldots$, with the following properties:

(*a*) $\quad Q_k(t) \geq 0$ *for* $t \in R^1$.

(*b*) $\quad \dfrac{1}{2\pi}\displaystyle\int_{-\pi}^{\pi} Q_k(t)\,dt = 1.$

(*c*) *If* $\eta_k(\delta) = \sup\{Q_k(t) : \delta \leq |t| \leq \pi\}$, *then*

$$\lim_{k\to\infty} \eta_k(\delta) = 0$$

for every $\delta > 0$.

Another way of stating (c) is to say that $Q_k(t) \to 0$ uniformly on $[-\pi, -\delta] \cup [\delta, \pi]$, for every $\delta > 0$.

To each $f \in C(T)$ we associate the functions P_k defined by

$$P_k(t) = \frac{1}{2\pi} \int_{-\pi}^{\pi} f(t-s) Q_k(s)\, ds \qquad (k = 1, 2, 3, \ldots). \tag{1}$$

If we replace s by $-s$ and then by $s - t$, the periodicity of f and Q_k shows that the value of the integral is not affected. Hence

$$P_k(t) = \frac{1}{2\pi} \int_{-\pi}^{\pi} f(s) Q_k(t-s)\, ds \qquad (k = 1, 2, 3, \ldots). \tag{2}$$

Since each Q_k is a trigonometric polynomial, Q_k is of the form

$$Q_k(t) = \sum_{n=-N_k}^{N_k} a_{n,k} e^{int}, \tag{3}$$

and if we replace t by $t - s$ in (3) and substitute the result in (2), we see that each P_k is a trigonometric polynomial.

Let $\epsilon > 0$ be given. Since f is uniformly continuous on T, there exists a $\delta > 0$ such that $|f(t) - f(s)| < \epsilon$ whenever $|t - s| < \delta$. By (b), we have

$$P_k(t) - f(t) = \frac{1}{2\pi} \int_{-\pi}^{\pi} \{f(t-s) - f(t)\} Q_k(s)\, ds,$$

and (a) implies, for all t, that

$$|P_k(t) - f(t)| \leq \frac{1}{2\pi} \int_{-\pi}^{\pi} |f(t-s) - f(t)| Q_k(s)\, ds = A_1 + A_2,$$

where A_1 is the integral over $[-\delta, \delta]$ and A_2 is the integral over

$$[-\pi, -\delta] \cup [\delta, \pi].$$

In A_1, the integrand is less than $\epsilon Q_k(s)$, so $A_1 < \epsilon$, by (b). In A_2, we have $Q_k(s) \leq \eta_k(\delta)$, hence

$$A_2 \leq 2\|f\|_\infty \cdot \eta_k(\delta) < \epsilon \tag{4}$$

for sufficiently large k, by (c). Since these estimates are independent of t, we have proved that

$$\lim_{k \to \infty} \|f - P_k\|_\infty = 0. \tag{5}$$

It remains to construct the Q_k. This can be done in many ways. Here is a simple one. Put

$$Q_k(t) = c_k \left(\frac{1 + \cos t}{2} \right)^k, \tag{6}$$

where c_k is chosen so that (*b*) holds. Since (*a*) is clear, we only need to show (*c*). Since Q_k is even, (*b*) shows that

$$1 = \frac{c_k}{\pi}\int_0^\pi \left(\frac{1+\cos t}{2}\right)^k dt > \frac{c_k}{\pi}\int_0^\pi \left(\frac{1+\cos t}{2}\right)^k \sin t\, dt = \frac{2c_k}{\pi(k+1)}.$$

Since Q_k is decreasing on $[0,\pi]$, it follows that

$$(7)\qquad Q_k(t) \le Q_k(\delta) \le \frac{\pi(k+1)}{2}\left(\frac{1+\cos\delta}{2}\right)^k \qquad (0 < \delta \le |t| \le \pi).$$

This implies (*c*), since $1 + \cos\delta < 2$ if $0 < \delta \le \pi$.

We have proved the following important result:

4.25 Theorem *If $f \in C(T)$ and $\epsilon > 0$, there is a trigonometric polynomial P such that*

$$|f(t) - P(t)| < \epsilon$$

for every real t.

A more precise result was proved by Fejér (1904): *The arithmetic means of the partial sums of the Fourier series of any $f \in C(T)$ converge uniformly to f.* For a proof (quite similar to the above) see Theorem 8.15 of [26].

4.26 Fourier Series For any $f \in L^1(T)$, we define the *Fourier coefficients* of f by the formula

$$(1)\qquad \hat{f}(n) = \frac{1}{2\pi}\int_{-\pi}^{\pi} f(t)e^{-int}\,dt \qquad (n \in Z),$$

where, we recall, Z is the set of all integers. We thus associate with each $f \in L^1(T)$ a function $\hat{f}$ on Z. The *Fourier series* of f is

$$(2)\qquad \sum_{-\infty}^{\infty} \hat{f}(n)e^{int},$$

and its *partial sums* are

$$(3)\qquad s_N(t) = \sum_{-N}^{N} \hat{f}(n)e^{int} \qquad (N = 0, 1, 2, \ldots).$$

Since $L^2(T) \subset L^1(T)$, (1) can be applied to every $f \in L^2(T)$. Comparing the definitions made in Secs. 4.23 and 4.13, we can now restate Theorems 4.17 and 4.18 in concrete terms:

The *Riesz-Fischer theorem* asserts that if $\{c_n\}$ is a sequence of complex numbers such that

$$(4)\qquad \sum_{n=-\infty}^{\infty} |c_n|^2 < \infty,$$

then there exists an $f \in L^2(T)$ such that

$$(5) \qquad c_n = \frac{1}{2\pi} \int_{-\pi}^{\pi} f(t)e^{-int}\, dt \qquad (n \in Z).$$

The *Parseval theorem* asserts that

$$(6) \qquad \sum_{n=-\infty}^{\infty} \hat{f}(n)\overline{\hat{g}(n)} = \frac{1}{2\pi} \int_{-\pi}^{\pi} f(t)\overline{g(t)}\, dt$$

whenever $f \in L^2(T)$ and $g \in L^2(T)$; the series on the left of (6) converges absolutely; and if s_N is as in (3), then

$$(7) \qquad \lim_{N\to\infty} \|f - s_N\|_2 = 0,$$

since a special case of (6) yields

$$(8) \qquad \|f - s_N\|_2^2 = \sum_{|n|>N} |\hat{f}(n)|^2.$$

Note that (7) says that every $f \in L^2(T)$ is the L^2-limit of the partial sums of its Fourier series; i.e., the Fourier series of f converges to f, in the L^2-sense. Pointwise convergence presents a more delicate problem, as we shall see in Chap. 5.

The Riesz-Fischer theorem and the Parseval theorem may be summarized by saying that the mapping $f \to \hat{f}$ is a Hilbert space isomorphism of $L^2(T)$ onto $\ell^2(Z)$.

The theory of Fourier series in other function spaces, for instance in $L^1(T)$, is much more difficult than in $L^2(T)$, and we shall touch only a few aspects of it.

Observe that the crucial ingredient in the proof of the Riesz-Fischer theorem is the fact that L^2 is complete. This is so well recognized that the name "Riesz-Fischer theorem" is sometimes given to the theorem which asserts the completeness of L^2, or even of any L^p.

Exercises

In this set of exercises, H always denotes a Hilbert space.

1 If M is a closed subspace of H, prove that $M = (M^\perp)^\perp$. Is there a similar true statement for subspaces M which are not necessarily closed?

2 For $n = 1, 2, 3, \ldots$, let $\{v_n\}$ be an independent set of vectors in H. Develop a *constructive* process which generates an orthonormal set $\{u_n\}$, such that u_n is a linear combination of $v_1, \ldots, v_n$. Note that this leads to a proof of the existence of a maximal orthonormal set in separable Hilbert spaces which makes no appeal to the Hausdorff maximality principle. (A space is *separable* if it contains a countable dense subset.)

3 Show that $L^p(T)$ is separable if $1 \leq p < \infty$, but that $L^\infty(T)$ is not separable.

4 Show that H is separable if and only if H contains a maximal orthonormal system which is at most countable.

5 If $M = \{x: Lx = 0\}$, where L is a continuous linear functional on H, prove that $M^\perp$ is a vector space of dimension 1 (unless $M = H$).

6 Let $\{u_n\}$ $(n = 1, 2, 3, \ldots)$ be an orthonormal set in H. Show that this gives an example of a closed and bounded set which is not compact. Let Q be the set of all $x \in H$ of the form

$$x = \sum_1^\infty c_n u_n, \text{ where } |c_n| \leq \frac{1}{n}.$$

Prove that Q is compact. (Q is called the Hilbert cube.)

More generally, let $\{\delta_n\}$ be a sequence of positive numbers, and let S be the set of all $x \in H$ of the form

$$x = \sum_1^\infty c_n u_n, \text{ where } |c_n| \leq \delta_n.$$

Prove that S is compact if and only if $\sum_1^\infty \delta_n^2 < \infty$.

Prove that H is not locally compact.

7 Suppose $\{a_n\}$ is a sequence of positive numbers such that $\Sigma a_n b_n < \infty$ whenever $b_n \geq 0$ and $\Sigma b_n^2 < \infty$. Prove that $\Sigma a_n^2 < \infty$.

8 If H_1 and H_2 are two Hilbert spaces, prove that one of them is isomorphic to a subspace of the other. (Note that every closed subspace of a Hilbert space is a Hilbert space.)

9 If $A \subset [0,2\pi]$ and A is measurable, prove that

$$\lim_{n\to\infty} \int_A \cos nx\,dx = \lim_{n\to\infty} \int_A \sin nx\,dx = 0.$$

10 Let $n_1 < n_2 < n_3 < \cdots$ be positive integers, and let E be the set of all $x \in [0,2\pi]$ at which $\{\sin n_k x\}$ converges. Prove that $m(E) = 0$. *Hint:* $2 \sin^2 \alpha = 1 - \cos 2\alpha$, so $\sin n_k x \to \pm 1/\sqrt{2}$ a.e. on E, by Exercise 9.

11 Prove that the identity

$$4(x,y) = \|x + y\|^2 - \|x - y\|^2 + i\|x + iy\|^2 - i\|x - iy\|^2$$

is valid in every inner product space, and show that it proves the implication (c) → (d) of Theorem 4.18.

12 The constants c_k in Sec. 4.24 were shown to be such that $k^{-1}c_k$ is bounded. Estimate the relevant integral more precisely and show that

$$0 < \lim_{k\to\infty} k^{-\frac{1}{2}} c_k < \infty.$$

13 Suppose f is a continuous function on R^1, with period 1. Prove that

$$\lim_{N\to\infty} \frac{1}{N} \sum_{n=1}^{N} f(n\alpha) = \int_0^1 f(t)\, dt$$

for every irrational real number α. *Hint:* Do it first for

$$f(t) = \exp(2\pi ikt),$$

$k = 0, \pm 1, \pm 2, \ldots .$

14 Compute

$$\min_{a,b,c} \int_{-1}^{1} |x^3 - a - bx - cx^2|^2\, dx$$

and find

$$\max \int_{-1}^{1} x^3 g(x)\, dx,$$

where g is subject to the restrictions

$$\int_{-1}^{1} g(x)\, dx = \int_{-1}^{1} xg(x)\, dx = \int_{-1}^{1} x^2 g(x)\, dx = 0; \qquad \int_{-1}^{1} |g(x)|^2\, dx = 1.$$

15 Compute

$$\min_{a,b,c} \int_0^\infty |x^3 - a - bx - cx^2|^2 e^{-x}\, dx.$$

State and solve the corresponding maximum problem, as in Exercise 14.

16 If $x_0 \in H$ and M is a closed linear subspace of H, prove that

$$\min \{\|x - x_0\| : x \in M\} = \max \{|(x_0, y)| : y \in M^\perp, \|y\| = 1\}.$$

17 Show that there is a continuous one-to-one mapping γ of $[0,1]$ into H such that $\gamma(b) - \gamma(a)$ is orthogonal to $\gamma(d) - \gamma(c)$ whenever $0 \le a \le b \le c \le d \le 1$. ($\gamma$ may be called a "curve with orthogonal increments.") *Hint:* Take $H = L^2$, and consider characteristic functions of certain subsets of $[0,1]$.

18 Give a direct proof of Theorem 4.16, i.e., one which does not depend on the more general considerations of Sec. 4.15.

5

Examples of Banach Space Techniques

Banach Spaces

5.1 In the preceding chapter we saw how certain analytic facts about trigonometric series can be made to emerge from essentially geometric considerations about general Hilbert spaces, involving the notions of convexity, subspaces, orthogonality, and completeness. There are many problems in analysis which can be attacked with greater ease when they are placed within a suitably chosen abstract framework. The theory of Hilbert spaces is not always suitable since orthogonality is something rather special. The class of all Banach spaces affords greater variety. In this chapter we shall develop some of the basic properties of Banach spaces and illustrate them by applications to concrete problems.

5.2 Definition A complex vector space X is said to be a *normed linear space* if to each $x \in X$ there is associated a nonnegative real number $\|x\|$, called the *norm* of x, such that

(*a*) $\|x + y\| \leq \|x\| + \|y\|$ for all x and $y \in X$,
(*b*) $\|\alpha x\| = |\alpha| \, \|x\|$ if $x \in X$ and α is a scalar,
(*c*) $\|x\| = 0$ implies $x = 0$.

By (*a*), the triangle inequality

$$\|x - y\| = \|x - z\| + \|z - y\| \qquad (x, y, z \in X)$$

holds. Combined with (*b*) (take $\alpha = 0$, $\alpha = -1$) and (*c*) this shows that every normed linear space may be regarded as a metric space, the distance between x and y being $\|x - y\|$.

A *Banach space* is a normed linear space which is *complete* in the metric defined by its norm.

For instance, every Hilbert space is a Banach space, so is every $L^p(\mu)$ normed by $\|f\|_p$ (provided we identify functions which are equal a.e.) if $1 \le p \le \infty$, and so is $C_0(X)$ with the supremum norm. The simplest Banach space is of course the complex field itself, normed by $\|x\| = |x|$.

One can equally well discuss *real* Banach spaces; the definition is exactly the same, except that all scalars are assumed to be real.

5.3 Definition Consider a linear transformation Λ from a normed linear space X into a normed linear space Y, and define its *norm* by

$$\|\Lambda\| = \sup\left\{\frac{\|\Lambda x\|}{\|x\|} : x \in X,\ x \neq 0\right\}. \tag{1}$$

If $\|\Lambda\| < \infty$, then Λ is called a *bounded linear transformation.*

In (1), $\|x\|$ is the norm of x in X, $\|\Lambda x\|$ is the norm of Λx in Y; it will frequently happen that several norms occur together, and the context will make it clear which is which.

Observe that we could restrict ourselves to *unit vectors* x in (1), i.e., to x with $\|x\| = 1$, without changing the supremum, since

$$\|\Lambda(\alpha x)\| = \|\alpha \Lambda x\| = |\alpha|\,\|\Lambda x\|. \tag{2}$$

Observe also that $\|\Lambda\|$ is the smallest number such that the inequality

$$\|\Lambda x\| \le \|\Lambda\|\,\|x\| \tag{3}$$

holds for *every* $x \in X$.

The following geometric picture is helpful: Λ maps the *closed unit ball* in X, i.e., the set

$$\{x \in X : \|x\| \le 1\}, \tag{4}$$

into the closed ball in Y with center at 0 and radius $\|\Lambda\|$.

An important special case is obtained by taking the complex field for Y; in that case we talk about *bounded linear functionals.*

5.4 Theorem *For a linear transformation Λ of a normed linear space X into a normed linear space Y, each of the following three conditions implies the other two:*

(*a*) *Λ is bounded.*
(*b*) *Λ is continuous.*
(*c*) *Λ is continuous at one point of X.*

PROOF Since $\|\Lambda(x_1 - x_2)\| \le \|\Lambda\|\,\|x_1 - x_2\|$, it is clear that (*a*) implies (*b*), and (*b*) implies (*c*) trivially. Suppose Λ is continuous at x_0. To each $\epsilon > 0$ one can then find a $\delta > 0$ so that $\|x - x_0\| < \delta$

implies $\|\Lambda x - \Lambda x_0\| < \epsilon$. In other words, $\|x\| < \delta$ implies

$$\|\Lambda(x_0 + x) - \Lambda x_0\| < \epsilon.$$

But then the linearity of Λ shows that $\|\Lambda x\| < \epsilon$. Hence $\|\Lambda\| \leq \epsilon/\delta$, and (*c*) implies (*a*).

Consequences of Baire's Theorem

5.5 The manner in which the completeness of a Banach space is frequently exploited depends on the following theorem about complete metric spaces, which also has many applications in other parts of mathematics. It implies two of the three most important theorems which make Banach spaces useful tools in analysis, the *Banach-Steinhaus theorem* and the *open mapping theorem.* The third is the *Hahn-Banach extension theorem,* in which completeness plays no role.

5.6 Baire's Theorem *If X is a complete metric space, the intersection of every countable collection of dense open subsets of X is dense in X.*

In particular (except in the trivial case $X = \varnothing$), the intersection is not empty. This is often the principal significance of the theorem.

PROOF Suppose $V_1, V_2, V_3, \ldots$ are dense and open in X. Let W be any open set in X. We have to show that $\bigcap V_n$ has a point in W if $W \neq \varnothing$.

Let ρ be the metric of X; let us write

$$S(x,r) = \{y \in X: \rho(x,y) < r\} \tag{1}$$

and let $\bar{S}(x,r)$ be the closure of $S(x,r)$. [*Note:* There exist situations in which $\bar{S}(x,r)$ does *not* contain all y with $\rho(x,y) \leq r$!]

Since V_1 is dense, $W \cap V_1$ is a nonempty open set, and we can therefore find x_1 and r_1 such that

$$\bar{S}(x_1,r_1) \subset W \cap V_1 \quad \text{and} \quad 0 < r_1 < 1. \tag{2}$$

If $n \geq 2$ and x_{n-1} and r_{n-1} are chosen, the denseness of V_n shows that $V_n \cap S(x_{n-1},r_{n-1})$ is not empty, and we can therefore find x_n and r_n such that

$$\bar{S}(x_n,r_n) \subset V_n \cap S(x_{n-1},r_{n-1}) \quad \text{and} \quad 0 < r_n < \frac{1}{n}. \tag{3}$$

By induction, this process produces a sequence $\{x_n\}$ in X. If $i > n$ and $j > n$, the construction shows that x_i and x_j both lie in $S(x_n,r_n)$, so that $\rho(x_i,x_j) < 2r_n < 2/n$, and hence $\{x_n\}$ is a Cauchy sequence. Since X is complete, there is a point $x \in X$ such that $x = \lim_{n\to\infty} x_n$.

Since x_i lies in the closed set $\bar{S}(x_n,r_n)$ if $i > n$, it follows that x lies in each $\bar{S}(x_n,r_n)$, and (3) shows that x lies in each V_n. By (2), $x \in W$. This completes the proof.

Corollary *In a complete metric space, the intersection of any countable collection of dense G_δ's is again a dense G_δ.*

This follows from the theorem, since every G_δ is the intersection of a countable collection of open sets, and since the union of countably many countable sets is countable.

5.7 Baire's theorem is sometimes called the *category theorem*, for the following reason.

Call a set $E \subset X$ *nowhere dense* if its closure $\bar{E}$ contains no nonempty open subset of X. Any countable union of nowhere dense sets is called a set of the *first category;* all other subsets of X are of the *second category* (Baire's terminology). Theorem 5.6 is equivalent to the statement that *no complete metric space is of the first category.* To see this, just take complements in the statement of Theorem 5.6.

5.8 The Banach-Steinhaus Theorem *Suppose X is a Banach space, Y is a normed linear space, and $\{\Lambda_\alpha\}$ is a collection of bounded linear transformations of X into Y, where α ranges over some index set A. Then either there exists an $M < \infty$ such that*

$$(1) \qquad \|\Lambda_\alpha\| \le M$$

for every $\alpha \in A$, or

$$(2) \qquad \sup_{\alpha \in A} \|\Lambda_\alpha x\| = \infty$$

for all x belonging to some dense G_δ in X.

In geometric terminology, the alternatives are as follows: *Either* there is a ball B in Y (with radius M and center at 0) such that every Λ_α maps the unit ball of X into B, *or* there exist $x \in X$ (in fact, a whole dense G_δ of them) such that no ball in Y contains $\Lambda_\alpha x$ for all α.

The theorem is sometimes referred to as the *uniform boundedness principle.*

PROOF Put

$$(3) \qquad \varphi(x) = \sup_{\alpha \in A} \|\Lambda_\alpha x\| \qquad (x \in X)$$

and let

$$(4) \qquad V_n = \{x: \varphi(x) > n\} \qquad (n = 1, 2, 3, \ldots).$$

Since each Λ_α is continuous and since the norm of Y is a continuous function on Y (an immediate consequence of the triangle inequality, as in the proof of Theorem 4.6), each function $x \to \|\Lambda_\alpha x\|$ is continuous on X. Hence φ is lower semicontinuous, and each V_n is open.

If one of these sets, say V_N, fails to be dense in X, then there exist an $x_0 \in X$ and an $r > 0$ such that $\|x\| \leq r$ implies $x_0 + x \notin V_N$; this means that $\varphi(x_0 + x) \leq N$, or

$$\|\Lambda_\alpha(x_0 + x)\| \leq N \tag{5}$$

for all $\alpha \in A$ and all x with $\|x\| \leq r$. Since $x = (x_0 + x) - x_0$, we then have

$$\|\Lambda_\alpha x\| \leq \|\Lambda_\alpha(x_0 + x)\| + \|\Lambda_\alpha x_0\| \leq 2N, \tag{6}$$

and it follows that (1) holds with $M = 2N/r$.

The other possibility is that every V_n is dense in X. In that case, $\bigcap V_n$ is a dense G_δ in X, by Baire's theorem; and since $\varphi(x) = \infty$ for every $x \in \bigcap V_n$, the proof is complete.

5.9 The Open Mapping Theorem *Let U and V be the open unit balls of the Banach spaces X and Y. To every bounded linear transformation Λ of X onto Y there corresponds a $\delta > 0$ so that*

$$\Lambda(U) \supset \delta V. \tag{1}$$

Note the word "onto" in the hypothesis. The symbol δV stands for the set $\{\delta y: y \in V\}$, i.e., the set of all $y \in Y$ with $\|y\| < \delta$.

It follows from (1) and the linearity of Λ that the image of every open ball in X, with center at x_0, say, contains an open ball in Y with center at Λx_0. Hence the image of every open set is open. This explains the name of the theorem.

Here is another way of stating (1): *To every y with $\|y\| < \delta$ there corresponds an x with $\|x\| < 1$ so that $\Lambda x = y$.*

PROOF Given $y \in Y$, there exists an $x \in X$ such that $\Lambda x = y$; if $\|x\| < k$, it follows that $y \in \Lambda(kU)$. Hence Y is the union of the sets $\Lambda(kU)$, for $k = 1, 2, 3, \ldots$. Since Y is complete, the Baire theorem implies that there is a nonempty open set W in the closure of some $\Lambda(kU)$. This means that every point of W is the limit of a sequence $\{\Lambda x_i\}$, where $x_i \in kU$; from now on, k and W are fixed.

Choose $y_0 \in W$, and choose $\eta > 0$ so that $y_0 + y \in W$ if $\|y\| < \eta$ For any such y there are sequences $\{x_i'\}$, $\{x_i''\}$ in kU such that

$$\Lambda x_i' \to y_0, \qquad \Lambda x_i'' \to y_0 + y \qquad (i \to \infty). \tag{2}$$

Setting $x_i = x_i'' - x_i'$, we have $\|x_i\| < 2k$ and $\Lambda x_i \to y$. Since this holds for every y with $\|y\| < \eta$, the linearity of Λ shows that the following is true, if $\delta = \eta/2k$:

To each $y \in Y$ *and to each* $\epsilon > 0$ *there corresponds an* $x \in X$ *such that*

$$\|x\| \leq \delta^{-1}\|y\| \quad \text{and} \quad \|y - \Lambda x\| < \epsilon. \tag{3}$$

This is almost the desired conclusion, as stated just before the start of the proof, except that there we had $\epsilon = 0$.

Fix $y \in \delta V$, and fix $\epsilon > 0$. By (3) there exists an x_1 with $\|x_1\| < 1$ and

$$\|y - \Lambda x_1\| < \tfrac{1}{2}\delta\epsilon. \tag{4}$$

Suppose $x_1, \ldots, x_n$ are chosen so that

$$\|y - \Lambda x_1 - \cdots - \Lambda x_n\| < 2^{-n}\,\delta\epsilon. \tag{5}$$

Use (3), with y replaced by the vector on the left side of (5), to obtain an x_{n+1} so that (5) holds with $n + 1$ in place of n, and

$$\|x_{n+1}\| < 2^{-n}\epsilon \qquad (n = 1, 2, 3, \ldots). \tag{6}$$

If we set $s_n = x_1 + \cdots + x_n$, (6) shows that $\{s_n\}$ is a Cauchy sequence in X. Since X is complete, there exists an $x \in X$ so that $s_n \to x$. The inequality $\|x_1\| < 1$, together with (6), shows that $\|x\| < 1 + \epsilon$. Since Λ is continuous, $\Lambda s_n \to \Lambda x$. By (5), $\Lambda s_n \to y$. Hence $\Lambda x = y$.

We have now proved that

$$\Lambda((1 + \epsilon)U) \supset \delta V, \tag{7}$$

or

$$\Lambda(U) \supset (1 + \epsilon)^{-1}\,\delta V, \tag{8}$$

for every $\epsilon > 0$. The union of the sets on the right of (8), taken over all $\epsilon > 0$, is δV. This proves (1).

5.10 Theorem *If* X *and* Y *are Banach spaces and if* Λ *is a bounded linear transformation of* X *onto* Y *which is also one-to-one, then there is a* $\delta > 0$ *such that*

$$\|\Lambda x\| \geq \delta\|x\| \qquad (x \in X). \tag{1}$$

In other words, Λ^{-1} *is a bounded linear transformation of* Y *onto* X.

PROOF If δ is chosen as in the statement of Theorem 5.9, the conclusion of that theorem, combined with the fact that Λ is now one-to-one, shows that $\|\Lambda x\| < \delta$ implies $\|x\| < 1$. Hence $\|x\| \geq 1$ implies $\|\Lambda x\| \geq \delta$, and (1) is proved.

The transformation Λ^{-1} is defined on Y by the requirement that $\Lambda^{-1}y = x$ if $y = \Lambda x$. A trivial verification shows that Λ^{-1} is linear, and (1) implies that $\|\Lambda^{-1}\| \leq 1/\delta$.

Fourier Series of Continuous Functions

5.11 A Convergence Problem *Is it true for every $f \in C(T)$ that the Fourier series of f converges to $f(x)$ at every point x?*

Let us recall that the nth partial sum of the Fourier series of f at the point x is given by

$$(1) \qquad s_n(f;x) = \frac{1}{2\pi} \int_{-\pi}^{\pi} f(t) D_n(x - t)\, dt \qquad (n = 0, 1, 2, \ldots),$$

where

$$(2) \qquad D_n(t) = \sum_{k=-n}^{n} e^{ikt}.$$

This follows directly from formulas 4.26(1) and 4.26(3).

The problem is to determine whether

$$(3) \qquad \lim_{n \to \infty} s_n(f;x) = f(x)$$

for every $f \in C(T)$ and for every real x. We observed in Sec. 4.26 that the partial sums do converge to f in the L^2-norm, and therefore Theorem 3.12 implies that each $f \in L^2(T)$ [hence also each $f \in C(T)$] is the pointwise limit a.e. of some subsequence of the full sequence of the partial sums. But this does not answer the present question.

We shall see that the Banach-Steinhaus theorem answers the question *negatively*. Put

$$(4) \qquad s^*(f;x) = \sup_n |s_n(f;x)|.$$

To begin with, take $x = 0$, and define

$$(5) \qquad \Lambda_n f = s_n(f;0) \qquad (f \in C(T);\ n = 1, 2, 3, \ldots).$$

We know that $C(T)$ is a Banach space, relative to the supremum norm $\|f\|_\infty$. It follows from (1) that each Λ_n is a bounded linear functional on $C(T)$, of norm

$$(6) \qquad \|\Lambda_n\| \le \frac{1}{2\pi} \int_{-\pi}^{\pi} |D_n(t)|\, dt = \|D_n\|_1.$$

We claim that

$$(7) \qquad \|\Lambda_n\| \to \infty \qquad \text{as } n \to \infty.$$

This will be proved by showing that equality holds in (6) and that

$$(8) \qquad \|D_n\|_1 \to \infty \qquad \text{as } n \to \infty.$$

Multiply (2) by $e^{it/2}$ and by $e^{-it/2}$ and subtract one of the resulting two equations from the other, to obtain

$$D_n(t) = \frac{\sin\,(n + \frac{1}{2})t}{\sin\,(t/2)}. \tag{9}$$

Since $|\sin x| \le |x|$ for all real x, (9) shows that

$$\|D_n\|_1 > \frac{2}{\pi}\int_0^\pi \left|\sin\left(n+\frac{1}{2}\right)t\right|\frac{dt}{t} = \frac{2}{\pi}\int_0^{(n+\frac{1}{2})\pi}|\sin t|\,\frac{dt}{t}$$

$$> \frac{2}{\pi}\sum_{k=1}^{n}\frac{1}{k\pi}\int_{(k-1)\pi}^{k\pi}|\sin t|\,dt = \frac{4}{\pi^2}\sum_{k=1}^{n}\frac{1}{k} \to \infty,$$

which proves (8).

Next, fix n, and put $g(t) = 1$ if $D_n(t) \ge 0$, $g(t) = -1$ if $D_n(t) < 0$. There exist $f_j \in C(T)$ such that $-1 \le f_j \le 1$ and $f_j(t) \to g(t)$ for every t, as $j \to \infty$. By the dominated convergence theorem,

$$\lim_{j\to\infty} \Lambda_n(f_j) = \lim_{j\to\infty}\frac{1}{2\pi}\int_{-\pi}^{\pi} f_j(-t)\,D_n(t)\,dt = \frac{1}{2\pi}\int_{-\pi}^{\pi} g(-t)\,D_n(t)\,dt$$

$$= \|D_n\|_1.$$

Thus equality holds in (6), and we have proved (7).

Since (7) holds, the Banach-Steinhaus theorem now asserts that $s^*(f;0) = \infty$ for every f in some dense G_δ-set in $C(T)$.

We chose $x = 0$ just for convenience. It is clear that the same result holds for every other x:

To each real number x there corresponds a set $E_x \subset C(T)$ which is a dense G_δ in $C(T)$, such that $s^*(f;x) = \infty$ for every $f \in E_x$.

In particular, the Fourier series of each $f \in E_x$ diverges at x, and we have a negative answer to our question.

It is interesting to observe that the above result can be strengthened by another application of Baire's theorem. Let us take countably many points x_i, and let E be the intersection of the corresponding sets

$$E_{x_i} \subset C(T).$$

By Baire's theorem, E is a dense G_δ in $C(T)$. Every $f \in E$ has

$$s^*(f;x_i) = \infty$$

at every point x_i.

For each f, $s^*(f;x)$ is a lower semicontinuous function of x, since (4) exhibits it as the supremum of a collection of continuous functions. Hence $\{x\colon s^*(f;x) = \infty\}$ is a G_δ in R^1, for each f. If the above points x_i are taken so that their union is dense in $(-\pi,\pi)$, we obtain the following result:

5.12 Theorem *There is a set $E \subset C(T)$ which is a dense G_δ in $C(T)$ and which has the following property: For each $f \in E$, the set*

$$Q_f = \{x\colon s^*(f;x) = \infty\}$$

is a dense G_δ in R^1.

This gains in interest if we realize that E, as well as each Q_f, is an *uncountable* set:

5.13 Theorem *In a complete metric space X which has no isolated points, no countable dense set is a G_δ.*

PROOF Let x_k be the points of a countable dense set E in X. Assume that E is a G_δ. Then $E = \bigcap V_n$, where each V_n is dense and open. Let

$$W_n = V_n - \bigcup_{k=1}^{n} \{x_k\}.$$

Then each W_n is still a dense open set, but $\bigcap W_n = \varnothing$, in contradiction to Baire's theorem.

Note: A slight change in the proof of Baire's theorem actually shows that every dense G_δ contains a perfect set if X is as above.

Fourier Coefficients of L^1-functions

5.14 As in Sec. 4.26, we associate to every $f \in L^1(T)$ a function $\hat{f}$ on Z defined by

$$\hat{f}(n) = \frac{1}{2\pi}\int_{-\pi}^{\pi} f(t)e^{-int}\,dt \qquad (n \in Z). \tag{1}$$

It is easy to prove that $\hat{f}(n) \to 0$ as $|n| \to \infty$, for every $f \in L^1$. For we know that $C(T)$ is dense in $L^1(T)$ (Theorem 3.14) and that the trigonometric polynomials are dense in $C(T)$ (Theorem 4.25). If $\epsilon > 0$ and $f \in L^1(T)$, this says that there is a $g \in C(T)$ and a trigonometric polynomial P such that $\|f - g\|_1 < \epsilon$ and $\|g - P\|_\infty < \epsilon$. Since

$$\|g - P\|_1 \leq \|g - P\|_\infty$$

it follows that $\|f - P\|_1 < 2\epsilon$; and if $|n|$ is large enough (depending on P), then

$$|\hat{f}(n)| = \left|\frac{1}{2\pi}\int_{-\pi}^{\pi} \{f(t) - P(t)\}e^{-int}\,dt\right| \leq \|f - P\|_1 < 2\epsilon. \tag{2}$$

Thus $\hat{f}(n) \to 0$ as $n \to \pm\infty$. This is known as the Riemann-Lebesgue lemma.

The question we wish to raise is whether the converse is true. That is to say, if $\{a_n\}$ is a sequence of complex numbers such that $a_n \to 0$ as $n \to \pm\infty$, does it follow that there is an $f \in L^1(T)$ such that $\hat{f}(n) = a_n$ for all $n \in Z$? In other words, is something like the Riesz-Fischer theorem true in this situation?

This can easily be answered (negatively) with the aid of the open mapping theorem.

Let c_0 be the space of all complex functions φ on Z such that $\varphi(n) \to 0$ as $n \to \pm\infty$, with the supremum norm

$$\|\varphi\|_\infty = \sup \{|\varphi(n)| : n \in Z\}. \tag{3}$$

Then c_0 is easily seen to be a Banach space. In fact, if we declare every subset of Z to be open, then Z is a locally compact Hausdorff space, and c_0 is nothing but $C_0(Z)$.

The following theorem contains the answer to our question:

5.15 Theorem *The mapping $f \to \hat{f}$ is a one-to-one bounded linear transformation of $L^1(T)$ into (but not onto) c_0.*

PROOF Define Λ by $\Lambda f = \hat{f}$. It is clear that Λ is linear. We have just proved that Λ maps $L^1(T)$ into c_0, and formula 5.14(1) shows that $|\hat{f}(n)| \le \|f\|_1$, so that $\|\Lambda\| \le 1$. (Actually, $\|\Lambda\| = 1$; to see this, take $f = 1$.) Let us now prove that Λ is one-to-one. Suppose $f \in L^1(T)$ and $\hat{f}(n) = 0$ for every $n \in Z$. Then

$$\int_{-\pi}^{\pi} f(t)g(t)\,dt = 0 \tag{1}$$

if g is any trigonometric polynomial. By Theorem 4.25 and the dominated convergence theorem, (1) holds for every $g \in C(T)$. Apply the dominated convergence theorem once more, in conjunction with the Corollary to Lusin's theorem, to conclude that (1) holds if g is the characteristic function of any measurable set in T. Now Theorem 1.39(b) shows that $f = 0$ a.e.

If the range of Λ were all of c_0, Theorem 5.10 would imply the existence of a $\delta > 0$ such that

$$\|\hat{f}\|_\infty \ge \delta \|f\|_1 \tag{2}$$

for every $f \in L^1(T)$. But if $D_n(t)$ is defined as in Sec. 5.11, then $D_n \in L^1(T)$, $\|\hat{D}_n\|_\infty = 1$ for $n = 1, 2, 3, \ldots$, and $\|D_n\|_1 \to \infty$ as $n \to \infty$. Hence there is no $\delta > 0$ such that the inequalities

$$\|\hat{D}_n\|_\infty \ge \delta \|D_n\|_1 \tag{3}$$

hold for every n.

This completes the proof.

The Hahn-Banach Theorem

5.16 Theorem *If M is a subspace of a normed linear space X and if f is a bounded linear functional on M, then f can be extended to a bounded linear functional F on X so that $\|F\| = \|f\|$.*

Note that M need not be closed.

Before we turn to the proof, some comments seem called for. First, to say (in the most general situation) that a function F is an *extension* of f means that the domain of F includes that of f and that $F(x) = f(x)$ for all x in the domain of f. Secondly, the norms $\|F\|$ and $\|f\|$ are computed relative to the domains of F and f; explicitly,

$$\|f\| = \sup\left\{\frac{|f(x)|}{\|x\|} : x \in M\right\}, \qquad \|F\| = \sup\left\{\frac{|F(x)|}{\|x\|} : x \in X\right\}.$$

The third comment concerns the field of scalars. So far everything has been stated for complex scalars, but the complex field could have been replaced by the real field without any changes in statements or proofs. The Hahn-Banach theorem is also true in both cases; nevertheless, it appears to be essentially a "real" theorem. The fact that the complex case was not yet proved when Banach wrote his classical book "Opérations linéaires" must be the reason that real scalars are the only ones considered in his work.

It will be helpful to introduce some temporary terminology. Recall that V is a complex (real) vector space if $x + y \in V$ for x and $y \in V$, and if $\alpha x \in V$ for all complex (real) numbers α. It follows trivially that *every complex vector space is also a real vector space.* A complex function φ on a complex vector space V is a *complex-linear functional* if

$$(1) \qquad \varphi(x + y) = \varphi(x) + \varphi(y) \qquad \text{and} \qquad \varphi(\alpha x) = \alpha\varphi(x)$$

for all x and $y \in V$ and all *complex* α. A real-valued function φ on a complex (or real) vector space V is a *real-linear functional* if (1) holds for all *real* α.

If u is the real part of a complex-linear functional f, i.e., if $u(x)$ is the real part of the complex number $f(x)$ for all $x \in V$, it is easily seen that u is a real-linear functional. The following relations hold between f and u:

5.17 Proposition *Let V be a complex vector space.*

(*a*) *If u is the real part of a complex-linear functional f on V, then*

$$(1) \qquad f(x) = u(x) - iu(ix) \qquad (x \in V).$$

(*b*) *If u is a real-linear functional on V and if f is defined by* (1), *then f is a complex-linear functional on V.*

(c) *If V is a normed linear space and f and u are related as in* (1), *then* $\|f\| = \|u\|$.

PROOF If α and β are real numbers and $z = \alpha + i\beta$, the real part of iz is $-\beta$. This gives the identity

$$(2) \qquad z = \text{Re } z - i \text{ Re } (iz)$$

for all complex numbers z. Since

$$(3) \qquad \text{Re } (if(x)) = \text{Re } f(ix) = u(ix),$$

(1) follows from (2) with $z = f(x)$.

Under the hypotheses (b), it is clear that $f(x + y) = f(x) + f(y)$ and that $f(\alpha x) = \alpha f(x)$ for all real α. But we also have

$$(4) \qquad f(ix) = u(ix) - iu(-x) = u(ix) + iu(x) = if(x),$$

which proves that f is complex-linear.

Since $|u(x)| \le |f(x)|$, we have $\|u\| \le \|f\|$. On the other hand, to every $x \in V$ there corresponds a complex number α, $|\alpha| = 1$, so that $\alpha f(x) = |f(x)|$. Then

$$(5) \qquad |f(x)| = f(\alpha x) = u(\alpha x) \le \|u\| \cdot \|\alpha x\| = \|u\| \cdot \|x\|,$$

which proves that $\|f\| \le \|u\|$.

5.18 Proof of Theorem 5.16 We first assume that X is a real normed linear space and, consequently, that f is a real-linear bounded functional on M. If $\|f\| = 0$, the desired extension is $F = 0$. Omitting this case, there is no loss of generality in assuming that $\|f\| = 1$.

Choose $x_0 \in X$, $x_0 \notin M$, and let M_1 be the vector space spanned by M and x_0. Then M_1 consists of all vectors of the form $x + \lambda x_0$, where $x \in M$ and λ is a real scalar. If we define $f_1(x + \lambda x_0) = f(x) + \lambda\alpha$, where α is any fixed real number, it is trivial to verify that an extension of f to a linear functional on M_1 is obtained. The problem is to choose α so that the extended functional still has norm 1. This will be the case provided that

$$(1) \qquad |f(x) + \lambda\alpha| \le \|x + \lambda x_0\| \qquad (x \in M, \lambda \text{ real}).$$

Replace x by $-\lambda x$ and divide both sides of (1) by $|\lambda|$. The requirement is then that

$$(2) \qquad |f(x) - \alpha| \le \|x - x_0\| \qquad (x \in M),$$

i.e., that $A_x \le \alpha \le B_x$ for all $x \in M$, where

$$(3) \qquad A_x = f(x) - \|x - x_0\| \qquad \text{and} \qquad B_x = f(x) + \|x - x_0\|.$$

There exists such an α if and only if all the intervals $[A_x,B_x]$ have a common point, i.e., if and only if

$$(4) \qquad A_x \le B_y$$

for all x and $y \in M$. But

$$(5) \quad f(x) - f(y) = f(x - y) \le \|x - y\| \le \|x - x_0\| + \|y - x_0\|,$$

and so (4) follows from (3).

We have now proved that there exists a norm-preserving extension f_1 of f on M_1.

Let $\mathcal{P}$ be the collection of all ordered pairs (M',f'), where M' is a subspace of X which contains M and where f' is a real-linear extension of f to M', with $\|f'\| = 1$. Partially order $\mathcal{P}$ by declaring $(M',f') \le (M'',f'')$ to mean that $M' \subset M''$ and $f''(x) = f'(x)$ for all $x \in M'$. The axioms of a partial order are clearly satisfied, $\mathcal{P}$ is not empty since it contains (M,f), and so the Hausdorff maximality theorem asserts the existence of a maximal totally ordered subcollection Ω of $\mathcal{P}$.

Let Φ be the collection of all M' such that $(M',f') \in \Omega$. Then Φ is totally ordered, by set inclusion, and *therefore* the union $\tilde{M}$ of all members of Φ is a subspace of X. (Note that in general the union of two subspaces is not a subspace. An example is two planes through the origin in R^3.) If $x \in \tilde{M}$, then $x \in M'$ for some $M' \in \Phi$; define $F(x) = f'(x)$, where f' is the function which occurs in the pair $(M',f') \in \Omega$. Our definition of the partial order in Ω shows that it is immaterial which $M' \in \Omega$ we choose to define $F(x)$, as long as M' contains x.

It is now easy to check that F is a linear functional on $\tilde{M}$, with $\|F\| = 1$. If $\tilde{M}$ were a proper subspace of X, the first part of the proof would give us a further extension of F, and this would contradict the maximality of Ω. Thus $\tilde{M} = X$, and the proof is complete for the case of real scalars.

If now f is a complex-linear functional on the subspace M of the complex normed linear space X, let u be the real part of f, use the real Hahn-Banach theorem to extend u to a real-linear functional U on X, with $\|U\| = \|u\|$, and define

$$(6) \qquad F(x) = U(x) - iU(ix) \qquad (x \in X).$$

By Proposition 5.17, F is a complex-linear extension of f, and

$$\|F\| = \|U\| = \|u\| = \|f\|.$$

This completes the proof.

Let us mention two important consequences of the Hahn-Banach theorem:

5.19 Theorem *Let M be a linear subspace of a normed linear space X, and let $x_0 \in X$. Then x_0 is in the closure $\bar{M}$ of M if and only if there is no bounded linear functional f on X such that $f(x) = 0$ for all $x \in M$ but $f(x_0) \neq 0$.*

PROOF If $x_0 \in \bar{M}$, f is a bounded linear functional on X, and $f(x) = 0$ for all $x \in M$, the continuity of f shows that we also have $f(x_0) = 0$.

Conversely, suppose $x_0 \notin \bar{M}$. Then there exists a $\delta > 0$ such that $\|x - x_0\| > \delta$ for all $x \in M$. Let M' be the subspace generated by M and x_0, and define $f(x + \lambda x_0) = \lambda$ if $x \in M$ and λ is a scalar. Since

$$\delta|\lambda| \leq |\lambda|\ \|x_0 + \lambda^{-1}x\| = \|\lambda x_0 + x\|,$$

we see that f is a linear functional on M' whose norm is at most δ^{-1}. Also $f(x) = 0$ on M, $f(x_0) = 1$. The Hahn-Banach theorem allows us to extend this f from M' to X.

5.20 Theorem *If X is a normed linear space and if $x_0 \in X$, $x_0 \neq 0$, there is a bounded linear functional f on X, of norm 1, so that $f(x_0) = \|x_0\|$.*

PROOF Let $M = \{\lambda x_0\}$, and define $f(\lambda x_0) = \lambda\|x_0\|$. Then f is a linear functional of norm 1 on M, and the Hahn-Banach theorem can again be applied.

5.21 Remarks If X is a normed linear space, let X^* be the collection of all bounded linear functionals on X. If addition and scalar multiplication of linear functionals are defined in the obvious manner, it is easy to see that X^* is again a normed linear space. In fact, X^* is a Banach space; this follows from the fact that the field of scalars is a complete metric space. We leave the verification of these properties of X^* as an exercise.

One of the consequences of Theorem 5.20 is that X^* is not the trivial vector space (i.e., X^* consists of more than 0) if X is not trivial. In fact, X^* *separates points on* X. This means that if $x_1 \neq x_2$ in X there exists an $f \in X^*$ such that $f(x_1) \neq f(x_2)$. To prove this, merely take

$$x_0 = x_2 - x_1$$

in Theorem 5.20.

Another consequence is that, for $x \in X$,

$$\|x\| = \sup\{|f(x)| : f \in X^*, \|f\| = 1\}.$$

Hence, for fixed $x \in X$, the mapping $f \to f(x)$ is a bounded linear functional on X^*, of norm $\|x\|$.

This interplay between X and X^* (the so-called "dual space" of X) forms the basis of a large portion of that part of mathematics which is known as *functional analysis*.

An Abstract Approach to the Poisson Integral

5.22 Successful applications of the Hahn-Banach theorem to concrete problems depend of course on a knowledge of the bounded linear functionals on the normed linear space under consideration. So far we have only determined the bounded linear functionals on a Hilbert space (where a much simpler proof of the Hahn-Banach theorem exists; see Exercise 6) and we know the positive linear functionals on $C_c(X)$.

We shall now describe a general situation in which the last-mentioned functionals occur naturally.

Let K be a compact Hausdorff space, let H be a compact subset of K, and let A be a subspace of $C(K)$ such that $1 \in A$ (1 denotes the function which assigns the number 1 to each $x \in K$) and such that

(1) $$\|f\|_K = \|f\|_H \qquad (f \in A).$$

Here we used the notation

(2) $$\|f\|_E = \sup\{|f(x)|: x \in E\}.$$

Because of the example discussed in Sec. 5.23, H is sometimes called a *boundary* of K, corresponding to the space A.

If $f \in A$ and $x \in K$, (1) says that

(3) $$|f(x)| \leq \|f\|_H.$$

In particular, if $f(y) = 0$ for every $y \in H$, then $f(x) = 0$ for all $x \in K$. Hence if f_1 and $f_2 \in A$ and $f_1(y) = f_2(y)$ for every $y \in H$, then $f_1 = f_2$; to see this, put $f = f_1 - f_2$.

Let M be the set of all functions on H which are restrictions to H of members of A. It is clear that M is a subspace of $C(H)$. The preceding remark shows that each member of M has a unique extension to a member of A. Thus we have a natural one-to-one correspondence between M and A, which is also norm-preserving, by (1). Hence it will cause no confusion if we use the same letter to designate a member of A and its restriction to H.

Fix a point $x \in K$. The inequality (3) shows that the mapping $f \to f(x)$ is a bounded linear functional on M, of norm 1 [since equality holds in (3) if $f = 1$]. By the Hahn-Banach theorem there is a linear functional Λ on $C(H)$, of norm 1, such that

(4) $$\Lambda f = f(x) \qquad (f \in M).$$

We claim that the properties

(5) $$\Lambda 1 = 1, \qquad \|\Lambda\| = 1$$

imply that Λ is a *positive* linear functional on $C(H)$.

To prove this, suppose $f \in C(H)$, $0 \le f \le 1$, put $g = 2f - 1$, and put $\Lambda g = \alpha + i\beta$, where α and β are real. Note that $-1 \le g \le 1$, so that $|g + ir|^2 \le 1 + r^2$ for every real constant r. Hence (5) implies that

$$(6) \qquad (\beta + r)^2 \le |\alpha + i(\beta + r)|^2 = |\Lambda(g + ir)|^2 \le 1 + r^2.$$

Thus $\beta^2 + 2r\beta \le 1$ for every real r, which forces $\beta = 0$. Since $\|g\|_H \le 1$, we have $|\alpha| \le 1$; hence

$$(7) \qquad \Lambda f = \tfrac{1}{2}\Lambda(1 + g) = \tfrac{1}{2}(1 + \alpha) \ge 0.$$

Now Theorem 2.14 can be applied. It shows that there is a regular positive Borel measure μ_x on H such that

$$(8) \qquad \Lambda f = \int_H f\, d\mu_x \qquad (f \in C(H)).$$

In particular, we get the representation formula

$$(9) \qquad f(x) = \int_H f\, d\mu_x \qquad (f \in A).$$

What we have proved is that *to each $x \in K$ there corresponds a positive measure μ_x on the "boundary" H which "represents" x in the sense that* (9) *holds for every $f \in A$.*

Note that Λ determines μ_x uniquely; but there is no reason to expect the Hahn-Banach extension to be unique. Hence, in general, we cannot say much about the uniqueness of the representing measures. Under special circumstances we do get uniqueness, as we shall see presently.

5.23 To see an example of the preceding situation, let $U = \{z: |z| < 1\}$ be the open unit disc in the complex plane, put $K = \bar{U}$ (the closed unit disc), and take for H the boundary T of U. We claim that every polynomial f, i.e., every function of the form

$$(1) \qquad f(z) = \sum_{n=0}^{N} a_n z^n,$$

where $a_0, \ldots, a_N$ are complex numbers, satisfies the relation

$$(2) \qquad \|f\|_U = \|f\|_T.$$

(Note that the continuity of f shows that the supremum of $|f|$ over U is the same as that over $\bar{U}$.)

Since $\bar{U}$ is compact, there exists a $z_0 \in \bar{U}$ such that $|f(z_0)| \ge |f(z)|$ for all $z \in \bar{U}$. Assume $z_0 \in U$. Then

$$(3) \qquad f(z) = \sum_{n=0}^{N} b_n (z - z_0)^n,$$

and if $0 < r < 1 - |z_0|$, we obtain

$$\sum_{n=0}^{N} |b_n|^2 r^{2n} = \frac{1}{2\pi} \int_{-\pi}^{\pi} |f(z_0 + re^{i\theta})|^2 \, d\theta \le \frac{1}{2\pi} \int_{-\pi}^{\pi} |f(z_0)|^2 \, d\theta = |b_0|^2,$$

so that $b_1 = b_2 = \cdots = b_N = 0$; i.e., f is constant. Thus $z_0 \in T$ for every nonconstant polynomial f, and this proves (2).

(We have just proved a special case of the *maximum modulus theorem;* we shall see later that this is an important property of all holomorphic functions.)

5.24 The Poisson Integral Let A be any subspace of $C(\bar{U})$ (where $\bar{U}$ is the closed unit disc, as above) such that A contains all polynomials and such that

(1) $$\|f\|_U = \|f\|_T$$

holds for every $f \in A$. We do not exclude the possibility that A consists of precisely the polynomials, but A might be larger.

The general result obtained in Sec. 5.22 applies to A and shows that to each $z \in U$ there corresponds a positive Borel measure μ_z on T such that

(2) $$f(z) = \int_T f \, d\mu_z \qquad (f \in A).$$

(This also holds for $z \in T$, but is then trivial: μ_z is simply the unit mass concentrated at the point z.)

We now fix $z \in U$ and write $z = re^{i\theta}$, $0 \le r < 1$, θ real.

If $u_n(w) = w^n$, then $u_n \in A$ for $n = 0, 1, 2, \ldots$; hence (2) shows that

(3) $$r^n e^{in\theta} = \int_T u_n \, d\mu_z \qquad (n = 0, 1, 2, \ldots).$$

Since $u_{-n} = \bar{u}_n$ on T, (3) leads to

(4) $$\int_T u_n \, d\mu_z = r^{|n|} e^{in\theta} \qquad (n = 0, \pm 1, \pm 2, \ldots).$$

This suggests that we look at the real function

(5) $$P_r(\theta - t) = \sum_{n=-\infty}^{\infty} r^{|n|} e^{in(\theta - t)} \qquad (t \text{ real}),$$

since

(6) $$\frac{1}{2\pi} \int_{-\pi}^{\pi} P_r(\theta - t) e^{int} \, dt = r^{|n|} e^{in\theta} \qquad (n = 0, \pm 1, \pm 2, \ldots).$$

Note that the series (5) is dominated by the convergent geometric series $\Sigma r^{|n|}$, so that it is legitimate to insert the series into the integral (6) and to integrate term by term, which gives (6). Comparison of (4) and (6) gives

$$\int_T f\,d\mu_z = \frac{1}{2\pi}\int_{-\pi}^{\pi} f(e^{it})P_r(\theta - t)\,dt \tag{7}$$

for $f = u_n$, hence for every trigonometric polynomial f, and Theorem 4.25 now implies that (7) holds for every $f \in C(T)$. [This shows that μ_z was uniquely determined by (2). Why?]

In particular, (7) holds if $f \in A$, and then (2) gives the representation

$$f(z) = \frac{1}{2\pi}\int_{-\pi}^{\pi} f(e^{it})P_r(\theta - t)\,dt \qquad (f \in A). \tag{8}$$

The series (5) can be summed explicitly, since it is the real part of

$$1 + 2\sum_{1}^{\infty} (ze^{-it})^n = \frac{e^{it} + z}{e^{it} - z} = \frac{1 - r^2 + 2ir\sin(\theta - t)}{|1 - ze^{-it}|^2}.$$

Thus

$$P_r(\theta - t) = \frac{1 - r^2}{1 - 2r\cos(\theta - t) + r^2}. \tag{9}$$

This is the so-called "Poisson kernel." Note that $P_r(\theta - t) \geq 0$ if $0 \leq r < 1$.

We now summarize what we have proved:

5.25 Theorem *Suppose A is a vector space of continuous complex functions on the closed unit disc $\bar{U}$. If A contains all polynomials, and if*

$$\sup_{z \in \bar{U}} |f(z)| = \sup_{z \in T} |f(z)| \tag{1}$$

for every $f \in A$ (where T is the unit circle, the boundary of U), then the Poisson integral representation

$$f(z) = \frac{1}{2\pi}\int_{-\pi}^{\pi} \frac{1 - r^2}{1 - 2r\cos(\theta - t) + r^2} f(e^{it})\,dt \qquad (z = re^{i\theta}) \tag{2}$$

is valid for every $f \in A$ and every $z \in U$.

Exercises

1 Let X consist of two points a and b, put $\mu(\{a\}) = \mu(\{b\}) = \frac{1}{2}$, and let $L^p(\mu)$ be the resulting *real* L^p-space. Identify each real function f on X with the point $(f(a), f(b))$ in the plane, and sketch the unit balls of $L^p(\mu)$, for $0 < p \leq \infty$. Note that they are convex if and only if $1 \leq p \leq \infty$. For which p is this unit ball a square? A circle? If $\mu(\{a\}) \neq \mu(\{b\})$, how does the situation differ from the preceding one?

2 Prove that the unit ball (open or closed) is convex in every normed linear space.

3 If $1 < p < \infty$, prove that the unit ball of $L^p(\mu)$ is *strictly convex;* this means that if

$$\|f\|_p = \|g\|_p = 1, \qquad f \neq g, \qquad h = \tfrac{1}{2}(f + g),$$

then $\|h\|_p < 1$. (Geometrically, the surface of the ball contains no straight lines.) Show that this fails in every $L^1(\mu)$, in every $L^\infty(\mu)$, and in every $C(X)$. (Ignore trivialities, such as spaces consisting of only one point.)

4 Let C be the space of all continuous functions on [0,1], with the supremum norm. Let M consist of all $f \in C$ for which

$$\int_0^{\frac{1}{2}} f(t)\, dt - \int_{\frac{1}{2}}^1 f(t)\, dt = 1.$$

Prove that M is a closed convex subset of C which contains no element of minimal norm.

5 Let M be the set of all $f \in L^1([0,1])$, relative to Lebesgue measure, such that

$$\int_0^1 f(t)\, dt = 1.$$

Show that M is a closed convex subset of $L^1([0,1])$ which contains infinitely many elements of minimal norm. (Compare this and Exercise 4 with Theorem 4.10.)

6 Let f be a bounded linear functional on a subspace M of a Hilbert space H. Prove that f has a *unique* norm-preserving extension to a bounded linear functional on H, and that this extension vanishes on $M^\perp$.

7 Construct a bounded linear functional on some subspace of some $L^1(\mu)$ which has two (hence infinitely many) distinct norm-preserving linear extensions to $L^1(\mu)$.

8 Let X be a normed linear space, and let X^* be its dual space, as defined in Sec. 5.21, with the norm

$$\|f\| = \sup\{|f(x)| : \|x\| \leq 1\}.$$

(*a*) Prove that X^* is a Banach space.

(*b*) Prove that the mapping $f \to f(x)$ is, for each $x \in X$, a bounded linear functional on X^*, of norm $\|x\|$. (This gives a natural imbedding of X in its "second dual" X^{**}, the dual space of X^*.)

(c) Prove that $\{\|x_n\|\}$ is bounded if $\{x_n\}$ is a sequence in X such that $\{f(x_n)\}$ is bounded for every $f \in X^*$.

9 Let c_0, ℓ^1, and ℓ^∞ be the Banach spaces consisting of all complex sequences $x = \{\xi_i\}$, $i = 1, 2, 3, \ldots$, defined as follows:

$x \in \ell^1$ if and only if $\|x\|_1 = \Sigma|\xi_i| < \infty$.
$x \in \ell^\infty$ if and only if $\|x\|_\infty = \sup |\xi_i| < \infty$.
c_0 is the subspace of ℓ^∞ consisting of all $x \in \ell^\infty$ for which $\xi_i \to 0$ as $i \to \infty$.

Prove that $(c_0)^* = \ell^1$ and that $(\ell^1)^* = \ell^\infty$, using the notation of Exercise 8, but that $(\ell^\infty)^* \neq \ell^1$.

Prove that c_0 and ℓ^1 are separable but that ℓ^∞ is not.

[The statement "$(c_0)^* = \ell^1$" means, more explicitly, that to every bounded linear functional Λ on c_0 there corresponds a unique sequence $\{\eta_i\}$ such that

$$\Sigma|\eta_i| = \|\Lambda\| \qquad \text{and} \qquad \Lambda x = \Sigma \xi_i \eta_i \qquad \text{for all } x \in c_0$$

and conversely. That $(\ell^\infty)^* \neq \ell^1$ depends on the fact that there is a nontrivial bounded linear functional on ℓ^∞ which vanishes on all of c_0.]

10 If $\Sigma \alpha_i \xi_i$ converges for every sequence $\{\xi_i\}$ such that $\xi_i \to 0$ as $i \to \infty$, prove that $\Sigma|\alpha_i| < \infty$.

11 For $0 < \alpha \leq 1$, let Lip α denote the space of all complex functions f on $[a,b]$ for which

$$M_f = \sup_{s \neq t} \frac{|f(s) - f(t)|}{|s - t|^\alpha} < \infty.$$

Prove that Lip α is a Banach space, if $\|f\| = |f(a)| + M_f$; also, if $\|f\| = M_f + \sup_x |f(x)|$. (The members of Lip α are said to satisfy a *Lipschitz condition* of order α.)

12 Let K be a triangle (two-dimensional figure) in the plane, let H be the set consisting of the vertices of K, and let A be the set of all real functions f on K, of the form

$$f(x,y) = \alpha x + \beta y + \gamma \qquad (\alpha, \beta, \text{ and } \gamma \text{ real}).$$

Show that to each $(x_0,y_0) \in K$ there corresponds a unique measure μ on H such that

$$f(x_0,y_0) = \int_H f\, d\mu.$$

(Compare Sec. 5.22.)

Replace K by a square, let H again be the set of its vertices, and let A be as above. Show that to each point of K there still corresponds a measure on H, with the above property, but that uniqueness is now lost.

Can you extrapolate to a more general theorem? (Think of other figures, higher dimensional spaces.)

13 Let $\{f_n\}$ be a sequence of continuous real functions on the line which converges at every point. Prove that there is an interval I and a number $M < \infty$ such that $|f_n(x)| < M$ for every $x \in I$ and $n = 1, 2, 3, \ldots$. Find some generalizations of this.

14 Let C be the space of all real continuous functions on $I = [0,1]$ with the supremum norm. Let X_n be the subset of C consisting of those f for which there exists a $t \in I$ such that $|f(s) - f(t)| \leq n|s - t|$ for all $s \in I$. Fix n and prove that each open set in C contains an open set which does not intersect X_n. (Each $f \in C$ can be uniformly approximated by a zigzag function g with very large slopes, and if $\|g - h\|$ is small, $h \notin X_n$.) Show that this implies the existence of a dense G_δ in C which consists entirely of nowhere differentiable functions.

15 Let $A = (a_{ij})$ be an infinite matrix with complex entries, where $i, j = 0, 1, 2, \ldots$. A associates with each sequence $\{s_j\}$ a sequence $\{\sigma_i\}$, defined by

$$\sigma_i = \sum_{j=0}^{\infty} a_{ij}s_j \qquad (i = 1, 2, 3, \ldots),$$

provided that these series converge.

Prove that A transforms every convergent sequence $\{s_j\}$ to a sequence $\{\sigma_i\}$ which converges to the same limit if and only if the following conditions are satisfied:

(a) $$\lim_{i \to \infty} a_{ij} = 0 \qquad \text{for each } j.$$

(b) $$\sup_i \sum_{j=0}^{\infty} |a_{ij}| < \infty.$$

(c) $$\lim_{i \to \infty} \sum_{j=0}^{\infty} a_{ij} = 1.$$

The process of passing from $\{s_j\}$ to $\{\sigma_i\}$ is called a *summability method*. Two examples are:

$$a_{ij} = \begin{cases} \dfrac{1}{i+1} & \text{if } 0 \leq j \leq i, \\ 0 & \text{if } i < j, \end{cases}$$

and $\quad a_{ij} = (1 - r_i)r_i^j, \qquad 0 < r_i < 1, \qquad r_i \to 1.$

Prove that each of these also transforms some divergent sequences $\{s_j\}$ (even some unbounded ones) to convergent sequences $\{\sigma_i\}$.

16 Suppose X and Y are Banach spaces, and suppose Λ is a linear mapping of X into Y, with the following property: For every sequence $\{x_n\}$ in X for which $x = \lim x_n$ and $y = \lim \Lambda x_n$ exist, it is true that $y = \Lambda x$. Prove that Λ is continuous.

This is the so-called "closed graph theorem." *Hint:* Let $X \oplus Y$ be the set of all ordered pairs (x,y), $x \in X$ and $y \in Y$, with addition and scalar multiplication defined componentwise. Prove that $X \oplus Y$ is a Banach space, if $\|(x,y)\| = \|x\| + \|y\|$. The graph G of Λ is the subset of $X \oplus Y$ formed by the pairs $(x,\Lambda x)$, $x \in X$. Note that our hypothesis says that G is closed; hence G is a Banach space. Note that $(x,\Lambda x) \to x$ is continuous, one-to-one, and linear and maps G onto X.

Observe that there exist *nonlinear* mappings (of R^1 onto R^1, for instance) whose graph is closed although they are not continuous: $f(x) = 1/x$ if $x \neq 0$, $f(0) = 0$.

17 If μ is a positive measure, each $f \in L^\infty(\mu)$ defines a multiplication operator M_f on $L^2(\mu)$ into $L^2(\mu)$, such that $M_f(g) = fg$. Prove that $\|M_f\| \leq \|f\|_\infty$. For which measures μ is it true that $\|M_f\| = \|f\|_\infty$ for all $f \in L^\infty(\mu)$? For which $f \in L^\infty(\mu)$ does M_f map $L^2(\mu)$ onto $L^2(\mu)$?

18 Suppose $\{\Lambda_n\}$ is a sequence of bounded linear transformations from a normed linear space X to a Banach space Y, suppose $\|\Lambda_n\| \leq M < \infty$ for all n, and suppose there is a dense set $E \subset X$ such that $\{\Lambda_n x\}$ converges for each $x \in E$. Prove that $\{\Lambda_n x\}$ converges for each $x \in X$.

19 If s_n is the nth partial sum of the Fourier series of a function $f \in C(T)$, prove that $s_n/\log n \to 0$ uniformly, as $n \to \infty$, for each $f \in C(T)$. That is, prove that

$$\lim_{n\to\infty} \frac{\|s_n\|_\infty}{\log n} = 0.$$

On the other hand, if $\lambda_n/\log n \to 0$, prove that there exists an $f \in C(T)$ such that the sequence $\{s_n(f;0)/\lambda_n\}$ is unbounded. *Hint:* Apply the reasoning of Exercise 18 and that of Sec. 5.11, with a better estimate of $\|D_n\|_1$ than was used there.

20 Is the lemma of Sec. 4.15 valid in every Banach space? In every normed linear space?

6

Complex Measures

Total Variation

6.1 Introduction Let $\mathfrak{M}$ be a σ-algebra in a set X. Call a countable collection $\{E_i\}$ of members of $\mathfrak{M}$ a *partition of* E if $E_i \cap E_j = \emptyset$ whenever $i \neq j$, and if $E = \bigcup E_i$. A *complex measure* μ on $\mathfrak{M}$ is then a complex function on $\mathfrak{M}$ such that

$$(1) \qquad \mu(E) = \sum_{i=1}^{\infty} \mu(E_i) \qquad (E \in \mathfrak{M})$$

for every partition $\{E_i\}$ of E.

Observe that the convergence of the series in (1) is now part of the requirement (unlike for positive measures, where the series either could converge or could diverge to ∞). Since the union of the sets E_i is not changed if the subscripts are permuted, every rearrangement of the series (1) must also converge. Hence ([26], Theorem 3.56) the series actually converges absolutely.

Let us consider the problem of finding a positive measure λ which dominates a given complex measure μ on $\mathfrak{M}$, in the sense that $|\mu(E)| \leq \lambda(E)$ for every $E \in \mathfrak{M}$, and let us try to keep λ as small as we can. Every solution to our problem (if there is one at all) must satisfy

$$(2) \qquad \lambda(E) = \sum_{i=1}^{\infty} \lambda(E_i) \geq \sum_{1}^{\infty} |\mu(E_i)|,$$

for every partition $\{E_i\}$ of any set $E \in \mathfrak{M}$, so that $\lambda(E)$ is at least equal to the supremum of the sums on the right of (2), taken over all partitions of E. This suggests that we *define a set function* $|\mu|$ *on* $\mathfrak{M}$ *by*

$$(3) \qquad |\mu|(E) = \sup \sum_{i=1}^{\infty} |\mu(E_i)| \qquad (E \in \mathfrak{M}),$$

the supremum being taken over all partitions $\{E_i\}$ *of* E.

This notation is perhaps not the best, but it is the customary one. Note that $|\mu|(E) \geq |\mu(E)|$, but that in general $|\mu|(E)$ is not equal to $|\mu(E)|$.

It turns out, as will be proved below, that $|\mu|$ actually *is* a measure, so that our problem does have a solution. The discussion which led to (3) then shows clearly that $|\mu|$ is the minimal solution, in the sense that any other solution λ has the property $\lambda(E) \geq |\mu|(E)$ for all $E \in \mathfrak{M}$.

The set function $|\mu|$ is called the *total variation* of μ, or sometimes, to avoid misunderstanding, the *total variation measure.* The term "total variation of μ" is also frequently used to denote the number $|\mu|(X)$.

If μ is a positive measure, then of course $|\mu| = \mu$.

Besides being a measure, $|\mu|$ has another unexpected property: $|\mu|(X) < \infty$. Since $|\mu(E)| \leq |\mu|(E) \leq |\mu|(X)$, this implies that every complex measure μ on any σ-algebra is bounded: if the range of μ lies in the complex plane, then it actually lies in some disc of finite radius. This property (proved in Theorem 6.4) is sometimes expressed by saying that μ *is of bounded variation.*

6.2 Theorem *The total variation $|\mu|$ of a complex measure μ on $\mathfrak{M}$ is a positive measure on $\mathfrak{M}$.*

PROOF Let $\{E_i\}$ be a partition of $E \in \mathfrak{M}$. Let t_i be real numbers such that $t_i < |\mu|(E_i)$. Then each E_i has a partition $\{A_{ij}\}$ such that

$$\sum_j |\mu(A_{ij})| > t_i \qquad (i = 1, 2, 3, \ldots). \tag{1}$$

Since $\{A_{ij}\}$ $(i, j = 1, 2, 3, \ldots)$ is a partition of E, it follows that

$$\sum_i t_i \leq \sum_{i,j} |\mu(A_{ij})| \leq |\mu|(E). \tag{2}$$

Taking the supremum of the left side of (2), over all admissible choices of $\{t_i\}$, we see that

$$\sum_i |\mu|(E_i) \leq |\mu|(E). \tag{3}$$

To prove the opposite inequality, let $\{A_j\}$ be any partition of E. Then for any fixed j, $\{A_j \cap E_i\}$ is a partition of A_j, and for any fixed i, $\{A_j \cap E_i\}$ is a partition of E_i. Hence

$$\begin{aligned} \sum_j |\mu(A_j)| &= \sum_j \Big| \sum_i \mu(A_j \cap E_i) \Big| \\ &\leq \sum_j \sum_i |\mu(A_j \cap E_i)| \\ &= \sum_i \sum_j |\mu(A_j \cap E_i)| \leq \sum_i |\mu|(E_i). \end{aligned} \tag{4}$$

Since (4) holds for every partition $\{A_j\}$ of E, we have

(5) $$|\mu|(E) \leq \sum_i |\mu|(E_i).$$

By (3) and (5), $|\mu|$ is countably additive.

Note that the Corollary to Theorem 1.27 was used in (2) and (4).

That $|\mu|$ is not identically ∞ is a trivial consequence of Theorem 6.4 but can also be seen right now, since $|\mu|(\varnothing) = 0$.

6.3 Lemma *If $z_1, z_2, \ldots, z_n$ are complex numbers, there is a subset S of $\{1, \ldots, n\}$ such that*

(1) $$\left| \sum_{j \in S} z_j \right| \geq \frac{1}{6} \sum_{j=1}^{n} |z_j|.$$

PROOF Put $w = |z_1| + \cdots + |z_n|$. The complex plane is the union of four closed quadrants, bounded by the lines $y = \pm x$, and at least one of these quadrants Q (assume, without loss of generality, that it is the one defined by $|y| \leq x$) has the property that the sum of the $|z_j|$ for which $z_j \in Q$ is at least $w/4$. For $z \in Q$, we have

$$\operatorname{Re} z \geq |z|/\sqrt{2};$$

if S is the set of all j such that $z_j \in Q$, it follows that

$$\left| \sum_{j \in S} z_j \right| \geq \sum_{j \in S} \operatorname{Re} z_j \geq \frac{1}{\sqrt{2}} \sum_{j \in S} |z_j| \geq \frac{w}{4\sqrt{2}} \geq \frac{w}{6}.$$

6.4 Theorem *If μ is a complex measure on X, then*

(1) $$|\mu|(X) < \infty.$$

PROOF We first show that if $|\mu|(E) = \infty$ for some $E \in \mathfrak{M}$, then $E = A \cup B$, where A and $B \in \mathfrak{M}$, $A \cap B = \varnothing$, and

(2) $$|\mu(A)| > 1, \qquad |\mu|(B) = \infty.$$

Indeed, the definition of $|\mu|$ shows that to every $t < \infty$ there corresponds a partition $\{E_j\}$ of E such that $\Sigma|\mu(E_j)| > t$. Let us take $t = 6(1 + |\mu(E)|)$. Then

(3) $$\sum_{j=1}^{n} |\mu(E_j)| > t$$

for some n; and if we apply Lemma 6.3 with $z_j = \mu(E_j)$ and put

(4) $$A = \bigcup_{j \in S} E_j,$$

it follows that $A \subset E$ and $|\mu(A)| > t/6 \geq 1$. If $B = E - A$, then

$$(5) \quad |\mu(B)| = |\mu(E) - \mu(A)| \geq |\mu(A)| - |\mu(E)| > \frac{t}{6} - |\mu(E)| = 1.$$

Since $|\mu|(E) = |\mu|(A) + |\mu|(B)$, by Theorem 6.2, we have $|\mu|(A) = \infty$ or $|\mu|(B) = \infty$ (or both), and we obtain (2) by interchanging A and B, if necessary.

Now assume that $|\mu|(X) = \infty$. Put $B_0 = X$. Suppose $n \geq 0$, and B_n is chosen so that $|\mu|(B_n) = \infty$. Then, applying (2) with B_n in place of E, we see that B_n is the union of two disjoint sets A_{n+1} and B_{n+1}, such that $|\mu(A_{n+1})| > 1$ and $|\mu|(B_{n+1}) = \infty$. We thus inductively obtain disjoint sets $A_1, A_2, A_3, \ldots$, with $|\mu(A_n)| > 1$. If $C = \bigcup A_n$, the countable additivity of μ shows that

$$(6) \qquad \mu(C) = \sum_1^\infty \mu(A_n).$$

But this series cannot converge, since $\mu(A_n)$ does not tend to 0 as $n \to \infty$. This contradiction shows that (1) must hold.

6.5 If μ and λ are complex measures on the same σ-algebra $\mathfrak{M}$, we define $\mu + \lambda$ and $c\mu$ by

$$(1) \qquad \begin{aligned} (\mu + \lambda)(E) &= \mu(E) + \lambda(E) \\ (c\mu)(E) &= c\mu(E) \end{aligned} \qquad (E \in \mathfrak{M})$$

for any scalar c, in the usual manner. It is then trivial to verify that $\mu + \lambda$ and $c\mu$ are complex measures. The collection of all complex measures on $\mathfrak{M}$ is thus a vector space. If we put

$$(2) \qquad \|\mu\| = |\mu|(X),$$

it is easy to verify that all axioms of a normed linear space are satisfied.

6.6 Positive and Negative Variations Let us now specialize and consider a *real* measure μ on a σ-algebra $\mathfrak{M}$. (Such measures are frequently called *signed* measures.) Define $|\mu|$ as before, and define

$$(1) \qquad \mu^+ = \tfrac{1}{2}(|\mu| + \mu), \qquad \mu^- = \tfrac{1}{2}(|\mu| - \mu).$$

Then both μ^+ and μ^- are positive measures on $\mathfrak{M}$, and they are bounded, by Theorem 6.4. Also,

$$(2) \qquad \mu = \mu^+ - \mu^-, \qquad |\mu| = \mu^+ + \mu^-.$$

The measures μ^+ and μ^- are called the *positive* and *negative variations* of μ, respectively. This representation of μ as the difference of the positive measures μ^+ and μ^- is known as the *Jordan decomposition* of μ.

Among all representations of μ as a difference of two positive measures, the Jordan decomposition has a certain minimum property which will be established as a corollary to Theorem 6.14.

Absolute Continuity

6.7 Definitions Let μ be a positive measure on a σ-algebra $\mathfrak{M}$, and let λ be an arbitrary measure on $\mathfrak{M}$; λ may be positive or complex. (Recall that a complex measure has its range in the complex plane, but that our usage of the term "positive measure" includes ∞ as an admissible value. Thus the positive measures do not form a subclass of the complex ones.)

We say that λ is *absolutely continuous* with respect to μ, and write

$$\lambda \ll \mu \tag{1}$$

if $\lambda(E) = 0$ for every $E \in \mathfrak{M}$ for which $\mu(E) = 0$.

If there is a set $A \in \mathfrak{M}$ such that $\lambda(E) = \lambda(A \cap E)$ for every $E \in \mathfrak{M}$, we say that λ is *concentrated on* A. This is equivalent to the hypothesis that $\lambda(E) = 0$ whenever $E \cap A = \varnothing$.

Suppose λ_1 and λ_2 are measures on $\mathfrak{M}$, and suppose there exists a pair of disjoint sets A and B such that λ_1 is concentrated on A and λ_2 is concentrated on B. Then we say that λ_1 and λ_2 are *mutually singular*, and write

$$\lambda_1 \perp \lambda_2. \tag{2}$$

Here are some elementary properties of these concepts.

6.8 Proposition *Suppose μ, λ, λ_1, and λ_2 are measures on a σ-algebra $\mathfrak{M}$, and μ is positive.*

(*a*) *If λ is concentrated on A, so is $|\lambda|$.*
(*b*) *If $\lambda_1 \perp \lambda_2$, then $|\lambda_1| \perp |\lambda_2|$.*
(*c*) *If $\lambda_1 \perp \mu$ and $\lambda_2 \perp \mu$, then $\lambda_1 + \lambda_2 \perp \mu$.*
(*d*) *If $\lambda_1 \ll \mu$ and $\lambda_2 \ll \mu$, then $\lambda_1 + \lambda_2 \ll \mu$.*
(*e*) *If $\lambda \ll \mu$, then $|\lambda| \ll \mu$.*
(*f*) *If $\lambda_1 \ll \mu$ and $\lambda_2 \perp \mu$, then $\lambda_1 \perp \lambda_2$.*
(*g*) *If $\lambda \ll \mu$ and $\lambda \perp \mu$, then $\lambda = 0$.*

PROOF

(*a*) If $E \cap A = \varnothing$ and $\{E_j\}$ is any partition of E, then $\lambda(E_j) = 0$ for all j. Hence $|\lambda|(E) = 0$.
(*b*) follows immediately from (*a*).
(*c*) There are disjoint sets A_1 and B_1 such that λ_1 is concentrated on A_1 and μ on B_1, and there are disjoint sets A_2 and B_2 such

that λ_2 is concentrated on A_2 and μ on B_2. Hence $\lambda_1 + \lambda_2$ is concentrated on $A = A_1 \cup A_2$, μ is concentrated on $B = B_1 \cap B_2$, and $A \cap B = \emptyset$.

(*d*) is obvious.

(*e*) Suppose $\mu(E) = 0$, and $\{E_j\}$ is a partition of E. Then $\mu(E_j) = 0$; and since $\lambda \ll \mu$, $\lambda(E_j) = 0$ for all j, hence $\Sigma|\lambda(E_j)| = 0$. This implies $|\lambda|(E) = 0$.

(*f*) Since $\lambda_2 \perp \mu$, there is a set A with $\mu(A) = 0$ on which λ_2 is concentrated. Since $\lambda_1 \ll \mu$, $\lambda_1(E) = 0$ for every $E \subset A$. So λ_1 is concentrated on the complement of A.

(*g*) By (*f*), the hypothesis of (*g*) implies that $\lambda \perp \lambda$, and this clearly forces $\lambda = 0$.

We now turn to the principal theorem concerning absolute continuity. In fact, it is probably the most important theorem in measure theory.

6.9 Theorem *Let μ and λ be positive bounded measures on a σ-algebra $\mathfrak{M}$ in a set X.*

(*a*) *There is a unique pair of measures λ_a and λ_s on $\mathfrak{M}$ such that*

$$\lambda = \lambda_a + \lambda_s, \qquad \lambda_a \ll \mu, \qquad \lambda_s \perp \mu. \tag{1}$$

These measures are positive, and $\lambda_a \perp \lambda_s$.

(*b*) *There is a unique $h \in L^1(\mu)$ such that*

$$\lambda_a(E) = \int_E h\,d\mu \qquad (E \in \mathfrak{M}). \tag{2}$$

The pair λ_a and λ_s is called the *Lebesgue decomposition* of λ relative to μ. The uniqueness of the decomposition is easily seen, for if λ_a' and λ_s' is another pair which satisfies (1), then

$$\lambda_a' - \lambda_a = \lambda_s - \lambda_s', \tag{3}$$

$\lambda_a' - \lambda_a \ll \mu$, and $\lambda_s - \lambda_s' \perp \mu$, hence both sides of (3) are 0; we have used 6.8(*c*), 6.8(*d*), and 6.8(*g*).

The *existence* of the decomposition is the significant part of (*a*).

Assertion (*b*) is known as the *Radon-Nikodym* theorem. Again, uniqueness of h is immediate, from Theorem 1.39(*b*). Also, if h is *any* member of $L^1(\mu)$, the integral in (2) defines a measure on $\mathfrak{M}$ (Theorem 1.29) which is clearly absolutely continuous with respect to μ. The point of the Radon-Nikodym theorem is the converse: *every* $\lambda \ll \mu$ (in which case $\lambda_a = \lambda$) is obtained in this way.

The function h which occurs in (2) is called the *Radon-Nikodym derivative* of λ_a with respect to μ. As noted after Theorem 1.29, we may express (2) in the form $d\lambda_a = h\,d\mu$, or even in the form $h = d\lambda_a/d\mu$.

The idea of the following proof, which yields both theorems at one stroke, is due to von Neumann.

PROOF Put $\varphi = \lambda + \mu$. Then φ is a positive bounded measure on $\mathfrak{M}$. The definition of the sum of two measures shows that

$$\int_X f\,d\varphi = \int_X f\,d\lambda + \int_X f\,d\mu \tag{4}$$

for $f = \chi_E$, hence for simple f, hence for any nonnegative measurable f. If $f \in L^2(\varphi)$, the Schwarz inequality gives

$$\left|\int_X f\,d\lambda\right| \leq \int_X |f|\,d\lambda \leq \int_X |f|\,d\varphi \leq \left\{\int_X |f|^2\,d\varphi\right\}^{\frac{1}{2}}\{\varphi(X)\}^{\frac{1}{2}};$$

since $\varphi(X) < \infty$, the mapping

$$f \to \int_X f\,d\lambda \tag{5}$$

is seen to be a bounded linear functional on $L^2(\varphi)$.

We know that every bounded linear functional on a Hilbert space H is given by an inner product with an element of H. Hence there exists a $g \in L^2(\varphi)$ such that

$$\int_X f\,d\lambda = \int_X fg\,d\varphi \qquad (f \in L^2(\varphi)). \tag{6}$$

Observe how the completeness of $L^2(\varphi)$ was used to guarantee the existence of the function g. Observe also that although g is defined uniquely as an element of $L^2(\varphi)$, g is determined only a.e. $[\varphi]$ as a point function on X.

Put $f = \chi_E$ in (6), for any $E \in \mathfrak{M}$ with $\varphi(E) > 0$. The left side of (6) is then $\lambda(E)$; and since $0 \leq \lambda \leq \varphi$, we have

$$0 \leq \frac{1}{\varphi(E)} \int_E g\,d\varphi \leq 1. \tag{7}$$

Hence $g(x) \in [0,1]$ for almost all x (with respect to φ), by Theorem 1.40. We may therefore assume that $0 \leq g(x) \leq 1$ for every $x \in X$, without affecting (6), and we rewrite (6) in the form

$$\int_X (1 - g)f\,d\lambda = \int_X fg\,d\mu \qquad (f \in L^2(\varphi)). \tag{8}$$

Put

$$A = \{x\colon 0 \leq g(x) < 1\}, \qquad B = \{x\colon g(x) = 1\}, \tag{9}$$

and define

$$\lambda_a(E) = \lambda(A \cap E), \qquad \lambda_s(E) = \lambda(B \cap E) \qquad (E \in \mathfrak{M}). \tag{10}$$

If we take $f = \chi_B$ in (8), we see that $\mu(B) = 0$. Thus $\lambda_s \perp \mu$. Since g is bounded, (8) holds if we replace f by

$$(1 + g + \cdots + g^n)\chi_E,$$

for $n = 1, 2, 3, \ldots, E \in \mathfrak{M}$. We then obtain

$$(11) \qquad \int_E (1 - g^{n+1})\, d\lambda = \int_E g(1 + g + \cdots + g^n)\, d\mu.$$

At every point of B, $g(x) = 1$, hence $1 - g^{n+1}(x) = 0$. At every point of A, $g^{n+1}(x) \to 0$ monotonically. The left side of (11) converges therefore to $\lambda(A \cap E) = \lambda_a(E)$, as $n \to \infty$.

The integrand on the right side of (11) increases monotonically to a nonnegative measurable limit h, and the monotone convergence theorem shows that the right side of (11) tends to $\int_E h\, d\mu$, as $n \to \infty$.

We have thus proved that (2) holds for every $E \in \mathfrak{M}$. Taking $E = X$, we see that $h \in L^1(\mu)$, since $\lambda_a(X) < \infty$.

Finally, (2) shows that $\lambda_a \ll \mu$, and the proof is complete.

6.10 Extensions of Theorem 6.9 The proof of Theorem 6.9 strongly depended on the assumption that $\varphi(X) < \infty$, i.e., that both μ and λ were bounded measures.

If μ is σ-finite, then (by definition) X is a union of countably many sets X_n such that $\mu(X_n) < \infty$. We may assume that the X_n are disjoint, for if not, we replace $\{X_n\}$ by $\{Y_n\}$, where $Y_1 = X_1$, and

$$Y_n = X_n - (Y_1 \cup \cdots \cup Y_{n-1})$$

for $n \geq 2$. If now $\lambda(X) < \infty$, we can apply Theorem 6.9 to each X_n. The Lebesgue decompositions of the measures $\lambda(E \cap X_n)$ add up to a Lebesgue decomposition of λ; we get functions h_n on X_n which define a function h on X, by setting $h(x) = h_n(x)$ if $x \in X_n$; and since $\lambda(X) < \infty$, it follows easily that $h \in L^1(\mu)$.

Next, if we keep μ σ-finite and let λ be a complex measure on $\mathfrak{M}$, then $\lambda = \lambda_1 + i\lambda_2$, with λ_1 and λ_2 real, and we can apply the preceding result to the positive and negative variations of λ_1 and λ_2 (see Sec. 6.6).

We may summarize as follows:

The Lebesgue decomposition theorem and the Radon-Nikodym theorem are valid if μ is a positive σ-finite measure on $\mathfrak{M}$ and if λ is a complex measure on $\mathfrak{M}$.

If both μ and λ are positive and σ-finite, most of Theorem 6.9 is still true. We can now write $X = \bigcup X_n$, where $\mu(X_n) < \infty$ and $\lambda(X_n) < \infty$, for $n = 1, 2, 3, \ldots$. The Lebesgue decompositions of the measures $\lambda(E \cap X_n)$ still give us a Lebesgue decomposition of λ, and we still get a function h which satisfies Eq. 6.9(2); however, it is no longer true that $h \in L^1(\mu)$, although h is "locally in L^1," i.e., $\int_{X_n} h\,d\mu < \infty$ for each n.

Finally, if we go beyond σ-finiteness, we meet situations where the two theorems under consideration actually fail. For example, let μ be Lebesgue measure on $(0,1)$, and let λ be the counting measure on the σ-algebra of all Lebesgue measurable sets in $(0,1)$. *Then λ has no Lebesgue decomposition relative to μ, and although $\mu \ll \lambda$ and μ is bounded, there is no $h \in L^1(\lambda)$ such that $d\mu = h\,d\lambda$.* We omit the easy proof.

The following theorem may explain why the word "continuity" is used in connection with the relation $\lambda \ll \mu$.

6.11 Theorem *Suppose μ and λ are measures on a σ-algebra $\mathfrak{M}$, μ is positive, and λ is complex. Then the following two conditions are equivalent:*

(*a*) $\lambda \ll \mu$.

(*b*) *To every $\epsilon > 0$ there corresponds a $\delta > 0$ such that $|\lambda(E)| < \epsilon$ for all $E \in \mathfrak{M}$ with $\mu(E) < \delta$.*

Property (*b*) is sometimes used as the definition of absolute continuity. However, (*a*) does not imply (*b*) if λ is a positive unbounded measure. For instance, let μ be Lebesgue measure on $(0,1)$, and put

$$\lambda(E) = \int_E t^{-1}\,dt$$

for every Lebesgue measurable set $E \subset (0,1)$.

PROOF Suppose (*b*) holds. If $\mu(E) = 0$, then $\mu(E) < \delta$ for every $\delta > 0$, hence $|\lambda(E)| < \epsilon$ for every $\epsilon > 0$, so $\lambda(E) = 0$. Thus (*b*) implies (*a*).

Suppose (*b*) is false. Then there exists an $\epsilon > 0$ and there exist sets $E_n \in \mathfrak{M}$ $(n = 1, 2, 3, \ldots)$ such that $\mu(E_n) < 2^{-n}$ but $|\lambda(E_n)| \geq \epsilon$. Hence $|\lambda|(E_n) \geq \epsilon$. Put

$$(1) \qquad A_n = \bigcup_{i=n}^{\infty} E_i, \qquad A = \bigcap_{n=1}^{\infty} A_n.$$

Then $\mu(A_n) < 2^{-n+1}$, $A_n \supset A_{n+1}$, and so Theorem 1.19(*e*) shows that $\mu(A) = 0$ and that

$$|\lambda|(A) = \lim_{n\to\infty} |\lambda|(A_n) \geq \epsilon > 0,$$

since $|\lambda|(A_n) \geq |\lambda|(E_n)$.

It follows that we do *not* have $|\lambda| \ll \mu$, hence (*a*) is false, by Proposition 6.8(*e*).

Consequences of the Radon-Nikodym Theorem

6.12 Theorem *Let μ be a complex measure on a σ-algebra $\mathfrak{M}$ in X. Then there is a measurable function h such that $|h(x)| = 1$ for all $x \in X$ and such that*

$$d\mu = h\,d|\mu|. \tag{1}$$

By analogy with the representation of a complex number as the product of its absolute value and a number of absolute value 1, Eq. (1) is sometimes referred to as the *polar representation* (or *polar decomposition*) of μ.

PROOF It is trivial that $\mu \ll |\mu|$, and therefore the Radon-Nikodym theorem guarantees the existence of some $h \in L^1(|\mu|)$ which satisfies (1).

Let $A_r = \{x: |h(x)| < r\}$, where r is some positive number, and let $\{E_j\}$ be a partition of A_r. Then

$$\sum_j |\mu(E_j)| = \sum_j \left| \int_{E_j} h\,d|\mu| \right| \le \sum_j r|\mu|(E_j) = r|\mu|(A_r),$$

so that $|\mu|(A_r) \le r|\mu|(A_r)$. If $r < 1$, this forces $|\mu|(A_r) = 0$. Thus $|h| \ge 1$ a.e.

On the other hand, if $|\mu|(E) > 0$, (1) shows that

$$\left| \frac{1}{|\mu|(E)} \int_E h\,d|\mu| \right| = \frac{|\mu(E)|}{|\mu|(E)} \le 1.$$

We now apply Theorem 1.40 (with the closed unit disc in place of S) and conclude that $|h| \le 1$ a.e.

Let $B = \{x \in X: |h(x)| \ne 1\}$. We have shown that $|\mu|(B) = 0$; and if we redefine h on B so that $h(x) = 1$ on B, we obtain a function with the desired properties.

6.13 Theorem *Suppose μ is a positive measure on $\mathfrak{M}$, $g \in L^1(\mu)$, and*

$$\lambda(E) = \int_E g\,d\mu \qquad (E \in \mathfrak{M}). \tag{1}$$

Then

$$|\lambda|(E) = \int_E |g|\,d\mu \qquad (E \in \mathfrak{M}). \tag{2}$$

PROOF By Theorem 6.12, there is a function h, of absolute value 1, such that $d\lambda = h\,d|\lambda|$. By hypothesis, $d\lambda = g\,d\mu$. Hence

$$h\,d|\lambda| = g\,d\mu.$$

This gives $d|\lambda| = \bar{h}g\,d\mu$. (Compare with Theorem 1.29.)

Since $|\lambda| \ge 0$ and $\mu \ge 0$, it follows that $\bar{h}g \ge 0$ a.e. $[\mu]$, so that $\bar{h}g = |g|$ a.e. $[\mu]$.

6.14 The Hahn Decomposition Theorem *Let μ be a real measure on a σ-algebra $\mathfrak{M}$ in a set X. Then there exist sets A and $B \in \mathfrak{M}$ such that $A \cup B = X$, $A \cap B = \varnothing$, and such that the positive and negative variations μ^+ and μ^- of μ satisfy*

$$(1) \qquad \mu^+(E) = \mu(A \cap E), \qquad \mu^-(E) = -\mu(B \cap E) \qquad (E \in \mathfrak{M}).$$

In other words, X is the union of two disjoint measurable sets A and B, such that "A carries all the positive mass of μ" [since (1) implies that $\mu(E) \geq 0$ if $E \subset A$] and "B carries all the negative mass of μ" [since $\mu(E) \leq 0$ if $E \subset B$]. The pair A and B is called a Hahn decomposition of X, induced by μ.

PROOF By Theorem 6.12, $d\mu = h\, d|\mu|$, where $|h| = 1$. Since μ is real, it follows that h is real (a.e., and therefore everywhere, by redefining on a set of measure 0), hence $h = \pm 1$. Put

$$(2) \qquad A = \{x: h(x) = 1\}, \qquad B = \{x: h(x) = -1\}.$$

Since $\mu^+ = \frac{1}{2}(|\mu| + \mu)$, and since

$$(3) \qquad \tfrac{1}{2}(1 + h) = \begin{cases} h & \text{on } A, \\ 0 & \text{on } B, \end{cases}$$

we have, for any $E \in \mathfrak{M}$,

$$(4) \qquad \mu^+(E) = \tfrac{1}{2} \int_E (1 + h)\, d|\mu| = \int_{E \cap A} h\, d|\mu| = \mu(E \cap A).$$

Since $\mu(E) = \mu(E \cap A) + \mu(E \cap B)$ and since $\mu = \mu^+ - \mu^-$, the second half of (1) follows from the first.

Corollary *If $\mu = \lambda_1 - \lambda_2$, where λ_1 and λ_2 are positive measures, then $\lambda_1 \geq \mu^+$ and $\lambda_2 \geq \mu^-$.*

This is the minimum property of the Jordan decomposition which was mentioned in Sec. 6.6.

PROOF Since $\mu \leq \lambda_1$, we have

$$\mu^+(E) = \mu(E \cap A) \leq \lambda_1(E \cap A) \leq \lambda_1(E).$$

Bounded Linear Functionals on L^p

6.15 Let μ be a positive measure, suppose $1 \leq p \leq \infty$, and let q be the exponent conjugate to p. The Hölder inequality (Theorem 3.8) shows that if $g \in L^q(\mu)$ and if Φ_g is defined by

$$(1) \qquad \Phi_g(f) = \int_X fg\, d\mu,$$

then Φ_g is a bounded linear functional on $L^p(\mu)$, of norm at most $\|g\|_q$. The question naturally arises whether all bounded linear functionals on $L^p(\mu)$ have this form, and whether the representation is unique.

For $p = \infty$, the answer is negative: $L^1(\mu)$ does not furnish all bounded linear functionals on $L^\infty(\mu)$. For $1 < p < \infty$, the answer is affirmative. It is also affirmative for $p = 1$, provided certain measure-theoretic pathologies are excluded. For σ-finite measure spaces, no difficulties arise, and we shall confine ourselves to this case.

6.16 Theorem *Suppose* $1 \leq p < \infty$, μ *is a* σ*-finite positive measure on* X, *and* Φ *is a bounded linear functional on* $L^p(\mu)$. *Then there is a unique* $g \in L^q(\mu)$, *where* q *is the exponent conjugate to* p, *such that*

$$\Phi(f) = \int_X fg\,d\mu \qquad (f \in L^p(\mu)). \tag{1}$$

Moreover, if Φ *and* g *are related as in* (1), *we have*

$$\|\Phi\| = \|g\|_q. \tag{2}$$

In other words, $L^q(\mu)$ is the dual space of $L^p(\mu)$, under the stated conditions.

PROOF The uniqueness of g is clear, for if g and g' satisfy (1), then the integral of $g - g'$ over any measurable set E of finite measure is 0 (as we see by taking χ_E for f), and the σ-finiteness of μ therefore implies that $g - g' = 0$ a.e.

Next, if (1) holds, Hölder's inequality implies

$$\|\Phi\| \leq \|g\|_q. \tag{3}$$

So it remains to prove that g exists and that equality holds in (3). If $\|\Phi\| = 0$, (1) and (2) hold with $g = 0$. So assume $\|\Phi\| > 0$.

We first consider the case $\mu(X) < \infty$.

For any measurable set $E \subset X$, define

$$\lambda(E) = \Phi(\chi_E).$$

Since Φ is linear, and since $\chi_{A\cup B} = \chi_A + \chi_B$ if A and B are disjoint, we see that λ is additive. To prove countable additivity, suppose E is the union of countably many disjoint measurable sets E_i, put $A_k = E_1 \cup \cdots \cup E_k$, and note that

$$\|\chi_E - \chi_{A_k}\|_p = [\mu(E - A_k)]^{1/p} \to 0 \qquad (k \to \infty); \tag{4}$$

the continuity of Φ now shows that $\lambda(A_k) \to \lambda(E)$. So λ is a complex measure. [In (4) the assumption $p < \infty$ was used.] It is clear that $\lambda(E) = 0$ if $\mu(E) = 0$, since then $\|\chi_E\|_p = 0$. Thus $\lambda \ll \mu$, and the

Radon-Nikodym theorem ensures the existence of a function $g \in L^1(\mu)$ such that, for every measurable $E \subset X$,

$$\Phi(\chi_E) = \int_E g\,d\mu = \int_X \chi_E g\,d\mu. \tag{5}$$

By linearity it follows that

$$\Phi(f) = \int_X fg\,d\mu \tag{6}$$

holds for every simple measurable f, and so also for every $f \in L^\infty(\mu)$, since every $f \in L^\infty(\mu)$ is a uniform limit of simple functions f_i. Note that the uniform convergence of f_i to f implies $\|f_i - f\|_p \to 0$, hence $\Phi(f_i) \to \Phi(f)$, as $i \to \infty$.

We want to conclude that $g \in L^q(\mu)$ and that (2) holds; it is best to split the argument into two cases.

CASE 1 $p = 1$. Here (5) shows that

$$\left| \int_E g\,d\mu \right| \le \|\Phi\| \cdot \|\chi_E\|_1 = \|\Phi\| \cdot \mu(E)$$

for every $E \in \mathfrak{M}$. By Theorem 1.40, $|g(x)| \le \|\Phi\|$ a.e., so that $\|g\|_\infty \le \|\Phi\|$.

CASE 2 $1 < p < \infty$. There is a measurable function α, $|\alpha| = 1$, such that $\alpha g = |g|$ [proposition 1.9(*e*)]. Let $E_n = \{x\colon |g(x)| \le n\}$, and put $f = \chi_{E_n}|g|^{q-1}\alpha$. Then $|f|^p = |g|^q$ on E_n, $f \in L^\infty(\mu)$, and (6) gives

$$\int_{E_n} |g|^q\,d\mu = \int_X fg\,d\mu = \Phi(f) \le \|\Phi\| \left\{ \int_{E_n} |g|^q \right\}^{1/p},$$

so that

$$\int_X \chi_{E_n}|g|^q\,d\mu \le \|\Phi\|^q \qquad (n = 1, 2, 3, \ldots). \tag{7}$$

If we apply the monotone convergence theorem to (7), we obtain $\|g\|_q \le \|\Phi\|$.

Thus (2) holds and $g \in L^q(\mu)$. It follows that both sides of (6) are continuous functions on $L^p(\mu)$. They coincide on the dense subset $L^\infty(\mu)$ of $L^p(\mu)$; hence they coincide on all of $L^p(\mu)$, and this completes the proof if $\mu(X) < \infty$.

In the σ-finite case, X is the union of countably many disjoint sets X_i with $\mu(X_i) < \infty$. Put $Y_k = X_1 \cup \cdots \cup X_k$. Note that

$$\|\chi_E f\|_p \le \|f\|_p$$

for every measurable set $E \subset X$, so that the mapping

$$f \to \Phi(\chi_E f) \tag{8}$$

is a linear functional on $L^p(\mu)$, of norm at most $\|\Phi\|$. The preceding result (applied to X_i in place of X) shows that there are functions g_i on X_i such that

$$(9) \qquad \Phi(\chi_{X_i} f) = \int_{X_i} f g_i \, d\mu \qquad (f \in L^p(\mu)).$$

Define $g_i(x) = 0$ for $x \notin X_i$, and put $g = g_1 + g_2 + g_3 + \cdots$. Since

$$(10) \quad \Phi(\chi_{Y_k} f) = \int_{Y_k} f(g_1 + \cdots + g_k) \, d\mu \qquad (f \in L^p(\mu))$$

and since $\mu(Y_k) < \infty$, the preceding result shows that

$$(11) \quad \|g_1 + \cdots + g_k\|_q \le \|\Phi\| \qquad (k = 1, 2, 3, \ldots),$$

whence $\|g\|_q \le \|\Phi\|$ (by Fatou's lemma, for instance). This concludes the proof.

6.17 Remark We have already encountered the special case $p = q = 2$ of Theorem 6.16. In fact, the proof of the general case was based on this special case, for we used the knowledge of the bounded linear functionals on $L^2(\mu)$ in the proof of the Radon-Nikodym theorem, and the latter was the key to the proof of Theorem 6.16. The special case $p = 2$, in turn, depended on the completeness of $L^2(\mu)$, on the fact that $L^2(\mu)$ is therefore a Hilbert space, and on the fact that the bounded linear functionals on a Hilbert space are given by inner products.

We now turn to the complex version of Theorem 2.14.

The Riesz Representation Theorem

6.18 Let X be a locally compact Hausdorff space. Theorem 2.14 characterizes the *positive* linear functionals on $C_C(X)$. We are now in a position to characterize the *bounded* linear functionals Φ on $C_C(X)$. Since $C_C(X)$ is a dense subspace of $C_0(X)$, relative to the supremum norm, every such Φ has a unique extension to a bounded linear functional on $C_0(X)$. Hence we may as well assume to begin with that we are dealing with the Banach space $C_0(X)$.

If μ is a complex Borel measure, Theorem 6.12 asserts that there is a complex Borel function h with $|h| = 1$ such that $d\mu = h \, d|\mu|$. It is therefore reasonable to define integration with respect to a complex measure μ by the formula

$$(1) \qquad \int f \, d\mu = \int fh \, d|\mu|.$$

The relation $\int \chi_E \, d\mu = \mu(E)$ is a special case of (1). Thus

$$(2) \quad \int_X \chi_E \, d(\mu + \lambda) = (\mu + \lambda)(E) = \mu(E) + \lambda(E) = \int_X \chi_E \, d\mu + \int_X \chi_E \, d\lambda$$

whenever μ and λ are complex measures on $\mathfrak{M}$ and $E \in \mathfrak{M}$. This leads to the addition formula

$$\int_X f\,d(\mu + \lambda) = \int_X f\,d\mu + \int_X f\,d\lambda, \tag{3}$$

which is valid (for instance) for every bounded measurable f.

We shall call a complex Borel measure μ on X *regular* if $|\mu|$ is regular in the sense of Definition 2.15.

If μ is a complex Borel measure on X, it is clear that the mapping

$$f \to \int_X f\,d\mu \tag{4}$$

is a bounded linear functional on $C_0(X)$, whose norm is no larger than $|\mu|(X)$. That *all* bounded linear functionals on $C_0(X)$ are obtained in this way is the content of the Riesz theorem:

6.19 Theorem *To each bounded linear functional Φ on $C_0(X)$, where X is a locally compact Hausdorff space, there corresponds a unique complex regular Borel measure μ such that*

$$\Phi(f) = \int_X f\,d\mu \qquad (f \in C_0(X)). \tag{1}$$

Moreover, if Φ and μ are related as in (1), *then*

$$\|\Phi\| = |\mu|(X). \tag{2}$$

PROOF We first settle the uniqueness question. Suppose μ is a regular complex Borel measure on X and $\int f\,d\mu = 0$ for all $f \in C_0(X)$. By Theorem 6.12 there is a Borel function h, with $|h| = 1$, such that $d\mu = h\,d|\mu|$. For any sequence $\{f_n\}$ in $C_0(X)$ we then have

$$|\mu|(X) = \int_X (\bar{h} - f_n)h\,d|\mu| \leq \int_X |\bar{h} - f_n|\,d|\mu|, \tag{3}$$

and since $C_c(X)$ is dense in $L^1(|\mu|)$ (Theorem 3.14), $\{f_n\}$ can be so chosen that the last expression in (3) tends to 0 as $n \to \infty$. Thus $|\mu|(X) = 0$, and $\mu = 0$. It is easy to see that the difference of two regular complex Borel measures on X is regular. This shows that at most one μ corresponds to each Φ.

Now consider a given bounded linear functional Φ on $C_0(X)$. Assume $\|\Phi\| = 1$, without loss of generality. We shall construct a *positive* linear functional Λ on $C_c(X)$, such that

$$|\Phi(f)| \leq \Lambda(|f|) \leq \|f\| \qquad (f \in C_c(X), \tag{4}$$

where $\|f\|$ denotes the supremum norm.

Once we have this Λ, we associate with it a positive Borel measure λ, as in Theorem 2.14. The conclusion of Theorem 2.14 shows that

λ is regular if $\lambda(X) < \infty$. Since

$$\lambda(X) = \{\sup \Lambda f\colon 0 \le f \le 1, f \in C_C(X)\}$$

and since $|\Lambda f| \le 1$ if $\|f\| \le 1$, we see that actually $\lambda(X) \le 1$.

We also deduce from (4) that

$$(5) \qquad |\Phi(f)| \le \Lambda(|f|) = \int_X |f|\, d\lambda = \|f\|_1 \qquad (f \in C_C(X)).$$

The last norm refers to the space $L^1(\lambda)$. Thus Φ is a linear functional on $C_C(X)$ of norm at most 1, *with respect to the* $L^1(\lambda)$*-norm on* $C_C(X)$. There is a norm-preserving extension of Φ to a linear functional on $L^1(\lambda)$, and therefore Theorem 6.16 (the case $p = 1$) gives a Borel function g, with $|g| \le 1$, such that

$$(6) \qquad \Phi(f) = \int_X fg\, d\lambda \qquad (f \in C_C(X)).$$

Each side of (6) is a continuous functional on $C_0(X)$, and $C_C(X)$ is dense in $C_0(X)$. Hence (6) holds for all $f \in C_0(X)$, and we obtain the representation (1) with $d\mu = g\, d\lambda$.

Since $\|\Phi\| = 1$, (6) shows that

$$(7) \qquad \int_X |g|\, d\lambda \ge \sup \{|\Phi(f)|\colon f \in C_0(X),\ \|f\| \le 1\} = 1.$$

We also know that $\lambda(X) \le 1$ and $|g| \le 1$. These facts are compatible only if $\lambda(X) = 1$ and $|g| = 1$ a.e. $[\lambda]$. Thus $d|\mu| = |g|\, d\lambda = d\lambda$, by Theorem 6.13, and

$$(8) \qquad |\mu|(X) = \lambda(X) = 1 = \|\Phi\|,$$

which proves (2).

So all depends on finding a positive linear functional Λ which satisfies (4). If $f \in C_C^+(X)$ [the class of all nonnegative real members of $C_C(X)$], define

$$(9) \qquad \Lambda f = \sup \{|\Phi(h)|\colon h \in C_C(X),\ |h| \le f\}.$$

Then $\Lambda f \ge 0$, Λ satisfies (4), $0 \le f_1 \le f_2$ implies $\Lambda f_1 \le \Lambda f_2$, and $\Lambda(cf) = c\Lambda f$ if c is a positive constant. We have to show that

$$(10) \qquad \Lambda(f + g) = \Lambda f + \Lambda g \qquad (f \text{ and } g \in C_C^+(X)),$$

and we then have to extend Λ to a linear functional on $C_C(X)$.

Fix f and $g \in C_C^+(X)$. If $\epsilon > 0$, there exist h_1 and $h_2 \in C_C(X)$ such that $|h_1| \le f$, $|h_2| \le g$, and

$$(11) \qquad \Lambda f \le |\Phi(h_1)| + \epsilon, \qquad \Lambda g \le |\Phi(h_2)| + \epsilon.$$

There are complex numbers α_i, $|\alpha_i| = 1$, so that $\alpha_i\Phi(h_i) = |\Phi(h_i)|$, $i = 1, 2$. Then

$$\begin{aligned}\Lambda f + \Lambda g &\le |\Phi(h_1)| + |\Phi(h_2)| + 2\epsilon \\ &= \Phi(\alpha_1 h_1 + \alpha_2 h_2) + 2\epsilon \\ &\le \Lambda(|h_1| + |h_2|) + 2\epsilon \\ &\le \Lambda(f + g) + 2\epsilon,\end{aligned}$$

so that the inequality $\ge$ holds in (10).

Next, choose $h \in C_c(X)$, subject only to the condition $|h| \le f + g$, let $V = \{x: f(x) + g(x) > 0\}$, and define

$$(12) \qquad \begin{aligned} &h_1(x) = \frac{f(x)h(x)}{f(x) + g(x)}, \qquad h_2(x) = \frac{g(x)h(x)}{f(x) + g(x)} \qquad (x \in V), \\ &h_1(x) = h_2(x) = 0 \qquad (x \notin V).\end{aligned}$$

It is clear that h_1 is continuous at every point of V. If $x_0 \notin V$, then $h(x_0) = 0$; since h is continuous and since $|h_1(x)| \le |h(x)|$ for all $x \in X$, it follows that x_0 is a point of continuity of h_1. Thus $h_1 \in C_c(X)$, and the same holds for h_2.

Since $h_1 + h_2 = h$ and $|h_1| \le f$, $|h_2| \le g$, we have

$$|\Phi(h)| = |\Phi(h_1) + \Phi(h_2)| \le |\Phi(h_1)| + |\Phi(h_2)| \le \Lambda f + \Lambda g.$$

Hence $\Lambda(f + g) \le \Lambda f + \Lambda g$, and we have proved (10).

If f is now a real function, $f \in C_c(X)$, then $2f^+ = |f| + f$, so that $f^+ \in C_c^+(X)$; likewise, $f^- \in C_c^+(X)$; and since $f = f^+ - f^-$, it is natural to define

$$(13) \qquad \Lambda f = \Lambda f^+ - \Lambda f^- \qquad (f \in C_c(X), f \text{ real})$$

and

$$(14) \qquad \Lambda(u + iv) = \Lambda u + i\Lambda v.$$

Simple algebraic manipulations, just like those which occur in the proof of Theorem 1.32, now show that our extended functional Λ is linear on $C_c(X)$.

This completes the proof.

Exercises

1 If μ is a complex measure on a σ-algebra $\mathfrak{M}$, and if $E \in \mathfrak{M}$, define

$$\lambda(E) = \sup \sum |\mu(E_i)|,$$

the supremum being taken over all *finite* partitions $\{E_i\}$ of E. Does it follow that $\lambda = |\mu|$?

2 Prove that the example given at the end of Sec. 6.10 has the stated properties.

3 Prove that the vector space $M(X)$ of all complex regular Borel measures on a locally compact Hausdorff space X is a Banach space if $\|\mu\| = |\mu|(X)$. *Hint:* Compare Exercise 8, Chap. 5. [That the difference of any two members of $M(X)$ is in $M(X)$ was used in the first paragraph of the proof of Theorem 6.19; supply a proof of this fact.]

4 Suppose $1 \leq p \leq \infty$, and q is the exponent conjugate to p. Suppose μ is a σ-finite measure and g is a measurable function such that $fg \in L^1(\mu)$ for every $f \in L^p(\mu)$. Prove that then $g \in L^q(\mu)$.

5 Suppose X consists of two points a and b; define $\mu(\{a\}) = 1$, $\mu(\{b\}) = \mu(X) = \infty$, and $\mu(\varnothing) = 0$. Is it true, for this μ, that $L^\infty(\mu)$ is the dual space of $L^1(\mu)$?

6 Suppose $1 < p < \infty$ and prove that $L^q(\mu)$ is the dual space of $L^p(\mu)$ even if μ is not σ-finite. (As usual, $1/p + 1/q = 1$.)

7 Suppose μ is a complex Borel measure on $[0,2\pi)$ (or on the unit circle T), and define

$$\hat{\mu}(n) = \int e^{-int}\,d\mu(t) \qquad (n = 0, \pm 1, \pm 2, \ldots).$$

Assume that $\hat{\mu}(n) \to 0$ as $n \to +\infty$ and prove that then $\hat{\mu}(n) \to 0$ as $n \to -\infty$. *Hint:* The assumption also holds with $f\,d\mu$ in place of $d\mu$ if f is any trigonometric polynomial, hence if f is continuous, hence if f is any bounded Borel function, hence if $d\mu$ is replaced by $d|\mu|$.

8 In the terminology of Exercise 7, find all μ such that $\hat{\mu}$ is periodic, with period k. [This means that $\hat{\mu}(n + k) = \hat{\mu}(n)$ for all integers n; of course, k is also assumed to be an integer.]

9 Let μ be a *finite* positive measure on a measure space X. A sequence $\{f_n\}$ in $L^1(\mu)$ is said to have *uniformly absolutely continuous integrals* if to each $\epsilon > 0$ there corresponds a $\delta > 0$ such that $\mu(E) < \delta$ implies

$$\left| \int_E f_n\,d\mu \right| < \epsilon \qquad (n = 1, 2, 3, \ldots).$$

Prove the following theorem of Vitali: If $\{f_n\}$ has uniformly absolutely continuous integrals and if $f_n(x) \to f(x)$ a.e., then $f \in L^1(\mu)$ and

$$\int_X f\,d\mu = \lim_{n\to\infty} \int_X f_n\,d\mu.$$

Hint: Show first that $\{|f_n|\}$ also has uniformly absolutely continuous integrals. X is a union of finitely many sets of small measure. This leads to $\int |f| < \infty$. For any $\epsilon > 0$, the set where $|f_n - f| > \epsilon$ has small measure for all large n.

10 (*a*) Show that Vitali's theorem implies Lebesgue's dominated convergence theorem, for finite measure spaces. Construct an example in which Vitali's theorem applies although the hypotheses of Lebesgue's theorem do not hold.

(*b*) Construct a sequence $\{f_n\}$, say on [0,1], so that $f_n(x) \to 0$ a.e., $\int f_n \to 0$, but $\{f_n\}$ does *not* have uniformly absolutely continuous integrals.

(*c*) However, the following converse of Vitali's theorem is true: Suppose μ is a finite positive measure on X, $\{f_n\}$ is a sequence in $L^1(\mu)$, $f \in L^1(\mu)$, $f_n(x) \to f(x)$ a.e., and

$$\lim_{n \to \infty} \int_E f_n \, d\mu = \int_E f \, d\mu$$

for every measurable set $E \subset X$. Then $\{f_n\}$ has uniformly absolutely continuous integrals. Prove this. (It is enough to consider the case $f = 0$.)

11 Show that pointwise convergence a.e. can be replaced by convergence in measure in Exercises 9 and 10.

7

Integration on Product Spaces

This chapter is devoted to the proof and discussion of the theorem of Fubini concerning integration of functions of two variables. We first present the theorem in its abstract form.

Measurability on Cartesian Products

7.1 Definitions If X and Y are two sets, their *cartesian product* $X \times Y$ is the set of all ordered pairs (x,y), with $x \in X$ and $y \in Y$. If $A \subset X$ and $B \subset Y$, it follows that $A \times B \subset X \times Y$. We call any set of the form $A \times B$ a *rectangle* in $X \times Y$.

Suppose now that $(X,\mathfrak{S})$ and $(Y,\mathfrak{T})$ are measurable spaces. Recall that this simply means that $\mathfrak{S}$ is a σ-algebra in X and $\mathfrak{T}$ is a σ-algebra in Y.

A *measurable rectangle* is any set of the form $A \times B$, where $A \in \mathfrak{S}$ and $B \in \mathfrak{T}$.

If $Q = R_1 \cup \cdots \cup R_n$, where each R_i is a measurable rectangle and $R_i \cap R_j = \emptyset$ for $i \neq j$, we say that $Q \in \mathcal{E}$, the class of all *elementary sets.*

$\mathfrak{S} \times \mathfrak{T}$ is defined to be the smallest σ-algebra in $X \times Y$ which contains every measurable rectangle.

A *monotone class* $\mathfrak{M}$ is a collection of sets with the following properties: If $A_i \in \mathfrak{M}$, $B_i \in \mathfrak{M}$, $A_i \subset A_{i+1}$, $B_i \supset B_{i+1}$, for $i = 1, 2, 3, \ldots$, and if

$$(1) \qquad A = \bigcup_{i=1}^{\infty} A_i, \qquad B = \bigcap_{i=1}^{\infty} B_i,$$

then $A \in \mathfrak{M}$ and $B \in \mathfrak{M}$.

If $E \subset X \times Y$, $x \in X$, $y \in Y$, we define

$$(2) \qquad E_x = \{y: (x,y) \in E\}, \; E^y = \{x: (x,y) \in E\}.$$

We call E_x and E^y the *x-section* and *y-section*, respectively, of E. Note that $E_x \subset Y$, $E^y \subset X$.

7.2 Theorem *If $E \in \mathcal{S} \times \mathcal{T}$, then $E_x \in \mathcal{T}$ and $E^y \in \mathcal{S}$, for every $x \in X$ and $y \in Y$.*

PROOF Let Ω be the class of all $E \in \mathcal{S} \times \mathcal{T}$ such that $E_x \in \mathcal{T}$ for every $x \in X$. If $E = A \times B$, then $E_x = B$ if $x \in A$, $E_x = \emptyset$ if $x \notin A$. Therefore every measurable rectangle belongs to Ω. Since $\mathcal{T}$ is a σ-algebra, the following three statements are true. They prove that Ω is a σ-algebra and hence that $\Omega = \mathcal{S} \times \mathcal{T}$:

(*a*) $X \times Y \in \Omega$.
(*b*) If $E \in \Omega$, then $(E^c)_x = (E_x)^c$, hence $E^c \in \Omega$.
(*c*) If $E_i \in \Omega$ $(i = 1, 2, 3, \ldots)$ and $E = \bigcup E_i$, then $E_x = \bigcup (E_i)_x$, hence $E \in \Omega$.

The proof is the same for E^y.

7.3 Theorem *$\mathcal{S} \times \mathcal{T}$ is the smallest monotone class which contains all elementary sets.*

PROOF Let $\mathfrak{M}$ be the smallest monotone class which contains $\mathcal{E}$; the proof that this class exists is exactly like that of Theorem 1.10. Since $\mathcal{S} \times \mathcal{T}$ is a monotone class, we have $\mathfrak{M} \subset \mathcal{S} \times \mathcal{T}$.

The identities

$$(A_1 \times B_1) \cap (A_2 \times B_2) = (A_1 \cap A_2) \times (B_1 \cap B_2),$$

$$(A_1 \times B_1) - (A_2 \times B_2) = [(A_1 - A_2) \times B_1] \cup [(A_1 \cap A_2) \times (B_1 - B_2)]$$

show that the intersection of two measurable rectangles is a measurable rectangle and that their difference is the union of two disjoint measurable rectangles, hence is an elementary set. If $P \in \mathcal{E}$ and $Q \in \mathcal{E}$, it follows easily that $P \cap Q \in \mathcal{E}$ and $P - Q \in \mathcal{E}$. Since

$$P \cup Q = (P - Q) \cup Q$$

and $(P - Q) \cap Q = \emptyset$, we also have $P \cup Q \in \mathcal{E}$.

For any set $P \subset X \times Y$, define $\Omega(P)$ to be the class of all

$$Q \subset X \times Y$$

such that $P - Q \in \mathfrak{M}$, $Q - P \in \mathfrak{M}$, and $P \cup Q \in \mathfrak{M}$. The following properties are obvious:

(*a*) $Q \in \Omega(P)$ if and only if $P \in \Omega(Q)$.
(*b*) Since $\mathfrak{M}$ is a monotone class, so is each $\Omega(P)$.

Fix $P \in \mathcal{E}$. Our preceding remarks about $\mathcal{E}$ show that $Q \in \Omega(P)$ for all $Q \in \mathcal{E}$, hence $\mathcal{E} \subset \Omega(P)$, and now (*b*) implies that $\mathfrak{M} \subset \Omega(P)$.

Next, fix $Q \in \mathfrak{M}$. We just saw that $Q \in \Omega(P)$ if $P \in \mathcal{E}$. By (*a*),

$P \in \Omega(Q)$, hence $\mathcal{E} \subset \Omega(Q)$, and if we use (*b*) once more we obtain $\mathfrak{M} \subset \Omega(Q)$.

Summing up: *If $P \in \mathfrak{M}$ and $Q \in \mathfrak{M}$, then $P - Q \in \mathfrak{M}$ and $P \cup Q \in \mathfrak{M}$.* It now follows that $\mathfrak{M}$ is a σ-algebra in $X \times Y$:

(i) $X \times Y \in \mathcal{E}$, hence $X \times Y \in \mathfrak{M}$.

(ii) If $Q \in \mathfrak{M}$, then $Q^c \in \mathfrak{M}$, since the difference of any two members of $\mathfrak{M}$ is in $\mathfrak{M}$.

(iii) If $P_i \in \mathfrak{M}$ for $i = 1, 2, 3, \ldots$, and $P = \bigcup P_i$, put

$$Q_n = P_1 \cup \cdots \cup P_n.$$

Since $\mathfrak{M}$ is closed under the formation of finite unions, $Q_n \in \mathfrak{M}$. Since $Q_n \subset Q_{n+1}$ and $P = \bigcup Q_n$, the monotonicity of $\mathfrak{M}$ shows that $P \in \mathfrak{M}$.

Thus $\mathfrak{M}$ is a σ-algebra, $\mathcal{E} \subset \mathfrak{M} \subset \mathcal{S} \times \mathfrak{T}$, and (by definition) $\mathcal{S} \times \mathfrak{T}$ is the smallest σ-algebra which contains $\mathcal{E}$. Hence $\mathfrak{M} = \mathcal{S} \times \mathfrak{T}$.

7.4 Definition With each function f on $X \times Y$ and with each $x \in X$ we associate a function f_x defined on Y by $f_x(y) = f(x,y)$.

Similarly, if $y \in Y$, f^y is the function defined on X by $f^y(x) = f(x,y)$.

Since we are now dealing with three σ-algebras, $\mathcal{S}$, $\mathfrak{T}$, and $\mathcal{S} \times \mathfrak{T}$, we shall, for the sake of clarity, indicate in the sequel to which of these three σ-algebras the word "measurable" refers.

7.5 Theorem *Let f be an $(\mathcal{S} \times \mathfrak{T})$-measurable function on $X \times Y$. Then*

(*a*) *For each $x \in X$, f_x is a $\mathfrak{T}$-measurable function.*

(*b*) *For each $y \in Y$, f^y is an $\mathcal{S}$-measurable function.*

PROOF For any open set V, put

$$Q = \{(x,y): f(x,y) \in V\}.$$

Then $Q \in \mathcal{S} \times \mathfrak{T}$, and

$$Q_x = \{y: f_x(y) \in V\}.$$

Theorem 7.2 shows that $Q_x \in \mathfrak{T}$. This proves (*a*); the proof of (*b*) is similar.

Product Measures

7.6 Theorem *Let $(X,\mathcal{S},\mu)$ and $(Y,\mathfrak{T},\lambda)$ be σ-finite measure spaces. Suppose $Q \in \mathcal{S} \times \mathfrak{T}$. If*

$$\varphi(x) = \lambda(Q_x), \qquad \psi(y) = \mu(Q^y) \tag{1}$$

for every $x \in X$ and $y \in Y$, then φ is $\mathcal{S}$-measurable, ψ is $\mathfrak{T}$-measurable, and

$$\int_X \varphi \, d\mu = \int_Y \psi \, d\lambda. \tag{2}$$

Notes: The assumptions on the measure spaces are, more explicitly, that μ and λ are positive measures on $\mathcal{S}$ and $\mathfrak{T}$, respectively, that X is the union of countably many disjoint sets X_n with $\mu(X_n) < \infty$, and that Y is the union of countably many disjoint sets Y_m with $\lambda(Y_m) < \infty$.

Theorem 7.2 shows that the definitions (1) make sense. Since

$$\lambda(Q_x) = \int_Y \chi_Q(x,y) \, d\lambda(y) \qquad (x \in X), \tag{3}$$

with a similar statement for $\mu(Q^y)$, the conclusion (2) can be written in the form

$$\int_X d\mu(x) \int_Y \chi_Q(x,y) \, d\lambda(y) = \int_Y d\lambda(y) \int_X \chi_Q(x,y) \, d\mu(x). \tag{4}$$

PROOF Let Ω be the class of all $Q \in \mathcal{S} \times \mathfrak{T}$ for which the conclusion of the theorem holds. We claim that Ω has the following four properties:

(*a*) Every measurable rectangle belongs to Ω.
(*b*) If $Q_1 \subset Q_2 \subset Q_3 \subset \cdots$, if each $Q_i \in \Omega$, and if $Q = \bigcup Q_i$, then $Q \in \Omega$.
(*c*) If $\{Q_i\}$ is a disjoint countable collection of members of Ω, and $Q = \bigcup Q_i$, then $Q \in \Omega$.
(*d*) If $\mu(A) < \infty$ and $\lambda(B) < \infty$, if

$$A \times B \supset Q_1 \supset Q_2 \supset Q_3 \supset \cdots,$$

if $Q = \bigcap Q_i$ and $Q_i \in \Omega$ for $i = 1, 2, 3, \ldots$, then $Q \in \Omega$.

If $Q = A \times B$, where $A \in \mathcal{S}$, $B \in \mathfrak{T}$, then

$$\lambda(Q_x) = \lambda(B)\chi_A(x) \qquad \text{and} \qquad \mu(Q^y) = \mu(A)\chi_B(y), \tag{5}$$

and therefore each of the integrals in (2) is equal to $\mu(A)\lambda(B)$. This gives (*a*).

To prove (*b*), let φ_i and ψ_i be associated with Q_i in the way in which (1) associates φ and ψ with Q. The countable additivity of μ and λ shows that

$$\varphi_i(x) \to \varphi(x), \qquad \psi_i(y) \to \psi(y) \qquad (i \to \infty), \tag{6}$$

the convergence being monotone increasing at every point. Since φ_i and ψ_i are assumed to satisfy the conclusion of the theorem, (*b*) follows from the monotone convergence theorem.

For finite unions of disjoint sets, (*c*) is clear, because the characteristic function of a union of *disjoint* sets is the sum of their characteristic functions. The general case of (*c*) now follows from (*b*).

The proof of (*d*) is like that of (*b*), except that we use the dominated convergence theorem in place of the monotone convergence theorem. This is legitimate, since $\mu(A) < \infty$ and $\lambda(B) < \infty$.

Now define

$$(7) \qquad Q_{mn} = Q \cap (X_n \times Y_m) \qquad (m, n = 1, 2, 3, \ldots)$$

and let $\mathfrak{M}$ be the class of all $Q \in \mathcal{S} \times \mathfrak{I}$ such that $Q_{mn} \in \Omega$ for all choices of m and n. Then (*b*) and (*d*) show that $\mathfrak{M}$ is a monotone class; (*a*) and (*c*) show that $\mathcal{E} \subset \mathfrak{M}$; and since $\mathfrak{M} \subset \mathcal{S} \times \mathfrak{I}$, Theorem 7.3 implies that $\mathfrak{M} = \mathcal{S} \times \mathfrak{I}$.

Thus $Q_{mn} \in \Omega$ for every $Q \in \mathcal{S} \times \mathfrak{I}$ and for all choices of m and n. Since Q is the union of the sets Q_{mn} and since these sets are disjoint, we conclude from (*c*) that $Q \in \Omega$. This completes the proof.

7.7 Definition If $(X,\mathcal{S},\mu)$ and $(Y,\mathfrak{I},\lambda)$ are as in Theorem 7.6, and if $Q \in \mathcal{S} \times \mathfrak{I}$, we define

$$(1) \qquad (\mu \times \lambda)(Q) = \int_X \lambda(Q_x)\, d\mu(x) = \int_Y \mu(Q^y)\, d\lambda(y).$$

The equality of the integrals in (1) is the content of Theorem 7.6. We call $\mu \times \lambda$ the *product* of the measures μ and λ. That $\mu \times \lambda$ is really a measure (i.e., that $\mu \times \lambda$ is countably additive on $\mathcal{S} \times \mathfrak{I}$) follows immediately from Theorem 1.27.

Observe also that $\mu \times \lambda$ is σ-finite.

The Fubini Theorem

7.8 Theorem *Let $(X,\mathcal{S},\mu)$ and $(Y,\mathfrak{I},\lambda)$ be σ-finite measure spaces, and let f be an $(\mathcal{S} \times \mathfrak{I})$-measurable function on $X \times Y$.*

(*a*) *If $0 \le f \le \infty$, and if*

$$(1) \quad \varphi(x) = \int_Y f_x\, d\lambda, \qquad \psi(y) = \int_X f^y\, d\mu \qquad (x \in X,\ y \in Y),$$

then φ is $\mathcal{S}$-measurable, ψ is $\mathfrak{I}$-measurable, and

$$(2) \qquad \int_X \varphi\, d\mu = \int_{X \times Y} f\, d(\mu \times \lambda) = \int_Y \psi\, d\lambda.$$

(*b*) *If f is complex and if*

$$(3) \quad \varphi^*(x) = \int_Y |f|_x\, d\lambda \qquad \text{and} \qquad \int_X \varphi^*\, d\mu < \infty,$$

then $f \in L^1(\mu \times \lambda)$.

(*c*) *If* $f \in L^1(\mu \times \lambda)$, *then* $f_x \in L^1(\lambda)$ *for almost all* $x \in X$, $f^y \in L^1(\mu)$ *for almost all* $y \in Y$; *the functions* φ *and* ψ, *defined by* (1) a.e., *are in* $L^1(\mu)$ *and* $L^1(\lambda)$, *respectively, and* (2) *holds.*

Notes: The first and last integrals in (2) can also be written in the more usual form

$$\int_X d\mu(x) \int_Y f(x,y)\, d\lambda(y) = \int_Y d\lambda(y) \int_X f(x,y)\, d\mu(x). \tag{4}$$

These are the so-called "iterated integrals" of f. The middle integral in (2) is often referred to as a *double integral.*

The combination of (*b*) and (*c*) gives the following useful result: *If* f *is* $(\mathcal{S} \times \mathfrak{T})$*-measurable and if*

$$\int_X d\mu(x) \int_Y |f(x,y)|\, d\lambda(y) < \infty, \tag{5}$$

then the two iterated integrals (4) *are finite and equal.*

In other words, "the order of integration may be reversed" for $(\mathcal{S} \times \mathfrak{T})$-measurable functions f whenever $f \geq 0$ and also whenever one of the iterated integrals of $|f|$ is finite.

PROOF We first consider (*a*). By Theorem 7.5, the definitions of φ and ψ make sense. Suppose $Q \in \mathcal{S} \times \mathfrak{T}$ and $f = \chi_Q$. By Definition 7.7, (2) is then exactly the conclusion of Theorem 7.6. Hence (*a*) holds for all nonnegative simple $(\mathcal{S} \times \mathfrak{T})$-measurable functions s. In the general case, there is a sequence of such functions s_n, such that $0 \leq s_1 \leq s_2 \leq \cdots$ and $s_n(x,y) \to f(x,y)$ at every point of $X \times Y$. If φ_n is associated with s_n in the same way in which φ was associated to f, we have

$$\int_X \varphi_n\, d\mu = \int_{X \times Y} s_n\, d(\mu \times \lambda) \qquad (n = 1, 2, 3, \ldots). \tag{6}$$

The monotone convergence theorem, applied on $(Y,\mathfrak{T},\lambda)$, shows that $\varphi_n(x)$ increases to $\varphi(x)$, for every $x \in X$, as $n \to \infty$. Hence the monotone convergence theorem applies again, to the two integrals in (6), and the first equality (2) is obtained. The second half of (2) follows by interchanging the roles of x and y. This completes (*a*).

If we apply (*a*) to $|f|$, we see that (*b*) is true.

Obviously, it is enough to prove (*c*) for *real* $f \in L^1(\mu \times \lambda)$; the complex case then follows. If f is real, (*a*) applies to f^+ and to f^-. Let φ_1 and φ_2 correspond to f^+ and f^- as φ corresponds to f in (1). Since $f \in L^1(\mu \times \lambda)$ and $f^+ \leq |f|$, and since (*a*) holds for f^+, we see that $\varphi_1 \in L^1(\mu)$. Similarly, $\varphi_2 \in L^1(\mu)$. Since

$$f_x = (f^+)_x - (f^-)_x \tag{7}$$

we have $f_x \in L^1(\lambda)$ for every x for which $\varphi_1(x) < \infty$ and $\varphi_2(x) < \infty$; since φ_1 and φ_2 are in $L^1(\mu)$, this happens for almost all x; and at any such x, we have $\varphi(x) = \varphi_1(x) - \varphi_2(x)$. Hence $\varphi \in L^1(\mu)$. Now (2) holds with φ_1 and f^+ and with φ_2 and f^-, in place of φ and f; if we subtract the resulting equations, we obtain one half of (c). The other half is proved in the same manner, with f^y and ψ in place of f_x and φ.

7.9 Counterexamples The following three examples will show that the various hypotheses in Theorems 7.6 and 7.8 cannot be dispensed with.

(a) Let $X = Y = [0,1]$, $\mu = \lambda =$ Lebesgue measure on $[0,1]$. Choose $\{\delta_n\}$ so that $0 = \delta_1 < \delta_2 < \delta_3 < \cdots$, $\delta_n \to 1$, and let g_n be a real continuous function with support in (δ_n,δ_{n+1}), such that $\int_0^1 g_n(t)\,dt = 1$, for $n = 1, 2, 3, \ldots$. Define

$$f(x,y) = \sum_{n=1}^{\infty} [g_n(x) - g_{n+1}(x)]g_n(y).$$

Note that at each point (x,y) at most one term in this sum is different from 0. Thus no convergence problem arises in the definition of f. An easy computation shows that

$$\int_0^1 dx \int_0^1 f(x,y)\,dy = 1 \neq 0 = \int_0^1 dy \int_0^1 f(x,y)\,dx,$$

so that the conclusion of the Fubini theorem fails, although both iterated integrals exist. Note that f is continuous in this example, except at the point $(1,1)$, but that

$$\int_0^1 dx \int_0^1 |f(x,y)|\,dy = \infty.$$

(b) Let $X = Y = [0,1]$, $\mu =$ Lebesgue measure on $[0,1]$, $\lambda =$ counting measure on Y, and put $f(x,y) = 1$ if $x = y$, $f(x,y) = 0$ if $x \neq y$. Then

$$\int_X f(x,y)\,d\mu(x) = 0, \qquad \int_Y f(x,y)\,d\lambda(y) = 1$$

for all x and y in $[0,1]$, so that

$$\int_Y d\lambda(y) \int_X f(x,y)\,d\mu(x) = 0 \neq 1 = \int_X d\mu(x) \int_Y f(x,y)\,d\lambda(y).$$

This time the failure is due to the fact that λ is not σ-finite.

Observe that our function f *is* $(\mathfrak{S} \times \mathfrak{I})$-measurable, if $\mathfrak{S}$ is the class of all Lebesgue measurable sets in $[0,1]$ and $\mathfrak{I}$ consists of all subsets of $[0,1]$. To see this, note that $f = \chi_D$, where D is the diagonal of the unit square. Given n, put

$$I_j = \left[\frac{j-1}{n}, \frac{j}{n}\right]$$

and put

$$Q_n = (I_1 \times I_1) \cup (I_2 \times I_2) \cup \cdots \cup (I_n \times I_n).$$

Then Q_n is a finite union of measurable rectangles, and $D = \bigcap Q_n$.

(*c*) In examples (*a*) and (*b*), the failure of the Fubini theorem was due to the fact that either the function or the space was "too big." We now turn to the role played by the requirement that f be measurable *with respect to the σ-algebra* $\mathfrak{S} \times \mathfrak{T}$.

To pose the question more precisely, suppose $\mu(X) = \lambda(Y) = 1$, $0 \le f \le 1$ (so that "bigness" is certainly avoided); assume f_x is $\mathfrak{T}$-measurable and f^y is $\mathfrak{S}$-measurable, for all x and y; and assume φ is $\mathfrak{S}$-measurable and ψ is $\mathfrak{T}$-measurable, where φ and ψ are defined as in 7.8(1). Then $0 \le \varphi \le 1$, $0 \le \psi \le 1$, and both iterated integrals are finite. (Note that no reference to product measures is needed to *define* iterated integrals.) Does it follow that the two iterated integrals of f are equal?

The (perhaps surprising) answer is no.

In the following example (due to Sierpinski), we take

$$(X,\mathfrak{S},\mu) = (Y,\mathfrak{T},\lambda) = [0,1]$$

with Lebesgue measure. The construction depends on the continuum hypothesis. It is a consequence of this hypothesis that there is a one-to-one mapping j of the unit interval [0,1] onto a well-ordered set W such that $j(x)$ has at most countably many predecessors in W, for each $x \in [0,1]$. Taking this for granted, let Q be the set of all (x,y) in the unit square such that $j(x)$ precedes $j(y)$ in W. For each $x \in [0,1]$, Q_x contains all but countably many points of [0,1]; for each $y \in [0,1]$, Q^y contains at most countably many points of [0,1]. If $f = \chi_Q$, it follows that f_x and f^y are Borel measurable and that

$$\varphi(x) = \int_0^1 f(x,y)\,dy = 1, \qquad \psi(y) = \int_0^1 f(x,y)\,dx = 0$$

for all x and y. Hence

$$\int_0^1 dx \int_0^1 f(x,y)\,dy = 1 \ne 0 = \int_0^1 dy \int_0^1 f(x,y)\,dx.$$

Completion of Product Measures

7.10 If $(X,\mathfrak{S},\mu)$ and $(Y,\mathfrak{T},\lambda)$ are complete measure spaces, it need not be true that $(X \times Y, \mathfrak{S} \times \mathfrak{T}, \mu \times \lambda)$ is complete. There is nothing pathological about this phenomenon: Suppose that there exists an $A \in \mathfrak{S}$,

$A \neq \emptyset$, with $\mu(A) = 0$; and suppose there exists a $B \subset Y$ so that $B \notin \mathfrak{I}$. Then $A \times B \subset A \times Y$, $(\mu \times \lambda)(A \times Y) = 0$, but $A \times B \notin \mathcal{S} \times \mathfrak{I}$. (The last assertion follows from Theorem 7.2.)

For instance, if $\mu = \lambda = m_1$ (Lebesgue measure on R^1), let A consist of any one point, and let B be any nonmeasurable set in R^1. Thus $m_1 \times m_1$ is not a complete measure; in particular, $m_1 \times m_1$ is not m_2, since the latter is complete, by its construction. However, *m_2 is the completion of $m_1 \times m_1$.* This result generalizes to arbitrary dimensions:

7.11 Theorem *Let m_k denote Lebesgue measure on R^k. If $k = r + s$, $r \geq 1$, $s \geq 1$, then m_k is the completion of the product measure $m_r \times m_s$.*

PROOF Let $\mathcal{B}_k$ and $\mathfrak{M}_k$ be the σ-algebras of all Borel sets and of all Lebesgue measurable sets in R^k, respectively. We shall first show that

$$(1) \qquad \mathcal{B}_k \subset \mathfrak{M}_r \times \mathfrak{M}_s \subset \mathfrak{M}_k.$$

Every k-cell belongs to $\mathfrak{M}_r \times \mathfrak{M}_s$. The σ-algebra generated by the k-cells is $\mathcal{B}_k$. Hence $\mathcal{B}_k \subset \mathfrak{M}_r \times \mathfrak{M}_s$. Next, suppose $E \in \mathfrak{M}_r$ and $F \in \mathfrak{M}_s$. It is easy to see, by Theorem 2.20(*b*), that both $E \times R^s$ and $R^r \times F$ belong to $\mathfrak{M}_k$. The same is true of their intersection $E \times F$. It follows that $\mathfrak{M}_r \times \mathfrak{M}_s \subset \mathfrak{M}_k$.

Choose $Q \in \mathfrak{M}_r \times \mathfrak{M}_s$. Then $Q \in \mathfrak{M}_k$, so there are sets P_1 and $P_2 \in \mathcal{B}_k$ such that $P_1 \subset Q \subset P_2$ and $m_k(P_2 - P_1) = 0$. Both m_k and $m_r \times m_s$ are translation invariant Borel measures on R^k. They assign the same value to each k-cell. Hence they agree on $\mathcal{B}_k$, by Theorem 2.20(*d*). In particular,

$$(m_r \times m_s)(Q - P_1) \leq (m_r \times m_s)(P_2 - P_1) = m_k(P_2 - P_1) = 0$$

and therefore

$$(m_r \times m_s)(Q) = (m_r \times m_s)(P_1) = m_k(P_1) = m_k(Q).$$

So $m_r \times m_s$ agrees with m_k on $\mathfrak{M}_r \times \mathfrak{M}_s$.

It now follows that $\mathfrak{M}_k$ is the $(m_r \times m_s)$-completion of $\mathfrak{M}_r \times \mathfrak{M}_s$, and this is what the theorem asserts.

We conclude this section with an alternative statement of Fubini's theorem which is of special interest in view of Theorem 7.11.

7.12 Theorem *Let $(X,\mathcal{S},\mu)$ and $(Y,\mathfrak{I},\lambda)$ be complete σ-finite measure spaces. Let $(\mathcal{S} \times \mathfrak{I})^*$ be the completion of $\mathcal{S} \times \mathfrak{I}$, relative to the measure $\mu \times \lambda$. Let f be an $(\mathcal{S} \times \mathfrak{I})^*$-measurable function on $X \times Y$. Then all conclusions of Theorem 7.8 hold, the only difference being as follows:*

The $\mathscr{T}$-measurability of f_x can be asserted only for almost all $x \in X$, so that $\varphi(x)$ is only defined a.e. $[\mu]$ by 7.8(1); a similar statement holds for f^y and ψ.

The proof depends on the following two lemmas:

Lemma 1 *Suppose ν is a positive measure on a σ-algebra $\mathfrak{M}$, $\mathfrak{M}^*$ is the completion of $\mathfrak{M}$ relative to ν, and f is an $\mathfrak{M}^*$-measurable function. Then there exists an $\mathfrak{M}$-measurable function g such that $f = g$ a.e. $[\nu]$.*

(An interesting special case of this arises when ν is Lebesgue measure on R^k and $\mathfrak{M}$ is the class of all Borel sets in R^k.)

Lemma 2 *Let h be an $(\mathscr{S} \times \mathscr{T})^*$-measurable function on $X \times Y$ such that $h = 0$ a.e. $[\mu \times \lambda]$. Then for almost all $x \in X$ it is true that $h(x,y) = 0$ for almost all $y \in Y$; in particular, h_x is $\mathscr{T}$-measurable for almost all $x \in X$. A similar statement holds for h^y.*

If we assume the lemmas, the proof of the theorem is immediate: If f is as in the theorem, Lemma 1 (with $\nu = \mu \times \lambda$) shows that $f = g + h$, where $h = 0$ a.e. $[\mu \times \lambda]$ and g is $(\mathscr{S} \times \mathscr{T})$-measurable. Theorem 7.8 applies to g. Lemma 2 shows that $f_x = g_x$ a.e. $[\lambda]$ for almost all x and that $f^y = g^y$ a.e. $[\mu]$ for almost all y. Hence the two iterated integrals of f, as well as the double integral, are the same as those of g, and the theorem follows

PROOF OF LEMMA 1 If f is a characteristic function, the conclusion of the lemma is just the definition of $\mathfrak{M}^*$ (see Theorem 1.36). Hence the lemma is true for simple functions f. If f is $\mathfrak{M}^*$-measurable and $f \geq 0$, and if $\{s_n\}$ is a sequence of $\mathfrak{M}^*$-measurable simple functions which converges pointwise to f, there are $\mathfrak{M}$-measurable simple functions t_n such that $t_n = s_n$ a.e. $[\nu]$ and such that $t_n(x) = 0$ at those x at which $t_n(x) \neq s_n(x)$. Then $g(x) = \lim t_n(x)$ exists for every x, g is $\mathfrak{M}$-measurable, and $g = f$ a.e. $[\nu]$. The general case (f real or complex) follows.

PROOF OF LEMMA 2 Let P be the set of all points in $X \times Y$ at which $h(x,y) \neq 0$. Then $P \in (\mathscr{S} \times \mathscr{T})^*$ and $(\mu \times \lambda)(P) = 0$. Hence there exists a $Q \in \mathscr{S} \times \mathscr{T}$ such that $P \subset Q$ and $(\mu \times \lambda)(Q) = 0$. By Theorem 7.6,

$$(1) \qquad \int_X \lambda(Q_x)\, d\mu(x) = 0.$$

Let N be the set of all $x \in X$ at which $\lambda(Q_x) > 0$. It follows from (1) that $\mu(N) = 0$. For every $x \notin N$, $\lambda(Q_x) = 0$. Since $P_x \subset Q_x$ and $(Y,\mathscr{T},\lambda)$ is a complete measure space, every subset of P_x belongs to $\mathscr{T}$ if $x \notin N$. If $y \notin P_x$, then $h_x(y) = 0$. Thus we see, for every $x \notin N$, that h_x is $\mathscr{T}$-measurable and that $h_x(y) = 0$ a.e. $[\lambda]$.

Convolutions

7.13 It happens occasionally that one can prove that a certain set is not empty by proving that it is actually large. The word "large" may of course refer to various properties. One of these (a rather crude one) is cardinality. An example is furnished by the familiar proof that there exist transcendental numbers: there are only countably many algebraic numbers but uncountably many real numbers, hence the set of transcendental real numbers is not empty. Applications of Baire's theorem are based on a topological notion of largeness: the dense G_δ's are "large" subsets of a complete metric space. A third type of largeness is measure-theoretic: One can try to show that a certain set in a measure space is not empty by showing that it has positive measure or, better still, by showing that its complement has measure zero. Fubini's theorem often occurs in this type of argument.

For example, let f and $g \in L^1(R^1)$, assume $f \geq 0$ and $g \geq 0$ for the moment, and consider the integral

$$(1) \qquad h(x) = \int_{-\infty}^{\infty} f(x-t)g(t)\,dt \qquad (-\infty < x < \infty).$$

For any fixed x, the integrand in (1) is a measurable function with range in $[0, \infty]$, so that $h(x)$ is certainly well defined by (1), and we see that $0 \leq h(x) \leq \infty$.

But is there any x for which $h(x) < \infty$? Note that the integrand in (1) is, for each fixed x, the product of two members of L^1, and such a product is not always in L^1. [Example: $f(x) = g(x) = 1/\sqrt{x}$ if $0 < x < 1$, 0 otherwise.] The Fubini theorem will give an affirmative answer. In fact, it will show that $h \in L^1(R^1)$, hence that $h(x) < \infty$ a.e.

7.14 Theorem *Suppose $f \in L^1(R^1)$, $g \in L^1(R^1)$. Then*

$$(1) \qquad \int_{-\infty}^{\infty} |f(x-y)g(y)|\,dy < \infty$$

for almost all x. For these x, define

$$(2) \qquad h(x) = \int_{-\infty}^{\infty} f(x-y)g(y)\,dy.$$

Then $h \in L^1(R^1)$, and

$$(3) \qquad \|h\|_1 \leq \|f\|_1 \|g\|_1,$$

where

$$(4) \qquad \|f\|_1 = \int_{-\infty}^{\infty} |f(x)|\,dx.$$

We call h the *convolution* of f and g, and write $h = f * g$.

PROOF There exist Borel functions f_0 and g_0 such that $f_0 = f$ a.e. and $g_0 = g$ a.e. The integrals (1) and (2) are unchanged, for every x, if we replace f by f_0 and g by g_0. Hence we may assume, to begin with, that f and g are Borel functions.

To apply Fubini's theorem, we shall first prove that the function F defined by

$$F(x,y) = f(x - y)g(y) \tag{5}$$

is a Borel function on R^2.

Associate with each $E \subset R^1$ the set $\tilde{E} \subset R^2$ defined by

$$\tilde{E} = \{(x,y) : x - y \in E\}. \tag{6}$$

If E is open, so is $\tilde{E}$. The collection of all $E \subset R^1$ for which $\tilde{E}$ is a Borel set is easily verified to be a σ-algebra in R^1, hence contains all Borel sets in R^1. It follows that $\tilde{E}$ is a Borel set in R^2 whenever E is a Borel set in R^1.

Now let V be open, and let $E = \{x : f(x) \in V\}$. Then E is a Borel set in R^1, and so is

$$\{(x,y) : f(x - y) \in V\} = \{(x,y) : x - y \in E\} = \tilde{E}. \tag{7}$$

This shows that $(x,y) \to f(x - y)$ is a Borel function. So is $(x,y) \to g(y)$. Since the product of two Borel functions is a Borel function, our assertion concerning F is proved.

Next we observe that

$$\int_{-\infty}^{\infty} dy \int_{-\infty}^{\infty} |F(x,y)|\, dx = \int_{-\infty}^{\infty} |g(y)|\, dy \int_{-\infty}^{\infty} |f(x - y)|\, dx = \|f\|_1 \|g\|_1, \tag{8}$$

since

$$\int_{-\infty}^{\infty} |f(x - y)|\, dx = \|f\|_1 \tag{9}$$

for every $y \in R^1$, by the translation invariance of Lebesgue measure.

Thus $F \in L^1(R^2)$, and Fubini's theorem implies that the integral (2) exists for almost all $x \in R^1$ and that $h \in L^1(R^1)$. Finally,

$$\begin{aligned} \|h\|_1 &= \int_{-\infty}^{\infty} |h(x)|\, dx \le \int_{-\infty}^{\infty} dx \int_{-\infty}^{\infty} |F(x,y)|\, dy \\ &= \int_{-\infty}^{\infty} dy \int_{-\infty}^{\infty} |F(x,y)|\, dx = \|f\|_1 \|g\|_1, \end{aligned}$$

by (8). This gives (3), and completes the proof.

Convolutions will play an important role in Chap. 9.

Exercises

1 Find an example of a monotone class $\mathfrak{M}$ in a set X such that $\varnothing \in \mathfrak{M}$, $X \in \mathfrak{M}$, but $\mathfrak{M}$ is not a σ-algebra.

2 Suppose f is a Lebesgue measurable nonnegative real function on R^1 and $A(f)$ is the *ordinate set* of f. This is the set of all points $(x,y) \in R^2$ for which $0 < y < f(x)$.

(*a*) Is it true that $A(f)$ is Lebesgue measurable, in the two-dimensional sense?

(*b*) If the answer to (*a*) is affirmative, is the integral of f over R^1 equal to the measure of $A(f)$?

(*c*) Is the graph of f a measurable subset of R^2?

(*d*) If the answer to (*c*) is affirmative, is the measure of the graph equal to zero?

3 Find an example of a positive continuous function f in the open unit square in R^2, whose integral (relative to Lebesgue measure) is finite but such that $\varphi(x)$ (in the notation of Theorem 7.8) is infinite for some $x \in (0,1)$.

4 Suppose $1 \leq p \leq \infty$, $f \in L^1(R^1)$, and $g \in L^p(R^1)$.

(*a*) Imitate the proof of Theorem 7.14 to show that the integral defining $(f * g)(x)$ exists for almost all x, that $f * g \in L^p(R^1)$, and that

$$\|f * g\|_p \leq \|f\|_1 \|g\|_p.$$

(*b*) Show that equality can hold in (*a*) if $p = 1$ and if $p = \infty$, and find the conditions under which this happens.

(*c*) Assume $1 < p < \infty$, and equality holds in (*a*). Show that then either $f = 0$ a.e. or $g = 0$ a.e.

(*d*) Assume $1 \leq p \leq \infty$, $\epsilon > 0$, and show that there exist $f \in L^1(R^1)$ and $g \in L^p(R^1)$ such that

$$\|f * g\|_p > (1 - \epsilon)\|f\|_1 \|g\|_p.$$

5 Let M be the Banach space of all complex Borel measures on R^1. The norm in M is $\|\mu\| = |\mu|(R^1)$. Associate to each Borel set $E \subset R^1$ the set

$$E_2 = \{(x,y): x + y \in E\} \subset R^2.$$

If μ and $\lambda \in M$, define their convolution $\mu * \lambda$ to be the set function given by

$$(\mu * \lambda)(E) = (\mu \times \lambda)(E^2)$$

for every Borel set $E \subset R^1$; $\mu \times \lambda$ is as in Definition 7.7.

(*a*) Prove that $\mu * \lambda \in M$ and that $\|\mu * \lambda\| \leq \|\mu\|\,\|\lambda\|$.

(*b*) Prove that $\mu * \lambda$ is the unique $\nu \in M$ such that

$$\int f\,d\nu = \iint f(x+y)\,d\mu(x)\,d\lambda(y)$$

for every $f \in C_0(R^1)$. (All integrals extend over R^1.)

(*c*) Prove that convolution in M is commutative, associative, and distributive with respect to addition.

(*d*) Prove the formula

$$(\mu * \lambda)(E) = \int \mu(E-t)\,d\lambda(t)$$

for every μ and $\lambda \in M$ and every Borel set E. Here

$$E - t = \{x - t : x \in E\}.$$

(*e*) Define μ to be *discrete* if μ is concentrated on a countable set; define μ to be *continuous* if $\mu(\{x\}) = 0$ for every point $x \in R^1$; let m be Lebesgue measure on R^1 (note that $m \notin M$). Prove that $\mu * \lambda$ is discrete if both μ and λ are discrete, that $\mu * \lambda$ is continuous if μ is continuous and $\lambda \in M$, and that $\mu * \lambda \ll m$ if $\mu \ll m$.

(*f*) If $d\mu = f\,dm$, $d\lambda = g\,dm$, $f \in L^1(R^1)$, and $g \in L^1(R^1)$, prove that $d(\mu * \lambda) = f * g\,dm$.

(*g*) Properties (*a*) and (*c*) show that the Banach space M is what one calls a *commutative Banach algebra*. Show that (*e*) and (*f*) imply that the set of all discrete measures in M is a subalgebra of M, that the continuous measures form an ideal in M, and that the absolutely continuous measures (relative to m) form an ideal in M which is isomorphic (as an algebra) to $L^1(R^1)$.

(*h*) Show that M has a unit, i.e., show that there exists a $\delta \in M$ such that $\delta * \mu = \mu$ for all $\mu \in M$.

(*i*) Only two properties of R^1 have been used in this discussion: R^1 is a commutative group (under addition), and there exists a translation invariant Borel measure m on R^1 which is not identically 0 and which is finite on all compact subsets of R^1. Show that the same results hold if R^1 is replaced by R^k or by T (the unit circle) or by T^k (the k-dimensional torus, the cartesian product of k copies of T), as soon as the definitions are properly formulated.

6 (Polar coordinates in R^k.) Let S_{k-1} be the unit sphere in R^k, i.e., the set of all $u \in R^k$ whose distance from the origin 0 is 1. Show that every $x \in R^k$, except for $x = 0$, has a unique representation of the form $x = ru$, where r is a positive real number and $u \in S_{k-1}$. Thus $R^k - \{0\}$ may be regarded as the cartesian product $(0, \infty) \times S_{k-1}$.

Let m_k be Lebesgue measure on R^k, and define a measure σ_{k-1} on S_{k-1} as follows: If $A \subset S_{k-1}$ and A is a Borel set, let $\tilde{A}$ be the set of all points ru, where $0 < r < 1$ and $u \in A$, and define

$$\sigma_{k-1}(A) = k \cdot m_k(\tilde{A}).$$

Prove that the formula

$$\int_{R^k} f\, dm_k = \int_0^\infty r^{k-1}\, dr \int_{S_{k-1}} f(ru)\, d\sigma_{k-1}(u)$$

is valid for every nonnegative Borel function f on R^k. Check that this coincides with familiar results when $k = 2$ and when $k = 3$.

Suggestion: If $0 < r_1 < r_2$ and if A is an open subset of S_{k-1}, let E be the set of all ru with $r_1 < r < r_2$, $u \in A$, and verify that the formula holds for the characteristic function of E. Pass from there to characteristic functions of Borel sets in R^k.

7 Suppose $(X,\mathcal{S},\mu)$ and $(Y,\mathfrak{I},\lambda)$ are σ-finite measure spaces, and suppose ψ is a measure on $\mathcal{S} \times \mathfrak{I}$ such that

$$\psi(A \times B) = \mu(A)\lambda(B)$$

whenever $A \in \mathcal{S}$ and $B \in \mathfrak{I}$. Prove that then $\psi(E) = (\mu \times \lambda)(E)$ for every $E \in \mathcal{S} \times \mathfrak{I}$.

8 (*a*) Suppose f is a real function on R^2 such that each section f_x is Borel measurable and each section f^y is continuous. Prove that f is Borel measurable on R^2.

Note the contrast between this and Example 7.9(*c*).

(*b*) Suppose g is a real function on R^k which is continuous in each of the k variables separately. More explicitly, for every choice of $x_2, \ldots, x_k$, the mapping $x_1 \to g(x_1,x_2, \ldots ,x_k)$ is continuous, etc. Prove that g is a Borel function.

Hint: If $(i - 1)/n = \alpha_{i-1} \le x \le \alpha_i = i/n$, put

$$f_n(x,y) = \frac{\alpha_i - x}{\alpha_i - \alpha_{i-1}} f(\alpha_{i-1},y) + \frac{x - \alpha_{i-1}}{\alpha_i - \alpha_{i-1}} f(\alpha_i,y).$$

9 Suppose E is a dense set in R^1 and f is a real function on R^2 such that (*a*) f_x is Lebesgue measurable for each $x \in E$ and (*b*) f^y is continuous for almost all $y \in R^1$. Prove that f is Lebesgue measurable on R^2.

10 Suppose f is a real function on R^2, f_x is Lebesgue measurable for each x, and f^y is continuous for each y. Suppose $g\colon R^1 \to R^1$ is continuous and $h(y) = f(g(y),y)$. Prove that h is Lebesgue measurable on R^1. Then use Lusin's theorem to obtain the same result if continuity of g is replaced by measurability.

11 Let $\mathcal{B}_k$ be the σ-algebra of all Borel sets in R^k. Prove that $\mathcal{B}_{m+n} = \mathcal{B}_m \times \mathcal{B}_n$. This is relevant in Theorem 7.14.

8

Differentiation

Derivatives of Measures

We begin with a theorem about derivatives of certain point functions, in order to motivate Definition 8.2.

8.1 Theorem *Suppose μ is a complex Borel measure on R^1 and*

$$f(x) = \mu((-\infty, x)) \qquad (x \in R^1). \tag{1}$$

For any $x \in R^1$, each of the following two statements implies the other:

(a) f is differentiable at x and $f'(x) = A$.
(b) To every $\epsilon > 0$ there exists a $\delta > 0$ such that

$$\left| \frac{\mu(I)}{m(I)} - A \right| < \epsilon \tag{2}$$

for every open segment I which contains x and whose length is less than δ.

Here m denotes Lebesgue measure on R^1.

PROOF Replace μ by $\mu - Am$, restricted to some segment containing x (so that the new measure is finite). This shows that there is no loss of generality in assuming $A = 0$.

If $f'(x) = 0$ and $\epsilon > 0$, there exists a $\delta > 0$ such that

$$|f(t) - f(x)| \leq \epsilon |t - x|$$

if $|t - x| < \delta$. Suppose $x \in I$, $I = (s,t)$, and $t - s < \delta$. Choose s_n so that $x > s_1 > s_2 > \cdots, s_n \to s$. Then

$$\begin{aligned} |\mu([s_n,t))| &= |f(t) - f(s_n)| \leq |f(t) - f(x)| + |f(x) - f(s_n)| \\ &\leq \epsilon(t - x) + \epsilon(x - s_n) = \epsilon(t - s_n) < \epsilon m(I), \end{aligned}$$

and since $I = \bigcup([s_n,t))$, it follows that $|\mu(I)| \le \epsilon m(I)$. Thus (*a*) implies (*b*).

Next, suppose (*b*) holds with $A = 0$, choose $\epsilon > 0$, and choose δ as in (*b*). If $s < x < t$ and $t - s < \delta$, then

$$\left|\mu\left(\left(s - \frac{1}{n}, t\right)\right)\right| < \epsilon\left(t - s + \frac{1}{n}\right)$$

for all large enough n. Since $[s,t) = \bigcap(s - 1/n, t)$ and

$$f(t) - f(s) = \mu([s,t)),$$

it follows that

$$(3) \qquad |f(t) - f(s)| \le \epsilon|t - s| \qquad (s < x < t < s + \delta).$$

If (*b*) holds, then $\mu(\{x\}) = 0$, where $\{x\}$ is the set consisting of x alone. Hence f is continuous at x. Hence either s or t can be replaced by x in (3), and we conclude that $f'(x) = 0$.

8.2 Definition Theorem 8.1 suggests that the derivative of μ at x might be defined as the limit of the quotients $\mu(I)/m(I)$ as the segments I shrink to the point x. Of course, one could also consider quotients $\mu(E)/m(E)$, where E runs over some other family of sets. On the line there seems little point in doing this, but in euclidean spaces of higher dimension it is appropriate.

A collection Ω of open sets in R^k will be called a *substantial family* if

(*a*) There is a constant $\beta < \infty$ such that each $E \in \Omega$ is contained in an open ball B with $m(B) < \beta m(E)$, where m denotes Lebesgue measure in R^k.

(*b*) To every $x \in R^k$ and $\delta > 0$ there exists an $E \in \Omega$, whose diameter is less than δ, such that $x \in E$.

Recall that

$$(1) \qquad \operatorname{diam} E = \sup\{|x - y| : x \in E, y \in E\}.$$

Condition (*a*) is a quantitative statement of the requirement that the members of Ω should not be too long and thin; if the volume is small, the diameter must be small. Simple examples of substantial families are the collection of all open balls, the collection of all open cubes, and the collection of all open k-cells whose longest edge is at most 1,000 times as long as the shortest edge.

Now suppose μ is a complex Borel measure on R^k, Ω is a substantial family, $x \in R^k$, and A is a complex number. If to each $\epsilon > 0$ there corresponds a $\delta > 0$ such that

$$(2) \qquad \left|\frac{\mu(E)}{m(E)} - A\right| < \epsilon$$

for every $E \varepsilon \Omega$ with $x \varepsilon E$ and diam $E < \delta$, then we say that μ *is differentiable at* x, and write

(3) $$(D\mu)(x) = A.$$

Note that this definition of $D\mu$ depends on Ω, so that we should perhaps be talking about Ω-derivatives and should perhaps use the notation D_Ω in place of D. Since we shall never be dealing with more than one family Ω at a time, this will not be necessary.

8.3 Definition If μ is a real (or a positive) Borel measure on R^k, we can define upper and lower derivatives of μ at every point $x \varepsilon R^k$. For every $r > 0$, put

(1) $$\bar{\Delta}_r(x) = \sup \left\{ \frac{\mu(E)}{m(E)} : x \varepsilon E, E \varepsilon \Omega, \text{diam } E < r \right\},$$

where Ω is a given substantial family, and define the *upper derivative* of μ at x by

(2) $$(\bar{D}\mu)(x) = \lim_{r \to 0} \bar{\Delta}_r(x).$$

Since $r \geq s$ implies $\bar{\Delta}_r(x) \geq \bar{\Delta}_s(x)$, the limit in (2) exists, as a number in $[-\infty, \infty]$.

If we replace sup by inf in (1), we obtain $\underline{\Delta}_r(x)$, and we define $(\underline{D}\mu)(x)$ to be lim $\underline{\Delta}_r(x)$, as $r \to 0$.

It is clear that μ is differentiable at x if and only if $(\bar{D}\mu)(x)$ and $(\underline{D}\mu)(x)$ are equal and finite; in that case, we have

(3) $$(\underline{D}\mu)(x) = (D\mu)(x) = (\bar{D}\mu)(x).$$

Also, $(\underline{D}\mu)(x) \leq (\bar{D}\mu)(x)$ always holds.

8.4 Proposition *Suppose μ and λ are real Borel measures on R^k, $\sigma = \mu + \lambda$, and $x \varepsilon R^k$. Then*

(1) $$(\bar{D}\sigma)(x) \leq (\bar{D}\mu)(x) + (\bar{D}\lambda)(x)$$

unless the right side of (1) *is undefined (i.e., is of the form $\infty - \infty$). If μ and λ are differentiable at x, so is σ, and*

(2) $$(D\sigma)(x) = (D\mu)(x) + (D\lambda)(x).$$

PROOF If either of the numbers on the right of (1) is $+\infty$, there is nothing to prove. If not, and if $A > (\bar{D}\mu)(x)$, $B > (\bar{D}\lambda)(x)$, there exists a $\delta > 0$ such that $\mu(E) < Am(E)$ and $\lambda(E) < Bm(E)$ for all $E \varepsilon \Omega$ with $x \varepsilon E$ and diam $E < \delta$. Hence

$$\frac{\sigma(E)}{m(E)} < A + B$$

for all such E, so that $(\bar{D}\sigma)(x) \leq A + B$. This gives (1).

The inequality

$$(3) \qquad (\underline{D}\sigma)(x) \geq (\underline{D}\mu)(x) + (\underline{D}\lambda)(x)$$

is proved similarly, and (2) is a consequence of (1) and (3).

The relevance of substantial families to the result we are aiming at (Theorem 8.6) depends on the following covering theorem.

8.5 Theorem *Let Ω be a substantial family in R^k, and suppose A is the union of a finite collection Φ of members of Ω. Then there is a disjoint subcollection Φ' of Φ whose union A' has the property*

$$(1) \qquad m(A) \leq \beta \cdot 3^k \cdot m(A').$$

Here β is the constant in Definition 8.2(*a*).

PROOF Order the elements $S_1, S_2, \ldots, S_p$ of Φ so that

$$\operatorname{diam} S_i \geq \operatorname{diam} S_{i+1}.$$

Put $i_1 = 1$, let i_2 be the smallest integer greater than i_1 such that $S_{i_2} \cap S_{i_1}$ is empty, let i_3 be the smallest integer greater than i_2 such that $S_{i_3} \cap (S_{i_1} \cup S_{i_2})$ is empty, and so on as long as possible. In a finite number of steps this gives us a disjoint collection $S_{i_1}, S_{i_2}, \ldots$ which we call Φ'.

Each S_{i_n} lies in an open ball B_n such that

$$(2) \qquad m(B_n) < \beta m(S_{i_n}).$$

Let V_n be the open ball which has the same center as B_n but whose radius is 3 times as large. To each S_j there corresponds at least one $i_n \leq j$ such that S_j intersects S_{i_n}. Then $S_j \subset V_n$. Hence $A \subset \bigcup V_n$; and since $A' = \bigcup S_{i_n}$, we have

$$m(A) \leq \sum_n m(V_n) = 3^k \sum_n m(B_n)$$

$$\leq 3^k \cdot \beta \cdot \sum_n m(S_{i_n}) = 3^k \cdot \beta \cdot m(A').$$

8.6 Theorem *Let Ω be a substantial family in R^k. If μ is a complex Borel measure on R^k, then*

(*a*) *μ is differentiable a.e.* $[m]$,
(*b*) $D\mu \in L^1(R^k)$,
(*c*) *For every Borel set E,*

$$\mu(E) = \mu_s(E) + \int_E (D\mu)(x)\, dx$$

where $\mu_s \perp m$ and $(D\mu_s)(x) = 0$ a.e. $[m]$.

Note that (c) is the Lebesgue decomposition of μ, relative to m. This leads to the following.

Corollary (i) *$\mu \perp m$ if and only if $(D\mu)(x) = 0$ a.e. $[m]$.* (ii) *$\mu \ll m$ if and only if*

$$\mu(E) = \int_E (D\mu)(x)\,dx;$$

in this case, the derivative $(D\mu)(x)$ (computed as a limit of quotients) coincides a.e. $[m]$ with the Radon-Nikodym derivative $d\mu/dm$.

We begin with some lemmas.

Lemma 1 *If μ is a positive or real Borel measure on R^k, then $\bar{D}\mu$ is a Borel function.*

PROOF If α is a real number and $\bar{\Delta}_r(x) > \alpha$ for some $x \in R^k$ and some $r > 0$ (the notation is as in Definition 8.3), then there exists an $E \in \Omega$ such that $x \in E$, diam $E < r$, and $\mu(E) > \alpha m(E)$. It follows that $\bar{\Delta}_r(y) > \alpha$ for every $y \in E$; and since E is open, we have proved that $\{x: \bar{\Delta}_r(x) > \alpha\}$ is open. Thus $\bar{\Delta}_r$ is lower semicontinuous, for every $r > 0$, and since

$$(\bar{D}\mu)(x) = \lim_{n\to\infty} \bar{\Delta}_{1/n}(x),$$

$\bar{D}\mu$ is a Borel function.

Lemma 2 *Suppose μ is a positive Borel measure on R^k which is finite on compact sets. Let A be a Borel set for which $\mu(A) = 0$. Then $(D\mu)(x) = 0$ a.e. $[m]$ on A.*

PROOF If P is the set of all x at which $(\bar{D}\mu)(x) > 0$, Lemma 1 shows that P is a Borel set, and hence so is $A \cap P$. We have to prove that $m(A \cap P) = 0$.

Assume this is false. Then there exists an $\alpha > 0$ and a Borel set $E_\alpha \subset A \cap P$ such that $m(E_\alpha) > 0$ and $(\bar{D}\mu)(x) > \alpha$ for all $x \in E_\alpha$. The regularity of m shows that E_α contains a compact set K, with $m(K) > 0$.

Fix $\delta > 0$. Each $x \in K$ then lies in some $S \in \Omega$ such that diam $S < \delta$ and $\mu(S) > \alpha m(S)$. Since K is compact, a finite collection Φ of these sets S covers K, and Theorem 8.5 shows that there is a subcollection $\{S_1, S_2, \ldots, S_n\}$ of Φ with the following properties:

(1) $\qquad S_i \cap S_j = \varnothing \quad \text{if } i \neq j, \qquad \mu(S_i) > \alpha m(S_i),$

and

(2) $$\sum_{i=1}^{n} m(S_i) \geq \beta^{-1} \cdot 3^{-k} \cdot m(K);$$

also, $S_i \subset K_\delta$, for $i = 1, \ldots, n$, where K_δ is the set of all points whose distance from K is less than δ. Hence

$$\text{(3)} \qquad \mu(K_\delta) \geq \mu\left(\bigcup_{i=1}^{n} S_i\right) = \sum_{i=1}^{n} \mu(S_i)$$

$$> \alpha \sum_{i=1}^{n} m(S_i) \geq \alpha \cdot \beta^{-1} \cdot 3^{-k} \cdot m(K).$$

Take $\delta = 1/n$, $n = 1, 2, 3, \ldots$. Then $\mu(K) = \lim \mu(K_{1/n})$, since K is the intersection of the decreasing sequence $\{K_{1/n}\}$ and $\mu(K_1) < \infty$. (K_1 has compact closure.) Hence (3) implies

$$\text{(4)} \qquad \mu(K) \geq \alpha \cdot \beta^{-1} \cdot 3^{-k} \cdot m(K) > 0.$$

But $K \subset A$ and $\mu(A) = 0$.

This contradiction proves that $(\bar{D}\mu)(x) \leq 0$ a.e. $[m]$ in A. Since $\mu \geq 0$, the inequality $(\underline{D}\mu)(x) \geq 0$ is obvious for all x. This proves the lemma.

Lemma 3 *If $\mu \perp m$, then $(D\mu)(x) = 0$ a.e. $[m]$.*

PROOF It is enough to prove this for real μ. In that case $\mu = \mu^+ - \mu^-$ (Jordan decomposition theorem), where $\mu^+ \geq 0$, $\mu^+ \perp m$, and similar statements apply to μ^-. Since $\mu^+ \perp m$, there is a Borel set A such that $\mu^+(A) = 0$ and $m(A^c) = 0$. By Lemma 2, $D\mu^+ = 0$ a.e. $[m]$. Similarly, $D\mu^- = 0$ a.e. $[m]$, and the lemma follows from Proposition 8.4.

Proof of Theorem 8.6 By Lemma 3 and the Lebesgue decomposition theorem we only need to consider the case $\mu \ll m$; also, it is enough to consider real μ. The Radon-Nikodym theorem then shows that there is a real Borel function $f \in L^1(R^k)$ such that

$$\text{(5)} \qquad \mu(E) = \int_E f(x)\,dx.$$

The theorem therefore follows from the equality

$$\text{(6)} \qquad (D\mu)(x) = f(x) \qquad \text{(a.e. } [m]),$$

which we shall now prove.

Let r be a rational number, put

$$\text{(7)} \qquad A = \{x : f(x) < r\}, \qquad B = \{x : r \leq f(x)\},$$

and define

$$\text{(8)} \qquad \lambda(E) = \int_{E \cap B} (f(x) - r)\,dx$$

for all Borel sets E in R^k. For every $E \in \Omega$,

(9) $$\mu(E) - rm(E) = \int_E (f(x) - r)\,dx \leq \lambda(E),$$

and since $(D\lambda)(x) = 0$ a.e. $[m]$ on A, by Lemma 2, we conclude from (9) that

(10) $$(\bar{D}\mu)(x) \leq r \qquad \text{(a.e. } [m] \text{ on } A).$$

In other words, if

(11) $$E_r = \{x : f(x) < r < (\bar{D}\mu)(x)\},$$

we have proved that $m(E_r) = 0$. But $f(x) < (\bar{D}\mu)(x)$ if and only if $x \in \bigcup E_r$, the union being taken over the countable set of all rational numbers. Thus

(12) $$(\bar{D}\mu)(x) \leq f(x) \qquad \text{(a.e. } [m]).$$

If we replace μ by $-\mu$, hence f by $-f$, (12) leads to $(\underline{D}\mu)(x) \geq f(x)$ a.e. $[m]$. This gives (6) and completes the proof of the theorem.

8.7 Remarks Theorem 8.6 evidently also holds if μ is defined only on the Borel sets in some open set $V \subset R^k$ (the conclusions then also just hold in V, of course), as an examination of the proof will show. Or we can simply define $\mu(E) = 0$ for all $E \subset V^c$ and apply the theorem as it stands.

If $f \in L^1(R^k)$ and

(1) $$\mu(E) = \int_E f(x)\,dx,$$

it is reasonable to call μ the *indefinite integral* of f. With this terminology, Theorem 8.6 asserts that the derivative of an indefinite integral equals the integrand a.e. $[m]$, and that every $\mu \ll m$ is the indefinite integral of its derivative. Note that this holds for *every* substantial family Ω; the exceptional set of measure 0 on which the derivative may fail to exist may of course depend on Ω.

The differentiability of indefinite integrals may be interpreted as a kind of "average continuity" of Lebesgue integrable functions. For if (1) holds, the assertion $(D\mu)(x_0) = f(x_0)$ is nothing but the statement that

(2) $$\frac{1}{m(E)} \int_E f(x)\,dx \to f(x_0)$$

as E shrinks to x_0, or that

(3) $$\frac{1}{m(E)} \int_E \{f(x) - f(x_0)\}\,dx \to 0.$$

The left side of (2) is the average of f over small neighborhoods E of x_0; the left side of (3) is the average of $f - f(x_0)$ over E.

Now (3) could be due to a cancellation effect caused by changes of sign of $f - f(x_0)$ in small neighborhoods of almost all points x_0; or a stronger statement might be true, namely, that the averages of $|f - f(x_0)|$ actually become small in small neighborhoods of almost all points x_0. The stronger result is in fact true:

8.8 Theorem *Suppose $f \in L^1(R^k)$, and Ω is a substantial family in R^k. Then*

$$\frac{1}{m(E)} \int_E |f(x) - f(x_0)|\, dx \to 0 \tag{1}$$

for almost all $x_0 \in R^k$.

More precisely, the conclusion is that to each $\epsilon > 0$ there corresponds a $\delta > 0$ such that the left side of (1) is less than ϵ for all $E \in \Omega$ such that $x_0 \in E$ and diam $E < \delta$.

PROOF Let S be a countable dense set in the complex plane. For each $r \in S$, the relation

$$\frac{1}{m(E)} \int_E |f(x) - r|\, dx \to |f(x_0) - r| \tag{2}$$

holds for almost all x_0, by Theorem 8.6. Let Q_r be the exceptional set, and put $Q = \bigcup Q_r$. Then $m(Q) = 0$. Fix $x_0 \notin Q$, and choose $\epsilon > 0$.

There exists an $r \in S$ such that $|f(x_0) - r| < \epsilon$, so

$$\frac{1}{m(E)} \int_E |f(x) - f(x_0)|\, dx \leq \frac{1}{m(E)} \int_E |f(x) - r|\, dx + \epsilon. \tag{3}$$

If we apply (2) to the integral on the right of (3), we see that the left side of (3) is less than 2ϵ for all $E \in \Omega$ which contain x_0 and whose diameter is sufficiently small. This proves (1).

Note: The set of all x_0 at which the relation (1) holds is usually called the *Lebesgue set* of f, especially when $k = 1$ and when Ω is the family of all segments in R^1.

We now turn to some results of a more special character:

8.9 Theorem *Suppose μ is a real Borel measure on R^1, $\mu \geq 0$, and $\mu \perp m$. Let Ω be the family of all open segments in R^1. Then $(D\mu)(x) = \infty$ a.e. $[\mu]$.*

Corollary *If*

$$S = \{x\colon (\bar{D}\mu)(x) > 0\} \cap \{x\colon (\underline{D}\mu)(x) < \infty\},$$

then $m(S) = \mu(S) = 0$.

PROOF There is a Borel set A, with $m(A) = 0$, on which μ is concentrated. If $0 < \alpha < \infty$, let E_α be the set of all $x \in A$ at which $(\underline{D}\mu)(x) < \alpha$, and let K be a compact subset of E_α. If we can prove that $\mu(K) = 0$, it will follow that $\mu(E_\alpha) = 0$, since μ is regular (Theorem 2.18), and this gives the desired result.

Fix $\epsilon > 0$. Since $K \subset A$, $m(K) = 0$, and K lies in an open set V with $m(V) < \epsilon$. Since $K \subset E_\alpha$, each $x \in K$ lies in a segment $I_x \subset V$ such that $\mu(I_x) < \alpha \cdot m(I_x)$. The compactness of K shows that there are points $x_1, \ldots, x_n \in K$ so that $K \subset I_{x_1} \cup \cdots \cup I_{x_n}$. If any point of R^1 lies in three segments, one of these lies in the union of the other two and can be removed without changing the union. In this way we can remove the superfluous segments I_{x_i} and arrive at a situation in which no point lies in more than two of the segments I_{x_i}. Then

$$\mu(K) \le \mu\left(\bigcup_i I_{x_i}\right) \le \sum_i \mu(I_{x_i}) < \alpha \sum_i m(I_{x_i})$$

$$\le 2\alpha m\left(\bigcup_i I_{x_i}\right) \le 2\alpha m(V) < 2\alpha\epsilon.$$

Since ϵ was arbitrary, $\mu(K) = 0$, and the proof is complete.

8.10 Examples Note that a very special property of the line was used in the preceding proof. To see that this was essential, let J be a compact interval on the line $y = x$ in R^2, let m_1 be one-dimensional Lebesgue measure on J, and define $\mu(E) = m_1(E \cap J)$ for every Borel set $E \subset R^2$. Then $\mu \perp m_2$, since $m_2(J) = 0$.

Let Ω consist of all open squares in the plane, with sides parallel to the axes. It is clear that $D\mu = 0$ at every point not in J. Each point of J lies in arbitrarily small members of Ω which intersect J in a very tiny segment. This shows that $\underline{D}\mu = 0$ at *every* point of R^2, unlike the conclusion of Theorem 8.9.

It is not hard to see that $\bar{D}\mu = \infty$ at every point of J, in this example. However, let us change Ω: Let Ω now consist of all open squares (sides parallel to the axes) which do not intersect J, plus those squares of area δ^2 (for every $\delta > 0$) which intersect J in a segment of length δ^3. This collection Ω is a substantial family, and we can verify that *the above* μ *even has* $\bar{D}\mu = 0$ *at every point of* R^2, although $\mu \perp m_2$ and $\mu \ne 0$.

This example shows that some special hypothesis on Ω is needed in the next theorem. (For an application, see Theorem 8.26.)

8.11 Theorem *Suppose μ is a real Borel measure on R^k, $\mu \ge 0$. Let Ω be the collection of all open cubes in R^k, with sides parallel to the coordinate axes. Assume $(\bar{D}\mu)(x) < \infty$ for every $x \in R^k$. Then μ is absolutely continuous with respect to Lebesgue measure.*

PROOF Assume there is a set E with $m(E) = 0$ but $\mu(E) > 0$. Put

(1) $E_n = \{x \in E: (\bar{D}\mu)(x) < n\}$ $(n = 1, 2, 3, \ldots)$.

Since $E = \bigcup E_n$, we have $\mu(E_n) > 0$ for some n. Fix this n. With the notation of Definition 8.3, put

(2) $A_j = \{x \in E_n: \bar{\Delta}_{1/j}(x) < n\}$ $(j = 1, 2, 3, \ldots)$.

Since $E_n = \bigcup A_j$, we have $\mu(A_j) > 0$ for some j. The regularity of μ (Theorem 2.18) now shows that there is a compact set $K \subset A_j$ with $\mu(K) > 0$.

Our construction shows that K has the following property: If $x \in K$, $x \in I$, $I \in \Omega$, and diam $I < 1/j$, then $\mu(I) < n \cdot m(I)$.

Let $\epsilon > 0$ be given. Since $K \subset E$, $m(K) = 0$, so there is an open set $V \supset K$ with $m(V) < \epsilon$.

Partition R^k into disjoint cubical boxes B, as in Sec. 2.19, whose diameter is less than $1/j$ and is so small that any box which intersects K lies in V. Keep those B's which intersect K, and enlarge each of them so as to obtain open cubes $I_i \supset B_i$ with $m(I_i) < 2m(B_i)$, diam $I_i < 1/j$. Then

$$\mu(K) \leq \Sigma\mu(B_i) \leq \Sigma\mu(I_i) < n \cdot \Sigma m(I_i)$$
$$< 2n \cdot \Sigma m(B_i) \leq 2n \cdot m(V) < 2n\epsilon.$$

Since ϵ was arbitrary, we have $\mu(K) = 0$, a contradiction.

Functions of Bounded Variation

8.12 Definitions We associate with each complex function f on R^1 its *total variation function* T_f defined by

(1) $$T_f(x) = \sup \sum_{j=1}^{N} |f(x_j) - f(x_{j-1})| \qquad (-\infty < x < \infty),$$

where the supremum is taken over all N and over all choices of $\{x_j\}$ such that

(2) $$-\infty < x_0 < x_1 < \cdots < x_N = x.$$

In general,

(3) $$0 \leq T_f(x) \leq T_f(y) \leq \infty \qquad (x < y).$$

If T_f is a bounded function, then (3) implies that

(4) $$V(f) = \lim_{x \to +\infty} T_f(x)$$

exists and is finite. In that case we say that f is of *bounded variation*, and we call $V(f)$ the *total variation of f;* the class of all such f will be denoted by BV.

If $-\infty < x \leq \infty$, f is said to have a *left-hand limit* at x, written $f(x-)$, if there corresponds to each $\epsilon > 0$ a real number $\alpha < x$ such that

$$(5) \qquad \alpha < t < x \quad \text{implies} \quad |f(t) - f(x-)| < \epsilon.$$

If $f(x-) = f(x)$, f is said to be *left-continuous* at x.

Right-hand limits and continuity from the right are defined similarly on $[-\infty, \infty)$.

We call a function $f \in BV$ *normalized* if $f(x) \to 0$ as $x \to -\infty$ and f is left-continuous at every point of R^1. The class of these functions will be denoted by NBV.

Instead of considering only functions defined on all of R^1 we could equally well consider functions defined on any segment or interval of R^1. Neither the preceding definitions nor the theorems which follow would be affected in any significant way.

8.13 Theorem

(*a*) *If $f \in BV$ and $x < y$, then*

$$|f(y) - f(x)| \leq T_f(y) - T_f(x).$$

(*b*) *If $f \in BV$, then $f(x-)$ exists at every point of $(-\infty, \infty]$, $f(x+)$ exists at every point of $[-\infty, \infty)$, the set of points at which f is discontinuous is at most countable, and there is a unique constant c and a unique function $g \in NBV$ such that*

$$f(x) = c + g(x)$$

at all points of continuity of f. Also, $V(g) \leq V(f)$.

(*c*) *If $f \in NBV$, then $T_f \in NBV$.*

PROOF

(*a*) If $x < y$ and $\epsilon > 0$, there are points $x_0 < x_1 < \cdots < x_n = x$ so that

$$(1) \qquad \sum_{i=1}^{n} |f(x_i) - f(x_{i-1})| > T_f(x) - \epsilon.$$

Hence

$$T_f(y) \geq |f(y) - f(x)| + \sum_{i=1}^{n} |f(x_i) - f(x_{i-1})| > |f(y) - f(x)| + T_f(x) - \epsilon.$$

This proves (*a*).

(*b*) It follows from (*a*) that if $\{x_i\}$ is a sequence for which $\{T_f(x_i)\}$ is a Cauchy sequence, then $\{f(x_i)\}$ is also a Cauchy sequence. Since monotone functions (and T_f in particular) have right- and left-hand limits at all points and since they have at most countably many discontinuities, the same therefore holds for f. Hence we can define

$$(2) \qquad c = \lim_{t \to -\infty} f(t), \qquad g(x) = f(x-) - c \qquad (x \in R^1).$$

It is clear that $g(x) \to 0$ as $x \to -\infty$. If $x \in R^1$ and $\epsilon > 0$, there exists an $\alpha < x$ such that $|f(t) - f(x-)| < \epsilon$ for all $t \in (\alpha,x)$. Since $f(t-)$ is a limit point of the set of all numbers $f(s)$, for $\alpha < s < t$, it follows that $|f(t-) - f(x-)| \leq \epsilon$ if $\alpha < t < x$. Thus g is left-continuous.

If $x_0 < x_1 < \cdots < x_n$ and $\delta > 0$, then

$$(3) \quad \sum_{i=1}^{n} |g(x_i) - g(x_{i-1})| = \lim_{\delta \to 0} \sum_{i=1}^{n} |f(x_i - \delta) - f(x_{i-1} - \delta)|,$$

and since none of the sums on the right of (3) exceeds $V(f)$, we have $V(g) \leq V(f)$. In particular, $g \in BV$.

This proves (*b*), except for the uniqueness. But if two left-continuous functions coincide on a dense subset of R^1, then they are identical. The uniqueness of g now follows easily.

(*c*) If $f \in NBV$, fix $x \in R^1$, $\epsilon > 0$, and choose points

$$x_0 < x_1 < \cdots < x_n = x$$

so that (1) holds. If $t_0 < \cdots < t_N = x_0$, then

$$(4) \qquad T_f(x) \geq \sum_{j=1}^{N} |f(t_j) - f(t_{j-1})| + \sum_{i=1}^{n} |f(x_i) - f(x_{i-1})|.$$

By (1), the first sum in (4) is less than ϵ. Hence $T_f(x_0) \leq \epsilon$, and this says that $T_f(t) \to 0$ as $t \to -\infty$.

Finally, choose t, so that $x_{n-1} < t < x_n$. Then

$$(5) \quad \sum_{i=1}^{n-1} |f(x_i) - f(x_{i-1})| + |f(t) - f(x_{n-1})| \leq T_f(t) \leq T_f(x-) \leq T_f(x).$$

If we let $t \to x_n = x$, the left side of (5) tends to the left side of (1), since $f(x) = f(x-)$, and this gives $T_f(x) - \epsilon < T_f(x-)$. Comparison with (5) now shows that $T_f(x-) = T_f(x)$, and the proof is complete.

The next theorem explains the importance of the class NBV. Observe how the correspondence between f and μ associates the total variation of f with that of μ, and how the existence of Lebesgue measure is used to construct μ in part (*b*).

8.14 Theorem

(*a*) *If* μ *is a complex Borel measure on* R^1 *and if*

(1) $$f(x) = \mu((-\infty,x)) \qquad (x \in R^1),$$

then $f \in NBV$.

(*b*) *Conversely, to every* $f \in NBV$ *there corresponds a unique complex Borel measure* μ *such that* (1) *holds; for this* μ,

(2) $$T_f(x) = |\mu|((-\infty,x)) \qquad (x \in R^1).$$

(*c*) *If* (1) *holds, then* f *is continuous precisely at those points* x *at which* $\mu(\{x\}) = 0$.

PROOF If f is defined by (1) and if $x_1 < x_2 < \cdots, x_n \to x$, then $f(x_n) \to f(x)$, since

(3) $$(-\infty,x) = \bigcup_{n=1}^{\infty} (-\infty,x_n).$$

Thus f is left-continuous. If $x_1 > x_2 > \cdots, x_n \to -\infty$, then $\bigcap(-\infty,x_n) = \emptyset$, so $f(x) \to 0$ as $x \to -\infty$, by Theorem 1.19(*e*). If $x_0 < x_1 < \cdots < x_n = x$, then

$$\sum_{i=1}^{n} |f(x_i) - f(x_{i-1})| = \sum_{i=1}^{n} |\mu([x_{i-1},x_i))| \le |\mu|((-\infty,x))$$

so that

(4) $$T_f(x) \le |\mu|((-\infty,x)).$$

This proves (*a*).

In the proof of (*b*), let us first assume that $f \in NBV$ and f is nondecreasing, $f \not\equiv 0$. Associate with each point $x \in R^1$ a set $\Phi[x]$, as follows: If f is continuous at x, $\Phi[x]$ is the point $f(x)$; if $f(x+) > f(x)$, then $\Phi[x]$ is the interval $[f(x),f(x+)]$. If $E \subset R^1$, let $\Phi[E]$ be the union of all sets $\Phi[x]$, for $x \in E$. We claim that the definition

(5) $$\mu(E) = m(\Phi[E])$$

gives us a measure which satisfies (1); here m is Lebesgue measure on R^1.

Put $J = \Phi[R^1]$. Then J is a 1-cell (i.e., a bounded interval with or without its end points). There are at most countably many points $y_i \in J$ such that $f^{-1}(y)$ consists of more than one point; for these y_i, $f^{-1}(y_i)$ is a 1-cell.

Let Σ be the class of all $E \subset R^1$ such that $\Phi[E]$ is a Borel set. If E is a 1-cell, so is $\Phi[E]$, hence $E \in \Sigma$. For any $E \subset R^1$, $\Phi[E^c]$ is the union of $J - \Phi[E]$ plus an at most countable set (a subset of $\{y_i\}$); thus $E \in \Sigma$ implies $E^c \in \Sigma$. Next,

$$\Phi[E_1 \cup E_2 \cup \cdots] = \Phi[E_1] \cup \Phi[E_2] \cup \cdots.$$

This proves that Σ is a σ-algebra which contains all segments, hence all Borel sets, so $m(\Phi[E])$ is defined for all Borel sets E. Moreover, μ is countably additive, for if $\{E_i\}$ is a disjoint collection of Borel sets in R^1, then $\{\Phi[E_i]\}$ is disjoint, except for our at most countable set $\{y_i\}$, and this does not affect the countable additivity of μ since $m(E) = 0$ for every countable set E.

Thus (5) defines a Borel measure. Since $\Phi[(-\infty,x)]$ is a 1-cell whose end points are 0 and $f(x)$, (5) shows that (1) holds.

We now turn to the general case of (*b*). If $f \in NBV$, then $f = u + iv$, u and v real, $u \in NBV$, and $T_u \in NBV$ by Theorem 8.13(*c*). Put

$$u_1 = \tfrac{1}{2}(T_u + u), \qquad u_2 = \tfrac{1}{2}(T_u - u). \tag{6}$$

Then u_1 and $u_2 \in NBV$, and they are nondecreasing; this follows easily from Theorem 8.13(*a*). The preceding construction associates measures μ_1 and μ_2 with u_1 and u_2, and $\mu_1 - \mu_2$ will be associated with $u = u_1 - u_2$. If we deal similarly with v and combine the results, we obtain a measure μ which corresponds to f in the sense that (1) holds.

If two regular measures (note Theorem 2.18) coincide on all segments of the form $(-\infty,x)$, they coincide on all 1-cells of the form $[\alpha,\beta)$, hence on all open sets, hence on all Borel sets. This proves the uniqueness assertion of (*b*).

Finally, let λ be the measure associated with T_f in the same way. If $\alpha < \beta$, then

$$\mu([\alpha,\beta)) = f(\beta) - f(\alpha), \qquad \lambda([\alpha,\beta)) = T_f(\beta) - T_f(\alpha). \tag{7}$$

The inequality

$$|\mu(E)| \leq \lambda(E) \tag{8}$$

therefore holds if $E = [\alpha,\beta)$. Since every open set in R^1 is a countable disjoint union of such 1-cells, (8) holds for every open set, hence for every Borel set. The definition of the total variation $|\mu|$ of μ now implies that $|\mu| \leq \lambda$. In particular,

$$|\mu|((-\infty,x)) \leq \lambda((-\infty,x)) = T_f(x). \tag{9}$$

Now (2) follows from (4) and (9).

The proof of (*c*) is left as an exercise.

Differentiation of Point Functions

8.15 Absolutely Continuous Functions A complex function f on R^1 is said to be *absolutely continuous* if to every $\epsilon > 0$ there corresponds a $\delta > 0$ such that

$$\sum_{i=1}^{N} (\beta_i - \alpha_i) < \delta \quad \text{implies} \quad \sum_{i=1}^{N} |f(\beta_i) - f(\alpha_i)| < \epsilon, \tag{1}$$

whenever $(\alpha_1,\beta_1), \ldots, (\alpha_N,\beta_N)$ are disjoint segments.

Observe that every absolutely continuous function is uniformly continuous (take $N = 1$) and that the restriction of any absolutely continuous function to a bounded interval is of bounded variation. However, if $f(x) = \sin x$, or if $f(x) = x + |x|$, then f is absolutely continuous, but $f \notin BV$.

The two meanings of the term "absolutely continuous" are related as follows:

8.16 Theorem *Suppose $f \in NBV$ and μ is associated with f as in Theorem 8.14. Then $\mu \ll m$ if and only if f is absolutely continuous.*

(Here m denotes Lebesgue measure on R^1.)

PROOF Suppose f is absolutely continuous. Let E be a Borel set such that $m(E) = 0$, choose $\epsilon > 0$, and choose $\delta > 0$ in accordance with Sec. 8.15. The regularity of μ shows that there are open sets $W_1 \supset W_2 \supset \cdots \supset E$ such that $m(W_1) < \delta$ and $\mu(W_n) \to \mu(E)$ as $n \to \infty$. Since W_n is a disjoint union of segments $I_j = (\alpha_j,\beta_j)$, and $\Sigma(\beta_j - \alpha_j) < \delta$, it follows that

$$|\mu(W_n)| \leq \sum_i |\mu(I_j)| = \sum_j |f(\beta_j) - f(\alpha_j)| \leq \epsilon.$$

Consequently, $\mu(E) = 0$. This proves that $\mu \ll m$.

The converse follows from Theorem 6.11.

We are now in a position to translate our earlier results on differentiation of set functions into point-function language. Theorems 8.17 to 8.19 are classical results, due to Lebesgue. Theorems 8.18 and 8.21 generalize the fundamental theorem of calculus.

8.17 Theorem *If $g \in L^1(R^1)$, and if*

$$f(x) = \int_{-\infty}^{x} g(t)\,dt \qquad (-\infty < x < \infty), \tag{1}$$

then $f \in NBV$, f is absolutely continuous, and

$$f'(x) = g(x) \text{ a.e. } [m]. \tag{2}$$

PROOF Define

(3) $$\mu(E) = \int_E g(t)\, dt$$

for every Borel set E. Then $f(x) = \mu((-\infty, x))$ and $\mu \ll m$. By Theorem 8.14, $f \in NBV$; by Theorem 8.16, f is absolutely continuous; Theorems 8.1 and 8.6 imply that

(4) $$f'(x) = (D\mu)(x) = g(x) \text{ a.e. } [m]$$

if $D\mu$ is computed relative to the family of all open segments in R^1.

8.18 Theorem *If $f \in NBV$, then f is differentiable a.e. $[m]$, $f' \in L^1(R^1)$, and there is a function $f_s \in NBV$ with $f_s'(x) = 0$ a.e. $[m]$ such that*

(1) $$f(x) = f_s(x) + \int_{-\infty}^{x} f'(t)\, dt \qquad (-\infty < x < \infty);$$

$f_s = 0$ if and only if f is absolutely continuous; if f is nondecreasing, so is f_s.

We call f_s the *singular part* of f. It is a perhaps unexpected fact that there exist continuous singular functions which are not constant. Examples are given in Sec. 8.20(*b*). The word "singular" as applied to measures has its origin in this phenomenon.

PROOF By Theorem 8.14 there is a complex measure μ on R^1 such that $\mu((-\infty, x)) = f(x)$. By Theorem 8.6,

(2) $$\mu(E) = \mu_s(E) + \int_E (D\mu)(t)\, dt,$$

where $D\mu$ is computed relative to the open segments in R^1. Put

(3) $$f_s(x) = \mu_s((-\infty, x)) \qquad (-\infty < x < \infty).$$

Theorems 8.6 and 8.1 show that $f_s'(x) = 0$ a.e. $[m]$ and that

$$f'(x) = (D\mu)(x) \text{ a.e. } [m].$$

Hence (1) follows from (2) if we take $E = (-\infty, x)$.

By Theorem 8.16, f is absolutely continuous if and only if $\mu \ll m$, i.e., if and only if $\mu_s = 0$.

Finally, if f is nondecreasing, then $\mu \geq 0$, hence $\mu_s \geq 0$, hence f_s is nondecreasing.

8.19 Theorem *If $f \in BV$, then f is differentiable a.e. $[m]$, and $f' \in L^1(R^1)$.*

PROOF By Theorem 8.13, there exists a $g \in NBV$ such that

$$f(x) = g(x) + c$$

at all points of continuity of f. Theorem 8.18 applies to g. Hence the following lemma (with $h = f - g$) implies the theorem:

Lemma *If $h \in BV$ and $h(x) = 0$ except on an at most countable set, then $h'(x) = 0$ a.e.*

To prove the lemma, let $S = \{x_i\}$ be the at most countable set at which $h(x_i) = c_i \neq 0$. Since $h \in BV$, it is easily seen that $\Sigma|c_i| < \infty$. Fix k, and let A_k be the set of all $x \notin S$ at which

$$\left| \frac{h(y) - h(x)}{y - x} \right| > \frac{1}{k} \tag{1}$$

for infinitely many y. Thus $x \in A_k$ if and only if $|x - x_i| < k|c_i|$ for infinitely many i. If J_i is the segment with center at x_i and length $2k|c_i|$, it follows that

$$\sum m(J_i) = 2k \sum |c_i| < \infty, \tag{2}$$

and hence $m(A_k) = 0$ for $k = 1, 2, 3, \ldots$, by Theorem 1.41.

But if $x \notin S \cup A_1 \cup A_2 \cup A_3 \cup \cdots$, then $h'(x) = 0$. This completes the proof.

Exercises 5 and 6 are relevant to this lemma.

8.20 Examples The preceding theorems show that the equation

$$f(x) - f(a) = \int_a^x f'(t)\, dt \tag{1}$$

(in which the right side is a Lebesgue integral) holds for all x in some interval $[a,b]$ if and only if f is absolutely continuous on $[a,b]$. One may ask whether the existence of f' implies the absolute continuity of f. Put this way, the question is not precise enough. We shall give two examples which show how (1) can fail, and then give a theorem in which (1) is deduced from another set of sufficient conditions.

(*a*) Put $f(x) = x^2 \sin(x^{-2})$ if $x \neq 0$, $f(0) = 0$. Then f is differentiable at every point, but

$$\int_0^1 |f'(t)|\, dt = \infty, \tag{2}$$

so $f' \notin L^1$. Also, $f \notin BV$ on $[0,1]$.

If we interpret the integral in (1) (with $[0,1]$ in place of $[a,b]$) as the limit, as $\epsilon \to 0$, of the integrals over $[\epsilon,1]$, then (1) still holds for this f.

More complicated situations can arise where this kind of passage to the limit is of no use. There are integration processes, due to Denjoy and Perron (see [18], [28]), which are so designed that (1) holds whenever f is differentiable at every point. These fail to have the property that the integrability of f implies that of $|f|$, and therefore do not play such an important role in analysis.

(*b*) Suppose f is continuous on $[a,b]$, f is differentiable at almost every point of $[a,b]$, and $f' \in L^1$ on $[a,b]$. Do these assumptions imply that (1) holds?

Answer: No.

Choose $\{\delta_n\}$ so that $1 = \delta_0 > \delta_1 > \delta_2 > \cdots, \delta_n \to 0$. Put $E_0 = [0,1]$. Suppose $n \geq 0$ and E_n is constructed so that E_n is the union of 2^n disjoint closed intervals, each of length $2^{-n}\delta_n$. Delete a segment in the center of each of these 2^n intervals, so that each of the remaining 2^{n+1} intervals has length $2^{-n-1}\delta_{n+1}$ (this is possible, since $\delta_{n+1} < \delta_n$), and let E_{n+1} be the union of these 2^{n+1} intervals. Then $E_1 \supset E_2 \supset \cdots, m(E_n) = \delta_n$, and if

$$E = \bigcap_{n=1}^{\infty} E_n, \tag{3}$$

then E is compact and $m(E) = 0$. (In fact, E is perfect.) Put

$$g_n = \delta_n^{-1}\chi_{E_n} \quad \text{and} \quad f_n(x) = \int_0^x g_n(t)\,dt \qquad (n = 0, 1, 2, \ldots). \tag{4}$$

Then $f_n(0) = 0$, $f_n(1) = 1$, and each f_n is a monotonic function which is constant on each segment in the complement of E_n. If I is one of the 2^n intervals whose union is E_n, then

$$\int_I g_n(t)\,dt = \int_I g_{n+1}(t)\,dt = 2^{-n}. \tag{5}$$

It follows from (5) that

$$f_{n+1}(x) = f_n(x) \qquad (x \notin E_n) \tag{6}$$

and that

$$|f_n(x) - f_{n+1}(x)| \leq \int_I |g_n - g_{n+1}| < 2^{-n+1} \qquad (x \in E_n). \tag{7}$$

Hence $\{f_n\}$ converges uniformly to a continuous monotonic function f, with $f(0) = 0$, $f(1) = 1$, and $f'(x) = 0$ for all $x \notin E$. Since $m(E) = 0$, we have $f' = 0$ a.e.

Thus (1) fails. Incidentally, we have now constructed examples of continuous singular functions as defined after the statement of Theorem 8.18.

If $\delta_n = (2/3)^n$, the set E is Cantor's "middle thirds" set.

8.21 Theorem *Suppose f is a real function on $[a,b]$ which is differentiable at every point of $[a,b]$, and assume that $f' \in L^1$ on $[a,b]$. Then*

$$f(x) - f(a) = \int_a^x f'(t)\,dt \qquad (a \leq x \leq b). \tag{1}$$

Note that differentiability is assumed to hold at *every* point of $[a,b]$.

PROOF It is clear that it is enough to prove this for $x = b$. Fix $\epsilon > 0$. Theorem 2.24 ensures the existence of a lower semicontinuous function g on $[a,b]$ such that $g > f'$ and

$$(2) \qquad \int_a^b g(t)\, dt < \int_a^b f'(t)\, dt + \epsilon.$$

Actually, Theorem 2.24 only gives $g \geq f'$, but since $m([a,b]) < \infty$, we can add a small constant to g without affecting (2). For any $\eta > 0$, define

$$(3) \quad F_\eta(x) = \int_a^x g(t)\, dt - f(x) + f(a) + \eta(x - a) \qquad (a \leq x \leq b).$$

Keep η fixed for the moment. To each $x \in [a,b)$ there corresponds a $\delta_x > 0$ such that

$$(4) \qquad g(t) > f'(x) \qquad \text{and} \qquad \frac{f(t) - f(x)}{t - x} < f'(x) + \eta$$

for all $t \in (x, x + \delta_x)$, since g is lower semicontinuous and $g(x) > f'(x)$. For any such t we therefore have

$$F_\eta(t) - F_\eta(x) = \int_x^t g(s)\, ds - [f(t) - f(x)] + \eta(t - x)$$
$$> (t - x)f'(x) - (t - x)[f'(x) + \eta] + \eta(t - x) = 0.$$

Since $F_\eta(a) = 0$ and F_η is *continuous*, there is a last point $x \in [a,b]$ at which $F_\eta(x) = 0$. If $x < b$, the preceding computation implies that $F_\eta(t) > 0$ for $t \in (x,b]$. In any case, $F_\eta(b) \geq 0$. Since this holds for every $\eta > 0$, (2) and (3) now give

$$(5) \qquad f(b) - f(a) \leq \int_a^b g(t)\, dt < \int_a^b f'(t)\, dt + \epsilon,$$

and since ϵ was arbitrary, we conclude that

$$(6) \qquad f(b) - f(a) \leq \int_a^b f'(t)\, dt.$$

If f satisfies the hypotheses of the theorem, so does $-f$; therefore (6) holds with $-f$ in place of f, and these two inequalities together give (1).

Differentiable Transformations

8.22 Definitions With any $x = (\xi_1, \ldots, \xi_k) \in R^k$ we associate the norm

$$(1) \qquad \|x\| = \max (|\xi_1|, \ldots, |\xi_k|).$$

This norm is better adapted for dealing with cubes than is the ordinary euclidean norm

$$(2) \qquad \|x\|_2 = (\xi_1^2 + \cdots + \xi_k^2)^{\frac{1}{2}}.$$

Since $\|x\| \le \|x\|_2 \le \sqrt{k}\,\|x\|$, the metrics induced by these two norms give rise to the same topology on R^k. In particular, $\|x_n\| \to 0$ as $n \to \infty$ if and only if $\|x_n\|_2 \to 0$.

Suppose V is an open set in R^k, T is a mapping of V into R^k, $x \in V$, and A is a linear operator on R^k (i.e., a linear mapping of R^k into R^k, as in Definition 2.1). If to every $\epsilon > 0$ there exists a $\delta > 0$ such that the inequality

$$(3) \qquad \|T(x+h) - T(x) - Ah\| \le \epsilon\|h\|$$

holds for all $h \in R^k$ with $\|h\| < \delta$, we say that T is *differentiable* at x, and define

$$(4) \qquad T'(x) = A.$$

The linear operator $T'(x)$ is called the *derivative* of T at x. The term *differential* is also very frequently used for $T'(x)$; then, rather than say that T is differentiable at x, one says that T *has a differential* at x, or that the differential of T exists at x.

Neither the differentiability of T nor the value of $T'(x)$ is affected by replacing the norm (1) by the norm (2) in (3).

We say that T is *differentiable in* V if T is differentiable at every point of V. In that case there corresponds to each $x \in V$ a linear operator $T'(x)$; for fixed x and small h, $T(x+h) - T(x)$ is approximated by $T'(x)h$, a *linear* function of h, in the sense of (3).

Since every real number α can be interpreted as a linear operator on R^1 (mapping t to αt), the above definition of $T'(x)$ coincides with the usual one when $k = 1$.

With each linear operator A on R^k we associate the number

$$(5) \qquad \Delta(A) = m(A(Q))$$

where m is Lebesgue measure on R^k and Q is the unit cube: $x \in Q$ if and only if $0 \le \xi_i < 1$ for $1 \le i \le k$.

8.23 Remark If A is a linear operator on R^k, then

$$(1) \qquad A'(x) = A \qquad (x \in R^k),$$

and if we define

$$(2) \qquad \mu(E) = m(A(E))$$

for all Borel sets E, then μ is translation invariant, since

$$\mu(E + x) = m(A(E + x)) = m(A(E) + Ax) = m(A(E)) = \mu(E).$$

It follows from Theorem 2.20(*d*) that

$$(3) \qquad \mu(E) = \Delta(A)m(E)$$

and hence that

$$(4)\qquad (D\mu)(x) = \Delta(A'(x)) \qquad (x \in R^k).$$

Since every differentiable transformation can be locally approximated by a constant plus a linear transformation, we may conjecture that (4) extends to differentiable transformations, under suitable conditions. This is indeed the case. We first state the result without any reference to any induced measure μ.

8.24 Theorem *Suppose T is a continuous open mapping of an open set $V \subset R^k$ into R^k, and suppose that T is differentiable at some point $x \in V$. Then to every $\epsilon > 0$ there corresponds a $\delta > 0$ such that*

$$(1)\qquad \left| \frac{m(T(C))}{m(C)} - \Delta(T'(x)) \right| < \epsilon$$

for every open cube C, with edges parallel to the axes and of length less than δ, which contains x.

PROOF We assume, without loss of generality, that $x = 0$ and $T(x) = 0$. Put $A = T'(0)$.

The following elementary fact about linear operators on finite-dimensional vector spaces will be used (for a proof, see any book on linear algebra): *A linear operator A on R^k is one-to-one if and only if the range of A is all of R^k.* In this case, the inverse A^{-1} of A is a linear operator on R^k, and A is said to be *nonsingular* or *invertible.*

The proof conveniently splits into two cases.

CASE 1 *A is nonsingular.* Consider the mapping S defined by

$$(2)\qquad S(x) = A^{-1}T(x) \qquad (x \in V).$$

It is clear that S is continuous and open and that $S'(0) = A^{-1}T'(0) = I$, the identity operator. We shall prove that then

$$(3)\qquad \left| \frac{m(S(C))}{m(C)} - 1 \right| < \epsilon$$

for all sufficiently small C which contain 0.

Since $T(x) = AS(x)$, we have

$$(4)\qquad m(T(C)) = m(A(S(C))) = \Delta(A)m(S(C)),$$

by 8.23(3). Hence (3) will give the desired result.

Fix $\eta > 0$ so that $\eta < \frac{1}{4}$ and

$$(5)\qquad 1 - \epsilon < (1 - 2\eta)^k < (1 + 2\eta)^k < 1 + \epsilon.$$

Since $S(0) = 0$ and $S'(0) = I$ there exists a $\delta > 0$ such that

$$(6)\qquad \|S(x) - x\| \le \eta\|x\| \qquad \text{if } \|x\| < \delta.$$

Let C be an open cube which contains 0 and whose edges are parallel to the axes and have length $\lambda < \delta$. Let C_1 and C_2 be open cubes concentric with C whose edges have lengths

$$\lambda_1 = (1 - 2\eta)\lambda, \qquad \lambda_2 = (1 + 2\eta)\lambda. \tag{7}$$

Note that (6) implies

$$\|S(x) - x\| < \eta\lambda \qquad (x \in \bar{C}), \tag{8}$$

where $\bar{C}$ is the closure of C.

If $x \in C$, (8) shows that $S(x) \in C_2$. Thus $S(C) \subset C_2$.

Our next objective is to prove that $C_1 \subset S(C)$. Put

$$E_1 = C_1 \cap S(C), \qquad E_2 = C_1 - S(C). \tag{9}$$

By (8), S maps no boundary point of C into C_1. Hence we could replace C by $\bar{C}$ in (9) without affecting the definitions of E_1 and E_2. Since C_1 is open and $S(\bar{C})$ is compact, we see that E_2 is open. Since $\eta < \frac{1}{4}$, (8) shows that S maps the center of C into C_1, so that E_1 is not empty. Finally, S is assumed to be an open mapping, so that $S(C)$ is open, and therefore E_1 is open. So C_1 is the union of two disjoint open sets E_1 and E_2, and $E_1 \neq \emptyset$. But C_1 is a connected set (every convex set in R^k is connected) and is therefore not the union of two disjoint nonempty open sets. We conclude that $E_2 = \emptyset$, hence $E_1 = C_1$, and this gives $C_1 \subset S(C)$.

We have now proved that $C_1 \subset S(C) \subset C_2$. Hence

$$(1 - 2\eta)^k \leq \frac{m(S(C))}{m(C)} \leq (1 + 2\eta)^k, \tag{10}$$

and (3) follows from (5).

This completes the proof in Case 1.

CASE 2 *A is singular.* In this case A maps R^k into a subspace of lower dimension, i.e., into a set of measure 0. In particular,

$$\Delta(A) = m(A(Q)) = 0. \tag{11}$$

If $\epsilon > 0$ is given, there exists an $\eta > 0$ such that $m(E_\eta) < \epsilon$ if E_η is the set of all points whose distance from $A(Q)$ is less than η. Since $A = T'(0)$, there exists a $\delta > 0$ such that

$$\|T(x) - Ax\| \leq \eta\|x\| \qquad \text{if } \|x\| < \delta. \tag{12}$$

Let C be an open cube as in Case 1, with edge of length $\lambda < \delta$. Then $\|T(x) - Ax\| < \eta\lambda$ for all $x \in C$, which means that $T(C)$ lies in the set E which consists of those points whose distance from $A(C)$ is less than $\eta\lambda$. Our choice of η shows that $m(E) < \epsilon\lambda^k$. Hence

$$\frac{m(T(C))}{m(C)} \leq \frac{m(E)}{m(C)} = \frac{m(E)}{\lambda^k} < \epsilon \tag{13}$$

as soon as $\lambda < \delta$; and since $\Delta(A) = 0$, we have proved that (1) holds also in Case 2.

The proof is now complete.

8.25 Remarks The preceding theorem is true, but harder to prove, if the first "open" is deleted from the hypotheses. We used the openness of T only to prove the following: If C and C_1 are concentric cubes, C_1 inside C, if the distance between corresponding faces of C and C_1 is ϵ, and if T moves no point of C by as much as ϵ, then $T(C) \supset C_1$. This is true for continuous T, but the proof depends on a deeper knowledge of the topology of R^k than we wish to assume here.

It should also be pointed out that if we assume that T is continuously differentiable, i.e., if we assume that $x \to T'(x)$ is a continuous mapping of V into the space of all linear operators on R^k, then the inverse function theorem ([26], Theorem 9.17) guarantees that T is open provided that $T'(x)$ is nonsingular. So "open" can be deleted from the hypotheses if we assume that T' is continuous.

In the application which follows, *existence* of $T'(x)$ is assumed, but no continuity assumption is imposed on T'. The topological assumptions imposed on T circumvent measurability difficulties.

8.26 Theorem *Suppose T is a differentiable mapping of an open set $V \subset R^k$ onto a bounded open set $W \subset R^k$. Suppose also that T is one-to-one and that the inverse of T is continuous. Then*

(*a*) *$T(E)$ is a Borel set for every Borel set $E \subset V$.*

(*b*) *If E is Lebesgue measurable, so is $T(E)$.*

(*c*) *If $\mu(E) = m(T(E))$, then μ is a positive bounded Borel measure on V, and for every $x \in V$*

$$(D\mu)(x) = \Delta(T'(x))$$

provided that $D\mu$ is computed relative to the collection of all open cubes with sides parallel to the coordinate axes.

(*d*) *$\mu \ll m$, and*

$$m(T(E)) = \int_E \Delta(T'(x))\, dx$$

for every Lebesgue measurable set $E \subset V$.

(*e*) *More generally, if $f \in L^1(W)$, we have*

$$\int_W f(y)\, dy = \int_V f(T(x))\, \Delta(T'(x))\, dx.$$

PROOF Since the inverse of T is continuous, $T(E)$ is open if E is open; the collection of all $E \subset V$ such that $T(E)$ is a Borel set is a σ-algebra in V; this implies (*a*).

If μ is defined as in (*c*), the countable additivity of μ follows from that of m, since T is one-to-one. Since $m(W) < \infty$, μ is bounded. The equation in (*c*) is just Theorem 8.24. Now Theorem 8.11 implies that $\mu \ll m$, and the equation in (*d*) follows from Theorem 8.6, for all Borel sets E. But if E is a Borel set and $m(E) = 0$, then also $m(T(E)) = 0$; it follows that $T(A)$ is Lebesgue measurable for all Lebesgue measurable sets $A \subset V$ with $m(A) = 0$ and that $m(T(A)) = 0$ in this case. This completes the proof of (*d*) and also establishes (*b*).

It remains to prove (*e*). If A is a Borel set in W and $E = T^{-1}(A)$, then E is a Borel set, $\chi_E(x) = \chi_A(T(x))$, so (*d*) implies that

$$\int_W \chi_A(y)\,dy = m(A) = m(T(E)) = \int_V \chi_A(T(x))\,\Delta(T'(x))\,dx.$$

Thus (*e*) holds if $f = \chi_A$, hence if f is any simple Borel function, and the general case follows.

8.27 Jacobians The change-of-variables formula 8.26(*e*) is usually stated in the form

$$\int_{T(V)} f(y)\,dy = \int_V f(T(x))|J_T(x)|\,dx \tag{1}$$

where $J_T(x)$ is the *Jacobian* of T at x. By definition, this is the determinant of the linear operator $T'(x)$. The equivalence of the two formulas will be established if we show that

$$\Delta(T'(x)) = |J_T(x)|, \tag{2}$$

and this is clearly a consequence of the following result.

8.28 Theorem *If A is a linear operator on R^k and if $\Delta(A)$ is the scale factor associated with A, so that*

$$m(A(E)) = \Delta(A)m(E) \tag{1}$$

for every measurable set E, then

$$\Delta(A) = |\det A|. \tag{2}$$

We chose to formulate and prove Theorems 8.24 and 8.26 in terms of the geometrically defined quantity $\Delta(A)$ in order to stress the geometric and measure-theoretic aspects of these theorems. That $\Delta(A)$ also happens to be the absolute value of the determinant of (a matrix associated with) A is additional information, of an algebraic nature, which is obviously important for computational reasons. However, earlier introduction of this determinant would not have simplified our work.

PROOF Let $\{e_1, \ldots, e_k\}$ be the standard basis for R^k: the ith coordinate of e_j is 1 if $i = j$, 0 if $i \neq j$. If A is a linear operator on R^k and

$$Ae_j = \sum_{i=1}^{k} \alpha_{ij} e_i \qquad (1 \le j \le k), \tag{3}$$

then det A is, by definition, the determinant of the matrix $[A]$ which has α_{ij} in the ith row and jth column.

If $A = A_1A_2$, (1) implies that $\Delta(A) = \Delta(A_1)\,\Delta(A_2)$, and the multiplication theorem for determinants therefore shows that if (2) holds for A_1 and A_2, then (2) also holds for A. Since every linear operator A on R^k is a product of finitely many operators of the following three types, it is sufficient to establish (2) for each of these:

(I) $\{Ae_1, \ldots ,Ae_k\}$ is a permutation of $\{e_1, \ldots ,e_k\}$.
(II) $Ae_1 = \alpha e_1$, $Ae_i = e_i$ for $i = 2, \ldots, k$.
(III) $Ae_1 = e_1 + e_2$, $Ae_i = e_i$ for $i = 2, \ldots, k$.

If A is of type (I), then $[A]$ has exactly one 1 in each row and each column and has 0 in all other places. So det $A = \pm 1$. If Q is the unit cube, then $A(Q) = Q$, hence $\Delta(A) = 1 = |\det A|$.

If A is of type (II), then clearly $\Delta(A) = |\alpha| = |\det A|$.

If A is of type (III), then det $A = 1$, and $A(Q)$ is the set of all points $\Sigma\xi_i e_i$ whose coordinates satisfy

$$\text{(4)} \qquad \xi_1 \le \xi_2 < \xi_1 + 1, \qquad 0 \le \xi_i < 1 \qquad \text{if } i \ne 2.$$

If S_1 is the set of those points in $A(Q)$ which have $\xi_2 < 1$ and if S_2 is the rest of $A(Q)$, then

$$\text{(5)} \qquad S_1 \cup (S_2 - e_2) = Q,$$

where $S_2 - e_2$ is a translate of S_2. Hence

$$\Delta(A) = m(S_1 \cup S_2) = m(S_1) + m(S_2 - e_2) = m(Q) = 1.$$

This completes the proof.

Exercises

1 The *symmetric derivative* of a complex Borel measure μ on R^k is defined to be

$$(D_{sym}\mu)(x) = \lim_{r\to 0} \frac{\mu(B(x;r))}{m(B(x;r))},$$

where $B(x;r)$ is the open ball in R^k with center at x and radius r. Prove that Theorem 8.6 implies the analogous theorem for D_{sym}.

2 Suppose $\{\mu_n\}$ is a sequence of positive Borel measures on R^k and

$$\mu(E) = \sum_{n=1}^{\infty} \mu_n(E).$$

Assume $\mu(R^k) < \infty$. Show that μ is a Borel measure. What is the relation between the Lebesgue decompositions of the μ_n and that of μ? Prove that

$$(D\mu)(x) = \sum_{n=1}^{\infty} (D\mu_n)(x) \qquad \text{a.e.}$$

3 Suppose each f_n is a positive nondecreasing function on R^1, and

$$f(x) = \sum_{n=1}^{\infty} f_n(x) < \infty$$

for all x. Prove that

$$f'(x) = \sum_{n=1}^{\infty} f_n'(x) \qquad \text{a.e.}$$

4 Construct a continuous monotonic function f on R^1 so that f is not constant on any segment although $f'(x) = 0$ a.e.

5 If f is as in the Lemma to Theorem 8.19, can there be an uncountable set E such that f is not differentiable at any point of E?

6 Suppose $\{c_i\}$ is a sequence of complex numbers such that $\Sigma|c_i| = \infty$. Show that there are segments $J_i = (x_i - c_i,\ x_i + c_i)$ such that $x_i \neq x_j$ if $i \neq j$, $\{x_i\}$ is dense in R^1, and every $x \in R^1$ lies in infinitely many J_i. Put $f(x_i) = c_i$ $(i = 1, 2, 3, \ldots)$, $f(x) = 0$ for all other x. Prove that f is nowhere differentiable.

7 Suppose E is a compact set in R^1 (or R^k) without isolated points (a *perfect* set). Show that E is the support (see Chap. 2, Exercise 11, for the definition) of a *continuous* positive Borel measure μ. If $m(E) = 0$, this gives examples of singular measures.

8 Suppose $E \subset [a,b]$, $m(E) = 0$. Construct an absolutely continuous monotonic function f on $[a,b]$ such that $f'(x) = +\infty$ for every $x \in E$. *Suggestion:* $E \subset \bigcap V_n$, $m(V_n) < 2^{-n}$, V_n open. Consider the sum of the χ_{V_n}.

9 Show that the product of two absolutely continuous functions on $[a,b]$ is absolutely continuous. Use this to derive a theorem about integration by parts.

10 If f is a real function on $[0,1]$ and

$$\gamma(t) = t + if(t),$$

the length of the graph of f is, by definition, the total variation of γ on $[0,1]$. Show that this length is finite if and only if $f \in BV$. Suppose $f(0) = 0$, f is continuous and nondecreasing, and f_s is the singular part of f (see Theorem 8.18). Prove that the length of the graph of f is

$$f_s(1) + \int_0^1 \sqrt{1 + [f'(t)]^2}\, dt.$$

How does this formula change if $f \in BV$ but f is not necessarily monotonic? How long is the graph of the function constructed in Example 8.20(*b*)?

11 If E is a Lebesgue measurable set in R^1, the upper and lower limits of the quotients

$$\frac{m(E \cap (x - \delta, x + \delta))}{2\delta}$$

are called the upper and lower densities of E at x, $\bar{D}_E(x)$ and $\underline{D}_E(x)$. If these are equal, their common value $D_E(x)$ is the *density* (sometimes called the *metric density*) of E at x. If $D_E(x) = 1$, x is a *point of density* of E.

Prove that $D_E(x) = 1$ at almost all $x \in E$ and that $D_E(x) = 0$ at almost all $x \notin E$.

Construct a set E such that $\underline{D}_E(0) \neq \bar{D}_E(0)$. Can it happen that $\underline{D}_E(0) = 0$ and $\bar{D}_E(0) = 1$?

12 If $A \subset R^1$ and $B \subset R^1$, put $A + B = \{a + b\colon a \in A,\ b \in B\}$. Suppose $m(A) > 0$ and $m(B) > 0$, and prove that $A + B$ contains a segment.

Suggestion: Either use the existence of points of density in A and B, or assume $m(A) < \infty$, $m(B) < \infty$, and show that the convolution of χ_A and χ_B is a continuous function whose integral over R^1 is not 0.

Let C be Cantor's middle thirds set and show that $C + C$ is an interval, although $m(C) = 0$.

Extend these results to sets in R^k.

13 Show (with the aid of the Hausdorff maximality theorem) that there exist real *discontinuous* functions f on R^1 such that

$$f(x + y) = f(x) + f(y) \tag{1}$$

for all x and $y \in R^1$.

Show that if (1) holds and f is Lebesgue measurable, then f is continuous.

Show that if (1) holds and the graph of f is not dense in the plane, then f is continuous.

Find all continuous functions which satisfy (1).

14 For $f \in L^\infty(R^1)$, define $f_t(x) = f(x - t)$, and assume that

$$\lim_{t \to 0} \|f_t - f\|_\infty = 0.$$

The norm is the *essential* supremum. Prove that under these conditions there is a *uniformly continuous* function g on R^1 such that $g(x) = f(x)$ a.e.

Suggestion: Put $h_n(t) = n$ if $|t| < 1/(2n)$, $h_n(t) = 0$ otherwise, and let g_n be the convolution $f * h_n$. Prove that $g_n(x) \to f(x)$ a.e. and that

$$|g_n(x + t) - g_n(x)| \leq \|f_t - f\|_\infty.$$

Exploit the equicontinuity of the sequence $\{g_n\}$ ([26], Theorem 7.23).

15 Show that there is at most one operator A which satisfies the requirements for $T'(x)$ in Definition 8.22.

16 Show that Lebesgue measure on R^k is rotation invariant.

17 Construct a monotonic function on R^1 whose derivative exists at every point but is not a continuous function on R^1.

18 Suppose G is a subgroup of R^1 (relative to addition), $G \neq R^1$, and G is Lebesgue measurable. Prove that then $m(G) = 0$. (Compare with Exercise 12.)

19 Call t a *period* of the function f on R^1 if $f(x + t) = f(x)$ for all $x \in R^1$. Suppose f is a real Lebesgue measurable function with periods s and t such that s/t is irrational. Prove that there is a constant λ such that $f(x) = \lambda$ a.e., but that f need not be constant. *Hint:* The periods of f form a dense set. Look at points of density of the sets $E_\alpha = \{x: f(x) > \alpha\}$, for real α.

20 Suppose f is a real function on the rectangle determined by the inequalities $a \leq x \leq b$ and $A \leq y \leq B$. Find conditions on f (make them as weak as you can) under which the following statement makes sense and is correct ($D_1 f$ denotes the partial derivative of f with respect to the first variable, x): If

$$g(x) = \int_A^B f(x,y)\, dy,$$

then
$$g(x) = \int_A^B dy\, [f(a,y) + \int_a^x (D_1 f)(t,y)\, dt]$$

$$= \int_a^x dt \int_A^B (D_1 f)(t,y)\, dy + \int_A^B f(a,y)\, dy,$$

so that
$$g'(x) = \int_A^B (D_1 f)(x,y)\, dy.$$

See also under what conditions you can derive the last formula by direct consideration of the quotients $[g(t) - g(x)]/(t - x)$.

21 Suppose f is a continuous complex function on $[a,b]$ with total variation V. Prove that to each $W < V$ there corresponds a $\delta > 0$ with the following property: If $a = x_0 < x_1 < \cdots < x_n = b$ and if $|x_i - x_{i-1}| < \delta$ for $i = 1, \ldots, n$, then

$$\sum_{i=1}^{n} |f(x_i) - f(x_{i-1})| > W.$$

22 Suppose f is a continuous *real* function on $[a,b]$. For each real y, let $M(y)$ be the number (finite or infinite) of points x on $[a,b]$ at which $f(x) = y$. (M may be called the *multiplicity function* of f.) Prove that M is a Borel function and that $\int M(y)\,dy$ is the total variation of f on $[a,b]$.

Hint: The result is clear for functions whose graph is a finite union of straight line intervals. Approximate f by a suitably chosen sequence of such functions. (Their multiplicity functions should increase to that of f.) Use Exercise 21.

23 Is every left-continuous complex function f on R^1 a Borel function? If V is open, what can you say about $f^{-1}(V)$?

9

Fourier Transforms

Formal Properties

9.1 Definitions In this chapter we shall depart from the previous notation and use the letter m not for Lebesgue measure on R^1 but for Lebesgue measure divided by $\sqrt{2\pi}$. This convention simplifies the appearance of results such as the inversion theorem and the Plancherel theorem. Accordingly, we shall use the notation

$$\int_{-\infty}^{\infty} f(x)\, dm(x) = \frac{1}{\sqrt{2\pi}} \int_{-\infty}^{\infty} f(x)\, dx, \tag{1}$$

where dx refers to ordinary Lebesgue measure, and we define

$$\|f\|_p = \left\{\int_{-\infty}^{\infty} |f(x)|^p\, dm(x)\right\}^{1/p} \qquad (1 \leq p < \infty), \tag{2}$$

$$(f * g)(x) = \int_{-\infty}^{\infty} f(x - y)g(y)\, dm(y) \qquad (x \in R^1), \tag{3}$$

and

$$\hat{f}(t) = \int_{-\infty}^{\infty} f(x)e^{-ixt}\, dm(x) \qquad (t \in R^1). \tag{4}$$

Throughout this chapter, we shall write L^p in place of $L^p(R^1)$, and C_0 will denote the space of all continuous functions on R^1 which vanish at infinity.

If $f \in L^1$, the integral (4) is well defined for every real t. The function $\hat{f}$ is called the *Fourier transform* of f. Note that the term "Fourier transform" is also applied to the *mapping* which takes f to $\hat{f}$.

The formal properties which are listed in Theorem 9.2 depend intimately on the translation invariance of m and on the fact that for each real α the mapping $x \to e^{i\alpha x}$ is a *character* of the additive group R^1. By definition, a function φ is a character of R^1 if $|\varphi(t)| = 1$ and if

$$\varphi(s + t) = \varphi(s)\varphi(t) \tag{5}$$

for all real s and t. In other words, φ is to be a homomorphism of the additive group R^1 into the multiplicative group of the complex numbers of absolute value 1. We shall see later (in the proof of Theorem 9.23) that every continuous character of R^1 is given by an exponential.

9.2 Theorem *Suppose $f \in L^1$, and α and λ are real numbers.*

(a) *If $g(x) = f(x)e^{i\alpha x}$, then $\hat{g}(t) = \hat{f}(t - \alpha)$.*
(b) *If $g(x) = f(x - \alpha)$, then $\hat{g}(t) = \hat{f}(t)e^{-i\alpha t}$.*
(c) *If $g \in L^1$ and $h = f * g$, then $\hat{h}(t) = \hat{f}(t)\hat{g}(t)$.*

Thus the Fourier transform converts multiplication by a character into translation, and vice versa, and it converts convolutions to pointwise products.

(d) *If $g(x) = \overline{f(-x)}$, then $\hat{g}(t) = \overline{\hat{f}(t)}$.*
(e) *If $g(x) = f(x/\lambda)$ and $\lambda > 0$, then $\hat{g}(t) = \lambda\hat{f}(\lambda t)$.*
(f) *If $g(x) = -ixf(x)$ and $g \in L^1$, then $\hat{f}$ is differentiable and $\hat{f}'(t) = \hat{g}(t)$.*

PROOF (a), (b), (d), and (e) are proved by direct substitution into formula 9.1(4). The proof of (c) is an application of Fubini's theorem (see Theorem 7.14 for the required measurability proof):

$$\begin{aligned}\hat{h}(t) &= \int_{-\infty}^{\infty} e^{-itx}\, dm(x) \int_{-\infty}^{\infty} f(x - y)g(y)\, dm(y)\\ &= \int_{-\infty}^{\infty} g(y)e^{-ity}\, dm(y) \int_{-\infty}^{\infty} f(x - y)e^{-it(x-y)}\, dm(x)\\ &= \int_{-\infty}^{\infty} g(y)e^{-ity}\, dm(y) \int_{-\infty}^{\infty} f(x)e^{-itx}\, dm(x)\\ &= \hat{g}(t)\hat{f}(t).\end{aligned}$$

Note how the translation invariance of m was used.

To prove (f), note that

$$(1)\qquad \frac{\hat{f}(s) - \hat{f}(t)}{s - t} = \int_{-\infty}^{\infty} f(x)e^{-ixt}\varphi(x, s - t)\, dm(x) \qquad (s \neq t),$$

where $\varphi(x,u) = (e^{-ixu} - 1)/u$. Since $|\varphi(x,u)| \leq |x|$ for all real $u \neq 0$ and since $\varphi(x,u) \to -ix$ as $u \to 0$, the dominated convergence theorem applies to (1), if s tends to t, and we conclude that

$$(2)\qquad \hat{f}'(t) = -i \int_{-\infty}^{\infty} xf(x)e^{-ixt}\, dm(x).$$

9.3 Remarks

(a) In the preceding proof, the appeal to the dominated convergence theorem may seem to be illegitimate since the dominated convergence theorem deals only with *countable* sequences of functions. However, it does enable us to conclude that

$$\lim_{n\to\infty} \frac{\hat{f}(s_n) - \hat{f}(t)}{s_n - t} = -i \int_{-\infty}^{\infty} xf(x)e^{-ixt}\, dm(t)$$

for every sequence $\{s_n\}$ which converges to t, and this says exactly that

$$\lim_{s\to t} \frac{\hat{f}(s) - \hat{f}(t)}{s - t} = -i \int_{-\infty}^{\infty} xf(x)e^{-ixt}\, dm(t).$$

We shall encounter similar situations again, and shall apply convergence theorems to them without further comment.

(*b*) Theorem 9.2(*b*) shows that the Fourier transform of

$$[f(x + \alpha) - f(x)]/\alpha$$

is

$$\hat{f}(t)\, \frac{e^{i\alpha t} - 1}{\alpha}.$$

This suggests that an analogue of Theorem 9.2(*f*) should be true under certain conditions, namely, that the Fourier transform of f' is $it\hat{f}(t)$. If $f \in L^1$, $f' \in L^1$, and if f is the indefinite integral of f', the result is easily established by an integration by parts. We leave this, and some related results, as exercises. The fact that the Fourier transform converts differentiation to multiplication by ti makes the Fourier transform a useful tool in the study of differential equations.

The Inversion Theorem

9.4 We have just seen that certain operations on functions correspond nicely to operations on their Fourier transforms. The usefulness and interest of this correspondence will of course be enhanced if there is a way of returning from the transforms to the functions, that is to say, if there is an inversion formula.

Let us see what such a formula might look like, by analogy with Fourier series. If

$$(1) \qquad c_n = \frac{1}{2\pi} \int_{-\pi}^{\pi} f(x)e^{-inx}\, dx \qquad (n \in Z),$$

then the inversion formula is

$$(2) \qquad f(x) = \sum_{-\infty}^{\infty} c_n e^{inx}.$$

We know that (2) holds, in the sense of L^2-convergence, if $f \in L^2(T)$. We also know that (2) does not necessarily hold in the sense of pointwise convergence, even if f is continuous. Suppose now that $f \in L^1(T)$, that $\{c_n\}$ is given by (1), and that

$$\sum_{-\infty}^{\infty} |c_n| < \infty. \tag{3}$$

Put

$$g(x) = \sum_{-\infty}^{\infty} c_n e^{inx}. \tag{4}$$

By (3), the series in (4) converges uniformly (hence g is continuous), and the Fourier coefficients of g are easily computed:

$$\begin{aligned} \frac{1}{2\pi}\int_{-\pi}^{\pi} g(x)e^{-ikx}\,dx &= \frac{1}{2\pi}\int_{-\pi}^{\pi}\left\{\sum_{n=-\infty}^{\infty} c_n e^{inx}\right\} e^{-ikx}\,dx \\ &= \sum_{n=-\infty}^{\infty} c_n \frac{1}{2\pi}\int_{-\pi}^{\pi} e^{i(n-k)x}\,dx = c_k. \end{aligned} \tag{5}$$

Thus f and g have the same Fourier coefficients. This implies $f = g$ a.e., so the Fourier series of f converges to $f(x)$ a.e.

The analogous assumptions in the context of Fourier transforms are that $f \in L^1$ and $\hat{f} \in L^1$, and we might then expect that a formula like

$$f(x) = \int_{-\infty}^{\infty} \hat{f}(t)e^{itx}\,dm(t) \tag{6}$$

is valid. Certainly, if $\hat{f} \in L^1$, the right side of (6) is well defined; call it $g(x)$; but if we want to argue as in (5), we run into the integral

$$\int_{-\infty}^{\infty} e^{i(t-s)x}\,dx, \tag{7}$$

which is meaningless as it stands. Thus even under the strong assumption that $\hat{f} \in L^1$, a proof of (6) (which *is* true) has to proceed over a more devious route.

[It should be mentioned that (6) may hold even if $\hat{f} \notin L^1$, if the integral over $(-\infty, \infty)$ is interpreted as the limit, as $A \to \infty$, of integrals over $(-A,A)$. (Analogue: a series may converge without converging absolutely.) We shall not go into this.]

9.5 Theorem *For any function f on R^1 and every $y \in R^1$, let f_y be the translate of f defined by*

$$f_y(x) = f(x - y) \qquad (x \in R^1). \tag{1}$$

If $1 \le p < \infty$ and if $f \in L^p$, the mapping

(2) $$y \to f_y$$

is a uniformly continuous mapping of R^1 into $L^p(R^1)$.

PROOF Fix $\epsilon > 0$. Since $f \in L^p$ there exists a continuous function g whose support lies in a bounded interval $[-A,A]$, such that

$$\|f - g\|_p < \epsilon$$

(Theorem 3.14). The uniform continuity of g shows that there exists a $\delta \in (0,A)$ such that $|s - t| < \delta$ implies

$$|g(s) - g(t)| < (3A)^{-1/p}\epsilon.$$

If $|s - t| < \delta$, it follows that

$$\int_{-\infty}^{\infty} |g(x - s) - g(x - t)|^p \, dx < (3A)^{-1}\epsilon^p(2A + \delta) < \epsilon^p,$$

so that $\|g_s - g_t\|_p < \epsilon$.

Note that L^p-norms (relative to Lebesgue measure) are translation invariant: $\|f\|_p = \|f_s\|_p$. Thus

$$\begin{aligned}\|f_s - f_t\|_p &\le \|f_s - g_s\|_p + \|g_s - g_t\|_p + \|g_t - f_t\|_p \\ &= \|(f - g)_s\|_p + \|g_s - g_t\|_p + \|(g - f)_t\|_p < 3\epsilon\end{aligned}$$

whenever $|s - t| < \delta$. This completes the proof.

9.6 Theorem *If $f \in L^1$, then $\hat{f} \in C_0$ and*

(1) $$\|\hat{f}\|_\infty \le \|f\|_1.$$

PROOF The inequality (1) is obvious from 9.1(4). If $t_n \to t$, then

(2) $$|\hat{f}(t_n) - \hat{f}(t)| \le \int_{-\infty}^{\infty} |f(x)| \, |e^{-it_nx} - e^{-itx}| \, dm(x).$$

The integrand is bounded by $2|f(x)|$ and tends to 0 for every x, as $n \to \infty$. Hence $\hat{f}(t_n) \to \hat{f}(t)$, by the dominated convergence theorem. Thus $\hat{f}$ is continuous.

Since $e^{\pi i} = -1$, 9.1(4) gives

(3) $$\begin{aligned}\hat{f}(t) &= -\int_{-\infty}^{\infty} f(x)e^{-it(x+\pi/t)} \, dm(x) \\ &= -\int_{-\infty}^{\infty} f(x - \pi/t)e^{-itx} \, dm(x).\end{aligned}$$

Hence

(4) $$2\hat{f}(t) = \int_{-\infty}^{\infty} \left\{f(x) - f\left(x - \frac{\pi}{t}\right)\right\} e^{-itx} \, dm(x),$$

so that

$$(5) \qquad 2|\hat{f}(t)| \le \|f - f_{\pi/t}\|_1,$$

which tends to 0 as $t \to \pm \infty$, by Theorem 9.5.

9.7 A Pair of Auxiliary Functions In the proof of the inversion theorem it will be convenient to know a positive function H which has a positive Fourier transform whose integral is easily calculated. Among the many possibilities we choose one which is of interest in connection with harmonic functions in a half plane. (See Exercise 17, Chap. 11.)

Put

$$(1) \qquad H(t) = e^{-|t|}$$

and define

$$(2) \qquad h_\lambda(x) = \int_{-\infty}^{\infty} H(\lambda t)e^{itx}\, dm(t) \qquad (\lambda > 0).$$

A simple computation gives

$$(3) \qquad h_\lambda(x) = \sqrt{\frac{2}{\pi}}\frac{\lambda}{\lambda^2 + x^2}$$

and hence

$$(4) \qquad \int_{-\infty}^{\infty} h_\lambda(x)\, dm(x) = 1.$$

Note also that $0 < H(t) \le 1$ and that $H(\lambda t) \to 1$ as $\lambda \to 0$.

9.8 Proposition *If $f \in L^1$, then*

$$(f * h_\lambda)(x) = \int_{-\infty}^{\infty} H(\lambda t)\hat{f}(t)e^{ixt}\, dm(t).$$

PROOF This is a simple application of Fubini's theorem.

$$\begin{aligned}(f * h_\lambda)(x) &= \int_{-\infty}^{\infty} f(x-y)\, dm(y) \int_{-\infty}^{\infty} H(\lambda t)e^{ity}\, dm(t)\\ &= \int_{-\infty}^{\infty} H(\lambda t)\, dm(t) \int_{-\infty}^{\infty} f(x-y)e^{ity}\, dm(y)\\ &= \int_{-\infty}^{\infty} H(\lambda t)\, dm(t) \int_{-\infty}^{\infty} f(y)e^{it(x-y)}\, dm(y)\\ &= \int_{-\infty}^{\infty} H(\lambda t)\hat{f}(t)e^{itx}\, dm(t).\end{aligned}$$

9.9 Theorem *If $g \in L^\infty$ and g is continuous at a point x, then*

$$(1) \qquad \lim_{\lambda \to 0} (g * h_\lambda)(x) = g(x).$$

PROOF On account of 9.7(4), we have

$$(g * h_\lambda)(x) - g(x) = \int_{-\infty}^{\infty} [g(x - y) - g(x)]h_\lambda(y)\, dm(y)$$

$$= \int_{-\infty}^{\infty} [g(x - y) - g(x)]\lambda^{-1}h_1\left(\frac{y}{\lambda}\right) dm(y)$$

$$= \int_{-\infty}^{\infty} [g(x - \lambda s) - g(x)]h_1(s)\, dm(s).$$

The last integrand is dominated by $2\|g\|_\infty h_1(s)$ and converges to 0 pointwise for every s, as $\lambda \to 0$. Hence (1) follows from the dominated convergence theorem.

9.10 Theorem *If $1 \le p < \infty$ and $f \in L^p$, then*

(1) $$\lim_{\lambda \to 0} \|f * h_\lambda - f\|_p = 0.$$

The cases $p = 1$ and $p = 2$ will be the ones of interest to us, but the general case is no harder to prove.

PROOF Since $h_\lambda \in L^q$, where q is the exponent conjugate to p, $(f * h_\lambda)(x)$ is defined for every x. (In fact, $f * h_\lambda$ is continuous; see Exercise 11.) Because of 9.7(4) we have

(2) $$(f * h_\lambda)(x) - f(x) = \int_{-\infty}^{\infty} [f(x - y) - f(x)]h_\lambda(y)\, dm(y)$$

and Theorem 3.3 gives

(3) $$|(f * h_\lambda)(x) - f(x)|^p \le \int_{-\infty}^{\infty} |f(x - y) - f(x)|^p h_\lambda(y)\, dm(y).$$

Integrate (3) with respect to x and apply Fubini's theorem:

(4) $$\|f * h_\lambda - f\|_p^p \le \int_{-\infty}^{\infty} \|f_y - f\|_p^p h_\lambda(y)\, dm(y).$$

If $g(y) = \|f_y - f\|_p^p$, then g is bounded and continuous, by Theorem 9.5, and $g(0) = 0$. Hence the right side of (4) tends to 0 as $\lambda \to 0$, by Theorem 9.9.

9.11 The Inversion Theorem *If $f \in L^1$ and $\hat{f} \in L^1$, and if*

(1) $$g(x) = \int_{-\infty}^{\infty} \hat{f}(t)e^{ixt}\, dm(t) \qquad (x \in R^1),$$

then $g \in C_0$ and $f(x) = g(x)$ a.e.

PROOF By Proposition 9.8,

(2) $$(f * h_\lambda)(x) = \int_{-\infty}^{\infty} H(\lambda t)\hat{f}(t)e^{ixt}\, dm(t).$$

The integrands on the right side of (2) are bounded by $|\hat{f}(t)|$, and since $H(\lambda t) \to 1$ as $\lambda \to 0$, the right side of (2) converges to $g(x)$, for every $x \in R^1$, by the dominated convergence theorem.

If we combine Theorems 9.10 and 3.12 we see that there is a sequence $\{\lambda_n\}$ such that $\lambda_n \to 0$ and

$$(3) \qquad \lim_{n\to\infty} (f * h_{\lambda_n})(x) = f(x) \text{ a.e.}$$

Hence $f(x) = g(x)$ a.e. That $g \in C_0$ follows from Theorem 9.6.

9.12 The Uniqueness Theorem *If $f \in L^1$ and $\hat{f}(t) = 0$ for all $t \in R^1$, then $f(x) = 0$ a.e.*

PROOF Since $\hat{f} = 0$ we have $\hat{f} \in L^1$, and the result follows from the inversion theorem.

The Plancherel Theorem

Since the Lebesgue measure of R^1 is infinite, L^2 is not a subset of L^1, and the definition of the Fourier transform by formula 9.1(4) is therefore not directly applicable to every $f \in L^2$. The definition does apply, however, if $f \in L^1 \cap L^2$, and it turns out that then $\hat{f} \in L^2$. In fact, $\|\hat{f}\|_2 = \|f\|_2$! This isometry of $L^1 \cap L^2$ into L^2 extends to an isometry of L^2 onto L^2, and this extension defines the Fourier transform (sometimes called the *Plancherel transform*) of every $f \in L^2$. The resulting L^2-theory has in fact a great deal more symmetry than is the case in L^1. In L^2, f and $\hat{f}$ play exactly the same role.

9.13 Theorem *One can associate to each $f \in L^2$ a function $\hat{f} \in L^2$ so that the following properties hold:*

(*a*) *If $f \in L^1 \cap L^2$, then $\hat{f}$ is the previously defined Fourier transform of f.*
(*b*) *For every $f \in L^2$, $\|\hat{f}\|_2 = \|f\|_2$.*
(*c*) *The mapping $f \to \hat{f}$ is a Hilbert space isomorphism of L^2 onto L^2.*
(*d*) *The following symmetric relation exists between f and $\hat{f}$: If*

$$\varphi_A(t) = \int_{-A}^{A} f(x)e^{-ixt}\,dm(x) \qquad \textit{and} \qquad \psi_A(x) = \int_{-A}^{A} \hat{f}(t)e^{ixt}\,dm(t),$$

then $\|\varphi_A - \hat{f}\|_2 \to 0$ and $\|\psi_A - f\|_2 \to 0$ as $A \to \infty$.

Note: Since $L^1 \cap L^2$ is dense in L^2, properties (*a*) and (*b*) determine the mapping $f \to \hat{f}$ uniquely. Property (*d*) may be called the L^2 *inversion theorem.*

PROOF Our first objective is the relation

$$(1) \qquad \|\hat{f}\|_2 = \|f\|_2 \qquad (f \in L^1 \cap L^2).$$

We fix $f \in L^1 \cap L^2$, put $\tilde{f}(x) = \overline{f(-x)}$, and define $g = f * \tilde{f}$. Then

$$(2)\quad g(x) = \int_{-\infty}^{\infty} f(x-y)\overline{f(-y)}\,dm(y) = \int_{-\infty}^{\infty} f(x+y)\overline{f(y)}\,dm(y),$$

or

$$(3)\qquad g(x) = (f_{-x}, f),$$

where the inner product is taken in the Hilbert space L^2 and f_{-x} denotes a translate of f, as in Theorem 9.5. By that theorem, $x \to f_{-x}$ is a continuous mapping of R^1 into L^2, and the continuity of the inner product (Theorem 4.6) therefore implies that g is a continuous function. The Schwarz inequality shows that

$$(4)\qquad |g(x)| \leq \|f_{-x}\|_2 \|f\|_2 = \|f\|_2^2,$$

so that g is bounded. Also, $g \in L^1$ since $f \in L^1$ and $\tilde{f} \in L^1$.

Since $g \in L^1$, we may apply Proposition 9.8:

$$(5)\qquad (g * h_\lambda)(0) = \int_{-\infty}^{\infty} H(\lambda t)\hat{g}(t)\,dm(t).$$

Since g is continuous and bounded, Theorem 9.9 shows that

$$(6)\qquad \lim_{\lambda \to 0} (g * h_\lambda)(0) = g(0) = \|f\|_2^2.$$

Theorem 9.2(d) shows that $\hat{g} = |\hat{f}|^2 \geq 0$, and since $H(\lambda t)$ increases to 1 as $\lambda \to 0$, the monotone convergence theorem gives

$$(7)\qquad \lim_{\lambda \to 0} \int_{-\infty}^{\infty} H(\lambda t)\hat{g}(t)\,dm(t) = \int_{-\infty}^{\infty} |\hat{f}(t)|^2\,dm(t).$$

Now (5), (6), and (7) show that $\hat{f} \in L^2$ and that (1) holds.

This was the crux of the proof.

For any $A > 0$, let f_A be the product of f and the characteristic function of the interval $[-A,A]$. If $f \in L^2$, then clearly $\|f_A - f\|_2 \to 0$ as $A \to \infty$. Also, $f_A \in L^1 \cap L^2$, and if φ_A is defined as in (d), we have $\varphi_A = \hat{f}_A$. Since $\{f_A\}$ is a Cauchy sequence in L^2, the relation (1) shows that $\{\varphi_A\}$ is a Cauchy sequence in L^2; and since L^2 is complete, $\{\varphi_A\}$ converges to an element of L^2, as $A \to \infty$, which we call $\hat{f}$. Note that if $f \in L^1 \cap L^2$, then $\varphi_A(t)$ converges pointwise to the previously defined Fourier transform of f, and this pointwise limit coincides a.e. with the L^2-limit (Theorem 3.12).

The domain of the mapping $f \to \hat{f}$ is now extended from $L^1 \cap L^2$ to L^2. Moreover, (1) implies that $\|\varphi_A\|_2 = \|f_A\|_2$, so that

$$(8)\qquad \|\hat{f}\|_2 = \lim_{A \to \infty} \|\varphi_A\|_2 = \lim_{A \to \infty} \|f_A\|_2 = \|f\|_2.$$

We have now proved (a), (b), and the first half of (d).

Let us introduce the temporary notation Φf for $\hat{f}$. Then Φf is the L^2-limit of the functions φ_A, if $f \in L^2$, and Φ is an isometry of L^2 into L^2. For $g \in L^2$, define Ψg analogously as the L^2-limit of the functions

$$(9) \qquad \int_{-A}^{A} g(t)e^{ixt}\,dm(t).$$

Then Ψ is an isometry of L^2 into L^2, since $(\Psi g)(x) = (\Phi g)(-x)$. If both f and $\hat{f}$ are in $L^1 \cap L^2$, it follows from Theorem 9.11 that

$$(10) \qquad \Psi\Phi f = f.$$

By Proposition 9.8, $f * h_\lambda$ satisfies these requirements if $f \in L^1 \cap L^2$ and $\lambda > 0$. Thus

$$(11) \qquad \Psi\Phi(f * h_\lambda) = f * h_\lambda.$$

As $\lambda \to 0$, $\|f * h_\lambda - f\|_2 \to 0$ (Theorem 9.10), and since $\Psi\Phi$ is an isometry, we obtain (10) for every $f \in L^1 \cap L^2$. Since $L^1 \cap L^2$ is dense in L^2, (10) holds for every $f \in L^2$. This proves the second half of (*d*).

But the relation $\Phi\Psi g = g$ is then also valid for every $g \in L^2$, since the roles of the operators Φ and Ψ can obviously be interchanged. This says that if $f = \Psi g$ then $g = \hat{f}$. The mapping $f \to \hat{f}$ therefore maps L^2 *onto* L^2.

Finally, the identity

$$(12) \qquad 4f\bar{g} = |f + g|^2 - |f - g|^2 + i|f + ig|^2 - i|f - ig|^2$$

shows that every isometry of L^2 onto L^2 also preserves inner products. In other words, the Parseval formula

$$(13) \qquad \int_{-\infty}^{\infty} f(x)\overline{g(x)}\,dm(x) = \int_{-\infty}^{\infty} \hat{f}(t)\overline{\hat{g}(t)}\,dm(t)$$

holds if $f \in L^2$ and $g \in L^2$.

This gives (*c*) and completes the proof.

9.14 Theorem *If $f \in L^2$ and $\hat{f} \in L^1$, then*

$$f(x) = \int_{-\infty}^{\infty} \hat{f}(t)e^{ixt}\,dm(t) \text{ a.e.}$$

PROOF This is a corollary of Theorem 9.13(*d*).

9.15 Remark If $f \in L^1$, formula 9.1(4) defines $\hat{f}(t)$ unambiguously for every t. If $f \in L^2$, the Plancherel theorem defines $\hat{f}$ uniquely as an element of the Hilbert space L^2, but as a point function $\hat{f}(t)$ is only determined almost everywhere. This is an important difference between the theory of Fourier transforms in L^1 and in L^2. The indeterminacy of $\hat{f}(t)$ as a point function will cause some difficulties in the problem to which we now turn.

9.16 Translation Invariant Subspaces of L^2 A subspace M of L^2 is said to be *translation invariant* if $f \in M$ implies that $f_\alpha \in M$ for all real α, where $f_\alpha(x) = f(x - \alpha)$. Translations have already played an important part in our study of Fourier transforms. We now pose a problem whose solution will afford an illustration of how the Plancherel theorem can be used. (Other applications will occur in Chap. 19.) The problem is:

Describe the closed translation invariant subspaces of L^2.

Let M be a closed translation invariant subspace of L^2, and let $\hat{M}$ be the image of M under the Fourier transform. Then $\hat{M}$ is closed (since the Fourier transform is an L^2-isometry). If f_α is a translate of f, the Fourier transform of f_α is $\hat{f}e_\alpha$, where $e_\alpha(t) = e^{-i\alpha t}$; we proved this for $f \in L^1$ in Theorem 9.2; the result extends to L^2, as can be seen from Theorem 9.13(d). *It follows that $\hat{M}$ is invariant under multiplication by e_α, for all $\alpha \in R^1$.*

Let E be any measurable set in R^1. If $\hat{M}$ is the set of all $\varphi \in L^2$ which vanish a.e. on E, then $\hat{M}$ certainly is a subspace of L^2, which is invariant under multiplication by all e_α (note that $|e_\alpha| = 1$, so $\varphi e_\alpha \in L^2$ if $\varphi \in L^2$), and $\hat{M}$ is also closed. *Proof:* $\varphi \in \hat{M}$ if and only if φ is orthogonal to every $\psi \in L^2$ which vanishes a.e. on the complement of E.

If M is the inverse image of this $\hat{M}$, under the Fourier transform, then M is a space with the desired properties.

One may now conjecture that every one of our spaces M is obtained in this manner, from a set $E \subset R^1$. To prove this, we have to show that to every closed translation invariant $M \subset L^2$ there corresponds a set $E \subset R^1$ such that $f \in M$ if and only if $\hat{f}(t) = 0$ a.e. on E. The obvious way of constructing E from M is to associate with each $f \in M$ the set E_f consisting of all points at which $\hat{f}(t) = 0$, and to define E as the intersection of these sets E_f. But this obvious attack runs into a serious difficulty: Each E_f is defined only up to sets of measure 0. If $\{A_i\}$ is a countable collection of sets, each determined up to sets of measure 0, then $\bigcap A_i$ is also determined up to sets of measure 0. But there are uncountably many $f \in M$, so we lose all control over $\bigcap E_f$.

This difficulty disappears entirely if we think of our functions as elements of the Hilbert space L^2, and not primarily as point functions.

We shall now prove the conjecture. Let $\hat{M}$ be the image of a closed translation invariant subspace $M \subset L^2$, under the Fourier transform. Let P be the orthogonal projection of L^2 onto $\hat{M}$ (Theorem 4.11): To each $f \in L^2$ there corresponds a unique $Pf \in \hat{M}$ such that $f - Pf$ is orthogonal to $\hat{M}$. Hence

$$f - Pf \perp Pg \qquad (f \text{ and } g \in L^2) \tag{1}$$

and since $\hat{M}$ is invariant under multiplication by e_α, we also have

$$f - Pf \perp (Pg)e_\alpha \qquad (f \text{ and } g \in L^2,\ \alpha \in R^1). \tag{2}$$

If we recall how the inner product is defined in L^2, we see that (2) is equivalent to

(3) $$\int_{-\infty}^{\infty} (f - Pf) \cdot \overline{Pg} \cdot e_{-\alpha}\, dm = 0 \qquad (f \text{ and } g \in L^2,\ \alpha \in R^1)$$

and this says that the Fourier transform of

(4) $$(f - Pf) \cdot \overline{Pg}$$

is 0. The function (4) is the product of two L^2-functions, hence is in L^1, and the uniqueness theorem for Fourier transforms now shows that the function (4) is 0 a.e. This remains true if $\overline{Pg}$ is replaced by Pg. Hence

(5) $$f \cdot Pg = (Pf) \cdot (Pg) \qquad (f \text{ and } g \in L^2).$$

Interchanging the roles of f and g leads from (5) to

(6) $$f \cdot Pg = g \cdot Pf \qquad (f \text{ and } g \in L^2).$$

Now let g be a fixed positive function in L^2; for instance, put $g(t) = e^{-|t|}$. Define

(7) $$\varphi(t) = \frac{(Pg)(t)}{g(t)}.$$

$(Pg)(t)$ may only be defined a.e.; choose any one determination in (7). Now (6) becomes

(8) $$Pf = \varphi \cdot f \qquad (f \in L^2).$$

If $f \in \hat{M}$, then $Pf = f$. This says that $P^2 = P$, and it follows that $\varphi^2 = \varphi$, because

(9) $$\varphi^2 \cdot g = \varphi \cdot Pg = P^2 g = Pg = \varphi \cdot g.$$

Since $\varphi^2 = \varphi$, we have $\varphi = 0$ or 1 a.e., and if we let E be the set of all t where $\varphi(t) = 0$, then $\hat{M}$ consists precisely of those $f \in L^2$ which are 0 a.e. on E, since $f \in \hat{M}$ if and only if $f = Pf = \varphi \cdot f$.

We therefore obtain the following solution to our problem:

9.17 Theorem *Associate to each measurable set $E \subset R^1$ the space M_E of all $f \in L^2$ such that $\hat{f} = 0$ a.e. on E. Then M_E is a closed translation invariant subspace of L^2. Every closed translation invariant subspace of L^2 is M_E for some E, and $M_A = M_B$ if and only if*

$$m((A - B) \cup (B - A)) = 0.$$

The uniqueness statement is easily proved; we leave the details to the reader.

The above problem can of course be posed in other function spaces. It has been studied in great detail in L^1. The known results show that the situation is infinitely more complicated there than in L^2.

The Banach Algebra L^1

9.18 Definition A Banach space A is said to be a *Banach algebra* if there is a multiplication defined in A which satisfies the inequality

$$(1) \qquad \|xy\| \le \|x\|\,\|y\| \qquad (x \text{ and } y \in A),$$

the associative law $x(yz) = (xy)z$, the distributive laws

$$(2) \quad x(y+z) = xy + xz, \qquad (y+z)x = yx + zx \qquad (x,\ y, \text{ and } z \in A),$$

and the relation

$$(3) \qquad (\alpha x)y = x(\alpha y) = \alpha(xy)$$

where α is any scalar.

9.19 Examples

(*a*) Let $A = C(X)$, where X is a compact Hausdorff space, with the supremum norm and the usual pointwise multiplication of functions: $(fg)(x) = f(x)g(x)$. This is a commutative Banach algebra ($fg = gf$) with unit (the constant function 1).

(*b*) $C_0(R^1)$ is a commutative Banach algebra without unit, i.e., without an element u such that $uf = f$ for all $f \in C_0(R^1)$.

(*c*) The set of all linear operators on R^k (or on any Banach space), with the operator norm as in Definition 5.3, and with addition and multiplication defined by

$$(A+B)(x) = Ax + Bx, \qquad (AB)x = A(Bx),$$

is a noncommutative Banach algebra (unless $k = 1$) with unit.

(*d*) L^1 is a Banach algebra if we define multiplication by convolution; since

$$\|f * g\|_1 \le \|f\|_1 \|g\|_1,$$

the norm inequality is satisfied. The associative law could be verified directly (an application of Fubini's theorem), but we can proceed as follows: We know that the Fourier transform of $f * g$ is $\hat{f} \cdot \hat{g}$, and we know that the mapping $f \to \hat{f}$ is one-to-one. For every $t \in R^1$,

$$\hat{f}(t)[\hat{g}(t)\hat{h}(t)] = [\hat{f}(t)\hat{g}(t)]\hat{h}(t),$$

by the associative law for complex numbers. It follows that $f * (g * h) = (f * g) * h$. In the same way we see immediately that $f * g = g * f$. The remaining requirements of Definition 9.18 are also easily seen to hold in L^1.

Thus L^1 is a commutative Banach algebra. The Fourier transform is an algebra isomorphism of L^1 into C_0. Hence there is no $f \in L^1$ with $\hat{f} \equiv 1$, and therefore L^1 has no unit.

9.20 Complex Homomorphisms The most important complex functions on a Banach algebra A are the homomorphisms of A into the complex field. These are precisely the linear functionals which also preserve multiplication, i.e., the functions φ such that

$$\varphi(\alpha x + \beta y) = \alpha\varphi(x) + \beta\varphi(y), \qquad \varphi(xy) = \varphi(x)\varphi(y)$$

for all x and $y \in A$ and all scalars α and β. Note that no boundedness assumption is made in this definition. It is a very interesting fact that this would be redundant:

9.21 Theorem *If φ is a complex homomorphism on a Banach algebra A, then the norm of φ, as a linear functional, is at most* 1.

PROOF Assume, to get a contradiction, that $|\varphi(x_0)| > \|x_0\|$ for some $x_0 \in A$. Put $\lambda = \varphi(x_0)$, and put $x = x_0/\lambda$. Then $\|x\| < 1$ and $\varphi(x) = 1$.

Since $\|x^n\| \leq \|x\|^n$ and $\|x\| < 1$, the elements

$$s_n = -x - x^2 - \cdots - x^n \tag{1}$$

form a Cauchy sequence in A. Since A is complete, being a Banach space, there exists a $y \in A$ such that $\|y - s_n\| \to 0$, and it is easily seen that $x + s_n = xs_{n-1}$, so that

$$x + y = xy. \tag{2}$$

Hence $\varphi(x) + \varphi(y) = \varphi(x)\varphi(y)$, which is impossible if $\varphi(x) = 1$.

9.22 The Complex Homomorphisms of L^1 Suppose φ is a complex homomorphism of L^1, i.e., a linear functional (of norm at most 1, by Theorem 9.21) which also satisfies the relation

$$\varphi(f * g) = \varphi(f)\varphi(g) \qquad (f \text{ and } g \in L^1). \tag{1}$$

By Theorem 6.16, there exists a $\beta \in L^\infty$ such that

$$\varphi(f) = \int_{-\infty}^{\infty} f(x)\beta(x)\,dm(x) \qquad (f \in L^1). \tag{2}$$

We now exploit the relation (1) to see what else we can say about β. On the one hand,

$$\begin{aligned}(3)\qquad \varphi(f * g) &= \int_{-\infty}^{\infty} (f * g)(x)\beta(x)\, dm(x) \\ &= \int_{-\infty}^{\infty} \beta(x)\, dm(x) \int_{-\infty}^{\infty} f(x-y)g(y)\, dm(y) \\ &= \int_{-\infty}^{\infty} g(y)\, dm(y) \int_{-\infty}^{\infty} f_y(x)\beta(x)\, dm(x) \\ &= \int_{-\infty}^{\infty} g(y)\varphi(f_y)\, dm(y).\end{aligned}$$

On the other hand,

$$(4)\qquad \varphi(f)\varphi(g) = \varphi(f) \int_{-\infty}^{\infty} g(y)\beta(y)\, dm(y).$$

Let us now assume that φ is not identically 0. Fix $f \varepsilon L^1$ so that $\varphi(f) \neq 0$. Since the last integral in (3) is equal to the right side of (4) for every $g \varepsilon L^1$, the uniqueness assertion of Theorem 6.16 shows that

$$(5)\qquad \varphi(f)\beta(y) = \varphi(f_y)$$

for almost all y. But $y \to f_y$ is a continuous mapping of R^1 into L^1 (Theorem 9.5) and φ is continuous on L^1. Hence the right side of (5) is a continuous function of y, and we may assume [by changing $\beta(y)$ on a set of measure 0 if necessary, which does not affect (2)] that β is continuous. If we replace y by $x + y$ and then f by f_x in (5), we obtain

$$\varphi(f)\beta(x+y) = \varphi(f_{x+y}) = \varphi((f_x)_y) = \varphi(f_x)\beta(y) = \varphi(f)\beta(x)\beta(y),$$

so that

$$(6)\qquad \beta(x+y) = \beta(x)\beta(y) \qquad (x \text{ and } y \;\varepsilon\; R^1).$$

Since β is not identically 0, (6) implies that $\beta(0) = 1$, and the continuity of β shows that there is a $\delta > 0$ such that

$$(7)\qquad \int_0^{\delta} \beta(y)\, dy = c \neq 0.$$

Then

$$(8)\qquad c\beta(x) = \int_0^{\delta} \beta(y)\beta(x)\, dy = \int_0^{\delta} \beta(y+x)\, dy = \int_x^{x+\delta} \beta(y)\, dy.$$

Since β is continuous, the last integral is a differentiable function of x; hence (8) shows that β is differentiable. Differentiate (6) with respect to y, then put $y = 0$; the result is

$$(9)\qquad \beta'(x) = A\beta(x), \qquad A = \beta'(0).$$

Hence the derivative of $\beta(x)e^{-Ax}$ is 0, and since $\beta(0) = 1$, we obtain

$$\beta(x) = e^{Ax}. \tag{10}$$

But β is bounded on R^1. Therefore A must be pure imaginary, and we conclude: There exists a $t \in R^1$ such that

$$\beta(x) = e^{-itx}. \tag{11}$$

We have thus arrived at the Fourier transform:

9.23 Theorem *To every complex homomorphism φ on L^1 (except to $\varphi = 0$) there corresponds a unique $t \in R^1$ such that $\varphi(f) = \hat{f}(t)$.*

The existence of t was proved above. The uniqueness follows from the observation that if $t \neq s$ then there exists an $f \in L^1$ such that $\hat{f}(t) \neq \hat{f}(s)$; take for $f(x)$ a suitable translate of $e^{-|x|}$.

Exercises

1 Compute the Fourier transform of the characteristic function of an interval. For $n = 1, 2, 3, \ldots$, let g_n be the characteristic function of $[-n,n]$, let h be the characteristic function of $[-1,1]$, and compute $g_n * h$ explicitly. (The graph is piecewise linear.) Show that $g_n * h$ is the Fourier transform of a function $f_n \in L^1$; except for a multiplicative constant,

$$f_n(x) = \frac{\sin x \sin nx}{x^2}.$$

Show that $\|f_n\|_1 \to \infty$ and conclude that the mapping $f \to \hat{f}$ maps L^1 into a *proper* subset of C_0.

Show, however, that the range of this mapping is dense in C_0.

2 Give examples of $f \in L^2$ such that $f \notin L^1$ but $\hat{f} \in L^1$. Under what circumstances can this happen?

3 If $f \in L^1$ and $\int |t\hat{f}(t)|\, dm(t) < \infty$, prove that f coincides a.e. with a differentiable function whose derivative is

$$i \int_{-\infty}^{\infty} t\hat{f}(t)e^{ixt}\, dm(t).$$

4 Suppose $f \in L^1$, f is differentiable almost everywhere, and $f' \in L^1$. Does it follow that the Fourier transform of f' is $ti\hat{f}(t)$?

5 Let S be the class of all functions f on R^1 which have the following property: f is infinitely differentiable, and there are numbers $A_{mn}(f) < \infty$, for m and $n = 0, 1, 2, \ldots$, such that

$$|x^n D^m f(x)| \leq A_{mn}(f) \qquad (x \in R^1).$$

Here D is the ordinary differentiation operator.

Prove that the Fourier transform maps S onto S.
Find examples of members of S.

6 The Fourier transform can be defined for $f \in L^1(R^k)$ by

$$\hat{f}(y) = \int_{R^k} f(x) e^{-ix \cdot y} \, dm_k(x) \qquad (y \in R^k),$$

where $x \cdot y = \Sigma \xi_i \eta_i$ if $x = (\xi_1, \ldots, \xi_k)$, $y = (\eta_1, \ldots, \eta_k)$, and m_k is Lebesgue measure on R^k, divided by $(2\pi)^{k/2}$ for convenience. Prove the inversion theorem and the Plancherel theorem in this context, as well as the analogue of Theorem 9.23.

7 If $f \in L^1(R^k)$, A is a linear operator on R^k, and $g(x) = f(Ax)$, how is $\hat{g}$ related to $\hat{f}$? If f is invariant under rotations, i.e., if $f(x)$ depends only on the euclidean distance of x from the origin, prove that the same is true of $\hat{f}$.

8 The *Laplacian* of a function f on R^k is

$$\Delta f = \sum_{j=1}^{k} \frac{\partial^2 f}{\partial x_j^2},$$

provided the partial derivatives exist. What is the relation between $\hat{f}$ and $\hat{g}$ if $g = \Delta f$ and all necessary integrability conditions are satisfied? It is clear that the Laplacian commutes with translations. Prove that it also commutes with rotations, i.e., that

$$\Delta(f \circ A) = (\Delta f) \circ A$$

whenever f has continuous second derivatives and A is a rotation of R^k. (Show that it is enough to do this under the additional assumption that f has compact support.)

9 Show that every Lebesgue measurable character of R^1 is continuous. Do the same for R^k. (Adapt part of the proof of Theorem 9.23.)

10 Suppose $f \in L^1$, $f > 0$. Prove that $|\hat{f}(y)| < \hat{f}(0)$ for every $y \neq 0$.

11 If p and q are conjugate exponents, $f \in L^p$, $g \in L^q$, and $h = f * g$, prove that h is uniformly continuous. If also $1 < p < \infty$, then $h \in C_0$; show that this fails for some $f \in L^1$, $g \in L^\infty$.

12 Suppose $1 \leq p < \infty$, $f \in L^p$, and

$$g(x) = \int_x^{x+1} f(t) \, dt.$$

Prove that $g \in C_0$. What can you say about g if $f \in L^\infty$?

13 Let C^∞ be the class of all infinitely differentiable complex functions on R^1, and let C_c^∞ consist of all $g \in C^\infty$ whose support is compact. Show that C_c^∞ does not consist of 0 alone.

Let L^1_{loc} be the class of all f which belong to L^1 locally; i.e.,

$f \in L^1_{loc}$ provided that f is measurable and $\int_I |f| < \infty$ for every bounded interval I.

If $f \in L^1_{loc}$ and $g \in C_c^\infty$, prove that $f * g \in C^\infty$.

Prove that there are sequences $\{g_n\}$ in C_c^∞ such that

$$\|f * g_n - f\|_1 \to 0$$

as $n \to \infty$, for every $f \in L^1$. (Compare Theorem 9.10.) Prove that $\{g_n\}$ can also be so chosen that $(f * g_n)(x) \to f(x)$ a.e., for every $f \in L^1_{loc}$; in fact, for suitable $\{g_n\}$ the convergence occurs at every point x at which f is the derivative of its indefinite integral.

Prove that $(f * h_\lambda)(x) \to f(x)$ a.e. if $f \in L^1$, as $\lambda \to 0$, and that $f * h_\lambda \in C^\infty$, although h_λ does not have compact support. (h_λ is defined in Sec. 9.7.)

14 Find

$$\lim_{A \to \infty} \int_{-A}^{A} \frac{\sin \lambda t}{t} e^{itx}\, dt \qquad (-\infty < x < \infty)$$

where λ is a positive constant.

15 Find conditions on f and/or $\hat{f}$ which ensure the correctness of the following formal argument: If

$$\varphi(t) = \frac{1}{2\pi} \int_{-\infty}^{\infty} f(x) e^{-itx}\, dx$$

and
$$F(x) = \sum_{k=-\infty}^{\infty} f(x + 2k\pi)$$

then F is periodic, with period 2π, the nth Fourier coefficient of F is $\varphi(n)$, hence $F(x) = \Sigma \varphi(n) e^{inx}$. In particular,

$$\sum_{k=-\infty}^{\infty} f(2k\pi) = \sum_{n=-\infty}^{\infty} \varphi(n).$$

More generally,

$$(*) \qquad \sum_{k=-\infty}^{\infty} f(k\beta) = \alpha \sum_{n=-\infty}^{\infty} \varphi(n\alpha) \qquad \text{if } \alpha > 0,\ \beta > 0,\ \alpha\beta = 2\pi.$$

What does (*) say about the limit, as $\alpha \to 0$, of the right-hand side (for "nice" functions, of course)? Is this in agreement with the inversion theorem?

[(*) is known as the Poisson summation formula.]

16 Take $f(x) = e^{-|x|}$ in Exercise 15 and derive the identity

$$\frac{e^{2\pi\alpha} + 1}{e^{2\pi\alpha} - 1} = \frac{1}{\pi} \sum_{n=-\infty}^{\infty} \frac{\alpha}{\alpha^2 + n^2}.$$

17 Take $f(x) = e^{-x^2}$ in Exercise 15. What is the resulting identity?

10

Elementary Properties of Holomorphic Functions

Complex Differentiation

We shall now study complex functions defined in subsets of the complex plane. It will be convenient to adopt some standard notations which will be used throughout the rest of this book.

10.1 Definitions If $r > 0$ and a is a complex number,

$$D(a;r) = \{z: |z - a| < r\} \tag{1}$$

is the open circular disc with center at a and radius r. $\bar{D}(a;r)$ is the closure of $D(a;r)$, and

$$D'(a;r) = \{z: 0 < |z - a| < r\} \tag{2}$$

is the punctured disc with center at a and radius r.

A set $E \subset X$, where X is a topological space, is said to be *connected* if there do *not* exist two disjoint open sets V and W such that $E \subset V \cup W$ and such that both V and W intersect E. A maximal connected subset of E is called a *component* of E. It is easy to see that any two components of E are disjoint and that E is the union of its components.

By a *region* we shall mean a nonempty connected open subset of the complex plane. Thus an open set $\Omega \neq \emptyset$ in the plane is a region if and only if Ω is not the union of two nonempty disjoint open sets. Each component of a plane open set Ω is clearly a region. The letter Ω will from now on denote a plane open set.

10.2 Definition Suppose f is a complex function defined in Ω. If $z_0 \in \Omega$ and if

$$\lim_{z \to z_0} \frac{f(z) - f(z_0)}{z - z_0} \tag{1}$$

exists, we denote this limit by $f'(z_0)$ and call it the *derivative* of f at z_0. If $f'(z_0)$ exists for every $z_0 \in \Omega$, we say that f is *holomorphic* (or *analytic*) in Ω. The class of all holomorphic functions in Ω will be denoted by $H(\Omega)$.

To be quite explicit, $f'(z_0)$ exists if to every $\epsilon > 0$ there corresponds a $\delta > 0$ such that

$$\left|\frac{f(z) - f(z_0)}{z - z_0} - f'(z_0)\right| < \epsilon \qquad \text{for all } z \in D'(z_0;\delta). \tag{2}$$

Thus $f'(z_0)$ is a complex number, obtained as a limit of quotients of complex numbers. Note that f is a mapping of Ω into R^2 and that Definition 8.22 associates with such mappings another kind of derivative, namely, a linear operator on R^2. In our present situation, if (2) is satisfied, this linear operator turns out to be multiplication by $f'(z_0)$ (regarding R^2 as the complex field). We leave it to the reader to verify this.

10.3 Remarks If $f \in H(\Omega)$ and $g \in H(\Omega)$, then also $f + g \in H(\Omega)$ and $fg \in H(\Omega)$, so that $H(\Omega)$ is a ring; the usual differentiation rules apply.

More interesting is the fact that superpositions of holomorphic functions are holomorphic: *If $f \in H(\Omega)$, if $f(\Omega) \subset \Omega_1$, if $g \in H(\Omega_1)$, and if $h = g \circ f$, then $h \in H(\Omega)$, and h' can be computed by the chain rule*

$$h'(z_0) = g'(f(z_0))f'(z_0) \qquad (z_0 \in \Omega). \tag{1}$$

To prove this, fix $z_0 \in \Omega$, and put $w_0 = f(z_0)$. Then

$$f(z) - f(z_0) = [f'(z_0) + \epsilon(z)](z - z_0), \tag{2}$$

$$g(w) - g(w_0) = [g'(w_0) + \eta(w)](w - w_0), \tag{3}$$

where $\epsilon(z) \to 0$ as $z \to z_0$ and $\eta(w) \to 0$ as $w \to w_0$. Put $w = f(z)$, and substitute (2) into (3): If $z \neq z_0$,

$$\frac{h(z) - h(z_0)}{z - z_0} = [g'(f(z_0)) + \eta(f(z))][f'(z_0) + \epsilon(z)]. \tag{4}$$

The differentiability of f forces f to be continuous at z_0. Hence (1) follows from (4).

10.4 Examples For $n = 0, 1, 2, \ldots, z^n$ is holomorphic in the whole plane, and the same is true of every polynomial in z. One easily verifies directly that $1/z$ is holomorphic in $\{z : z \neq 0\}$. Hence, taking $g(w) = 1/w$ in the chain rule, we see that if f_1 and f_2 are in $H(\Omega)$ and Ω_0 is an open subset of Ω in which f_2 has no zero, then $f_1/f_2 \in H(\Omega_0)$.

Another example of a function which is holomorphic in the whole plane (such functions are called *entire*) is the exponential function defined in the Prologue. In fact, we saw there that exp is differentiable everywhere, in the sense of Definition 10.2, and that $\exp'(z) = \exp(z)$ for every complex z.

10.5 Power Series From the theory of power series we shall assume only one fact as known, namely, that to each power series

$$(1) \qquad \sum_{n=0}^{\infty} c_n(z-a)^n$$

there corresponds a number $R \in [0, \infty]$ such that the series converges absolutely and uniformly in $\bar{D}(a;r)$, for every $r < R$, and diverges if $z \notin \bar{D}(a;R)$. The "radius of convergence" R is given by the root test:

$$(2) \qquad \frac{1}{R} = \limsup_{n \to \infty} |c_n|^{1/n}.$$

Let us say that a function f defined in Ω is *representable by power series in* Ω if to every disc $D(a;r) \subset \Omega$ there corresponds a series (1) which converges to $f(z)$ for all $z \in D(a;r)$.

10.6 Theorem *If f is representable by power series in Ω, then $f \in H(\Omega)$ and f' is also representable by power series in Ω. In fact, if*

$$(1) \qquad f(z) = \sum_{n=0}^{\infty} c_n(z-a)^n$$

for $z \in D(a;r)$, then for these z we also have

$$(2) \qquad f'(z) = \sum_{n=1}^{\infty} nc_n(z-a)^{n-1}.$$

PROOF If the series (1) converges in $D(a;r)$, the root test shows that the series (2) also converges there. Take $a = 0$, without loss of generality, denote the sum of the series (2) by $g(z)$, fix $w \in D(a;r)$, and choose ρ so that $|w| < \rho < r$. If $z \neq w$, we have

$$(3) \qquad \frac{f(z) - f(w)}{z - w} - g(w) = \sum_{n=1}^{\infty} c_n \left[\frac{z^n - w^n}{z - w} - nw^{n-1}\right].$$

The expression in brackets is 0 if $n = 1$ and is

$$(4) \qquad (z - w) \sum_{k=1}^{n-1} kw^{k-1}z^{n-k-1}$$

if $n \geq 2$. If $|z| < \rho$, the absolute value of the sum in (4) is less than

$$(5) \qquad \frac{n(n-1)}{2} \rho^{n-2}$$

so

$$(6) \qquad \left|\frac{f(z) - f(w)}{z - w} - g(w)\right| \leq |z - w| \sum_{n=2}^{\infty} n^2|c_n|\rho^{n-2}.$$

Since $\rho < r$, the last series converges. Hence the left side of (6) tends to 0 as $z \to w$. This says that $f'(w) = g(w)$, and completes the proof.

Corollary *Since f' is seen to satisfy the same hypothesis as f does, the theorem can be applied to f'. It follows that f has derivatives of all orders, that each derivative is representable by power series in Ω, and that*

$$f^{(k)}(z) = \sum_{n=k}^{\infty} n(n-1)\cdots(n-k+1)c_n(z-a)^{n-k} \tag{7}$$

if (1) *holds. Hence* (1) *implies that*

$$k!c_k = f^{(k)}(a) \qquad (k = 0, 1, 2, \ldots), \tag{8}$$

so that for each $a \in \Omega$ there is a unique sequence $\{c_n\}$ for which (1) *holds.*

We now describe a process which manufactures functions that are representable by power series. Special cases will be of importance later.

10.7 Theorem *Suppose μ is a complex (finite) measure on a measurable space X, φ is a complex measurable function on X, Ω is an open set in the plane which does not intersect $\varphi(X)$, and*

$$f(z) = \int_X \frac{d\mu(\zeta)}{\varphi(\zeta) - z} \qquad (z \in \Omega). \tag{1}$$

Then f is representable by power series in Ω.

PROOF Suppose $D(a;r) \subset \Omega$. Since

$$\left| \frac{z-a}{\varphi(\zeta) - a} \right| \le \frac{|z-a|}{r} < 1 \tag{2}$$

for every $z \in D(a;r)$ and every $\zeta \in X$, the geometric series

$$\sum_{n=0}^{\infty} \frac{(z-a)^n}{(\varphi(\zeta) - a)^{n+1}} = \frac{1}{\varphi(\zeta) - z} \tag{3}$$

converges uniformly on X, for every fixed $z \in D(a;r)$. Hence the series (3) may be substituted into (1), and $f(z)$ may be computed by interchanging summation and integration. It follows that

$$f(z) = \sum_{0}^{\infty} c_n(z-a)^n \qquad (z \in D(a;r)) \tag{4}$$

where

$$c_n = \int_X \frac{d\mu(\zeta)}{(\varphi(\zeta) - a)^{n+1}} \qquad (n = 0, 1, 2, \ldots). \tag{5}$$

Note: The convergence of the series (4) in $D(a;r)$ is a consequence of the proof. We can also derive it from (5), since (5) shows that

$$|c_n| \leq \frac{|\mu|(X)}{r^{n+1}} \qquad (n = 0, 1, 2, \ldots). \tag{6}$$

Integration over Paths

Our first major objective in this chapter is the converse of Theorem 10.6: Every $f \in H(\Omega)$ is representable by power series in Ω. The quickest route to this is via Cauchy's theorem which leads to an important integral representation of holomorphic functions. In this section the required integration theory will be developed; we shall keep it as simple as possible and shall regard it merely as a useful tool in the investigation of properties of holomorphic functions.

10.8 Definitions If X is a topological space, a *curve in X* is a continuous mapping γ of a compact interval $[\alpha,\beta] \subset R^1$ into X; here $\alpha < \beta$. We call $[\alpha,\beta]$ the *parameter interval* of γ and denote the range of γ by γ^*. Thus γ is a mapping, and γ^* is the set of all points $\gamma(t)$, for $\alpha \leq t \leq \beta$.

If the *initial point* $\gamma(\alpha)$ of γ coincides with its *end point* $\gamma(\beta)$, we call γ a *closed curve.*

A *path* is a piecewise continuously differentiable curve in the plane. More explicitly, a path with parameter interval $[\alpha,\beta]$ is a continuous complex function γ on $[\alpha,\beta]$, such that the following holds: There are finitely many points s_j, $\alpha = s_0 < s_1 < \cdots < s_n = \beta$, and the restriction of γ to each interval $[s_{j-1},s_j]$ has a continuous derivative on $[s_{j-1},s_j]$; however, at the points $s_1, \ldots, s_{n-1}$ the left- and right-hand derivatives of γ may differ.

A *closed path* is a closed curve which is also a path.

Now suppose γ is a path, and f is a continuous function on γ^*. The integral of f over γ is defined as an integral over the parameter interval $[\alpha,\beta]$ of γ:

$$\int_\gamma f(z)\,dz = \int_\alpha^\beta f(\gamma(t))\gamma'(t)\,dt. \tag{1}$$

Let φ be a continuously differentiable one-to-one mapping of an interval $[\alpha_1,\beta_1]$ onto $[\alpha,\beta]$, such that $\varphi(\alpha_1) = \alpha$, $\varphi(\beta_1) = \beta$, and put $\gamma_1 = \gamma \circ \varphi$. Then γ_1 is a path with parameter interval $[\alpha_1,\beta_1]$; the integral of f over γ_1 is

$$\int_{\alpha_1}^{\beta_1} f(\gamma_1(t))\gamma_1'(t)\,dt = \int_{\alpha_1}^{\beta_1} f(\gamma(\varphi(t)))\gamma'(\varphi(t))\varphi'(t)\,dt = \int_\alpha^\beta f(\gamma(s))\gamma'(s)\,ds,$$

so that our "reparametrization" has not changed the integral:

$$\int_{\gamma_1} f(z)\,dz = \int_\gamma f(z)\,dz. \tag{2}$$

Whenever (2) holds for a pair of paths γ and γ_1 (and for all f), we shall regard γ and γ_1 as equivalent.

It is convenient to be able to replace a path by an equivalent one, i.e., to choose parameter intervals at will. For instance, if the end point of γ_1 coincides with the initial point of γ_2, we may locate their parameter intervals so that γ_1 and γ_2 join to form one path γ, with the property that

(3)
$$\int_\gamma f = \int_{\gamma_1} f + \int_{\gamma_2} f$$

for every continuous f on $\gamma^* = \gamma_1^* \cup \gamma_2^*$.

However, suppose $[0,1]$ is the parameter interval of a path γ, and $\gamma_1(t) = \gamma(1-t)$, $0 \le t \le 1$. We call γ_1 the path *opposite* to γ, for the following reason: For any f continuous on $\gamma_1^* = \gamma^*$, we have

$$\int_0^1 f(\gamma_1(t))\gamma_1'(t)\,dt = -\int_0^1 f(\gamma(1-t))\gamma'(1-t)\,dt = -\int_0^1 f(\gamma(s))\gamma'(s)\,ds,$$

so that

(4)
$$\int_{\gamma_1} f = -\int_\gamma f.$$

From (1) we obtain the inequality

(5)
$$\left|\int_\gamma f(z)\,dz\right| \le \|f\|_\infty \int_\alpha^\beta |\gamma'(t)|\,dt,$$

where $\|f\|_\infty$ is the maximum of $|f|$ on γ^* and the last integral in (5) is (by definition) the *length* of γ.

10.9 Special Cases

(*a*) If a is a complex number and $r > 0$, the path defined by

(1)
$$\gamma(t) = a + re^{it} \qquad (0 \le t \le 2\pi)$$

is called the *positively oriented circle* with center at a and radius r; we have

(2)
$$\int_\gamma f(z)\,dz = ir\int_0^{2\pi} f(a + re^{i\theta})e^{i\theta}\,d\theta,$$

and the length of γ is $2\pi r$, as expected.

(*b*) If a and b are complex numbers, the path γ given by

(3)
$$\gamma(t) = a + (b-a)t \qquad (0 \le t \le 1)$$

is the *oriented interval* $[a,b]$; its length is $|b-a|$, and

(4)
$$\int_{[a,b]} f(z)\,dz = (b-a)\int_0^1 f[a + (b-a)t]\,dt.$$

If

$$(5)\quad \gamma_1(t) = \frac{a(\beta - t) + b(t - \alpha)}{\beta - \alpha} \qquad (\alpha \le t \le \beta),$$

we obtain an equivalent path, which we still denote by $[a,b]$. The path opposite to $[a,b]$ is $[b,a]$.

(*c*) Let $\{a,b,c\}$ be an ordered triple of complex numbers, let

$$\Delta = \Delta(a,b,c)$$

be the triangle with vertices at a, b, and c (Δ is the smallest convex set which contains a, b, and c), and define

$$(6)\qquad \int_{\partial\Delta} f = \int_{[a,b]} f + \int_{[b,c]} f + \int_{[c,a]} f,$$

for any f continuous on the boundary of Δ. We may regard (6) as the definition of its left side. Or we may regard $\partial\Delta$ as a path obtained by joining $[a,b]$ to $[b,c]$ to $[c,a]$, as outlined in Definition 10.8, in which case (6) is easily proved to be true.

If $\{a,b,c\}$ is permuted cyclically, we see from (6) that the left side of (6) is unaffected. If $\{a,b,c\}$ is replaced by $\{a,c,b\}$, then the left side of (6) changes sign.

We now come to a theorem which plays a very important role in function theory.

10.10 Theorem *Let γ be a closed path, let Ω be the complement of γ^* (relative to the plane), and define*

$$(1)\qquad \mathrm{Ind}_\gamma\,(z) = \frac{1}{2\pi i}\int_\gamma \frac{d\zeta}{\zeta - z} \qquad (z \in \Omega).$$

Then Ind_γ is an integer-valued function on Ω which is constant in each component of Ω and which is 0 in the unbounded component of Ω.

We call $\mathrm{Ind}_\gamma\,(z)$ the *index* of z with respect to γ. Note that γ^* is compact, hence γ^* lies in a bounded disc D whose complement D^c is connected; thus D^c lies in some component of Ω. This shows that Ω has precisely one unbounded component.

PROOF Let $[\alpha,\beta]$ be the parameter interval of γ, fix $z \in \Omega$, then

$$(2)\qquad \mathrm{Ind}_\gamma\,(z) = \frac{1}{2\pi i}\int_\alpha^\beta \frac{\gamma'(s)}{\gamma(s) - z}\,ds.$$

Since $w/2\pi i$ is an integer if and only if $e^w = 1$, the first assertion of the theorem, namely, that $\mathrm{Ind}_\gamma\,(z)$ is an integer, is equivalent to the assertion that $\varphi(\beta) = 1$, where

$$\varphi(t) = \exp\left\{\int_\alpha^t \frac{\gamma'(s)}{\gamma(s) - z}\, ds\right\} \qquad (\alpha \le t \le \beta). \tag{3}$$

Differentiation of (3) shows that

$$\frac{\varphi'(t)}{\varphi(t)} = \frac{\gamma'(t)}{\gamma(t) - z} \tag{4}$$

except possibly on a finite set S where γ is not differentiable. Therefore $\varphi/(\gamma - z)$ is a continuous function on $[\alpha,\beta]$ whose derivative is zero in $[\alpha,\beta] - S$. Since S is finite, $\varphi/(\gamma - z)$ is constant on $[\alpha,\beta]$; and since $\varphi(\alpha) = 1$, we obtain

$$\varphi(t) = \frac{\gamma(t) - z}{\gamma(\alpha) - z} \qquad (\alpha \le t \le \beta). \tag{5}$$

We now use the assumption that γ is a closed path, i.e., that $\gamma(\beta) = \gamma(\alpha)$; (5) shows that $\varphi(\beta) = 1$, and this, as we observed above, implies that $\text{Ind}_\gamma(z)$ is an integer.

By Theorem 10.7, (1) shows that $\text{Ind}_\gamma \in H(\Omega)$. The image of a connected set under a continuous mapping is connected ([26], Theorem 4.22), and since Ind_γ is an integer-valued function, Ind_γ must be constant on each component of Ω.

Finally, (2) shows that $|\text{Ind}_\gamma(z)| < 1$ if $|z|$ is sufficiently large. This implies that $\text{Ind}_\gamma(z) = 0$ in the unbounded component of Ω.

Remark: If $\lambda(t)$ denotes the integral in (3), the preceding proof shows that $2\pi\, \text{Ind}_\gamma(z)$ is the net increase in the imaginary part of $\lambda(t)$, as t runs from α to β, and this is the same as the net increase of the argument of $\gamma(t) - z$. (We have not defined "argument" and will have no need for it.) If we divide this increase by 2π, we obtain "the number of times that γ winds around z," and this explains why the term "winding number" is frequently used for the index. One virtue of the preceding proof is that it establishes the main properties of the index without any reference to the (multiple-valued) argument of a complex number.

10.11 Theorem *If γ is the positively oriented circle with center at a and radius r, then*

$$\text{Ind}_\gamma(z) = \begin{cases} 1 & \textit{if } |z - a| < r, \\ 0 & \textit{if } |z - a| > r. \end{cases}$$

PROOF We take γ as in Sec. 10.9(*a*). By Theorem 10.10, it is enough to compute $\text{Ind}_\gamma(a)$, and 10.9(2) shows that this equals

$$\frac{1}{2\pi i}\int_\gamma \frac{dz}{z - a} = \frac{r}{2\pi}\int_0^{2\pi} (re^{it})^{-1} e^{it}\, dt = 1.$$

The Cauchy Theorem

There are several forms of Cauchy's theorem. They all assert that if γ is a closed path in Ω, and if γ and Ω satisfy certain topological conditions, then the integral of every $f \in H(\Omega)$ over γ is 0. We shall first derive a simple version of this (Theorem 10.14) which is quite sufficient for many applications. A more general form will be established later, with the aid of Runge's theorem on approximation by rational functions.

10.12 Theorem *Suppose $F \in H(\Omega)$ and F' is continuous in Ω. Then*

$$\int_\gamma F'(z)\,dz = 0$$

for every closed path γ in Ω.

PROOF If $[\alpha,\beta]$ is the parameter interval of γ, the fundamental theorem of calculus shows that

$$\int_\gamma F'(z)\,dz = \int_\alpha^\beta F'(\gamma(t))\gamma'(t)\,dt = F(\gamma(\beta)) - F(\gamma(\alpha)) = 0,$$

since $\gamma(\beta) = \gamma(\alpha)$.

Corollary *Since z^n is the derivative of $z^{n+1}/(n+1)$ for all integers $n \neq -1$, we have*

$$\int_\gamma z^n\,dz = 0$$

for every closed path γ if $n = 0, 1, 2, \ldots$, and for those closed paths γ for which $0 \notin \gamma^*$ if $n = -2, -3, -4, \ldots$.

The case $n = -1$ was dealt with in Theorem 10.10.

10.13 Cauchy's Theorem for a Triangle *Suppose Δ is a closed triangle in a plane open set Ω, $p \in \Omega$, f is continuous on Ω, and $f \in H(\Omega - \{p\})$. Then*

$$\int_{\partial\Delta} f(z)\,dz = 0. \tag{1}$$

For the definition of $\partial\Delta$ we refer to Sec. 10.9(*c*). We shall see later that our hypothesis actually implies that $f \in H(\Omega)$, i.e., that the exceptional point p is not really exceptional. However, the above formulation of the theorem will be useful in the proof of the Cauchy formula.

PROOF We assume first that $p \notin \Delta$. Let a, b, and c be the vertices of Δ, let a', b', and c' be the midpoints of $[b,c]$, $[c,a]$, and $[a,b]$, respectively, and consider the four triangles Δ^j formed by the ordered triples

$$\{a,c',b'\}, \qquad \{b,a',c'\}, \qquad \{c,b',a'\}, \qquad \{a',b',c'\}. \tag{2}$$

If J is the value of the integral (1), it follows from 10.9(6) that

$$J = \sum_{j=1}^{4} \int_{\partial \Delta^j} f(z)\, dz. \tag{3}$$

The absolute value of at least one of the integrals on the right of (3) is therefore at least $|J/4|$. Call the corresponding triangle Δ_1, repeat the argument with Δ_1 in place of Δ, and so forth. This generates a sequence of triangles Δ_n such that $\Delta \supset \Delta_1 \supset \Delta_2 \supset \cdots$, such that the length of $\partial \Delta_n$ is $2^{-n}L$, if L is the length of $\partial \Delta$, and such that

$$|J| \leq 4^n \left| \int_{\partial \Delta_n} f(z)\, dz \right| \qquad (n = 1, 2, 3, \ldots). \tag{4}$$

There is a (unique) point z_0 which the triangles Δ_n have in common. Since Δ is compact, $z_0 \in \Delta$, so f is differentiable at z_0.

Let $\epsilon > 0$ be given. There exists an $r > 0$ such that

$$|f(z) - f(z_0) - f'(z_0)(z - z_0)| \leq \epsilon |z - z_0| \tag{5}$$

whenever $|z - z_0| < r$, and there exists an n such that $|z - z_0| < r$ for all $z \in \Delta_n$. For this n we also have $|z - z_0| \leq 2^{-n}L$ for all $z \in \Delta_n$. By the Corollary to Theorem 10.12,

$$\int_{\partial \Delta_n} f(z)\, dz = \int_{\partial \Delta_n} [f(z) - f(z_0) - f'(z_0)(z - z_0)]\, dz, \tag{6}$$

so that (5) implies

$$\left| \int_{\partial \Delta_n} f(z)\, dz \right| \leq \epsilon (2^{-n}L)^2, \tag{7}$$

and now (4) shows that $|J| \leq \epsilon L^2$. Hence $J = 0$ if $p \notin \Delta$.

Assume next that p is a vertex of Δ, say $p = a$. If a, b, and c are collinear, then (1) is trivial, for any continuous f. If not, choose points $x \in [a,b]$ and $y \in [a,c]$, both close to a, and observe that the integral of f over $\partial \Delta$ is the sum of the integrals over the boundaries of the triangles $\{a,x,y\}$, $\{x,b,y\}$, and $\{b,c,y\}$. The last two of these are 0, since these triangles do not contain p. Hence the integral over $\partial \Delta$ is the sum of the integrals over $[a,x]$, $[x,y]$, and $[y,a]$, and since these intervals can be made arbitrarily short and f is bounded on Δ, we again obtain (1).

Finally, if p is an arbitrary point of Δ, apply the preceding result to $\{a,b,p\}$, $\{b,c,p\}$, and $\{c,a,p\}$ to complete the proof.

10.14 Cauchy's Theorem in a Convex Set *Suppose Ω is a convex open set, $p \in \Omega$, f is continuous on Ω, and $f \in H(\Omega - \{p\})$. Then*

$$\int_\gamma f(z)\, dz = 0 \tag{1}$$

for every closed path γ in Ω.

PROOF Fix $a \in \Omega$. Since Ω is convex, Ω contains the straight line interval from a to z for every $z \in \Omega$, so we can define

$$(2) \qquad F(z) = \int_{[a,z]} f(\xi)\, d\xi \qquad (z \in \Omega).$$

For any z and $z_0 \in \Omega$, the triangle with vertices at a, z_0, and z lies in Ω; hence $F(z) - F(z_0)$ is the integral of f over $[z_0,z]$, by Theorem 10.13. Fixing z_0, we thus obtain

$$(3) \qquad \frac{F(z) - F(z_0)}{z - z_0} - f(z_0) = \frac{1}{z - z_0} \int_{[z_0,z]} [f(\xi) - f(z_0)]\, d\xi,$$

if $z \neq z_0$. Given $\epsilon > 0$, the continuity of f at z_0 shows that there is a $\delta > 0$ such that $|f(\xi) - f(z_0)| < \epsilon$ if $|\xi - z_0| < \delta$; hence the absolute value of the left side of (3) is less than ϵ as soon as $|z - z_0| < \delta$. This proves that $f = F'$, and the desired result follows from Theorem 10.12.

10.15 Cauchy's Formula in a Convex Set *Suppose γ is a closed path in a convex open set Ω, and $f \in H(\Omega)$. If $z \in \Omega$ and $z \notin \gamma^*$, then*

$$(1) \qquad f(z) \cdot \operatorname{Ind}_\gamma(z) = \frac{1}{2\pi i} \int_\gamma \frac{f(\xi)}{\xi - z}\, d\xi.$$

The case of greatest interest is, of course, $\operatorname{Ind}_\gamma(z) = 1$.

PROOF Fix z so that the above conditions hold, and define

$$(2) \qquad g(\xi) = \begin{cases} \dfrac{f(\xi) - f(z)}{\xi - z} & \text{if } \xi \in \Omega,\ \xi \neq z, \\ f'(z) & \text{if } \xi = z. \end{cases}$$

Then g satisfies the hypotheses of Theorem 10.14. Hence

$$(3) \qquad \frac{1}{2\pi i} \int_\gamma g(\xi)\, d\xi = 0.$$

If we substitute (2) into (3) we obtain (1).

The theorem concerning the representability of holomorphic functions by power series is an easy consequence of Theorem 10.15, if we take a circle for γ:

10.16 Theorem *For every open set Ω in the plane, every $f \in H(\Omega)$ is representable by power series in Ω.*

PROOF Suppose $f \in H(\Omega)$ and $D(a;R) \subset \Omega$. If γ is a positively oriented circle with center at a and radius $r < R$, the convexity of $D(a;R)$ allows us to apply Theorem 10.15; by Theorem 10.11, we obtain

$$(1) \qquad f(z) = \frac{1}{2\pi i} \int_\gamma \frac{f(\xi)}{\xi - z}\, d\xi \qquad (z \in D(a;r)).$$

But now we can apply Theorem 10.7, with $X = [0,2\pi]$, $\varphi = \gamma$, and $d\mu(t) = f(\gamma(t))\gamma'(t)\,dt$, and we conclude that there is a sequence $\{c_n\}$ such that

$$f(z) = \sum_{n=0}^{\infty} c_n(z-a)^n \qquad (z \in D(a;r)). \tag{2}$$

The uniqueness of $\{c_n\}$ (see the Corollary to Theorem 10.6) shows that the same power series is obtained for every $r < R$ (as long as a is fixed). Hence the representation (2) is valid for every $z \in D(a;R)$, and the proof is complete.

Corollary *If $f \in H(\Omega)$, then $f' \in H(\Omega)$.*

PROOF Combine Theorems 10.6 and 10.16.

The Cauchy theorem has a useful converse:

10.17 Morera's Theorem *Suppose f is a continuous complex function in an open set Ω such that*

$$\int_{\partial\Delta} f(z)\,dz = 0$$

for every closed triangle $\Delta \subset \Omega$. Then $f \in H(\Omega)$.

PROOF Let V be a convex open set in Ω. As in the proof of Theorem 10.14, we can construct $F \in H(V)$ such that $F' = f$. Since derivatives of holomorphic functions are holomorphic (Theorem 10.16), we have $f \in H(V)$, for every convex open $V \subset \Omega$, hence $f \in H(\Omega)$.

The Power Series Representation

The fact that every holomorphic function is locally the sum of a convergent power series has a large number of interesting consequences. A few of these are developed in this section.

10.18 Theorem *Suppose Ω is a region, $f \in H(\Omega)$, and*

$$Z(f) = \{a \in \Omega : f(a) = 0\}. \tag{1}$$

Then either $Z(f) = \Omega$, or $Z(f)$ has no limit point in Ω. In the latter case there corresponds to each $a \in Z(f)$ a unique positive integer $m = m(a)$ such that

$$f(z) = (z-a)^m g(z) \qquad (z \in \Omega), \tag{2}$$

where $g \in H(\Omega)$ and $g(a) \neq 0$; furthermore, $Z(f)$ is at most countable.

(We recall that regions are *connected* open sets.)

The integer m is called the *order* of the zero which f has at the point a. Clearly, $Z(f) = \Omega$ if and only if f is identically 0 in Ω. We call $Z(f)$ the *zero set* of f. Analogous results hold of course for the set of α-points of f, i.e., the zero set of $f - \alpha$, where α is any complex number.

PROOF Let A be the set of all limit points of $Z(f)$ in Ω. Since f is continuous, $A \subset Z(f)$.

Fix $a \in Z(f)$, and choose $r > 0$ so that $D(a;r) \subset \Omega$. By Theorem 10.16,

$$f(z) = \sum_{n=0}^{\infty} c_n(z - a)^n \qquad (z \in D(a;r)). \tag{3}$$

There are now two possibilities. Either all c_n are 0, in which case $D(a;r) \subset A$ and a is an interior point of A, or there is a smallest integer m [necessarily positive, since $f(a) = 0$] such that $c_m \neq 0$. In that case, define

$$g(z) = \begin{cases} (z - a)^{-m}f(z) & (z \in \Omega - \{a\}), \\ c_m & (z = a). \end{cases} \tag{4}$$

Then (2) holds. It is clear that $g \in H(\Omega - \{a\})$. But (3) implies

$$g(z) = \sum_{k=0}^{\infty} c_{m+k}(z - a)^k \qquad (z \in D(a;r)). \tag{5}$$

Hence $g \in H(D(a;r))$, so actually $g \in H(\Omega)$.

Moreover, $g(a) \neq 0$, and the continuity of g shows that there is a neighborhood of a in which g has no zero. Thus a is an isolated point of $Z(f)$, by (2).

If $a \in A$, the first case must therefore occur. So A is open. If $B = \Omega - A$, it is clear from the definition of A as a set of limit points that B is open. Thus Ω is the union of the disjoint open sets A and B; and since Ω is connected, we have either $A = \Omega$, in which case $Z(f) = \Omega$, or $A = \varnothing$. In the latter case, $Z(f)$ has at most finitely many points in each compact subset of Ω, and since Ω is σ-compact, $Z(f)$ is at most countable.

Corollary *If f and g are holomorphic functions in a region Ω and if $f(z) = g(z)$ for all z in some set which has a limit point in Ω, then $f(z) = g(z)$ for all $z \in \Omega$.*

In other words, a holomorphic function in a region Ω is determined by its values on any set which has a limit point in Ω. This is an important uniqueness theorem.

Note: The theorem fails if we drop the assumption that Ω is connected: if $\Omega = \Omega_0 \cup \Omega_1$, and Ω_0 and Ω_1 are disjoint open sets, put $f = 0$ in Ω_0 and $f = 1$ in Ω_1.

10.19 Definition If $a \in \Omega$ and $f \in H(\Omega - \{a\})$, then f is said to have an *isolated singularity* at the point a. If f can be so defined at a that the extended function is holomorphic in Ω, the singularity is said to be *removable*.

10.20 Theorem *Suppose $f \in H(\Omega - \{a\})$ and f is bounded in $D'(a;r)$, for some $r > 0$. Then f has a removable singularity at a.*

Recall that $D'(a;r) = \{z: 0 < |z - a| < r\}$.

PROOF Define $h(a) = 0$, and $h(z) = (z - a)^2 f(z)$ in $\Omega - \{a\}$. Our boundedness assumption shows that $h'(a) = 0$. Since h is evidently differentiable at every other point of Ω, we have $h \in H(\Omega)$, so

$$h(z) = \sum_{n=2}^{\infty} c_n(z - a)^n \qquad (z \in D(a;r)).$$

We obtain the desired holomorphic extension of f by setting $f(a) = c_2$, for then

$$f(z) = \sum_{n=0}^{\infty} c_{n+2}(z - a)^n \qquad (z \in D(a;r)).$$

10.21 Theorem *If $a \in \Omega$ and $f \in H(\Omega - \{a\})$, then one of the following three cases must occur:*

(*a*) *f has a removable singularity at a.*
(*b*) *There are complex numbers $c_1, \ldots, c_m$, where m is a positive integer and $c_m \neq 0$, such that*

$$f(z) - \sum_{k=1}^{m} \frac{c_k}{(z - a)^k}$$

has a removable singularity at a.
(*c*) *If $r > 0$ and $D(a;r) \subset \Omega$, then $f(D'(a;r))$ is dense in the plane.*

In case (*b*), f is said to have a *pole of order m* at a. The function

$$\sum_{k=1}^{m} c_k(z - a)^{-k},$$

a polynomial in $(z - a)^{-1}$, is called the *principal part* of f at a. It is clear in this situation that $|f(z)| \to \infty$ as $z \to a$.

In case (*c*), f is said to have an *essential singularity* at a. A statement equivalent to (*c*) is that to each complex number w there corresponds a sequence $\{z_n\}$ such that $z_n \to a$ and $f(z_n) \to w$ as $n \to \infty$.

PROOF Suppose (*c*) fails. Then there exist $r > 0$, $\delta > 0$, and a complex number w such that $|f(z) - w| > \delta$ in $D'(a;r)$. Let us write D for $D(a;r)$ and D' for $D'(a;r)$. Define

$$(1) \qquad g(z) = \frac{1}{f(z) - w} \qquad (z \in D').$$

Then $g \in H(D')$ and $|g| < 1/\delta$. By Theorem 10.20, g extends to a holomorphic function in D.

If $g(a) \neq 0$, (1) shows that f is bounded in $D'(a;\rho)$ for some $\rho > 0$. Hence (*a*) holds, by Theorem 10.20.

If g has a zero of order $m \geq 1$ at a, Theorem 10.18 shows that

$$(2) \qquad g(z) = (z - a)^m g_1(z) \qquad (z \in D),$$

where $g_1 \in H(D)$ and $g_1(a) \neq 0$. Also, g_1 has no zero in D', by (1). Put $h = 1/g_1$ in D. Then $h \in H(D)$, h has no zero in D, and

$$(3) \qquad f(z) - w = (z - a)^{-m} h(z) \qquad (z \in D').$$

But h has an expansion of the form

$$(4) \qquad h(z) = \sum_{n=0}^{\infty} b_n (z - a)^n \qquad (z \in D),$$

with $b_0 \neq 0$. Now (3) shows that (*b*) holds, with $c_k = b_{m-k}$, $k = 1, \ldots, m$.

This completes the proof.

We shall now exploit the fact that the restriction of a power series $\Sigma c_n (z - a)^n$ to a circle with center at a is a trigonometric series.

10.22 Theorem *If*

$$(1) \qquad f(z) = \sum_{n=0}^{\infty} c_n (z - a)^n \qquad (z \in D(a;R))$$

and if $0 < r < R$, *then*

$$(2) \qquad \sum_{n=0}^{\infty} |c_n|^2 r^{2n} = \frac{1}{2\pi} \int_{-\pi}^{\pi} |f(a + re^{i\theta})|^2 \, d\theta.$$

PROOF We have

$$(3) \qquad f(a + re^{i\theta}) = \sum_{n=0}^{\infty} c_n r^n e^{in\theta}.$$

For $r < R$, the series (3) converges uniformly on $[-\pi,\pi]$. Hence

$$(4) \quad c_n r^n = \frac{1}{2\pi} \int_{-\pi}^{\pi} f(a + re^{i\theta})e^{-in\theta}\, d\theta \qquad (n = 0, 1, 2, \ldots),$$

and (2) is seen to be a special case of Parseval's formula.

Here are some consequences:

10.23 Liouville's Theorem *Every bounded entire function is constant.*

Recall that a function is *entire* if it is holomorphic in the whole plane.

PROOF Suppose f is entire, $|f(z)| < M$ for all z, and $f(z) = \Sigma c_n z^n$ for all z. By Theorem 10.22,

$$\sum_{n=0}^{\infty} |c_n|^2 r^{2n} < M^2$$

for all r, which is possible only if $c_n = 0$ for all $n \geq 1$.

10.24 The Maximum Modulus Theorem *Suppose Ω is a region, $f \in H(\Omega)$, and $a \in \Omega$. Then either f is constant in Ω, or each neighborhood of a contains a point b such that $|f(a)| < |f(b)|$.*

In other words, either f is constant or $|f|$ has no local maximum at any point of Ω.

PROOF Assume there exists an $R > 0$ such that $D(a;R) \subset \Omega$ and such that $|f(z)| \leq |f(a)|$ for all $z \in D(a;R)$. Theorem 10.22, applied to the expansion

$$f(z) = \sum_{n=0}^{\infty} c_n(z - a)^n,$$

shows for every $r < R$ that

$$\sum_{n=0}^{\infty} |c_n|^2 r^{2n} \leq |f(a)|^2 = |c_0|^2.$$

Hence $c_1 = c_2 = c_3 = \cdots = 0$, $f(z) = f(a)$ in $D(a;R)$, and since Ω is connected, f is constant in Ω, by Theorem 10.18.

10.25 Theorem (Cauchy's Estimates) *If $f \in H(D(a;R))$ and $|f(z)| \leq M$ for all $z \in D(a;R)$, then*

$$(1) \qquad |f^{(n)}(a)| \leq \frac{n!M}{R^n} \qquad (n = 1, 2, 3, \ldots).$$

PROOF For each $r < R$, each term of the series 10.22(2) is bounded above by M^2.

If we take $a = 0$, $R = 1$, and $f(z) = z^n$, then $M = 1$, $f^{(n)}(0) = n!$, and we see that (1) cannot be improved.

10.26 Definition A sequence $\{f_j\}$ of functions in Ω is said to *converge to* f *uniformly on compact subsets of* Ω if to every compact $K \subset \Omega$ and to every $\epsilon > 0$ there corresponds an $N = N(K,\epsilon)$ such that $|f_j(z) - f(z)| < \epsilon$ for all $z \in K$ if $j > N$.

For instance, the sequence $\{z^n\}$ converges to 0 uniformly on compact subsets of $D(0;1)$, but the convergence is *not* uniform in $D(0;1)$.

It is uniform convergence on compact subsets which arises most naturally in connection with limit operations on holomorphic functions. The term "almost uniform convergence" is sometimes used for this concept.

10.27 Theorem *Suppose $f_j \in H(\Omega)$, for $j = 1, 2, 3, \ldots$, and $f_j \to f$ uniformly on compact subsets of Ω. Then $f \in H(\Omega)$, and $f_j' \to f'$ uniformly on compact subsets of Ω.*

PROOF Since the convergence is uniform on each compact disc in Ω, f is continuous. Let Δ be a triangle in Ω. Then Δ is compact, so

$$\int_{\partial\Delta} f(z)\,dz = \lim_{j\to\infty} \int_{\partial\Delta} f_j(z)\,dz = 0,$$

by Cauchy's theorem. Hence Morera's theorem implies that $f \in H(\Omega)$.

Let K be compact, $K \subset \Omega$. There exists an $r > 0$ such that the union E of the closed discs $\bar{D}(z;r)$, for all $z \in K$, is a compact subset of Ω. Applying Theorem 10.25 to $f - f_j$, we have

$$|f'(z) - f_j'(z)| \le r^{-1}\|f - f_j\|_E \qquad (z \in K),$$

where $\|f\|_E$ denotes the supremum of $|f|$ on E. Since $f_j \to f$ uniformly on E, it follows that $f_j' \to f'$ uniformly on K.

Corollary *Under the same hypothesis, $f_j^{(n)} \to f^{(n)}$ uniformly, as $j \to \infty$, on every compact set $K \subset \Omega$.*

Compare this with the situation on the real line, where sequences of infinitely differentiable functions can converge uniformly to nowhere differentiable functions!

The Open Mapping Theorem

If Ω is a region and $f \in H(\Omega)$, then $f(\Omega)$ is either a region or a point.

This will be proved, in more detailed form, in Theorem 10.32. The proof will depend on facts about the index, on Cauchy's theorem, and on the notion of residue:

10.28 Definition Suppose $a \in \Omega$, $f \in H(\Omega - \{a\})$, and f has a pole at a, with principal part

$$(1) \qquad Q(z) = \sum_{k=1}^{m} c_k(z-a)^{-k},$$

as defined in Theorem 10.21. We call the number c_1 the *residue* of f at a:

$$(2) \qquad c_1 = \operatorname{Res}(f;a).$$

10.29 Theorem *Suppose Ω is a convex region, $a_1, \ldots, a_n$ are distinct points in Ω, f is holomorphic in $\Omega - (\{a_1\} \cup \cdots \cup \{a_n\})$, and f has a pole at each of the points a_k $(1 \le k \le n)$. If γ is a closed path in Ω such that $a_k \notin \gamma^*$ $(k = 1, \ldots, n)$, then*

$$(1) \qquad \frac{1}{2\pi i}\int_\gamma f(z)\,dz = \sum_{k=1}^{n} \operatorname{Res}(f;a_k)\cdot \operatorname{Ind}_\gamma(a_k).$$

PROOF Let Q_k be the principal part of f at a_k. Since

$$f - (Q_1 + \cdots + Q_n)$$

has only removable singularities in Ω, Cauchy's theorem (Theorem 10.14) shows that the integral in (1) is the same as the integral of $Q_1 + \cdots + Q_n$ over γ. This latter integral is equal to the right side of (1), by the Corollary to Theorem 10.12.

A more general version of this so-called "residue theorem" (for non-convex regions) will be derived in Chap. 13.

10.30 Theorem *Suppose $f \in H(\Omega)$ and f has a zero of order m at a point $a \in \Omega$. Then f'/f has a simple pole at a, and*

$$(1) \qquad \operatorname{Res}\left(\frac{f'}{f};a\right) = m.$$

If f has a pole of order m at a, and $f \in H(\Omega - \{a\})$, then

$$(2) \qquad \operatorname{Res}\left(\frac{f'}{f};a\right) = -m.$$

PROOF If f has a zero of order m at a, then

$$(3) \qquad f(z) = (z-a)^m g(z),$$

where $g \in H(\Omega)$, $g(a) \neq 0$. For $z \neq a$,

$$(4) \qquad \frac{f'(z)}{f(z)} = \frac{m}{z-a} + \frac{g'(z)}{g(z)}.$$

Since $g(a) \neq 0$, $1/g$ is holomorphic in a neighborhood of a. Hence the principal part of f'/f at a is $m(z-a)^{-1}$. This proves (1). The proof of (2) is analogous.

10.31 Theorem *Suppose $f \in H(\Omega)$, γ is a positively oriented circle in Ω whose interior D also lies in Ω, and Γ is the path defined by*

$$\Gamma(t) = f(\gamma(t)) \qquad (0 \leq t \leq 2\pi), \tag{1}$$

where $[0,2\pi]$ is the parameter interval of γ. Fix w so that $w \notin \Gamma^*$. Then the number of zeros of $f - w$ in D (counted according to their multiplicities) is equal to $\mathrm{Ind}_\Gamma(w)$.

To count the zeros of a function according to their multiplicities means that a zero of order m, say, is counted as m zeros.

PROOF The number of zeros of $f - w$ in D is equal to the sum of the residues of $f'/(f-w)$ in D, by Theorem 10.30, and since γ^* lies in a convex subregion of Ω, Theorem 10.29 shows that this sum is equal to

$$\frac{1}{2\pi i}\int_\gamma \frac{f'(z)}{f(z)-w}\,dz = \frac{1}{2\pi i}\int_0^{2\pi} \frac{f'(\gamma(t))}{f(\gamma(t))-w}\,\gamma'(t)\,dt$$

$$= \frac{1}{2\pi i}\int_0^{2\pi} \frac{\Gamma'(t)}{\Gamma(t)-w}\,dt = \frac{1}{2\pi i}\int_\Gamma \frac{d\xi}{\xi - w} = \mathrm{Ind}_\Gamma(w).$$

10.32 The Open Mapping Theorem *Suppose Ω is a region, $f \in H(\Omega)$, f is not constant, $z_0 \in \Omega$, and $w_0 = f(z_0)$. Let m be the order of the zero which the function $f - w_0$ has at z_0.*

Then there exist open sets V and W such that $z_0 \in V \subset \Omega$, $W = f(V)$, and for each $w \in W - \{w_0\}$ there are exactly m distinct points $z \in V$ at which $f(z) = w$.

It follows that each $w_0 \in f(\Omega)$ is an interior point of $f(\Omega)$, hence $f(\Omega)$ is open. (Exercise 17, Chap. 13, gives a more precise statement.)

See page 267

PROOF Since f is not constant, f' is not identically 0. Hence z_0 is not a limit of zeros of $f - w_0$, nor is z_0 a limit point of zeros of f'. Hence there exists an $r > 0$ such that $D(z_0;2r) \subset \Omega$ and such that neither $f - w_0$ nor f' has a zero in $D'(z_0;2r)$. Let γ be the positively oriented circle with center at z_0 and radius r, and put $\Gamma = f \circ \gamma$, as in Theorem 10.31. Then $w_0 \notin \Gamma^*$. Let W be that component of the complement of Γ^* which contains w_0, and put

$$V = D(z_0;r) \cap f^{-1}(W).$$

Since W is open, the continuity of f shows that V is open.

By Theorem 10.31, $\mathrm{Ind}_\Gamma(w_0) = m$. Since Ind_Γ is constant in W (Theorem 10.10), we can use Theorem 10.31 again to conclude that the function $f - w$ has exactly m zeros in $D(z_0;r)$ (hence in V) for each $w \in W$. Since f' has no zero in $D'(z_0;r)$, these zeros of $f - w$ must all be distinct if $w \neq w_0$, for if $f - w$ had a zero of order $k > 1$ at some point, then f' would have a zero of order $k - 1$ at that point. This completes the proof.

10.33 Let us restate Theorem 10.32: *If $z_0 \in \Omega$, $f \in H(\Omega)$, and $f - w_0$ has a zero of order $m \geq 1$ at z_0, then there are neighborhoods V of z_0 and W of w_0 such that f is an exactly m-to-1 mapping of $V - \{z_0\}$ onto $W - \{w_0\}$.*

It is clear that the maximum modulus theorem is a corollary of this, and so is the following analogue:

If $f \in H(\Omega)$, where Ω is a region, then neither the real part of f nor the imaginary part of f can have a local maximum or minimum, unless f is constant.

The case $m = 1$ in Theorem 10.32 is of particular interest:

10.34 Theorem *Suppose Ω is a region, $f \in H(\Omega)$, $z_0 \in \Omega$, $f(z_0) = w_0$, $f'(z_0) \neq 0$. Then there exist neighborhoods V and W of z_0 and w_0 such that f is a one-to-one mapping of V onto W. If g is defined in W by*

$$(1) \qquad g(f(z)) = z \qquad (z \in V),$$

then $g \in H(W)$.

In other words, f has a holomorphic inverse in W.

PROOF The only assertion which is not already contained in Theorem 10.32 is the claim that g is holomorphic in W. Fix $w_1 \in W$; then $f(z_1) = w_1$ for a unique $z_1 \in V$. If $w \in W$ and $g(w) = z$, we have

$$(2) \qquad \frac{g(w) - g(w_1)}{w - w_1} = \frac{z - z_1}{f(z) - f(z_1)}.$$

Since f is an open mapping, g is continuous; hence $z \to z_1$ if $w \to w_1$. Also, $f'(z_1) \neq 0$ since f is one-to-one in a neighborhood of z_1 (Theorem 10.32). If we let $w \to w_1$, (2) now shows that $g'(w_1) = 1/f'(z_1)$. So g is differentiable at every point of W, and the proof is complete.

We already know that $\text{Ind}_\gamma(z)$, for $z \notin \gamma^*$, is unchanged if γ is fixed and z is varied slightly. But we can also fix z and vary γ. Our next theorem deals with this situation; it leads to Rouché's theorem, which enables us to estimate the number of zeros of one holomorphic function in a disc if we know how many zeros some "nearby" function has.

10.35 Theorem *Suppose γ_1 and γ_2 are closed paths with parameter interval $[\alpha,\beta]$, and suppose that*

$$(1) \qquad |\gamma_1(t) - \gamma_2(t)| < |\gamma_1(t)| \qquad (\alpha \leq t \leq \beta).$$

Then

(2) $$\mathrm{Ind}_{\gamma_1}(0) = \mathrm{Ind}_{\gamma_2}(0).$$

PROOF Note first that (1) implies that $0 \notin \gamma_1^*$ and $0 \notin \gamma_2^*$. Put $\gamma(t) = \gamma_2(t)/\gamma_1(t)$. Then

(3) $$\frac{\gamma'}{\gamma} = \frac{\gamma_2'}{\gamma_2} - \frac{\gamma_1'}{\gamma_1}$$

and (1) shows that

(4) $$|1 - \gamma(t)| < 1 \qquad (\alpha \le t \le \beta).$$

Thus $\gamma^* \subset D(1;1)$, hence 0 lies in the unbounded component of the complement of γ^*, so $\mathrm{Ind}_\gamma(0) = 0$. Now integration of (3) over $[\alpha,\beta]$ gives (2).

10.36 Rouché's Theorem *Suppose* $f \in H(\Omega)$, $g \in H(\Omega)$, $\bar{D}(a;r) \subset \Omega$, *and*

(1) $$|f(z) - g(z)| < |f(z)| \qquad \text{if } |z - a| = r.$$

Then f and g have the same number of zeros in $D(a;r)$ (if they are counted according to their multiplicities).

PROOF Let γ be the positively oriented circle with center at a and radius r. Put $\gamma_1 = f \circ \gamma$ and $\gamma_2 = g \circ \gamma$, and let N_1 and N_2 be the number of zeros of f and g in $D(a;r)$. By Theorems 10.31 and 10.35,

$$N_1 = \mathrm{Ind}_{\gamma_1}(0) = \mathrm{Ind}_{\gamma_2}(0) = N_2.$$

10.37 An Application *If n is a positive integer and*

$$g(z) = z^n + a_{n-1}z^{n-1} + \cdots + a_1 z + a_0,$$

where $a_0, \ldots, a_{n-1}$ are complex numbers, then g has precisely n zeros in the plane.

Of course, these zeros are counted according to their multiplicities. This theorem contains the fact that the complex field is algebraically closed, i.e., that every nonconstant polynomial with complex coefficients has at least one complex zero. This can also be derived as a corollary of Liouville's theorem. (Apply Liouville's theorem to $1/g$.)

PROOF Put $f(z) = z^n$. If $r > 1$ and $r > |a_0| + \cdots + |a_{n-1}|$, and if $|z| = r$, then

$$|f(z) - g(z)| = \left|\sum_{k=0}^{n-1} a_k z^k\right| \le r^{n-1}\sum_{k=0}^{n-1}|a_k| < r^n = |f(z)|.$$

Hence f and g have the same number of zeros in $D(0;r)$, by Rouché's theorem; and since f has n zeros, the proof is complete.

Exercises

1 The following fact was tacitly used in this chapter: If A and B are disjoint subsets of the plane, if A is compact and if B is closed, then there exists a $\delta > 0$ such that $|\alpha - \beta| \geq \delta$ for all $\alpha \in A$ and $\beta \in B$. Prove this, with an arbitrary metric space in place of the plane.

2 Suppose P and Q are polynomials, the degree of Q exceeds that of P by at least 2, and the rational function $R = P/Q$ has no pole on the real axis. Prove that the integral of R over $(-\infty,\infty)$ is $2\pi i$ times the sum of the residues of R in the upper half plane. [Replace the integral over $(-A,A)$ by one over a suitable semicircle, and apply the residue theorem.] What is the analogous statement for the lower half plane? Use this method to compute

$$\int_{-\infty}^{\infty} \frac{x^2}{1 + x^4}\, dx.$$

3 Compute $\int_{-\infty}^{\infty} e^{itx}/(1 + x^2)\, dx$ for real t, by the method described in Exercise 2. Check your answer against the inversion theorem for Fourier transforms.

4 Let γ be the positively oriented unit circle, and compute

$$\frac{1}{2\pi i} \int_\gamma \frac{e^z - e^{-z}}{z^4}\, dz.$$

5 Suppose α is a complex number, $|\alpha| \neq 1$, and compute

$$\int_0^{2\pi} \frac{d\theta}{1 - 2\alpha \cos\theta + \alpha^2}$$

by integrating $(z - \alpha)^{-1}(z - 1/\alpha)^{-1}$ over the unit circle.

6 Suppose $f \in H(\Omega)$, $\bar{D}(a;r) \subset \Omega$, γ is the positively oriented circle with center at a and radius r, and f has no zero on γ^*. For $p = 0$, the integral

$$\frac{1}{2\pi i} \int_\gamma \frac{f'(z)}{f(z)} z^p\, dz$$

is equal to the number of zeros of f in $D(a;r)$. What is the value of this integral (in terms of the zeros of f) for $p = 1, 2, 3, \ldots$? What is the answer if z^p is replaced by any $\varphi \in H(\Omega)$?

7 Consider a polynomial in two variables with complex coefficients $P(z,w)$. Suppose w_0 is chosen so that all zeros of $P(z,w_0)$ are distinct. Use Rouché's theorem to prove that this property holds for all w in some neighborhood of w_0. Can you generalize this, from polynomials to other functions?

8 Suppose Ω is a region, $f_n \in H(\Omega)$ for $n = 1, 2, 3, \ldots$, none of the functions f_n has a zero in Ω, and $\{f_n\}$ converges to f uniformly on compact subsets of Ω. Prove that either f has no zero in Ω or $f(z) = 0$ for all $z \in \Omega$.

9 Suppose $P_n(z) = 1 + z/1! + \cdots + z^n/n!$, $Q_n(z) = P_n(z) - 1$, where $n = 1, 2, 3, \ldots$. What can you say about the location of the zeros of P_n and Q_n for large n? Be as specific as you can.

10 Suppose f and g are entire functions, and $|f(z)| \leq |g(z)|$ for every z. What conclusion can you draw?

11 Suppose f is an entire function, and

$$|f(z)| \leq A + B|z|^k$$

for all z, where A, B, and k are positive numbers. Prove that f must be a polynomial.

12 Suppose $f \in H(\Omega)$, Ω contains the closed unit disc, and $|f(z)| < 1$ if $|z| = 1$. How many fixed points must f have in the disc? That is, how many solutions does the equation $f(z) = z$ have there?

13 Suppose $f \in H(\Omega)$, Ω contains the closed unit disc, $|f(z)| > 2$ if $|z| = 1$, and $f(0) = 1$. Must f have a zero in the unit disc?

14 Suppose Ω is a region, $\varphi \in H(\Omega)$, φ' has no zero in Ω, $f \in H(\varphi(\Omega))$, $g = f \circ \varphi$, $z_0 \in \Omega$, and $w_0 = \varphi(z_0)$. Prove that if f has a zero of order m at w_0, then g also has a zero of order m at z_0. How is this modified if φ' has a zero of order k at z_0?

15 Suppose μ is a complex measure on a measure space X, Ω is an open set in the plane, φ is a bounded function on $\Omega \times X$ such that $\varphi(z,t)$ is a measurable function of t, for each $z \in \Omega$, and $\varphi(z,t)$ is holomorphic in Ω, for each $t \in X$. Define

$$f(z) = \int_X \varphi(z,t)\, d\mu(t)$$

for $z \in \Omega$. Prove that $f \in H(\Omega)$. *Hint:* Show that to every compact $K \subset \Omega$ there corresponds a constant $M < \infty$ such that

$$\left| \frac{\varphi(z,t) - \varphi(z_0,t)}{z - z_0} \right| < M \qquad (z \text{ and } z_0 \in K,\ t \in X).$$

16 Use Exercise 15 to determine the regions in which the following functions are defined and holomorphic:

$$f(z) = \int_0^1 \frac{dt}{1 + tz}, \qquad g(z) = \int_0^\infty \frac{e^{tz}}{1 + t^2}\, dt, \qquad h(z) = \int_{-1}^1 \frac{e^{tz}}{1 + t^2}\, dt.$$

17 Suppose $\{f_n\}$ is a uniformly bounded sequence of holomorphic functions in Ω such that $\{f_n(z)\}$ converges for every $z \in \Omega$. Prove that the convergence is uniform on every compact subset of Ω.

Hint: Apply the dominated convergence theorem to the Cauchy formula for $f_n - f_m$.

18 Suppose $f \in H(U)$, where U is the open unit disc, f is one-to-one in U, $\Omega = f(U)$, and $f(z) = \Sigma c_n z^n$. Prove that the area of Ω is

$$\pi \sum_{n=1}^{\infty} n|c_n|^2.$$

Hint: The Jacobian of f is $|f'|^2$.

19 There is a region Ω such that $\exp(\Omega) = D(1;1)$. Show that exp is one-to-one in Ω, but that there are many such Ω. Fix one, and define $\log z$, for $|z - 1| < 1$, to be that $w \in \Omega$ for which $e^w = z$. Prove that $\log'(z) = 1/z$. Find the coefficients a_n in

$$\frac{1}{z} = \sum_{n=0}^{\infty} a_n(z-1)^n$$

and hence find the coefficients c_n in the expansion

$$\log z = \sum_{n=0}^{\infty} c_n(z-1)^n.$$

In what other discs can this be done?

20 Suppose Ω_1 and Ω_2 are plane regions, f and g are nonconstant complex functions defined in Ω_1 and Ω_2, respectively, and $f(\Omega_1) \subset \Omega_2$. Put $h = g \circ f$. If f and g are holomorphic, we know that h is holomorphic. Suppose we know that f and h are holomorphic. Can we conclude anything about g? What if we know that g and h are holomorphic?

21 Suppose $f \in H(U)$, $g \in H(U)$, and neither f nor g has a zero in U. If

$$\frac{f'}{f}\left(\frac{1}{n}\right) = \frac{g'}{g}\left(\frac{1}{n}\right) \qquad (n = 1, 2, 3, \ldots)$$

find another simple relation between f and g.

22 Compute

$$\int_0^{\infty} \frac{dx}{1+x^n} \qquad (n = 2, 3, 4, \ldots).$$

[For even n, the method of Exercise 2 can be used. However, a different path can be chosen which simplifies the computation and which also works for odd n: from 0 to R to $R \exp(2\pi i/n)$ to 0.]

Answer: $(\pi/n)/\sin(\pi/n)$.

11

Harmonic Functions

The Cauchy-Riemann Equations

11.1 The Operators ∂ and $\bar{\partial}$ Suppose f is a complex function defined in a plane open set Ω. Regard f as a transformation which maps Ω into R^2, and assume that f has a differential at some point $z_0 \in \Omega$, in the sense of Definition 8.22. For simplicity, suppose $z_0 = f(z_0) = 0$. Our differentiability assumption is then equivalent to the existence of two complex numbers α and β (the partial derivatives of f with respect to x and y at $z_0 = 0$) such that

$$(1) \qquad f(z) = \alpha x + \beta y + \eta(z)z \qquad (z = x + iy),$$

where $\eta(z) \to 0$ as $z \to 0$.

Since $2x = z + \bar{z}$ and $2iy = z - \bar{z}$, (1) can be rewritten in the form

$$(2) \qquad f(z) = \frac{\alpha - i\beta}{2} z + \frac{\alpha + i\beta}{2} \bar{z} + \eta(z)z.$$

This suggests the introduction of the differential operators

$$(3) \qquad \partial = \frac{1}{2}\left(\frac{\partial}{\partial x} - i\frac{\partial}{\partial y}\right), \qquad \bar{\partial} = \frac{1}{2}\left(\frac{\partial}{\partial x} + i\frac{\partial}{\partial y}\right).$$

Now (2) becomes

$$(4) \qquad \frac{f(z)}{z} = (\partial f)(0) + (\bar{\partial} f)(0) \cdot \frac{\bar{z}}{z} + \eta(z) \qquad (z \neq 0).$$

For real z, $\bar{z}/z = 1$; for pure imaginary z, $\bar{z}/z = -1$. Hence $f(z)/z$ has a limit at 0 if and only if $(\bar{\partial} f)(0) = 0$, and we obtain the following characterization of holomorphic functions:

11.2 Theorem *Suppose f is a complex function in Ω which has a differential at every point of Ω. Then $f \in H(\Omega)$ if and only if the Cauchy-Riemann equation*

$$(1) \qquad (\bar{\partial} f)(z) = 0$$

holds for every $z \in \Omega$. *In that case we have*

$$f'(z) = (\partial f)(z) \qquad (z \in \Omega). \tag{2}$$

If $f = u + iv$, u and v real, (1) splits into the pair of equations

$$u_x = v_y, \qquad u_y = -v_x$$

where the subscripts refer to partial differentiation with respect to the indicated variable. These are the *Cauchy-Riemann equations* which must be satisfied by the real and imaginary parts of a holomorphic function.

11.3 The Laplacian If f has continuous second-order partial derivatives, then $f_{xy} = f_{yx}$, and therefore

$$f_{xx} + f_{yy} = 4\partial\bar{\partial} f. \tag{1}$$

This is the Laplacian of f. The *harmonic functions* in an open set Ω are those which satisfy the *Laplace equation*

$$\partial\bar{\partial} f = 0 \tag{2}$$

at every point of Ω. It is clear from (1) that the Laplacian of a real function is real. Hence *a complex function is harmonic in* Ω *if and only if both its real part and its imaginary part are harmonic in* Ω.

If f is holomorphic, then $\bar{\partial} f = 0$, f has continuous derivatives of all orders, and therefore (1) shows:

11.4 Theorem *Holomorphic functions are harmonic.*

We shall now turn our attention to an integral representation of harmonic functions which is closely related to the Cauchy formula for holomorphic functions. It will show, among other things, that every real harmonic function is locally the real part of a holomorphic function, and it will yield information about the boundary behavior of certain classes of holomorphic functions in open discs.

The Poisson Integral

11.5 The Poisson Kernel This is the function

$$P_r(t) = \sum_{-\infty}^{\infty} r^{|n|} e^{int} \qquad (0 \le r < 1,\ t \text{ real}). \tag{1}$$

We may regard $P_r(t)$ as a function of two variables r and t or as a family of functions of t, indexed by r.

If $z = re^{i\theta}$ $(0 \le r < 1,\ \theta$ real), a simple calculation, made in Sec. 5.24, shows that

$$P_r(\theta - t) = \operatorname{Re}\left[\frac{e^{it} + z}{e^{it} - z}\right] = \frac{1 - r^2}{1 - 2r\cos(\theta - t) + r^2}. \tag{2}$$

From (1) we see that

(3) $$\frac{1}{2\pi}\int_{-\pi}^{\pi} P_r(t)\,dt = 1 \qquad (0 \le r < 1).$$

From (2) it follows that $P_r(t) > 0$, $P_r(t) = P_r(-t)$, that

(4) $$P_r(t) < P_r(\delta) \qquad (0 < \delta < |t| \le \pi),$$

and that

(5) $$\lim_{r\to 1} P_r(\delta) = 0 \qquad (0 < \delta \le \pi).$$

11.6 Notation From now on, U will denote the open unit disc, i.e., $U = D(0;1)$, and T will be the unit circle, the boundary of U in the complex plane.

If f is a function on T and μ is a measure on T it will often be desirable to write

(1) $$\int_{\alpha}^{\alpha+2\pi} f(t)\,d\mu(t)$$

in place of $\int_T f\,d\mu$, where α is a conveniently chosen real number. The integration in (1) is understood to be over the half-open interval

$$[\alpha, \alpha + 2\pi).$$

Of course, a literal interpretation of (1) makes no sense; f and μ are defined on T, not on an interval of the real axis. However, if f and μ are defined on T, and if we define

(2) $$\tilde{f}(t) = f(e^{it}), \qquad \tilde{\mu}(E) = \mu(\varphi(E)),$$

for $\alpha \le t < \alpha + 2\pi$, $E \subset [\alpha, \alpha + 2\pi)$ where $\varphi(t) = e^{it}$, then it is true that

(3) $$\int_{\alpha}^{\alpha+2\pi} \tilde{f}(t)\,d\tilde{\mu}(t) = \int_T f\,d\mu.$$

The notation (1) thus amounts to an identification of $\tilde{f}$ with f and $\tilde{\mu}$ with μ and should cause no confusion.

The reason for preferring (1) to $\int_T f\,d\mu$ is simply that it is easier to manipulate the integrals in the form (1).

We shall also continue to identify the spaces $L^p(T)$ and $C(T)$ with the related spaces of 2π-periodic functions on R^1, as in Sec. 4.23.

11.7 The Poisson Integral If $f \in L^1(T)$ and

(1) $$F(re^{i\theta}) = \frac{1}{2\pi}\int_{-\pi}^{\pi} P_r(\theta - t) f(t)\,dt,$$

the function F so defined in U is called the *Poisson integral* of f; we shall sometimes abbreviate the relation (1) to

(2) $$F = P[f].$$

The Poisson integral $F = P[d\mu]$ of a complex Borel measure μ on T is defined analogously by

(3) $$F(re^{i\theta}) = \frac{1}{2\pi}\int_{-\pi}^{\pi} P_r(\theta - t)\, d\mu(t).$$

If we associate with each $f \in L^1(T)$ its indefinite integral $\mu(E) = \int_E f(t)\, dt$, we see that the functions F of the form (1) form a subclass of those defined by (3).

If μ is real, formula 11.5(2) shows that $P[d\mu]$ is the real part of

(4) $$\frac{1}{2\pi}\int_{-\pi}^{\pi} \frac{e^{it} + z}{e^{it} - z}\, d\mu(t) \qquad (z = re^{i\theta};\ z \in U).$$

But (4) defines a holomorphic function in U, by Theorem 10.7. Hence $P[d\mu]$ is a harmonic function. Since linear combinations (with constant coefficients) of harmonic functions are harmonic, we have proved the following:

11.8 Theorem *For every complex Borel measure μ on T its Poisson integral $P[d\mu]$ is a harmonic function in U. Hence $P[f]$ is harmonic in U for every $f \in L^1(T)$.*

Our next concern will be the behavior of $P[d\mu](re^{i\theta})$, for fixed θ, as $r \to 1$. In other words, we are going to study the radial limits (if they exist) of Poisson integrals of measures. The following lemma contains the computational part of this investigation.

11.9 Lemma *Suppose μ is a real Borel measure on T, fix θ, put*

(1) $$J(\theta;s) = \{e^{it}: \theta - s < t < \theta + s\},$$

so that $J(\theta;s)$ is the open circular arc of length $2s$ with center at $e^{i\theta}$, and assume there exists a δ, $0 < \delta < \pi$, and a real number A such that

(2) $$\mu(J(\theta;s)) < 2sA \qquad \text{if } 0 < s < \delta.$$

If $F = P[d\mu]$, these conditions imply that

(3) $$F(re^{i\theta}) < A + \frac{1}{2\pi} P_r(\delta)\|\mu\| \qquad (0 \le r < 1),$$

where $\|\mu\| = |\mu|(T)$ is the total variation of μ.

PROOF We have

(4) $$F(re^{i\theta}) = \frac{1}{2\pi}\int_{\theta-\pi}^{\theta+\pi} P_r(\theta - t)\, d\mu(t).$$

Split the integral into two parts. If $\delta \le |\theta - t| \le \pi$, then

$$P_r(\theta - t) \le P_r(\delta),$$

and therefore the integral over this range is not larger than the last term of (3). The remaining integral over $I(\delta) = (\theta - \delta, \theta + \delta)$ can be estimated by an integration by parts, using Fubini's theorem. We integrate

$$P_r'(s)\, ds\, d\mu(t) \tag{5}$$

(the differentiation is with respect to s) over the triangle

$$\{(s,t): \theta - s < t < \theta + s,\ 0 < s < \delta\} \tag{6}$$

and obtain

$$\int_0^\delta \mu(I(s))P_r'(s)\, ds = \int_{I(\delta)} [P_r(\delta) - P_r(\theta - t)]\, d\mu(t). \tag{7}$$

The left side of (7) was obtained by first integrating with respect to t; on the right the s-integration came first. Since $\mu(I(s)) < 2sA$, by assumption (note that we have identified μ and $\tilde{\mu}$, as in Sec. 11.6), and since $P_r'(s) < 0$ on $(0,\pi)$ [this follows from the inequality 11.5(4)], we conclude from (7) that

$$\begin{aligned}\int_{I(\delta)} P_r(\theta - t)\, d\mu(t) &= P_r(\delta)\mu(I(\delta)) + \int_0^\delta \mu(I(s))[-P_r'(s)]\, ds \\ &< 2A[\delta P_r(\delta) - \int_0^\delta sP_r'(s)\, ds] \\ &= 2A \int_0^\delta P_r(s)\, ds < 2A \int_0^\pi P_r(s)\, ds = 2\pi A,\end{aligned}$$

and this gives (3).

11.10 Theorem *Suppose μ is a real Borel measure on T, $J(\theta;s)$ is as in Lemma* 11.9, *define*

$$(\bar{D}\mu)(\theta) = \limsup_{s\to 0} \frac{\mu(J(\theta;s))}{2s}, \tag{1}$$

and define$(D\mu)(\theta)$ *and* $(\underline{D}\mu)(\theta)$ *analogously, with* lim *and* lim inf *in place of* lim sup. *Put*

$$F(re^{i\theta}) = \frac{1}{2\pi}\int_{-\pi}^{\pi} P_r(\theta - t)\, d\mu(t) \qquad (0 \le r < 1). \tag{2}$$

Then

$$(\underline{D}\mu)(\theta) \le \liminf_{r\to 1} F(re^{i\theta}) \le \limsup_{r\to 1} F(re^{i\theta}) \le (\bar{D}\mu)(\theta) \tag{3}$$

for every θ, and

$$\lim_{r\to 1} F(re^{i\theta}) = (D\mu)(\theta) \tag{4}$$

exists and is finite for almost all θ (with respect to Lebesgue measure).

PROOF Fix θ, and suppose $A > (\bar{D}\mu)(\theta)$. Then there exists a $\delta > 0$ so that the hypotheses of Lemma 11.9 hold. As $r \to 1$, $P_r(\delta) \to 0$, and so the last inequality in (3) follows from Lemma 11.9. The first inequality in (3) now follows if we apply the last one to $-\mu$ in place of μ, and (4) is a consequence of the one-dimensional case of Theorem 8.6.

Corollary *If $f \in L^1(T)$ and $F = P[f]$, then*

$$\lim_{r\to 1} F(re^{i\theta}) = f(e^{i\theta}) \text{ a.e.}$$

This follows from (4) since f is almost everywhere equal to the derivative of its indefinite integral.

If we take f continuous we get an even stronger result:

11.11 Theorem *Suppose $f \in C(T)$, $F = P[f]$, and*

$$u(re^{i\theta}) = \begin{cases} f(e^{i\theta}) & \text{if } r = 1, \\ F(re^{i\theta}) & \text{if } 0 \le r < 1. \end{cases} \tag{1}$$

Then u is a continuous function on the closed unit disc $\bar{U}$.

PROOF F is harmonic in U, hence continuous in U, so the continuity of u on $\bar{U}$ will follow if we can show that to every $\epsilon > 0$ there exists an $r_0 < 1$ such that

$$|f(e^{i\theta}) - F(re^{i\theta})| < \epsilon \qquad (r_0 < r < 1). \tag{2}$$

This is most easily proved by an elementary argument almost identical to the one used in Sec. 4.24. But we can also obtain (2) as a consequence of Lemma 11.9.

Assume f is real. (The complex case then follows trivially.) For any Borel set $E \subset T$, define $\mu(E) = \int_E f$. Fix $\epsilon > 0$. The uniform continuity of f shows that there exists a $\delta > 0$ such that

$$\left| \frac{\mu(J(\theta;s))}{2s} - f(e^{i\theta}) \right| < \epsilon \tag{3}$$

for all θ and for $0 < s < \delta$. Hence Lemma 11.9 applies, with $A = f(e^{i\theta}) + \epsilon$, and the conclusion of the lemma, combined with the analogous estimate from below, shows that

$$|F(re^{i\theta}) - f(e^{i\theta})| < \epsilon + P_r(\delta) \cdot \frac{1}{2\pi} \int_{-\pi}^{\pi} |f(t)|\, dt \tag{4}$$

for $0 \le r < 1$. Since $P_r(\delta) \to 0$ as $r \to 1$, (4) shows that (2) holds if r_0 is close enough to 1.

Now suppose $r_0 < r \le 1$ and $|\alpha - \beta| < \delta$, where δ is so chosen that $|f(e^{i\alpha}) - f(e^{i\beta})| < \epsilon$. By (2), $|u(e^{i\alpha}) - u(re^{i\beta})| < 2\epsilon$. Hence $u \in C(\bar{U})$.

Note: This theorem provides the solution of a boundary value problem (the *Dirichlet problem*): a continuous function f is given on T and it is required to find a harmonic function F in U "whose boundary values are f." The theorem exhibits a solution, by means of the Poisson integral of f, and it states the relation between f and F more precisely. The uniqueness theorem which corresponds to this existence theorem is contained in the following result.

11.12 Theorem *Suppose u is a continuous real function on the closed unit disc $\bar{U}$, and suppose u is harmonic in U. Then (in U) u is the Poisson integral of its restriction to T, and u is the real part of the holomorphic function*

$$(1) \qquad f(z) = \frac{1}{2\pi} \int_{-\pi}^{\pi} \frac{e^{it} + z}{e^{it} - z} u(e^{it})\, dt \qquad (z \in U).$$

PROOF Theorem 10.7 shows that $f \in H(U)$. If $u_1 = \operatorname{Re} f$, then (1) shows that u_1 is the Poisson integral of the boundary values of u, and the theorem will be proved as soon as we show that $u = u_1$.

Put $h = u - u_1$. Then h is continuous on $\bar{U}$ (apply Theorem 11.11 to u_1), h is harmonic in U, and $h = 0$ at all points of T. Assume (this will lead to a contradiction) that $h(z_0) > 0$ for some $z_0 \in U$. Fix ϵ so that $0 < 4\epsilon < h(z_0)$, and define

$$(2) \qquad g(z) = h(z) + \epsilon[(x - x_0)^2 - 4] \qquad (z \in \bar{U}),$$

where $z = x + iy$, $z_0 = x_0 + iy_0$. Then $g(z_0) > 0$. Since g is continuous on $\bar{U}$ and since $g < 0$ at all points of T, there exists a point $z_1 \in U$ at which g has a local maximum. This implies that $g_{xx} \le 0$ and $g_{yy} \le 0$ at z_1. But (2) shows that the Laplacian of g is $2\epsilon > 0$, and we have a contradiction.

Thus $u - u_1 \le 0$. The same argument shows that $u_1 - u \le 0$. Hence $u = u_1$, and the proof is complete.

11.13 So far we have considered only the unit disc $U = D(0;1)$. It is clear that the preceding work can be carried over to arbitrary circular discs, by a simple change of variables. Hence we shall merely summarize some of the results:

If u is a continuous real function on the boundary of the disc $D(a;R)$ and if u is defined in $D(a;R)$ by the Poisson integral

$$(1) \quad u(a + re^{i\theta}) = \frac{1}{2\pi} \int_{-\pi}^{\pi} \frac{R^2 - r^2}{R^2 - 2Rr\cos(\theta - t) + r^2} u(a + Re^{it})\, dt \qquad (0 \le r < R),$$

then u is continuous on $\bar{D}(a;R)$ and harmonic in $D(a;R)$.

If u is harmonic (and real) in an open set Ω and if $\bar{D}(a;R) \subset \Omega$, then u satisfies (1) in $D(a;R)$ and there is a holomorphic function f defined in

$D(a;R)$ whose real part is u. This f is uniquely defined, up to a pure imaginary additive constant. For if two functions, holomorphic in the same region, have the same real part, their difference must be constant (a corollary of the open mapping theorem, or the Cauchy-Riemann equations).

We may summarize this by saying that *every real harmonic function is locally the real part of a holomorphic function.*

Consequently, every harmonic function has continuous partial derivatives of all orders.

The Poisson integral also yields information about sequences of harmonic functions:

11.14 Harnack's Theorem *Let $\{u_n\}$ be a sequence of harmonic functions in a region Ω.*

(*a*) *If $u_n \to u$ uniformly on compact subsets of Ω, then u is harmonic in Ω.*

(*b*) *If $u_1 \le u_2 \le u_3 \le \cdots$, then either $\{u_n\}$ converges uniformly on compact subsets of Ω, or $u_n(z) \to \infty$ for every $z \in \Omega$.*

PROOF To prove (*a*), assume $\bar{D}(a;R) \subset \Omega$, and replace u by u_n in the Poisson integral 11.13(1). Since $u_n \to u$ uniformly on the boundary of $\bar{D}(a;R)$, we conclude that u itself satisfies 11.13(1) in $D(a;R)$.

In the proof of (*b*), we may assume that $u_1 \ge 0$. (If not, replace u_n by $u_n - u_1$.) Put $u = \sup u_n$, let $A = \{z \in \Omega\colon u(z) < \infty\}$, and $B = \Omega - A$. Choose $\bar{D}(a;R) \subset \Omega$. The Poisson kernel satisfies the inequalities

$$\frac{R-r}{R+r} \le \frac{R^2 - r^2}{R^2 - 2rR\cos(\theta - t) + r} \le \frac{R+r}{R-r}$$

for $0 \le r < R$. Hence

$$\frac{R-r}{R+r}\, u_n(a) \le u_n(a + re^{i\theta}) \le \frac{R+r}{R-r}\, u_n(a).$$

The same inequalities hold with u in place of u_n. It follows that either $u(z) = \infty$ for all $z \in D(a;R)$ or $u(z) < \infty$ for all $z \in D(a;R)$.

Thus both A and B are open; and since Ω is connected, we have either $A = \varnothing$ (in which case there is nothing to prove) or $A = \Omega$. In the latter case, the monotone convergence theorem shows that the Poisson formula holds for u in every disc in Ω. Hence u is harmonic in Ω. Whenever a sequence of continuous functions converges monotonically to a continuous limit, the convergence is uniform on compact sets ([26], Theorem 7.13). This completes the proof.

The Mean Value Property

11.15 Definition We say that a continuous function u in an open set Ω has the *mean value property* if to every $z \in \Omega$ there corresponds a sequence $\{r_n\}$ such that $r_n > 0$, $r_n \to 0$ as $n \to \infty$, and

$$(1) \qquad u(z) = \frac{1}{2\pi} \int_{-\pi}^{\pi} u(z + r_n e^{it})\, dt \qquad (n = 1, 2, 3, \ldots).$$

In other words, $u(z)$ is to be equal to the mean value of u on the circles of radius r_n and with center at z.

Note that the Poisson formula shows that (1) holds for every harmonic function u, and for *every* r such that $\bar{D}(z;r) \subset \Omega$. Thus harmonic functions satisfy a much stronger mean value property than the one that we just defined. The following theorem may therefore come as a surprise:

11.16 Theorem *If a continuous function u has the mean value property in an open set Ω, then u is harmonic in Ω.*

PROOF It is enough to prove this for real u. Fix $\bar{D}(a;R) \subset \Omega$. The Poisson integral gives us a continuous function h on $\bar{D}(a;R)$ which is harmonic in $D(a;R)$ and which coincides with u on the boundary of $D(a;R)$. Put $v = u - h$, and let $m = \sup \{v(z)\colon z \in \bar{D}(a;R)\}$. Assume $m > 0$, and let E be the set of all $z \in \bar{D}(a;R)$ at which $v(z) = m$. Since $v = 0$ on the boundary of $D(a;R)$, E is a compact subset of $D(a;R)$. Hence there exists a $z_0 \in E$ such that

$$|z_0 - a| \geq |z - a|$$

for all $z \in E$. For *all* small enough r, at least half the circle with center at z_0 and radius r lies outside E, so that the corresponding mean values of v are all less than $m = v(z_0)$. But v has the mean value property, and we have a contradiction. Thus $m = 0$, so $v \leq 0$. The same reasoning applies to $-v$. Hence $v = 0$, or $u = h$ in $D(a;R)$, and since $\bar{D}(a;R)$ was an arbitrary closed disc in Ω, u is harmonic in Ω.

Theorem 11.16 leads to a reflection theorem for holomorphic functions. By the *upper half plane* Π^+ we mean the set of all $z = x + iy$ with $y > 0$; the *lower half plane* Π^- consists of all z whose imaginary part is negative.

11.17 Theorem (The Schwarz reflection principle) *Suppose L is a segment on the real axis, Ω^+ is a region in Π^+, and every $t \in L$ is the center of an open disc D_t such that $\Pi^+ \cap D_t$ lies in Ω^+. Let Ω^- be the reflection of Ω^+:*

$$(1) \qquad \Omega^- = \{z\colon \bar{z} \in \Omega^+\}.$$

Suppose $f = u + iv$ is holomorphic in Ω^+, and

(2) $$\lim_{n\to\infty} v(z_n) = 0$$

for every sequence $\{z_n\}$ in Ω^+ which converges to a point of L.

Then there is a function F, holomorphic in $\Omega^+ \cup L \cup \Omega^-$, such that $F(z) = f(z)$ in Ω^+; this F satisfies the relation

(3) $$F(\bar{z}) = \overline{F(z)} \qquad (z \in \Omega^+ \cup L \cup \Omega^-).$$

The theorem asserts that f can be extended to a function which is holomorphic in a region symmetric with respect to the real axis, and (3) states that F preserves this symmetry. Note that the continuity hypothesis (2) is merely imposed on the imaginary part of f.

PROOF Put $\Omega = \Omega^+ \cup L \cup \Omega^-$. We extend v to Ω by defining $v(z) = 0$ for $z \in L$ and $v(z) = -v(\bar{z})$ for $z \in \Omega^-$. It is then immediate that v is continuous and that v has the mean value property in Ω, so that v is harmonic in Ω, by Theorem 11.16.

Hence v is locally the imaginary part of a holomorphic function. This means that to each of the discs D_t there corresponds an $f_t \in H(D_t)$ such that $\operatorname{Im} f_t = v$. Each f_t is determined by v up to a real additive constant. If this constant is chosen so that $f_t(z) = f(z)$ for *some* $z \in D_t \cap \Pi^+$, the same will hold for all $z \in D_t \cap \Pi^+$, since $f - f_t$ is constant in the region $D_t \cap \Pi^+$. We assume that the functions f_t are so adjusted.

The power series expansion of f_t in powers of $z - t$ has only real coefficients, since $v = 0$ on L, so that all derivatives of f_t are real at t. It follows that

(4) $$f_t(\bar{z}) = \overline{f_t(z)} \qquad (z \in D_t).$$

Next, assume that $D_s \cap D_t \neq \varnothing$. Then $f_t = f = f_s$ in $D_t \cap D_s \cap \Pi^+$; and since $D_t \cap D_s$ is connected, Theorem 10.18 shows that

(5) $$f_t(z) = f_s(z) \qquad (z \in D_t \cap D_s).$$

Thus it is consistent to define

(6) $$F(z) = \begin{cases} f(z) & \text{for } z \in \Omega^+ \\ f_t(z) & \text{for } z \in D_t \\ \overline{f(\bar{z})} & \text{for } z \in \Omega^- \end{cases}$$

and it remains to show that F is holomorphic in Ω^-. If $D(a;r) \subset \Omega^-$ then $D(\bar{a};r) \subset \Omega^+$, so for every $z \in D(a;r)$ we have

(7) $$f(\bar{z}) = \sum_{n=0}^{\infty} c_n(\bar{z} - \bar{a})^n.$$

Hence

$$(8)\qquad F(z) = \sum_{n=0}^{\infty} \bar{c}_n (z-a)^n \qquad (z \in D(a;r)).$$

This completes the proof.

Positive Harmonic Functions

11.18 It is clear that the Poisson integral $P[d\mu]$ of every positive finite Borel measure μ on the unit circle T is a positive harmonic function in the open disc U. The question arises whether every positive harmonic function in U is obtained in this manner.

The following observation will lead to an affirmative answer. If $h = P[d\mu]$, where μ is *any* complex Borel measure on T, Fubini's theorem shows that

$$(1)\qquad \int_{-\pi}^{\pi} |h(re^{i\theta})|\, d\theta \le \int_{-\pi}^{\pi} \left[\frac{1}{2\pi} \int_{-\pi}^{\pi} P_r(\theta - t)\, d\theta \right] d|\mu|(t) = \|\mu\|,$$

where $\|\mu\|$ is the total variation of μ on T. Thus the first integral in (1) is a bounded function of r on $[0,1)$, a condition which must be satisfied by all Poisson integrals.

Now if h is a positive harmonic function, then $|h| = h$, so the first integral in (1) is $2\pi h(0)$, for every $r \in [0,1)$. Thus positive harmonic functions satisfy the necessary condition which we just found, and we are led to the following stronger theorem.

11.19 Theorem *The mapping $\mu \to P[d\mu]$ is a linear one-to-one correspondence between the space of all complex Borel measures on T and the space of all harmonic functions h in U which satisfy the growth condition*

$$(1)\qquad \sup_{0 \le r < 1} \int_{-\pi}^{\pi} |h(re^{i\theta})|\, d\theta < \infty.$$

The set of all positive finite Borel measures on T is thereby put in one-to-one correspondence with the set of all positive harmonic functions in U.

Corollary *Every harmonic function h in U which satisfies* (1) *has finite radial limits at almost all* (*with respect to Lebesgue measure*) *points of T.*

PROOF It is clear that the mapping $\mu \to P[d\mu]$ is linear. The discussion in Sec. 11.18 showed that (1) holds for every $P[d\mu]$.

To prove that $\mu \to P[d\mu]$ is one-to-one, assume $P[d\mu] = 0$ in U. We have to show that $\mu = 0$. Choose $f \in C(T)$. Theorem 11.11

shows that

$$\int_{-\pi}^{\pi} f(\theta)\, d\mu(\theta) = \lim_{r\to 1} \int_{-\pi}^{\pi} d\mu(\theta) \frac{1}{2\pi} \int_{-\pi}^{\pi} f(t) P_r(\theta - t)\, dt$$

$$= \lim_{r\to 1} \int_{-\pi}^{\pi} f(t)\, dt \frac{1}{2\pi} \int_{-\pi}^{\pi} P_r(t - \theta)\, d\mu(\theta)$$

$$= \lim_{r\to 1} \int_{-\pi}^{\pi} f(t) P\,[d\mu]\,(re^{it})\, dt = 0.$$

Thus $\int f\, d\mu = 0$ for *every* $f \in C(T)$, and the uniqueness assertion of Theorem 6.19 now implies that $\mu = 0$.

We turn to the proof of the most significant part of the theorem: *Every* harmonic function in U which satisfies (1) is $P[d\mu]$ for some complex Borel measure μ on T. The proof depends on the notion of "weak convergence," which is defined, in more general situations, in Exercise 14.

Let h be a harmonic function in U for which

$$\int_{-\pi}^{\pi} |h(re^{i\theta})|\, d\theta \le M < \infty \qquad (0 \le r < 1). \tag{2}$$

For $0 < s < 1$, define

$$\Lambda_s f = \int_{-\pi}^{\pi} h(se^{it}) f(t)\, dt \qquad (f \in C(T)). \tag{3}$$

Each Λ_s is then a linear functional on $C(T)$, of norm $\|\Lambda_s\| \le M$. Let $\{f_j\}$ be a countable dense subset of $C(T)$. (For instance, take all trigonometric polynomials whose coefficients lie in some countable dense subset of the complex plane.) For each j the numbers $\Lambda_s f_j$ form a bounded set. The diagonal process (see [26], page 145) therefore guarantees the existence of a sequence $\{s_n\}$ such that $s_n \to 1$ and such that

$$\lim_{n\to\infty} \Lambda_{s_n} f_j \tag{4}$$

exists for each f_j.

We claim that $\{\Lambda_{s_n} f\}$ is a Cauchy sequence for *every* $f \in C(T)$: Fix $f \in C(T)$, $\epsilon > 0$, choose f_j so that $\|f - f_j\|_\infty < \epsilon/M$, then choose N so large that

$$|\Lambda_{s_n} f_j - \Lambda_{s_m} f_j| < \epsilon \qquad \text{if } n > N,\ m > N. \tag{5}$$

Since

$$|\Lambda_{s_n} f - \Lambda_{s_m} f| \le |\Lambda_{s_n}(f - f_j)| + |\Lambda_{s_n} f_j - \Lambda_{s_m} f_j| + |\Lambda_{s_m}(f_j - f)|,$$

it follows that $|\Lambda_{s_n} f - \Lambda_{s_m} f| < 3\epsilon$ if $n > N$ and $m > N$. Hence

$$\Lambda f = \lim_{n\to\infty} \Lambda_{s_n} f \tag{6}$$

exists for every $f \in C(T)$, and (6) defines a linear functional Λ on $C(T)$, with $\|\Lambda\| \leq M$. The Riesz representation theorem 6.19 now yields a complex Borel measure μ on T such that the relation

$$(7) \qquad \lim_{n\to\infty} \int_{-\pi}^{\pi} f(t)h(s_n e^{it})\, dt = \int_{-\pi}^{\pi} f(t)\, d\mu(t)$$

holds for every $f \in C(T)$; this follows from (3) and (6).

For each n, $h(s_n re^{i\theta})$ is harmonic in the disc $D(0;1/s_n)$ which contains $\bar{U}$. In U this function is therefore the Poisson integral of its restriction to T. In other words,

$$(8) \quad \frac{1}{2\pi}\int_{-\pi}^{\pi} P_r(\theta - t)h(s_n e^{it})\, dt = h(s_n re^{i\theta}) \qquad (0 \leq r < 1).$$

If we let $n \to \infty$ in (8) and use (7), we obtain

$$(9) \quad \frac{1}{2\pi}\int_{-\pi}^{\pi} P_r(\theta - t)\, d\mu(t) = h(re^{i\theta}) \qquad (0 \leq r < 1,\ -\pi \leq \theta < \pi),$$

which is the desired representation of h: $h = P[d\mu]$.

If h is real, so is μ, by the previously established uniqueness property. If $h > 0$, then each Λ_s is a positive linear functional on T, hence so is Λ, and the positivity of μ follows from the Riesz representation theorem 2.14.

This completes the proof. The corollary is a consequence of Theorem 11.10.

There are of course many applications of this theorem. We shall now give one which shows that there is a Cauchy formula for bounded holomorphic functions in U, in which the path of integration is moved to T. Other applications occur in Chap. 17.

11.20 Definition We let H^∞ be the space of all bounded holomorphic functions in U, normed by

$$\|f\|_\infty = \sup_{z \in U} |f(z)|.$$

As before, $L^\infty(T)$ will be the space of all (equivalence classes of) essentially bounded functions on T, normed by the essential supremum norm (relative to Lebesgue measure). For $g \in L^\infty(T)$, $\|g\|_\infty$ stands for the essential supremum of $|g|$.

11.20 Theorem *To every $f \in H^\infty$ there corresponds a function $f^* \in L^\infty(T)$, defined almost everywhere by*

$$(1) \qquad f^*(e^{it}) = \lim_{r\to 1} f(re^{it}).$$

The equality $\|f\|_\infty = \|f^*\|_\infty$ *holds. For every* $z \in U$, *the Cauchy formula*

$$(2) \qquad f(z) = \frac{1}{2\pi i} \int_\gamma \frac{f^*(\xi)}{\xi - z}\, d\xi$$

holds, where γ *is the positively oriented unit circle:* $\gamma(t) = e^{it}$, $0 \le t \le 2\pi$.

The functions $f^* \in L^\infty(T)$ *which are obtained in this manner are precisely those which satisfy the relations*

$$(3) \qquad \frac{1}{2\pi} \int_{-\pi}^{\pi} f^*(e^{it}) e^{-int}\, dt = 0 \qquad (n = -1, -2, -3, \ldots).$$

The fact that every $f \in H^\infty$ has radial limits at almost all points of T was proved by Fatou in one of the earliest applications of the Lebesgue integral to the study of holomorphic functions.

PROOF The existence a.e. of f^* follows from the Corollary to Theorem 11.19, and (1) makes it obvious that $\|f^*\|_\infty \le \|f\|_\infty$.

If $z \in U$ and $|z| < r < 1$, put $\gamma_r(t) = re^{it}$ $(0 \le t \le 2\pi)$. Then

$$(4) \qquad f(z) = \frac{1}{2\pi i} \int_{\gamma_r} \frac{f(\xi)}{\xi - z}\, d\xi = \frac{r}{2\pi} \int_{-\pi}^{\pi} \frac{f(re^{it})}{re^{it} - z}\, e^{it}\, dt.$$

Let $\{r_n\}$ be a sequence, $r_n \to 1$, and apply Lebesgue's dominated convergence theorem to the last integral in (4). The result is

$$(5) \qquad f(z) = \frac{1}{2\pi} \int_{-\pi}^{\pi} \frac{f^*(e^{it})}{1 - ze^{-it}}\, dt$$

which is the same as (2). The Cauchy theorem gives

$$(6) \qquad \int_{\gamma_r} f(\xi)\xi^n\, d\xi = 0 \qquad (n = 0, 1, 2, \ldots).$$

Hence a passage to the limit, similar to the above, shows that f^* satisfies (3). We can therefore convert (5) into a Poisson integral: If $z = re^{i\theta}$,

$$(7) \qquad f(z) = \frac{1}{2\pi} \int_{-\pi}^{\pi} f^*(e^{it}) \sum_{n=0}^{\infty} r^n e^{in(\theta - t)}\, dt$$

$$= \frac{1}{2\pi} \int_{-\pi}^{\pi} f^*(e^{it}) \sum_{n=-\infty}^{\infty} r^{|n|} e^{in(\theta - t)}\, dt$$

$$= \frac{1}{2\pi} \int_{-\pi}^{\pi} P_r(\theta - t) f^*(e^{it})\, dt.$$

From this we conclude that $\|f\|_\infty \le \|f^*\|_\infty$, so that the two norms are equal.

Finally, if $f^* \in L^\infty(T)$ is such that (3) holds, and if we define f by (5) for all $z \in U$, then (5) shows that $f \in H(U)$, (3) implies that the Cauchy integral (5) is equal to the Poisson integral (7), so that f is bounded, and the representation of f as the Poisson integral of f^* shows that (1) holds almost everywhere, by the Corollary to Theorem 11.10.

There is a uniqueness theorem which follows easily from the above Cauchy formula:

11.22 Theorem *Suppose $f \in H^\infty$, J is a subarc of T, and $f^*(e^{it}) = 0$ a.e. on J. Then $f(z) = 0$ for all $z \in U$.*

(A considerably stronger statement will be obtained later, in Theorem 15.19. See also Theorem 17.18 and Sec. 17.19.)

PROOF Let n be a positive integer such that the length of J is larger than $2\pi/n$, let $\eta = \exp\{2\pi i/n\}$, and put

$$g(z) = \prod_{k=1}^{n} f(\eta^k z) \qquad (z \in U). \tag{1}$$

Since f is bounded and $f^* = 0$ a.e. on J, we see that $g^* = 0$ a.e. on T, and $g \in H^\infty$. Since g is the Cauchy integral of g^*, $g(z) = 0$ for all $z \in U$. If $Z(f)$, the zero set of f in U, is at most countable, then so is $Z(g)$, since $Z(g)$ is the union of n sets obtained from $Z(f)$ by rotations. But $Z(g) = U$. Hence $f = 0$, by Theorem 10.18.

Exercises

1 Suppose u and v are real harmonic functions in a plane region Ω. Under what conditions is uv harmonic? (Note that the answer depends strongly on the fact that the question is one about *real* functions.) Show that u^2 cannot be harmonic in Ω, unless u is constant. For which $f \in H(\Omega)$ is $|f|^2$ harmonic?

2 Suppose f is a complex function in a region Ω, and both f and f^2 are harmonic in Ω. Prove that either f or $\bar{f}$ is holomorphic in Ω.

3 If u is a harmonic function in a region Ω, what can you say about the set of points at which the gradient of u is 0? (This is the set on which $u_x = u_y = 0$.)

4 Prove that every partial derivative of every harmonic function is harmonic.

Verify, by direct computation, that $P_r(\theta - t)$ is, for each fixed t, a harmonic function of $re^{i\theta}$. Deduce (without referring to holomorphic functions) that the Poisson integral $P[d\mu]$ of every finite Borel measure μ on T is harmonic in U, by showing that every partial derivative of $P[d\mu]$ is equal to the integral of the corresponding partial derivative of the kernel.

5 Suppose u is a Lebesgue measurable function in a region Ω, and u is locally in L^1. This means that the integral of $|u|$ over any compact subset of Ω is finite. Prove that u is harmonic if it satisfies the following form of the mean value property:

$$u(a) = \frac{1}{\pi r^2} \iint\limits_{D(a;r)} u(x,y)\, dx\, dy$$

whenever $\bar{D}(a;r) \subset \Omega$.

6 (*a*) Suppose u is a positive harmonic function in U and $u(0) = 1$. How large can $u(\frac{1}{2})$ be? How small? Get the best possible bounds.

(*b*) Suppose $f = u + iv$, $f \in H(U)$, $f(0) = 0$, and $|u| \leq 1$ in U. If $0 < r < 1$, how large can $|f(re^{i\theta})|$ be?

7 Suppose Ω is a region, K is a compact subset of Ω, $z_0 \in \Omega$. Prove that there exist positive numbers α and β (depending on z_0, K, and Ω) such that

$$\alpha u(z_0) \leq u(z) \leq \beta u(z_0)$$

for every positive harmonic function u in Ω and for all $z \in K$.

If $\{u_n\}$ is a sequence of positive harmonic functions in Ω and if $u_n(z_0) \to 0$, describe the behavior of $\{u_n\}$ in the rest of Ω. Do the same if $u_n(z_0) \to \infty$. Show that the assumed positivity of $\{u_n\}$ is essential for these results.

8 Suppose u is a positive harmonic function in U, and $u(re^{i\theta}) \to 0$ as $r \to 1$, for every $e^{i\theta} \neq 1$. Prove that there is a constant c such that

$$u(re^{i\theta}) = cP_r(\theta).$$

9 Here is an example of a harmonic function in U which is not identically 0 but *all* of whose radial limits are 0:

$$u(z) = \operatorname{Im}\left[\left(\frac{1+z}{1-z}\right)^2\right].$$

Prove that this u is not the Poisson integral of any measure on T and that it is not the difference of two positive harmonic functions in U.

10 Suppose μ is a positive Borel measure on T, not identically 0, and μ is singular (relative to Lebesgue measure). If $u = P[d\mu]$, prove that $u(re^{i\theta}) \to \infty$ as $r \to 1$, for at least one θ. *Hint:* Theorem 8.9.

11 Let Φ be the set of all positive harmonic functions u in U such that $u(0) = 1$. Show that Φ is a convex set and find the extreme points of Φ. (A point x in a convex set Φ is called an *extreme point* of Φ if x lies on no segment both of whose end points lie in Φ and are different from x.) *Hint:* If C is the convex set whose members are the positive Borel measures on T, of total variation 1, show that the extreme points of C are precisely those $\mu \in C$ whose support consists of only one point of T.

12 Suppose $f \in L^p(T)$, $1 \leq p < \infty$, and $F = P[f]$. Prove that

$$\lim_{r \to 1} \int_{-\pi}^{\pi} |F(re^{i\theta}) - f(e^{i\theta})|^p \, d\theta = 0.$$

(Compare with Theorems 9.5 and 9.10. Exercise 17 of Chap. 3 can also be applied here.)

13 Suppose $f \in H(\Omega)$ and f has no zero in Ω. Prove that $\log |f|$ is harmonic in Ω, by computing its Laplacian. Is there an easier way?

14 Let X^* be the dual space of the Banach space X. A sequence $\{\Lambda_n\}$ in X^* is said to *converge weakly* to $\Lambda \in X^*$ if $\Lambda_n x \to \Lambda x$ as $n \to \infty$, for every $x \in X$. Note that $\Lambda_n \to \Lambda$ weakly whenever $\Lambda_n \to \Lambda$ in the norm of X^*. (See Exercise 8, Chap. 5.) The converse need not be true. For example, the functionals $f \to \hat{f}(n)$ on $L^2(T)$ tend to 0 weakly (by the Bessel inequality), but each of these functionals has norm 1.

(*a*) Prove that $\{\|\Lambda_n\|\}$ must be bounded if $\{\Lambda_n\}$ converges weakly.

(*b*) Suppose X is a separable Banach space and $\{\Lambda_n\}$ is a sequence in X^* such that $\{\|\Lambda_n\|\}$ is bounded. Prove that $\{\Lambda_n\}$ contains a weakly convergent subsequence. (The proof is quite similar to the special case of Theorem 11.19.)

15 Suppose $I = [a,b]$ is an interval on the real axis, φ is a continuous function on I, and

$$f(z) = \frac{1}{2\pi i} \int_a^b \frac{\varphi(t)}{t - z} \, dt \qquad (z \notin I).$$

Show that

$$\lim_{\epsilon \to 0} [f(x + i\epsilon) - f(x - i\epsilon)] \qquad (\epsilon > 0)$$

exists for every real x, and find it in terms of φ.

How is the result affected if we assume merely that $\varphi \in L^1$? What happens then at points x at which φ has right- and left-hand limits?

16 Suppose $I = [a,b]$, Ω is a region, $I \subset \Omega$, f is continuous in Ω, and $f \in H(\Omega - I)$. Prove that actually $f \in H(\Omega)$.

Replace I by some other sets for which the same conclusion can be drawn.

17 If $1 \leq p \leq \infty$ and $f \in L^p(R^1)$, prove that $(f * h_\lambda)(x)$ is a harmonic function of $x + i\lambda$ in the upper half plane. (h_λ is defined in Sec. 9.7; it is the Poisson kernel for the half plane.)

18 Suppose Ω is a region, $f_n \in H(\Omega)$ for $n = 1, 2, 3, \ldots$, u_n is the real part of f_n, $\{u_n\}$ converges uniformly on compact subsets of Ω, and $\{f_n(z)\}$ converges for at least one $z \in \Omega$. Prove that then $\{f_n\}$ converges uniformly on compact subsets of Ω.

19 The device used in the proof of Lemma 11.9 yields a general theorem which makes it legitimate to apply the process of integration by parts to integrals of the form $\int_I f\, d\mu$, where μ is a Borel measure on a segment I of the real line. State such a theorem and prove it.

12

The Maximum Modulus Principle

Introduction

12.1 The maximum modulus theorem (10.24) asserts that the constants are the only holomorphic functions in a region Ω whose absolute value has a local maximum at any point of Ω.

Here is a restatement: *If K is the closure of a bounded region Ω, if f is continuous on K and holomorphic in Ω, then*

$$|f(z)| \leq \|f\|_{\partial K} \tag{1}$$

for every $z \in \Omega$. If equality holds at one point $z \in \Omega$, then f is constant.

[The right side of (1) is the supremum of $|f|$ on the boundary ∂K of K.]

For if $|f(z)| \geq \|f\|_{\partial K}$ at some $z \in \Omega$, then the maximum of $|f|$ on K (which is attained at some point of K, since K is compact) is actually attained at some point of Ω, so f is constant, by Theorem 10.24.

The equality $\|f\|_\infty = \|f^*\|_\infty$, which is part of Theorem 11.21, implies that

$$|f(z)| \leq \|f^*\|_\infty \qquad (z \in U, f \in H^\infty(U)). \tag{2}$$

This says (roughly speaking) that $|f(z)|$ is no larger than the supremum of the boundary values of f, a statement similar to (1). But this time boundedness on U is enough; we do not need continuity on $\bar{U}$.

This chapter contains further generalizations of the maximum modulus theorem, as well as some rather striking applications of it, and it concludes with a theorem which shows that the maximum property "almost" characterizes the class of holomorphic functions.

The Schwarz Lemma

This is the name usually given to the following theorem. We use the notation established in Definition 11.20.

12.2 Theorem *Suppose $f \in H^\infty$, $\|f\|_\infty \le 1$, and $f(0) = 0$. Then*

$$(1)\qquad |f(z)| \le |z| \qquad (z \in U),$$

$$(2)\qquad |f'(0)| \le 1;$$

if equality holds in (1) *for one $z \in U - \{0\}$, or if equality holds in* (2), *then $f(z) = \lambda z$, where λ is a constant, $|\lambda| = 1$.*

In geometric language, the hypothesis is that f is a holomorphic mapping of U into U which keeps the origin fixed; part of the conclusion is that either f is a rotation or f moves each $z \in U - \{0\}$ closer to the origin than it was.

PROOF Since $f(0) = 0$, $f(z)/z$ has a removable singularity at $z = 0$, hence there exists a $g \in H(U)$ such that $f(z) = zg(z)$. Since $1/|z|$ is bounded near the boundary of U, $g \in H^\infty$. Its radial limits satisfy the relation $|g^*| = |f^*|$. Thus $\|g^*\|_\infty \le 1$. By Theorem 11.21, $\|g\|_\infty \le 1$, and now the maximum modulus theorem shows that $|g(z)| = 1$ for some $z \in U$ if and only if g is constant. Since $f'(0) = g(0)$, this completes the proof.

Note: We did not really have to use the existence of radial limits a.e. on T; we could have applied Theorem 10.24 to g on discs $D(0; 1 - \epsilon)$ and let $\epsilon \to 0$ to obtain the final result.

Many variants of the Schwarz lemma can be obtained with the aid of the following mappings of U onto U:

12.3 Definition *For any $\alpha \in U$, define*

$$\varphi_\alpha(z) = \frac{z - \alpha}{1 - \bar{\alpha} z}.$$

12.4 Theorem *Fix $\alpha \in U$. Then φ_α is a one-to-one mapping which carries T onto T, U onto U, and α to 0. The inverse of φ_α is $\varphi_{-\alpha}$. We have*

$$(1)\qquad \varphi'_\alpha(0) = 1 - |\alpha|^2, \qquad \varphi'_\alpha(\alpha) = \frac{1}{1 - |\alpha|^2}.$$

PROOF φ_α is holomorphic in the whole plane, except for a pole at $1/\bar{\alpha}$ which lies outside $\bar{U}$. Straightforward substitution shows that

$$(2)\qquad \varphi_{-\alpha}(\varphi_\alpha(z)) = z.$$

Thus φ_α is one-to-one, and $\varphi_{-\alpha}$ is its inverse. Since, for real t,

$$(3)\qquad \left| \frac{e^{it} - \alpha}{1 - \bar{\alpha} e^{it}} \right| = \frac{|e^{it} - \alpha|}{|e^{-it} - \bar{\alpha}|} = 1$$

(z and $\bar{z}$ have the same absolute value), φ_α maps T into T; the same is true of $\varphi_{-\alpha}$; hence $\varphi_\alpha(T) = T$. It now follows from the maximum modulus theorem that $\varphi_\alpha(U) \subset U$, and consideration of $\varphi_{-\alpha}$ shows again that actually $\varphi_\alpha(U) = U$.

12.5 An Extremal Problem Suppose α and β are complex numbers, $|\alpha| < 1$, and $|\beta| < 1$. *How large can $|f'(\alpha)|$ be if f is subject to the conditions $f \in H^\infty$, $\|f\|_\infty \le 1$, and $f(\alpha) = \beta$?*

To solve this, put

(1) $$g = \varphi_\beta \circ f \circ \varphi_{-\alpha}.$$

Since $\varphi_{-\alpha}$ and φ_β map U onto U, we see that $g \in H^\infty$ and $\|g\|_\infty \le 1$; also, $g(0) = 0$. The passage from f to g has reduced our problem to the Schwarz lemma, which gives $|g'(0)| \le 1$. By (1), the chain rule gives

(2) $$g'(0) = \varphi_\beta'(\beta)f'(\alpha)\varphi_{-\alpha}'(0).$$

If we use Eqs. 12.4(1), we obtain the inequality

(3) $$|f'(\alpha)| \le \frac{1 - |\beta|^2}{1 - |\alpha|^2}.$$

This solves our problem, since equality can occur in (3). This happens if and only if $|g'(0)| = 1$, in which case g is a rotation (Theorem 12.2), so that

(4) $$f(z) = \varphi_{-\beta}(\lambda\varphi_\alpha(z)) \qquad (z \in U)$$

for some constant λ with $|\lambda| = 1$.

A remarkable feature of the solution should be stressed. We imposed no smoothness conditions (such as continuity on $\bar{U}$, for instance) on the behavior of f near the boundary of U. Nevertheless, it turns out that the functions f which maximize $|f'(\alpha)|$ under the stated restrictions are actually rational functions. Note also that these extremal functions map U onto U (not just into) and that they are one-to-one. This observation may serve as the motivation for the proof of the Riemann mapping theorem in Chap. 14.

At present, we shall merely show how this extremal problem can be used to characterize the one-to-one holomorphic mappings of U onto U.

12.6 Theorem *Suppose $f \in H(U)$, f is one-to-one, $f(U) = U$, $\alpha \in U$, and $f(\alpha) = 0$. Then there is a constant λ, $|\lambda| = 1$, such that*

(1) $$f(z) = \lambda\varphi_\alpha(z) \qquad (z \in U).$$

In other words, we obtain f by composing the mapping φ_α with a rotation.

PROOF Let g be the inverse of f, defined by $g(f(z)) = z$, $z \in U$. Since f is one-to-one, f' has no zero in U, so $g \in H(U)$, by Theorem

10.34. By the chain rule,

$$g'(0)f'(\alpha) = 1. \tag{2}$$

The solution of 12.5, applied to f and to g, yields the inequalities

$$|f'(\alpha)| \le \frac{1}{1 - |\alpha|^2}, \qquad |g'(0)| \le 1 - |\alpha|^2. \tag{3}$$

By (2), equality must hold in (3). As we observed in the preceding problem (with $\beta = 0$), this forces f to satisfy (1).

The Phragmen-Lindelöf Method

12.7 For a bounded region Ω, we saw in Sec. 12.1 that if f is continuous on the closure of Ω and if $f \in H(\Omega)$, the maximum modulus theorem implies

$$\|f\|_\Omega = \|f\|_{\partial\Omega}. \tag{1}$$

For unbounded regions, this is no longer true.

To see an example, let

$$\Omega = \left\{z = x + iy\colon -\frac{\pi}{2} < y < \frac{\pi}{2}\right\}; \tag{2}$$

Ω is the open strip bounded by the parallel lines $y = \pm\pi/2$; its boundary $\partial\Omega$ is the union of these two lines. Put

$$f(z) = \exp(\exp(z)). \tag{3}$$

For real x,

$$f\left(x \pm \frac{\pi i}{2}\right) = \exp(\pm ie^x) \tag{4}$$

since $\exp(\pi i/2) = i$, so $|f(z)| = 1$ for $z \in \partial\Omega$. But $f(x) \to \infty$ very rapidly as $x \to \infty$ along the positive real axis, which lies in Ω.

"Very" is the key word in the preceding sentence. A method developed by Phragmen and Lindelöf makes it possible to prove theorems of the following kind: If $f \in H(\Omega)$ and if $|f| < g$, where $g(z) \to \infty$ "slowly" as $z \to \infty$ in Ω (just what "slowly" means depends on Ω), then f is actually bounded in Ω, and this usually implies further conclusions about f, by the maximum modulus theorem.

Rather than describe the method by a theorem which would cover a large number of situations, we shall show how it works in two cases. In both, Ω will be a strip. In the first, f will be assumed to be bounded, and the theorem will improve the bound; in the second, a growth condition will be imposed on f which just excludes the function (3). In view of later applications, Ω will be a vertical strip in Theorem 12.8.

First, however, let us mention another example which also has this general flavor: *Suppose f is an entire function and*

(5) $$|f(z)| < 1 + |z|^{\frac{1}{2}}$$

for all z. Then f is constant.

This follows immediately from the Cauchy estimates 10.25, since they show that $f^{(n)}(0) = 0$ for $n = 1, 2, 3, \ldots$.

12.8 Theorem *Suppose*

(1) $$\Omega = \{x + iy: a < x < b\}, \qquad \bar{\Omega} = \{x + iy: a \le x \le b\},$$

f is continuous on $\bar{\Omega}$, $f \in H(\Omega)$, *and suppose that* $|f(z)| < B$ *for all* $z \in \Omega$ *and some fixed* $B < \infty$. *If*

(2) $$M(x) = \sup \{|f(x + iy)|: -\infty < y < \infty\} \qquad (a \le x \le b)$$

then we actually have

(3) $$M(x)^{b-a} \le M(a)^{b-x} M(b)^{x-a} \qquad (a < x < b).$$

Note: (3) implies that the inequality $|f| < B$ can be replaced by $|f| < \max (M(a), M(b))$, so that $|f|$ is no larger in Ω than the supremum of $|f|$ on the *boundary* of Ω.

If we apply the theorem to strips bounded by lines $x = \alpha$ and $x = \beta$, where $a \le \alpha < \beta \le b$, the conclusion can be stated in the following way:

Corollary *Under the hypotheses of the theorem, log M is a convex function on (a,b).*

PROOF We assume first that $M(a) = M(b) = 1$. In this case we have to prove that $|f(z)| \le 1$ for all $z \in \Omega$.

For each $\epsilon > 0$, we define an auxiliary function

(4) $$h_\epsilon(z) = \frac{1}{1 + \epsilon(z - a)} \qquad (z \in \bar{\Omega}).$$

Since $\text{Re}\{1 + \epsilon(z - a)\} = 1 + \epsilon(x - a) \ge 1$ in $\bar{\Omega}$, we have $|h_\epsilon| \le 1$ in $\bar{\Omega}$, so that

(5) $$|f(z)h_\epsilon(z)| \le 1 \qquad (z \in \partial\Omega).$$

Also, $|1 + \epsilon(z - a)| \ge \epsilon|y|$, so that

(6) $$|f(z)h_\epsilon(z)| \le \frac{B}{\epsilon|y|} \qquad (z = x + iy \in \bar{\Omega}).$$

Let R be the rectangle cut off from $\bar{\Omega}$ by the lines $y = \pm B/\epsilon$. By (5) and (6), $|fh_\epsilon| \le 1$ on ∂R, hence $|fh_\epsilon| \le 1$ on R, by the maximum modulus theorem. But (6) shows that $|fh_\epsilon| \le 1$ on the rest of $\bar{\Omega}$.

Thus $|f(z)h_\epsilon(z)| \leq 1$ for all $z \in \Omega$ and all $\epsilon > 0$. If we fix $z \in \Omega$ and then let $\epsilon \to 0$, we obtain the desired result $|f(z)| \leq 1$.

We now turn to the general case. Put

(7) $$g(z) = M(a)^{(b-z)/(b-a)} M(b)^{(z-a)/(b-a)},$$

where, for $M > 0$ and w complex, M^w is defined by

(8) $$M^w = \exp(w \log M),$$

and $\log M$ is real. Then g is entire, g has no zero, $1/g$ is bounded in $\bar{\Omega}$,

(9) $$|g(a + iy)| = M(a), \qquad |g(b + iy)| = M(b),$$

and hence f/g satisfies our previous assumptions. Thus $|f/g| \leq 1$ in Ω, and this gives (3).

12.9 Theorem *Suppose*

(1) $$\Omega = \left\{x + iy: |y| < \frac{\pi}{2}\right\}, \qquad \bar{\Omega} = \left\{x + iy: |y| \leq \frac{\pi}{2}\right\}.$$

Suppose f is continuous on $\bar{\Omega}$, $f \in H(\Omega)$, there are constants $\alpha < 1$, $A < \infty$, such that

(2) $$|f(z)| < \exp\{A \exp(\alpha|x|)\} \qquad (z = x + iy \in \Omega),$$

and

(3) $$\left|f\left(x \pm \frac{\pi i}{2}\right)\right| \leq 1 \qquad (-\infty < x < \infty).$$

Then $|f(z)| \leq 1$ for all $z \in \Omega$.

Note that the conclusion does not follow if $\alpha = 1$, as is shown by the function $\exp(\exp z)$.

PROOF Choose $\beta > 0$ so that $\alpha < \beta < 1$. For $\epsilon > 0$, define

(4) $$h_\epsilon(z) = \exp\{-\epsilon(e^{\beta z} + e^{-\beta z})\}.$$

For $z \in \bar{\Omega}$,

(5) $$\text{Re}\,[e^{\beta z} + e^{-\beta z}] = (e^{\beta x} + e^{-\beta x}) \cos \beta y \geq \delta(e^{\beta x} + e^{-\beta x})$$

where $\delta = \cos(\beta\pi/2) > 0$, since $|\beta| < 1$. Hence

(6) $$|h_\epsilon(z)| \leq \exp\{-\epsilon\delta(e^{\beta x} + e^{-\beta x})\} < 1 \qquad (z \in \bar{\Omega}).$$

It follows that $|fh_\epsilon| \leq 1$ on $\partial\Omega$ and that

(7) $$|f(z)h_\epsilon(z)| \leq \exp\{Ae^{\alpha|x|} - \epsilon\delta(e^{\beta x} + e^{-\beta x})\} \qquad (z \in \bar{\Omega}).$$

Fix $\epsilon > 0$. Since $\epsilon\delta > 0$ and $\beta > \alpha$, the exponent in (7) tends to $-\infty$ as $x \to \pm\infty$. Hence there exists an x_0 so that the right side of (7) is less than 1 for all $x > x_0$. Since $|fh_\epsilon| \leq 1$ on the boundary of the rectangle whose vertices are $\pm x_0 \pm (\pi i/2)$, the maximum modulus theorem shows that actually $|fh_\epsilon| \leq 1$ on this rectangle. Thus $|fh_\epsilon| \leq 1$ at every point of Ω, for every $\epsilon > 0$. As $\epsilon \to 0$, $h_\epsilon(z) \to 1$ for every z, so we conclude that $|f(z)| \leq 1$ for all $z \in \Omega$.

An Interpolation Theorem

12.10 The convexity theorem 12.8 can sometimes be used to prove that certain linear transformations are bounded with respect to certain L^p-norms. Rather than discuss this in full generality, let us look at a particular situation of this kind.

Let X be a measure space, with a positive measure μ, and suppose $\{\psi_n\}$ $(n = 1, 2, 3, \ldots)$ is an orthonormal set of functions in $L^2(\mu)$; we recall what this means:

$$(1) \qquad \int_X \psi_n \bar{\psi}_m \, d\mu = \begin{cases} 1 & \text{if } m = n, \\ 0 & \text{if } m \neq n. \end{cases}$$

Let us also assume that $\{\psi_n\}$ is a bounded sequence in $L^\infty(\mu)$: There exists an $M < \infty$ such that

$$(2) \qquad |\psi_n(x)| \leq M \qquad (n = 1, 2, 3, \ldots; x \in X).$$

Then for any $f \in L^p(\mu)$, where $1 \leq p \leq 2$, the integrals

$$(3) \qquad \hat{f}(n) = \int_X f\bar{\psi}_n \, d\mu \qquad (n = 1, 2, 3, \ldots)$$

exist and define a function $\hat{f}$ on the set of all positive integers.

There are now two very easy theorems: For $f \in L^1(\mu)$, (2) gives

$$(4) \qquad \|\hat{f}\|_\infty \leq M\|f\|_1,$$

and for $f \in L^2(\mu)$, the Bessel inequality gives

$$(5) \qquad \|\hat{f}\|_2 \leq \|f\|_2,$$

where the norms are defined as usual:

$$(6) \qquad \|f\|_p = \left[\int |f|^p \, d\mu\right]^{1/p}, \qquad \|\hat{f}\|_q = [\Sigma|\hat{f}(n)|^q]^{1/q},$$

and $\|\hat{f}\|_\infty = \sup\limits_n |\hat{f}(n)|$.

Since $(1, \infty)$ and $(2,2)$ are pairs of conjugate exponents, one may conjecture that $\|\hat{f}\|_q$ is finite whenever $f \in L^p(\mu)$ and $1 < p < 2$, $q = p/(p-1)$. This is indeed true and can be proved by "interpolation" between the preceding trivial cases $p = 1$ and $p = 2$:

12.11 The Hausdorff-Young Theorem *Under the above assumptions, the inequality*

(1) $$\|\hat{f}\|_q \le M^{(2-p)/p}\|f\|_p$$

holds if $1 \le p \le 2$ *and if* $f \in L^p(\mu)$.

PROOF We first prove a reduced form of the theorem.

Fix p, $1 < p < 2$. Let f be a *simple* complex function such that $\|f\|_p = 1$, and let $b_1, \ldots, b_N$ be complex numbers such that $\Sigma|b_n|^p = 1$. Our objective is the inequality

(2) $$\left|\sum_{n=1}^{N} b_n\hat{f}(n)\right| \le M^{(2-p)/p}.$$

Put $F = |f|^p$, and put $B_n = |b_n|^p$. Then there is a function φ and there are complex numbers $\beta_1, \ldots, \beta_N$ such that

(3) $$f = F^{1/p}\varphi, \qquad |\varphi| = 1, \qquad \int_X F\,d\mu = 1,$$

and

(4) $$b_n = B_n{}^{1/p}\beta_n, \qquad |\beta_n| = 1, \qquad \sum_{n=1}^{N} B_n = 1.$$

If we use these relations and the definition of $\hat{f}(n)$ given in Sec. 12.10, we obtain

(5) $$\sum_{n=1}^{N} b_n\hat{f}(n) = \sum_{n=1}^{N} B_n{}^{1/p}\beta_n \int_X F^{1/p}\varphi\psi_n\,d\mu.$$

Now replace $1/p$ by z in (5), and define

(6) $$\Phi(z) = \sum_{n=1}^{N} B_n{}^z\beta_n \int_X F^z\varphi\psi_n\,d\mu$$

for any complex number z. Recall that $A^z = \exp(z \log A)$ if $A > 0$; if $A = 0$, we agree that $A^z = 0$. Since F is simple, since $F \ge 0$, and since $B_n \ge 0$, we see that Φ is a finite linear combination of such exponentials, so Φ is an entire function which is bounded on

$$\{z\colon a \le \operatorname{Re}(z) \le b\}$$

for any finite a and b. We shall take $a = \frac{1}{2}$ and $b = 1$, shall estimate Φ on the edges of this strip, and shall then apply Theorem 12.8 to estimate $\Phi(1/p)$.

For $-\infty < y < \infty$, define

(7) $$c_n(y) = \int_X F^{\frac{1}{2}}F^{iy}\varphi\psi_n\,d\mu.$$

The Bessel inequality gives

$$(8) \qquad \sum_{n=1}^{N} |c_n(y)|^2 \le \int_X |F^{\frac{1}{2}} F^{iy} \varphi|^2 \, d\mu = \int_X |F| \, d\mu = 1,$$

and then the Schwarz inequality shows that

$$(9) \quad |\Phi(\tfrac{1}{2} + iy)| = \Big| \sum_{n=1}^{N} B_n^{\frac{1}{2}} B_n^{iy} \beta_n c_n \Big| \le \Big\{ \sum_{n=1}^{N} B_n \cdot \sum_{n=1}^{N} |c_n|^2 \Big\}^{\frac{1}{2}} \le 1.$$

The estimate

$$(10) \qquad |\Phi(1 + iy)| \le M \qquad (-\infty < y < \infty)$$

follows trivially from (3), (4), and (6), since $\|\psi_n\|_\infty \le M$.
We now conclude from (9), (10), and Theorem 12.8 that

$$(11) \quad |\Phi(x + iy)| \le M^{2x-1} \qquad (\tfrac{1}{2} \le x \le 1, \, -\infty < y < \infty).$$

With $x = 1/p$ and $y = 0$, this gives the desired inequality (2).
The proof is now easily completed. Note first that

$$(12) \qquad \Big\{ \sum_{n=1}^{N} |\hat{f}(n)|^q \Big\}^{1/q} = \sup \Big| \sum_{n=1}^{N} b_n \hat{f}(n) \Big|,$$

the supremum being taken over all $\{b_1, \ldots, b_N\}$ with $\Sigma |b_n|^p = 1$, since the L^q norm of any function on any measure space is equal to its norm as a linear functional on L^p. Hence (2) shows that

$$(13) \qquad \Big\{ \sum_{n=1}^{N} |\hat{f}(n)|^q \Big\}^{1/q} \le M^{(2-p)/p} \|f\|_p$$

for every simple complex $f \in L^p(\mu)$.

If now $f \in L^p(\mu)$, there are simple functions f_j such that $\|f_j - f\|_p \to 0$ as $j \to \infty$. Then $\hat{f}_j(n) \to \hat{f}(n)$ for every n, because $\psi_n \in L^q(\mu)$. Thus since (13) holds for each f_j, it also holds for f. Since N was arbitrary, we finally obtain (1).

A Converse of the Maximum Modulus Theorem

We now come to the theorem which was alluded to in the introduction of the present chapter.

The letter j will denote the identity function: $j(z) = z$.

The function which assigns the number 1 to each $z \in \bar{U}$ will be denoted by 1.

12.12 Theorem *Suppose M is a vector space of continuous complex functions on the closed unit disc $\bar{U}$, with the following properties:*

(a) $1 \in M$.
(b) *If $f \in M$, then also $jf \in M$.*
(c) *If $f \in M$, then $\|f\|_U = \|f\|_T$.*

Then every $f \in M$ is holomorphic in U.

Note that (c) is a rather weak form of the maximum modulus principle; (c) asserts only that the overall maximum of $|f|$ on $\bar{U}$ is attained at some point of the boundary T, but (c) does not a priori exclude the existence of *local* maxima of $|f|$ in U.

PROOF By (a) and (b), M contains all polynomials. In conjunction with (c), this shows that M satisfies the hypotheses of Theorem 5.25. Thus every $f \in M$ is harmonic in U. We shall use (b) to show that every $f \in M$ actually satisfies the Cauchy-Riemann equation.

Let ∂ and $\bar{\partial}$ be the differential operators introduced in Sec. 11.1. The product rule for differentiation gives

$$(\partial\bar{\partial})(fg) = f \cdot (\partial\bar{\partial}g) + (\partial f) \cdot (\bar{\partial}g) + (\bar{\partial}f) \cdot (\partial g) + (\partial\bar{\partial}f) \cdot g.$$

Fix $f \in M$, and take $g = j$. Then $fj \in M$. Hence f and fj are harmonic, so $\partial\bar{\partial}f = 0$ and $(\partial\bar{\partial})(fj) = 0$. Also, $\bar{\partial}j = 0$ and $\partial j = 1$. The above identity therefore reduces to $\bar{\partial}f = 0$. Thus $f \in H(U)$.

Exercises

1 Give a proof of Theorem 12.2 which requires no knowledge of the boundary values of f.

2 Suppose $f \in H(\Pi^+)$, where Π^+ is the upper half plane, and $|f| \leq 1$. How large can $|f'(i)|$ be? Find the extremal functions. (Compare the discussion in Sec. 12.5.)

3 Suppose $f \in H(\Omega)$. Under what conditions can $|f|$ have a local *minimum* in Ω?

4 Suppose $f \in H(U)$. Prove that there is a sequence $\{z_n\}$ in U such that $|z_n| \to 1$ and $\{f(z_n)\}$ is bounded.

5 If $0 < R_1 < R_2 < \infty$, let $A(R_1,R_2)$ denote the annulus

$$\{z: R_1 < |z| < R_2\}.$$

There is a vertical strip which the exponential function maps onto $A(R_1,R_2)$. Use this to prove Hadamard's *three-circle theorem:* If $f \in H(A(R_1,R_2))$, if

$$M(r) = \max_{\theta} |f(re^{i\theta})| \qquad (R_1 < r < R_2),$$

and if $R_1 < a < r < b < R_2$, then

$$\log M(r) \le \frac{\log (b/r)}{\log (b/a)} \log M(a) + \frac{\log (r/a)}{\log (b/a)} \log M(b).$$

[In other words, $\log M(r)$ is a convex function of $\log r$.] For which f does equality hold in this inequality?

6 Let Π be the open right half plane ($z \in \Pi$ if and only if $\operatorname{Re} z > 0$). Suppose f is continuous on the closure of Π ($\operatorname{Re} z \ge 0$), $f \in H(\Pi)$, and there are constants $A < \infty$ and $\alpha < 1$ such that

$$|f(z)| < A \exp (|z|^{\alpha})$$

for all $z \in \Pi$. Furthermore, $|f(iy)| \le 1$ for all real y. Prove that $|f(z)| \le 1$ in Π.

Show that the conclusion is false for $\alpha = 1$.

How does the result have to be modified if Π is replaced by a region bounded by two rays through the origin, at an angle not equal to π?

7 Suppose Γ is the boundary of an unbounded region Ω, $f \in H(\Omega)$, f is continuous on $\Omega \cup \Gamma$, and there are constants $B < \infty$ and $M < \infty$ such that $|f| \le M$ on Γ and $|f| \le B$ in Ω. Prove that we then actually have $|f| \le M$ in Ω.

Suggestion: Show that it involves no loss of generality to assume that $U \cap \Omega = \varnothing$. Fix $z_0 \in \Omega$, let n be a large integer, let V be a large disc with center at 0, and apply the maximum modulus theorem to the function $f^n(z)/z$ in the component of $V \cap \Omega$ which contains z_0.

8 Let f be an entire function. If there is a continuous mapping γ of $[0,1)$ into the complex plane such that $\gamma(t) \to \infty$ and $f(\gamma(t)) \to \alpha$ as $t \to 1$, we say that α is an *asymptotic value* of f. [In the complex plane, "$\gamma(t) \to \infty$ as $t \to 1$" means that to each $R < \infty$ there corresponds a $t_R < 1$ such that $|\gamma(t)| > R$ if $t_R < t < 1$.] Prove that every nonconstant entire function has ∞ as an asymptotic value.

Suggestion: Let $E_n = \{z: |f(z)| > n\}$. Each component of E_n is unbounded (proof?) and contains a component of E_{n+1}, by Exercise 7.

9 Show that exp has exactly two asymptotic values: 0 and ∞. How about sin and cos? *Note:* $\sin z$ and $\cos z$ are defined, for all complex z, by

$$\sin z = \frac{e^{iz} - e^{-iz}}{2i}, \qquad \cos z = \frac{e^{iz} + e^{-iz}}{2}.$$

10 If f is entire and if α is not in the range of f, prove that α is an asymptotic value of f.

11 Suppose Ω is a bounded region, $\{f_n\}$ is a sequence of continuous functions on $\bar{\Omega}$ which are holomorphic in Ω, and $\{f_n\}$ converges uniformly on the boundary of Ω. Prove that $\{f_n\}$ converges uniformly on $\bar{\Omega}$.

12 Suppose Ω is a bounded region, $f \in H(\Omega)$, and

$$\limsup_{n \to \infty} |f(z_n)| \leq M$$

for every sequence $\{z_n\}$ in Ω which converges to a boundary point of Ω. Prove that $|f(z)| \leq M$ for all $z \in \Omega$.

13 Suppose Ω is a region, D is a disc, $\bar{D} \subset \Omega$, $f \in H(\Omega)$, f is not constant, and $|f|$ is constant on the boundary of D. Prove that f has at least one zero in D.

13

Approximation by Rational Functions

Preparation

13.1 The Riemann Sphere It is often convenient in the study of holomorphic functions to compactify the complex plane by the adjunction of a new point called ∞. The resulting set S^2 (the *Riemann sphere*, the union of R^2 and $\{\infty\}$) is topologized in the following manner. For any $r > 0$, let $D'(\infty;r)$ be the set of all complex numbers z such that $|z| > r$, put $D(\infty;r) = D'(\infty;r) \cup \{\infty\}$, and declare a subset of S^2 to be open if and only if it is the union of discs $D(a;r)$, where the a's are arbitrary points of S^2 and the r's are arbitrary positive numbers. On $S^2 - \{\infty\}$, this gives of course the ordinary topology of the plane. It is easy to see that S^2 is homeomorphic to a sphere (hence the notation). In fact, a homeomorphism φ of S^2 onto the unit sphere in R^3 can be explicitly exhibited: Put $\varphi(\infty) = (0,0,1)$, and put

$$\varphi(re^{i\theta}) = \left(\frac{2r\cos\theta}{r^2+1}, \frac{2r\sin\theta}{r^2+1}, \frac{r^2-1}{r^2+1}\right) \tag{1}$$

for all complex numbers $re^{i\theta}$. We leave it to the reader to construct the geometric picture that goes with (1).

If f is holomorphic in $D'(\infty;r)$, we say that f has an isolated singularity at ∞. The nature of this singularity is the same as that which the function $\tilde{f}$, defined in $D'(0;1/r)$ by $\tilde{f}(z) = f(1/z)$, has at 0.

Thus if f is bounded in $D'(\infty;r)$, then $\lim_{z\to\infty} f(z)$ exists and is a complex number (as we see if we apply Theorem 10.20 to $\tilde{f}$), we define $f(\infty)$ to be this limit, and we thus obtain a function in $D(\infty;r)$ which we call holomorphic; note that this is defined in terms of the behavior of $\tilde{f}$ near 0, and not in terms of differentiability of f at ∞.

If $\tilde{f}$ has a pole of order m at 0, then f is said to have a pole of order m at ∞; the *principal part* of f at ∞ is then an ordinary polynomial of degree m (compare Theorem 10.21), and if we subtract this polynomial from f, we obtain a function with a removable singularity at ∞.

Finally, if $\tilde{f}$ has an essential singularity at 0, then f is said to have an essential singularity at ∞. For instance, every entire function which is not a polynomial has an essential singularity at ∞.

Later in this chapter we shall encounter the condition "$S^2 - \Omega$ is connected," where Ω is an open set in the plane. Note that this is not equivalent to the condition "the complement of Ω relative to the plane is connected." For example, if Ω consists of all complex $z = x + iy$ with $0 < y < 1$, the complement of Ω relative to the plane has two components, but $S^2 - \Omega$ is connected.

13.2 Rational Functions A rational function f is, by definition, a quotient of two polynomials P and Q: $f = P/Q$. It follows from the theorem in Sec. 10.37 (combined with some elementary algebra or with Theorem 10.18) that every nonconstant polynomial is a product of factors of degree 1. We may assume that P and Q have no such factors in common. Then f has a pole at each zero of Q (the pole of f has the same order as the zero of Q); and if we subtract the corresponding principal parts, we obtain a rational function whose only singularity is at ∞ and which is therefore a polynomial.

Thus every rational function $f = P/Q$ has a representation of the form

$$f(z) = A_0(z) + \sum_{j=1}^{k} A_j((z - a_j)^{-1}) \tag{1}$$

where $A_0, A_1, \ldots, A_k$ are polynomials, $A_1, \ldots, A_k$ have no constant term, and $a_1, \ldots, a_k$ are the distinct zeros of Q; (1) is called the *partial fractions decomposition* of f.

We turn to some topological considerations. We know that every open set in the plane is a countable union of compact sets (closed discs, for instance). However, it will be convenient to have some additional properties satisfied by these compact sets:

13.3 Theorem *Every open set Ω in the plane is the union of a sequence $\{K_n\}$, $n = 1, 2, 3, \ldots$, of compact sets such that*

(*a*) *K_n lies in the interior of K_{n+1}, for $n = 1, 2, 3, \ldots$.*
(*b*) *Every compact subset of Ω lies in some K_n.*
(*c*) *Every component of $S^2 - K_n$ contains a component of $S^2 - \Omega$, for $n = 1, 2, 3, \ldots$.*

Property (*c*) is, roughly speaking, that K_n has no holes except those which are forced upon it by the holes in Ω. Note that Ω is not assumed to be connected. The *interior* of a set E is, by definition, the largest open subset of E.

PROOF For $n = 1, 2, 3, \ldots$, put

$$V_n = D(\infty; n) \cup \bigcup_{a \notin \Omega} D\left(a; \frac{1}{n}\right) \tag{1}$$

and put $K_n = S^2 - V_n$. [Of course, $a \neq \infty$ in (1).] Then K_n is a closed and bounded (hence compact) subset of Ω, and $\Omega = \bigcup K_n$. If $z \in K_n$ and $r = n^{-1} - (n+1)^{-1}$, one verifies easily that $D(z;r) \subset K_{n+1}$. This gives (a). Hence Ω is the union of the interiors W_n of K_n. If K is a compact subset of Ω, then $K \subset W_1 \cup \cdots \cup W_N$ for some N, hence $K \subset K_N$.

Finally, each of the discs in (1) intersects $S^2 - \Omega$; each disc is connected; hence each component of V_n intersects $S^2 - \Omega$; since $V_n \supset S^2 - \Omega$, no component of $S^2 - \Omega$ can intersect two components of V_n. This gives (c).

13.4 Theorem *Suppose a and b are complex numbers, $b \neq 0$, and γ is the path consisting of the oriented intervals*

$$[a + i^n b,\ a + i^{n+1} b] \qquad (n = 0, 1, 2, 3). \tag{1}$$

Then

$$\operatorname{Ind}_\gamma(z) = 1 \tag{2}$$

for every z in the interior of the square with vertices at the points $a + i^n b$ $(n = 0, 1, 2, 3)$.

PROOF Let γ_n be the nth oriented interval in (1). For any z in the interior of the square, the integral of $(\xi - z)^{-1}$ over γ_n is the same as its integral over the circular arc Γ_n defined by

$$\Gamma_n(t) = a + i^n b e^{it} \qquad \left(0 \le t \le \frac{\pi}{2}\right), \tag{3}$$

as we see from Cauchy's theorem, applied to a convex region which contains $\gamma_n^* \cup \Gamma_n^*$ but excludes z. The result now follows from Theorem 10.11.

13.5 Theorem *If K is a compact subset of a plane open set Ω, there exist oriented line intervals $\gamma_1, \ldots, \gamma_n$ in $\Omega - K$ such that the Cauchy formula*

$$f(z) = \sum_{j=1}^{n} \frac{1}{2\pi i} \int_{\gamma_j} \frac{f(\zeta)}{\zeta - z}\, d\zeta \tag{1}$$

holds for every $f \in H(\Omega)$ and for every $z \in K$.

PROOF Since K is compact and Ω is open, there exists an $\eta > 0$ such that the distance from any point of K to any point outside Ω is at least 2η. Construct a grid of horizontal and vertical lines in the plane, such that the distance between any two adjacent horizontal lines is η, and likewise for the vertical lines. Let $Q_1, \ldots, Q_m$ be those squares (closed 2-cells) of edge η which are formed by this grid and which intersect K. Then $Q_r \subset \Omega$ for $r = 1, \ldots, m$.

Let ∂Q_r be the positively oriented boundary of Q_r. By this we mean that ∂Q_r consists of four oriented line intervals, as in Theorem 13.4, with a at the center of Q_r. Some of these line intervals may appear twice, but with opposite orientation; this happens whenever two of the Q_r's have an edge in common; discard these intervals, and let $\gamma_1, \ldots, \gamma_n$ be the remaining ones. It is then clear that

$$(2) \qquad \sum_{j=1}^{n} \frac{1}{2\pi i} \int_{\gamma_j} \varphi(\zeta)\, d\zeta = \sum_{r=1}^{m} \frac{1}{2\pi i} \int_{\partial Q_r} \varphi(\zeta)\, d\zeta$$

for any φ continuous on the union of the boundaries of the squares $Q_1, \ldots, Q_m$.

Any edge of any of the Q_r's which intersects K lies in the boundary of two Q_r's. For if an edge intersects K, then so do the two squares in whose boundary it lies. It follows that the intervals $\gamma_1, \ldots, \gamma_n$ lie in $\Omega - K$.

Now suppose $f \varepsilon H(\Omega)$ and fix z in the interior of some Q_r. Put $\varphi(\zeta) = [f(\zeta) - f(z)]/(\zeta - z)$, and apply (2). By the Cauchy theorem (which, since it holds for triangles, holds equally well for squares), the right side of (2) is 0. Hence

$$\sum_{j=1}^{n} \frac{1}{2\pi i} \int_{\gamma_j} \frac{f(\zeta)}{\zeta - z}\, d\zeta = \sum_{j=1}^{n} \frac{1}{2\pi i} \int_{\gamma_j} \frac{f(z)}{\zeta - z}\, d\zeta$$

$$= f(z) \sum_{r=1}^{m} \frac{1}{2\pi i} \int_{\partial Q_r} \frac{d\zeta}{\zeta - z} = f(z),$$

since the last integral is 0 for all but one value of r, and for that value it is 1, by Theorem 13.4.

This proves (1), provided z is in the interior of some Q_r. If $z \varepsilon K$, then z does not lie on any γ_j^*, and z is a limit point of the interior of some Q_r; hence (1) also holds for these z, by continuity.

Runge's Theorem

The main objective of this section is Theorem 13.9. We begin with a slightly different version in which the emphasis is on uniform approximation on one compact set.

13.6 Theorem *Suppose K is a compact set in the plane and $\{\alpha_j\}$ is a set which contains one point in each component of $S^2 - K$. If Ω is open, $\Omega \supset K$, $f \in H(\Omega)$, and $\epsilon > 0$, there exists a rational function R, all of whose poles lie in the prescribed set $\{\alpha_j\}$, such that*

$$|f(z) - R(z)| < \epsilon \tag{1}$$

for every $z \in K$.

Note that $S^2 - K$ has at most countably many components. Note also that the preassigned point in the unbounded component of $S^2 - K$ may very well be ∞; in fact, this happens to be the most interesting choice.

PROOF We consider the Banach space $C(K)$ whose members are the continuous complex functions on K, with the supremum norm. Let M be the subspace of $C(K)$ which consists of the restrictions to K of those rational functions which have all their poles in $\{\alpha_j\}$. The theorem asserts that f is in the closure of M. By Theorem 5.19 (a consequence of the Hahn-Banach theorem), this is equivalent to saying that every bounded linear functional on $C(K)$ which vanishes on M also vanishes at f, and hence the Riesz representation theorem (Theorem 6.19) shows that we must prove the following assertion:

If μ is a complex Borel measure on K such that

$$\int_K R\, d\mu = 0 \tag{2}$$

for every rational function R with poles only in the set $\{\alpha_j\}$, and if $f \in H(\Omega)$, then we also have

$$\int_K f\, d\mu = 0. \tag{3}$$

So let us assume that μ satisfies (2). Define

$$h(z) = \int_K \frac{d\mu(\zeta)}{\zeta - z} \qquad (z \in S^2 - K). \tag{4}$$

By Theorem 10.7 (with $X = K$, $\varphi(\zeta) = \zeta$), $h \in H(S^2 - K)$.

Let V_j be the component of $S^2 - K$ which contains α_j, and suppose $D(\alpha_j;r) \subset V_j$. If $\alpha_j \neq \infty$ and if z is fixed in $D(\alpha_j;r)$, then

$$\frac{1}{\zeta - z} = \lim_{N \to \infty} \sum_{n=0}^{N} \frac{(z - \alpha_j)^n}{(\zeta - \alpha_j)^{n+1}} \tag{5}$$

uniformly for $\zeta \in K$. Each of the functions on the right of (5) is one to which (2) applies. Hence $h(z) = 0$ for all $z \in D(\alpha_j;r)$. This implies that $h(z) = 0$ for all $z \in V_j$, by the uniqueness theorem 10.18.

If $\alpha_j = \infty$, (5) is replaced by

$$\frac{1}{\zeta - z} = -\lim_{N\to\infty} \sum_{n=0}^{N} z^{-n-1}\zeta^n \qquad (\zeta \in K, |z| > r), \tag{6}$$

which implies again that $h(z) = 0$ in $D(\infty; r)$, hence in V_j. We have thus proved from (2) that

$$h(z) = 0 \qquad (z \in S^2 - K). \tag{7}$$

Now choose oriented line intervals $\gamma_1, \ldots, \gamma_n$ in $\Omega - K$, as in Theorem 13.5, and integrate this Cauchy integral representation of f with respect to μ. An application of Fubini's theorem (legitimate, since we are dealing with Borel measures and continuous functions on compact spaces), combined with (7), gives

$$\int_K f\,d\mu = \int_K d\mu(\zeta)\left[\sum_{j=1}^{n} \frac{1}{2\pi i}\int_{\gamma_j} \frac{f(w)}{w - \zeta}\,dw\right]$$

$$= \sum_{j=1}^{n} \frac{1}{2\pi i}\int_{\gamma_j} f(w)\left[\int_K \frac{d\mu(\zeta)}{w - \zeta}\right]dw$$

$$= -\sum_{j=1}^{n} \frac{1}{2\pi i}\int_{\gamma_j} f(w)h(w)\,dw = 0.$$

The last equality depends on the fact that each γ_j is an interval in $S^2 - K$, where h vanishes.

Thus (3) holds, and the proof is complete.

The following special case is of particular interest.

13.7 Theorem *Suppose K is a compact set in the plane, $S^2 - K$ is connected, and $f \in H(\Omega)$, where Ω is some open set containing K. Then there is a sequence $\{P_n\}$ of polynomials such that $P_n(z) \to f(z)$ uniformly on K.*

PROOF Since now $S^2 - K$ has only one component, we need only one point α_j to apply Theorem 13.6, and we may take $\alpha_j = \infty$.

13.8 Remark The preceding result is false for *every* compact K in the plane such that $S^2 - K$ is not connected. For in that case $S^2 - K$ has a bounded component V. Choose $\alpha \in V$, put $f(z) = (z - \alpha)^{-1}$, and put $m = \max\{|z - \alpha| : z \in K\}$. Suppose P is a polynomial, such that $|P(z) - f(z)| < 1/m$ for all $z \in K$. Then

$$|(z - \alpha)P(z) - 1| < 1 \qquad (z \in K). \tag{1}$$

In particular, (1) holds if z is in the boundary of V; since the closure of V is compact, the maximum modulus theorem shows that (1) holds for every $z \in V$; taking $z = \alpha$, we obtain $1 < 1$. Hence the uniform approximation is not possible.

The same argument shows that none of the α_j can be dispensed with in Theorem 13.6.

We now apply the preceding approximation theorems to approximation in open sets. Let us emphasize that K was *not* assumed to be connected in Theorems 13.6 and 13.7 and that Ω will *not* be assumed to be connected in the theorem which follows.

13.9 Theorem *Let Ω be an open set in the plane, let A be a set which has one point in each component of $S^2 - \Omega$, and assume $f \in H(\Omega)$. Then there is a sequence $\{R_n\}$ of rational functions, with poles only in A, such that $R_n \to f$ uniformly on compact subsets of Ω.*

In the special case in which $S^2 - \Omega$ is connected, we may take $A = \{\infty\}$ and thus obtain polynomials P_n such that $P_n \to f$ uniformly on compact subsets of Ω.

Observe that $S^2 - \Omega$ may have uncountably many components; for instance, we may have $S^2 - \Omega = \{\infty\} \cup C$, where C is a Cantor set.

PROOF Choose a sequence of compact sets K_n in Ω, with the properties specified in Theorem 13.3. Fix n, for the moment. Since each component of $S^2 - K_n$ contains a component of $S^2 - \Omega$, each component of $S^2 - K_n$ contains a point of A, so Theorem 13.6 gives us a rational function R_n with poles in A such that

$$(1) \qquad |R_n(z) - f(z)| < \frac{1}{n} \qquad (z \in K_n).$$

If now K is any compact set in Ω, there exists an N such that $K \subset K_n$ for all $n \geq N$. It follows from (1) that

$$(2) \qquad |R_n(z) - f(z)| < \frac{1}{n} \qquad (z \in K,\ n \geq N),$$

which completes the proof.

13.10 Remark The power series representation of holomorphic functions provides us with a very specific procedure of approximation by polynomials, but this process can only be applied locally (i.e., in a circular disc contained in the set in which the given function is holomorphic). Runge's theorem provides a global approximation by rational functions (and, in some cases, by polynomials), in a much less specific manner, of course.

This global approximation leads to very simple proofs of general versions of the Cauchy theorem and the residue theorem. Essentially, any integration theorem that holds for rational functions with poles outside Ω holds for every $f \in H(\Omega)$. For if γ is a path in Ω, then γ^* is compact and f can therefore be uniformly approximated on γ^* by such rational functions. The only other significant ingredient of the proofs which follow is the residue theorem for rational functions (Theorem 10.29, with Ω the whole plane): *If γ is any closed path in the plane which passes through no pole of the rational function R, then*

$$\frac{1}{2\pi i}\int_\gamma R(z)\,dz = \sum_{k=1}^{n} \operatorname{Res}\,(R;a_k)\,\operatorname{Ind}_\gamma\,(a_k),$$

where $a_1, \ldots, a_n$ are the poles of R in the plane.

Cauchy's Theorem

13.11 Theorem *Suppose Ω is a plane open set, and $f \in H(\Omega)$.*

(*a*) *If γ is a closed path in Ω such that*

(1) $\operatorname{Ind}_\gamma(\alpha) = 0$ *for every* $\alpha \in S^2 - \Omega$,

then

(2) $$\int_\gamma f(z)\,dz = 0.$$

(*b*) *If γ_0 and γ_1 are closed paths in Ω such that*

(3) $\operatorname{Ind}_{\gamma_0}(\alpha) = \operatorname{Ind}_{\gamma_1}(\alpha)$ *for every* $\alpha \in S^2 - \Omega$,

then

(4) $$\int_{\gamma_0} f(z)\,dz = \int_{\gamma_1} f(z)\,dz.$$

(*c*) *If $S^2 - \Omega$ is connected, then* (1) *holds for every closed path γ in Ω; hence, so does* (2).

Note: We define $\operatorname{Ind}_\gamma(\infty) = 0$.

PROOF By Theorem 10.29, (*a*) and (*b*) hold for all rational functions without poles in Ω; as we observed above, the general case therefore follows from Theorem 13.9. As to (*c*), $\operatorname{Ind}_\gamma(\alpha) = 0$ for every α in the unbounded component of the complement of γ^*, and if $S^2 - \Omega$ is connected, $S^2 - \Omega$ lies in that component. This completes the proof.

Part (*b*) shows under what conditions integration over one path can be replaced by integration over another one, without changing the value of the integral.

If Ω is convex, then $S^2 - \Omega$ is connected. Hence (*a*) is a generalization of Theorem 10.14.

13.12 Definition A function f is said to be *meromorphic* in an open set Ω if there is a set $A \subset \Omega$ such that

(*a*) A has no limit point in Ω.
(*b*) $f \in H(\Omega - A)$.
(*c*) f has a pole at each point of A.

Note that the possibility $A = \varnothing$ is not excluded. Thus every $f \in H(\Omega)$ is meromorphic in Ω.

Note also that (*a*) implies that no compact subset of Ω can contain infinitely many points of A and that A is therefore at most countable.

We now state a general form of the residue theorem:

13.13 Theorem *Suppose f is a meromorphic function in the plane open set Ω. Let A be the set of points in Ω at which f has poles. If γ is any closed path in $\Omega - A$ such that* $\text{Ind}_\gamma(\alpha) = 0$ *for every $\alpha \in S^2 - \Omega$, then*

(1)
$$\frac{1}{2\pi i}\int_\gamma f(z)\,dz = \sum_{a\in A} \text{Res}\,(f;a)\,\text{Ind}_\gamma\,(a).$$

PROOF Let $B = \{a \in A : \text{Ind}_\gamma\,(a) \neq 0\}$. Every point of B lies in a bounded component V of $S^2 - \gamma^*$ such that V does not intersect $S^2 - \Omega$. Hence B lies in the union of γ^* and these V's; this union is a compact subset of Ω, and since A has no limit point in Ω, we conclude that B is a finite set. The sum in (1), though formally infinite, is therefore actually finite.

Let $a_1, \ldots, a_n$ be the points of B, let $\varphi_1, \ldots, \varphi_n$ be the principal parts of f at $a_1, \ldots, a_n$, and put $g = f - (\varphi_1 + \cdots + \varphi_n)$. Then g has removable singularities at $a_1, \ldots, a_n$. If $\Omega_0 = \Omega - (A - B)$, Theorem 13.11(*a*) applies to the function g and the open set Ω_0. Hence $\int_\gamma g = 0$. Since the only pole of φ_k is at a_k, it follows that

$$\frac{1}{2\pi i}\int_\gamma f(z)\,dz = \sum_{k=1}^{n} \frac{1}{2\pi i}\int_\gamma \varphi_k(z)\,dz = \sum_{k=1}^{n} \text{Res}\,(\varphi_k;a_k)\,\text{Ind}_\gamma\,(a_k),$$

and since f and φ_k have the same residue at a_k we obtain (1).

13.14 Homology and Homotopy We now give a brief discussion of the topological concepts which are relevant to Cauchy's theorem.

Two closed paths γ_0 and γ_1 in Ω are said to be Ω-*homologous* if they satisfy condition (3) of Theorem 13.11; if γ satisfies condition (1) of that theorem, we say that γ is Ω-homologous to 0. Intuitively, γ_0 is Ω-homologous to γ_1 if γ_0 and γ_1 wind around each point of $S^2 - \Omega$ the same number of times, and γ is Ω-homologous to 0 if γ does not wind around any point of $S^2 - \Omega$. It is clear that Ω-homology is an equivalence relation in the set of all closed paths in Ω.

The notion of homotopy (also an equivalence relation) formalizes the notion of deforming one curve to another:

Suppose γ_0 and γ_1 are closed curves in a topological space X, both with parameter interval $I = [0,1]$. We say that γ_0 and γ_1 are *X-homotopic* if there is a continuous mapping of the unit square $I^2 = I \times I$ into X such that

$$(1) \qquad h(0,t) = \gamma_0(t), \qquad h(1,t) = \gamma_1(t), \qquad h(s,0) = h(s,1),$$

for all $s \in I$ and $t \in I$. Setting $\gamma_s(t) = h(s,t)$, (1) gives what one calls a *one-parameter family* of closed curves γ_s in X, which connects γ_0 and γ_1.

If γ_0 is X-homotopic to a constant mapping γ_1 (i.e., if γ_1^* consists of just one point), we say that γ_0 is *null-homotopic in X*. Intuitively, this means that γ_0 can be shrunk to a point within X.

The class of *simply connected regions* is defined in terms of homotopy, as we shall see presently, and there are important relations between homotopy and analytic continuation. As far as Cauchy's theorem is concerned, homology is of greater significance. Theorem 13.11 shows this. The two concepts are related in the following manner.

13.15 Theorem *Suppose γ_0 and γ_1 are closed paths in Ω. If these paths are Ω-homotopic, they are also Ω-homologous. If γ_0 is null-homotopic in Ω, then γ_0 is also Ω-homologous to* 0.

PROOF Clearly, it is enough to prove the first assertion. So assume γ_0 and γ_1 are Ω-homotopic, with parameter interval $[0,1]$, let h be a mapping of I^2 into Ω with the properties listed in 13.14(1), and let $\{\gamma_s\}$ be the corresponding one-parameter family of closed curves in Ω, for $0 \leq s \leq 1$.

There is now a minor difficulty, due to the fact that we have defined the index only for closed *paths*, not for closed curves. We can circumvent this in two ways. One is to prove that if γ_0 and γ_1 are differentiable, and if there is a continuous mapping h with the required properties, then there is also a differentiable mapping h with these properties, so that the resulting γ_s will actually be paths.

The other way is to define the index for all closed *curves,* in the following way. Let Γ be a closed curve, with parameter interval $[0,2\pi]$, say, and assume $\alpha \notin \Gamma^*$. Γ can be uniformly approximated on $[0,2\pi]$ by trigonometric polynomials Γ_n. As soon as n and m are large enough, Theorem 10.35 can be applied to $\Gamma_n - \alpha$ and $\Gamma_m - \alpha$ and it shows that $\text{Ind}_{\Gamma_n}(\alpha) = \text{Ind}_{\Gamma_m}(\alpha)$. Define this common value to be $\text{Ind}_\Gamma(\alpha)$. It is easy to see that the result does not depend on the particular choice of $\{\Gamma_n\}$, and it is also easy to verify that Theorem 10.35 now holds for closed curves and not merely for closed paths. We leave it to the reader to check the details.

In any case, the uniform continuity of our mapping h of I^2 into Ω now implies that $\text{Ind}_{\gamma_s}(\alpha)$ is, for each $\alpha \in S^2 - \Omega$, a continuous function of s on $[0,1]$. Every integer-valued continuous function is constant on $[0,1]$. Hence γ_0 and γ_1 are Ω-homologous.

13.16 Example The converse of Theorem 13.15 is false. To show this, we shall construct a path γ_0 in a region Ω so that γ_0 is Ω-homologous to 0 without being null-homotopic in Ω.

Let M be the center of a square with vertices A, B, C, and D; let P and Q be interior points of the triangles AMD and BCM, respectively; and let Ω be the plane region whose complement consists of the points P and Q. Let γ_0 be the piecewise linear path $ADBCDACBA$. That is to say, γ_0 consists of the interval $[AD]$, followed by $[DB]$, etc. Since $[AD]$ cancels $[DA]$ and $[BC]$ cancels $[CB]$ in every integral over γ_0, we see that γ_0 is Ω-homologous to the path γ_1: $ACDBA$. Since P and Q are in the unbounded component of the complement of γ_1^*, γ_1 is Ω-homologous to 0, and hence the same is true of γ_0. But γ_0 cannot be shrunk to a point within Ω. This should be clear from a picture of γ_0. A formal proof (using the tools of algebraic topology) would depend on properties of the fundamental group of Ω.

Simply Connected Regions

13.17 Definition A plane region Ω is said to be *simply connected* if every closed curve in Ω is null-homotopic in Ω.

(A similar definition can of course be made in the class of all arcwise connected topological spaces.)

Simply connected regions play a particularly important role in the theory of holomorphic functions, for the following reason.

13.18 Theorem *For a plane region Ω, each of the following eight conditions implies all the others.*

(*a*) *Ω is homeomorphic to the open unit disc U.*
(*b*) *Ω is simply connected.*
(*c*) *$S^2 - \Omega$ is connected.*
(*d*) $\text{Ind}_\gamma(\alpha) = 0$ *for every closed path γ in Ω and for every $\alpha \in S^2 - \Omega$.*

(*e*) *For every* $f \in H(\Omega)$ *and every closed path* γ *in* Ω,

$$\int_\gamma f(z)\,dz = 0.$$

(*f*) *To every* $f \in H(\Omega)$ *there corresponds an* $F \in H(\Omega)$ *such that* $F' = f$.

(*g*) *If* $f \in H(\Omega)$ *and* f *has no zero in* Ω, *there exists a* $g \in H(\Omega)$ *such that* $f = \exp(g)$.

(*h*) *If* $f \in H(\Omega)$ *and* f *has no zero in* Ω, *there exists a* $\varphi \in H(\Omega)$ *such that* $f = \varphi^2$.

The assertion of (*g*) is that f has a "holomorphic logarithm" g in Ω; (*h*) asserts that f has a "holomorphic square root" φ in Ω; and (*e*) says that the Cauchy theorem holds for every closed path in a simply connected region.

PROOF (*a*) implies (*b*). To say that Ω is homeomorphic to U means that there is a continuous one-to-one mapping ψ of Ω onto U whose inverse ψ^{-1} is also continuous. If γ is a closed curve in Ω, with parameter interval $[0,1]$, put

$$h(s,t) = \psi^{-1}(s\psi(\gamma(t))) \qquad (0 \le s \le 1,\ 0 \le t \le 1). \tag{1}$$

Then h is a continuous mapping of the unit square into Ω;

$$h(s,0) = h(s,1)$$

since $\gamma(0) = \gamma(1)$; $h(0,t) = \psi^{-1}(0)$, a constant; and $h(1,t) = \gamma(t)$. Thus Ω is simply connected.

(*b*) implies (*c*). Assume (*c*) is false. Then there are disjoint open sets V and W in S^2 whose union covers $S^2 - \Omega$ and such that both V and W intersect $S^2 - \Omega$. Let W be the one which contains ∞, and put

$$K = V \cap (S^2 - \Omega). \tag{2}$$

Then $K \ne \varnothing$, and K is compact since $\bar{V}$ is compact and

$$V \cap (S^2 - \Omega) = \bar{V} \cap (S^2 - \Omega).$$

There is a positive number η such that every closed square of edge η which intersects K lies in V. Construct a grid whose horizontal and vertical lines partition the plane into squares of edge η, let A be the union of those (finitely many!) closed grid squares which intersect K, let B be one component of A (so $B \cap K \ne \varnothing$), and let C be the union of B and the bounded components of the complement of B (C is obtained by filling the holes of B). The boundary of C consists of finitely many intervals which join to a closed curve γ in $V - K$, such that $\text{Ind}_\gamma(\alpha) = 1$ for all $\alpha \in B \cap K$. Since $\alpha \notin \Omega$, Theorem 13.15 shows that γ is not null-homotopic in Ω, so (*b*) fails.

(*c*) implies (*d*) and (*d*) implies (*e*). This is part of Theorem 13.11.

(*e*) implies (*f*). Assume (*e*) holds, fix $z_0 \in \Omega$, and put

$$F(z) = \int_{\Gamma(z)} f(\zeta)\, d\zeta \qquad (z \in \Omega) \tag{3}$$

where $\Gamma(z)$ is any path in Ω from z_0 to z. This defines a function F in Ω. For if $\Gamma_1(z)$ is another path from z_0 to z (in Ω), then Γ followed by the opposite of Γ_1 is a closed path in Ω, the integral of f over this closed path is 0, so (3) is not affected if $\Gamma(z)$ is replaced by $\Gamma_1(z)$. We now verify that $F' = f$. Fix $a \in \Omega$. There exists an $r > 0$ such that $D(a;r) \subset \Omega$. For $z \in D(a;r)$ we can compute $F(z)$ by integrating f over a path $\Gamma(a)$, followed by the interval $[a,z]$. Hence, for $z \in D'(a;r)$,

$$\frac{F(z) - F(a)}{z - a} = \frac{1}{z - a} \int_{[a,z]} f(\zeta)\, d\zeta, \tag{4}$$

and the continuity of f at a now implies that $F'(a) = f(a)$, as in the proof of Theorem 10.14.

(*f*) implies (*g*). If $f \in H(\Omega)$ and f has no zero in Ω, then $f'/f \in H(\Omega)$, and (*f*) implies that there exists a $g \in H(\Omega)$ so that $g' = f'/f$. We can add a constant to g, so that $\exp\{g(z_0)\} = f(z_0)$ for some $z_0 \in \Omega$. Our choice of g shows that the derivative of fe^{-g} is 0 in Ω, hence fe^{-g} is constant (since Ω is connected), and it follows that $f = e^g$.

(*g*) implies (*h*). By (*g*), $f = e^g$. Put $\varphi = \exp(\frac{1}{2}g)$.

(*h*) implies (*a*). If Ω is the whole plane, then Ω is homeomorphic to U: map z to $z/(1 + |z|)$.

If Ω is a proper subregion of the plane which satisfies (*h*), then there actually exists a *holomorphic* homeomorphism of Ω onto U (a conformal mapping). This assertion is the Riemann mapping theorem, which is the main objective of the next chapter. Hence the proof of Theorem 13.18 will be complete as soon as the Riemann mapping theorem is proved. (See the note following the statement of Theorem 14.8.)

The fact that (*g*) holds in every simply connected region has the following consequence (which can also be proved by quite elementary means):

13.19 Theorem *If $f \in H(\Omega)$, where Ω is any open set in the plane, and if f has no zero in Ω, then* $\log |f|$ *is harmonic in Ω.*

PROOF To every disc $D \subset \Omega$ there corresponds a function $g \in H(D)$ such that $f = e^g$ in D. If $u = \operatorname{Re} g$, then u is harmonic in D, and $|f| = e^u$. Thus $\log |f|$ is harmonic in every disc in Ω, and this gives the desired conclusion.

Exercises

1 Complete the details in the proof of Theorem 13.15.

2 Prove that every meromorphic function on S^2 is rational.

3 Suppose Ω is a simply connected region, $f \in H(\Omega)$, f has no zero in Ω, and n is a positive integer. Prove that there exists a $g \in H(\Omega)$ such that $g^n = f$.

4 Let $\Omega = \{z: |z| < 1 \text{ and } |2z - 1| > 1\}$, and suppose $f \in H(\Omega)$.

(*a*) Must there exist a sequence of polynomials P_n such that $P_n \to f$ uniformly on compact subsets of Ω?

(*b*) Must there exist such a sequence which converges to f uniformly in Ω?

(*c*) Is the answer to (*b*) changed if we require more of f, namely, that f be holomorphic in some open set which contains the closure of Ω?

5 Is there a sequence of polynomials P_n such that $P_n(0) = 1$ for $n = 1, 2, 3, \ldots$, but $P_n(z) \to 0$ for every $z \neq 0$, as $n \to \infty$?

6 Is there a sequence of polynomials P_n such that

$$\lim_{n\to\infty} P_n(z) = \begin{cases} 1 & \text{if } \operatorname{Im} z > 0, \\ 0 & \text{if } z \text{ is real}, \\ -1 & \text{if } \operatorname{Im} z < 0? \end{cases}$$

7 For $n = 1, 2, 3, \ldots$, let Δ_n be a closed disc in U, and let L_n be an arc (a homeomorphic image of $[0,1]$) in $U - \Delta_n$ which intersects every radius of U. There are polynomials P_n which are very small on Δ_n and more or less arbitrary on L_n. Show that $\{\Delta_n\}$, $\{L_n\}$, and $\{P_n\}$ can be so chosen that the series $f = \Sigma P_n$ defines a function $f \in H(U)$ which has no radial limit at any point of T. In other words, for no real θ does $\lim_{r\to 1} f(re^{i\theta})$ exist.

8 Here is another construction of such a function. Let $\{n_k\}$ be a sequence of integers such that $n_1 > 1$ and $n_{k+1} > 2kn_k$. Define

$$h(z) = \sum_{k=1}^{\infty} 5^k z^{n_k}.$$

Prove that the series converges if $|z| < 1$ and prove that there is a constant $c > 0$ such that $|h(z)| > c \cdot 5^m$ for all z with $|z| = 1 - (1/n_m)$. [*Hint:* For such z the mth term in the series defining $h(z)$ is much larger than the sum of all the others.]

Hence h has no finite radial limits.

Prove also that h must have infinitely many zeros in U. (Compare with Exercise 4, Chap. 12.) In fact, prove that to every complex number α there correspond infinitely many $z \in U$ at which $h(z) = \alpha$.

9 Show that in Theorem 13.9 we need not assume that A intersects each component of $S^2 - \Omega$. It is enough to assume that the closure of A intersects each component of $S^2 - \Omega$.

10 Prove the following general form of Rouché's theorem: Let Ω be the interior of a compact set K in the plane. Suppose f and g are continuous on K and holomorphic in Ω, and $|f(z) - g(z)| < |f(z)|$ for all $z \in K - \Omega$. Then f and g have the same number of zeros in Ω.

11 Let A be the annulus $\{z: r_1 < |z| < r_2\}$, where r_1 and r_2 are given positive numbers.

(*a*) Show that the Cauchy formula

$$f(z) = \frac{1}{2\pi i}\left(\int_{\gamma_1} + \int_{\gamma_2}\right)\frac{f(\zeta)}{\zeta - z}\,d\zeta$$

is valid under the following conditions: $f \in H(A)$,

$$r_1 + \epsilon < |z| < r_2 - \epsilon,$$

and

$$\gamma_1(t) = (r_1 + \epsilon)e^{-it}, \qquad \gamma_2(t) = (r_2 - \epsilon)e^{it} \qquad (0 \le t \le 2\pi).$$

(*b*) Show by means of (*a*) that every $f \in H(A)$ can be decomposed into a sum $f = f_1 + f_2$, where $f_1 \in H(D(\infty; r_1))$ and $f_2 \in H(D(0; r_2))$; the decomposition is unique if we require that $f_1(\infty) = 0$.

(*c*) Use this decomposition to associate with each $f \in H(A)$ its so-called "Laurent series"

$$\sum_{-\infty}^{\infty} c_n z^n$$

which converges to f in A. Show that there is only one such series for each f. Show that it converges to f uniformly on compact subsets of A.

(*d*) If $f \in H(A)$ and f is bounded in A, show that the components f_1 and f_2 are also bounded. Show that f then has radial limits f^* at almost all points of the boundary of A and that the Cauchy formula (*a*) holds with $\epsilon = 0$ and with f^* in place of f in the integrand.

(*e*) How much of the foregoing can you extend to the case $r_1 = 0$ (or $r_2 = \infty$, or both)?

(*f*) How much of the foregoing can you extend to regions bounded by finitely many (more than two) circles?

12 It is required to expand the function

$$\frac{1}{1 - z^2} + \frac{1}{3 - z}$$

in a series of the form $\sum_{-\infty}^{\infty} c_n z^n$.

How many such expansions are there? In which region is each of them valid? Find the coefficients c_n explicitly for each of these expansions.

13 Suppose Ω is a horizontal strip, determined by the inequalities $a < y < b$, say. Suppose $f \in H(\Omega)$, and $f(z) = f(z + 1)$ for all $z \in \Omega$. Prove that f has a Fourier expansion in Ω,

$$f(z) = \sum_{-\infty}^{\infty} c_n e^{2\pi i n z},$$

which converges uniformly in $\{z: a + \epsilon \leq y \leq b - \epsilon\}$, for every $\epsilon > 0$. *Hint:* The map $z \rightarrow e^{2\pi i z}$ converts f to a function in an annulus.

Find integral formulas by means of which the coefficients c_n can be computed from f.

14 Suppose $f_n \in H(\Omega)$ $(n = 1, 2, 3, \ldots)$, f is a complex function in Ω, and $f(z) = \lim_{n \rightarrow \infty} f_n(z)$ for every $z \in \Omega$. Prove that Ω has a dense open subset V on which f is holomorphic. *Hint:* Put $\varphi = \sup |f_n|$. Use Baire's theorem to prove that every disc in Ω contains a disc on which φ is bounded. Apply Exercise 17, Chap. 10. (In general, $V \neq \Omega$. Compare Exercises 5 and 6.)

15 Prove Theorem 13.4 by direct computation (without intervention of a circle).

16 Suppose Ω is a region, $f \in H(\Omega)$, and $f \not\equiv 0$. Prove that f has a holomorphic logarithm in Ω if and only if f has holomorphic nth roots in Ω for every positive integer n.

17 Suppose $f \in H(\Omega)$, $z_0 \in \Omega$, m is a positive integer, and f has a zero of order m at z_0. Prove the existence of a neighborhood V of z_0 and of a function $g \in H(V)$ which maps V in a one-to-one fashion onto $D(0;r)$, for some $r > 0$, and such that $f(z) = [g(z)]^m$ for all $z \in V$.

Observe that this is a more precise statement than that furnished by Theorem 10.32. Namely, $f = h \circ g$, where g is one-to-one in V, and $h(w) = w^m$.

see pg 216

14

Conformal Mapping

Preservation of Angles

14.1 Definition Each complex number $z \neq 0$ determines a *direction* from the origin, defined by the point

(1) $$A[z] = \frac{z}{|z|}$$

on the unit circle.

Suppose f is a mapping of a region Ω into the plane, $z_0 \in \Omega$, and z_0 has a deleted neighborhood $D'(z_0;r) \subset \Omega$ in which $f(z) \neq f(z_0)$. We say that *f preserves angles at z_0* if

(2) $$\lim_{r\to 0} e^{-i\theta} A[f(z_0 + re^{i\theta}) - f(z_0)] \qquad (r > 0)$$

exists and *is independent of θ.*

In less precise language, the requirement is that for any two rays L' and L'', starting at z_0, the angle which their images $f(L')$ and $f(L'')$ make at $f(z_0)$ is the same as that made by L' and L'', in size as well as in orientation.

The property of preserving angles at each point of a region is characteristic of holomorphic functions whose derivative has no zero in that region. This is a corollary of Theorem 14.2 and is the reason for calling holomorphic functions with nonvanishing derivative *conformal mappings.*

14.2 Theorem *Let f map a region Ω into the plane. If $f'(z_0)$ exists at some $z_0 \in \Omega$ and $f'(z_0) \neq 0$, then f preserves angles at z_0. Conversely, if the differential of f exists and is different from 0 at z_0, and if f preserves angles at z_0, then $f'(z_0)$ exists and is different from 0.*

Here $f'(z_0) = \lim\, [f(z) - f(z_0)]/(z - z_0)$, as usual. The differential of f at z_0 is a linear transformation L of R^2 into R^2 such that, writing $z_0 = (x_0,y_0)$,

(1) $$f(x_0 + x,\, y_0 + y) = f(x_0,y_0) + L(x,y) + (x^2 + y^2)^{\frac{1}{2}}\eta(x,y),$$

where $\eta(x,y) \to 0$ as $x \to 0$ and $y \to 0$, as in Definition 8.22.

PROOF Take $z_0 = f(z_0) = 0$, for simplicity. If $f'(0) = a \neq 0$, then it is immediate that

$$e^{-i\theta}A[f(re^{i\theta})] = \frac{e^{-i\theta}f(re^{i\theta})}{|f(re^{i\theta})|} \to \frac{a}{|a|} \qquad (r \to 0), \tag{2}$$

so f preserves angles at 0. Conversely, if the differential of f exists at 0 and is different from 0, then (1) can be rewritten in the form

$$f(z) = \alpha z + \beta \bar{z} + |z|\eta(z), \tag{3}$$

where $\eta(z) \to 0$ as $z \to 0$, and α and β are complex numbers, not both 0. If f also preserves angles at 0, then

$$\lim_{r \to 0} e^{-i\theta}A[f(re^{i\theta})] = \frac{\alpha + \beta e^{-2i\theta}}{|\alpha + \beta e^{-2i\theta}|} \tag{4}$$

exists and is independent of θ. We may exclude those θ for which the denominator in (4) is 0; there are at most two such θ in $[0,2\pi)$. For all other θ, we conclude that $\alpha + \beta e^{-2i\theta}$ lies on a fixed ray through 0, and this is possible only when $\beta = 0$. Hence $\alpha \neq 0$, and (3) implies that $f'(0) = \alpha$.

Note: No holomorphic function preserves angles at any point where its derivative is 0. We omit the easy proof of this. However, the differential of a transformation may be 0 at a point where angles are preserved. Example: $f(z) = |z|z$, $z_0 = 0$.

Linear Fractional Transformations

14.3 If a, b, c, and d are complex numbers such that $ad - bc \neq 0$, the mapping

$$z \to \frac{az + b}{cz + d} \tag{1}$$

is called a *linear fractional transformation*. It is convenient to regard (1) as a mapping of the sphere S^2 into S^2, with the obvious conventions concerning the point ∞. For instance, $-d/c$ maps to ∞ and ∞ maps to a/c, if $c \neq 0$. It is then easy to see that each linear fractional transformation is a one-to-one mapping of S^2 onto S^2. Furthermore, each is obtained by a superposition of transformations of the following types:

(*a*) Translations: $z \to z + b$.
(*b*) Rotations: $z \to az$, $|a| = 1$.
(*c*) Homotheties: $z \to rz$, $r > 0$.
(*d*) Inversion: $z \to 1/z$.

If $c = 0$ in (1), this is obvious. If $c \neq 0$, it follows from the identity

$$\frac{az+b}{cz+d} = \frac{a}{c} + \frac{\lambda}{cz+d}, \qquad \lambda = \frac{bc-ad}{c}. \tag{2}$$

The first three types evidently carry lines to lines and circles to circles. This is not true of (*d*). But if we let $\mathfrak{F}$ be the family consisting of all straight lines and all circles, then $\mathfrak{F}$ *is* preserved by (*d*), and hence we have the important result that $\mathfrak{F}$ *is preserved by every linear fractional transformation.* (It may be noted that when $\mathfrak{F}$ is regarded as a family of subsets of S^2, then $\mathfrak{F}$ consists of all circles on S^2, via the stereographic projection 13.1(1); we shall not use this property of $\mathfrak{F}$ and omit its proof.)

The proof that $\mathfrak{F}$ is preserved by inversion is quite easy. Elementary analytic geometry shows that every member of $\mathfrak{F}$ is the locus of an equation

$$\alpha z\bar{z} + \beta z + \bar{\beta}\bar{z} + \gamma = 0, \tag{3}$$

where α and γ are real constants and β is a complex constant, provided that $\beta\bar{\beta} > \alpha\gamma$. If $\alpha \neq 0$, (3) defines a circle; $\alpha = 0$ gives the straight lines. Replacement of z by $1/z$ transforms (3) into

$$\alpha + \beta\bar{z} + \bar{\beta}z + \gamma z\bar{z} = 0, \tag{4}$$

which is an equation of the same type.

Suppose a, b, and c are distinct complex numbers. We construct a linear fractional transformation φ which maps the ordered triple $\{a,b,c\}$ into $\{0,1,\infty\}$, namely,

$$\varphi(z) = \frac{(b-c)(z-a)}{(b-a)(z-c)}. \tag{5}$$

There is only one such φ. For if $\varphi(a) = 0$, we must have $z - a$ in the numerator; if $\varphi(c) = \infty$, we must have $z - c$ in the denominator; and if $\varphi(b) = 1$, we are led to (5). If a or b or c is ∞, formulas analogous to (5) can easily be written down. If we follow (5) by the inverse of a transformation of the same type, we obtain the following result:

For any two ordered triples $\{a,b,c\}$ *and* $\{a',b',c'\}$ *in* S^2 *there is one and only one linear fractional transformation which maps* a *to* a', b *to* b', *and* c *to* c'.

(It is of course assumed that $a \neq b$, $a \neq c$, and $b \neq c$, and likewise for a', b', and c'.)

We conclude from this that every circle can be mapped onto every circle by a linear fractional transformation. Of more interest is the fact that every circle can be mapped onto every straight line (if ∞ is regarded as part of the line) and hence that *every open disc can be conformally mapped onto every open half plane.*

Let us discuss one such mapping more explicitly, namely,

$$\varphi(z) = \frac{1 + z}{1 - z}. \tag{6}$$

This φ maps $\{-1,0,1\}$ to $\{0,1,\infty\}$; the segment $(-1,1)$ maps onto the positive real axis. The unit circle T passes through -1 and 1; hence $\varphi(T)$ is a straight line through $\varphi(-1) = 0$. Since T makes a right angle with the real axis at -1, $\varphi(T)$ makes a right angle with the real axis at 0. Thus $\varphi(T)$ is the imaginary axis. Since $\varphi(0) = 1$, it follows that *φ is a conformal one-to-one mapping of the open unit disc onto the open right half plane.*

The role of linear fractional transformations in the theory of conformal mapping is also well illustrated by Theorem 12.6.

14.4 Linear fractional transformations make it possible to transfer theorems concerning the behavior of holomorphic functions near straight lines to situations where circular arcs occur instead. It will be enough to illustrate the method with an informal discussion of the reflection principle.

Suppose Ω is a region in U, bounded in part by an arc L on the unit circle, and f is continuous on $\bar{\Omega}$, holomorphic in Ω, and real on L. The function

$$\psi(z) = \frac{z - i}{z + i} \tag{1}$$

maps the upper half plane onto U. If $g = f \circ \psi$, Theorem 11.17 gives us a holomorphic extension G of g, and then $F = G \circ \psi^{-1}$ gives a holomorphic extension F of f which satisfies the relation

$$F(z^*) = \overline{F(z)}, \tag{2}$$

where $z^* = 1/\bar{z}$.

The last assertion follows from a property of ψ: If $w = \psi(z)$ and $w_1 = \psi(\bar{z})$, then $w_1 = w^*$, as is easily verified by computation.

Exercises 2 to 5 furnish other applications of this technique.

Normal Families

The Riemann mapping theorem will be proved by exhibiting the mapping function as the solution of a certain extremum problem. The existence of this solution depends on a very useful compactness property of certain families of holomorphic functions which we now formulate.

14.5 Definition Suppose $\mathfrak{F} \subset H(\Omega)$, for some region Ω. We call $\mathfrak{F}$ a *normal family* if every sequence of members of $\mathfrak{F}$ contains a subsequence which converges uniformly on compact subsets of Ω. The limit function is not required to belong to $\mathfrak{F}$.

(Sometimes a wider definition is adopted, by merely requiring that every sequence in $\mathfrak{F}$ either converges or tends to ∞, uniformly on compact subsets of Ω. This is well adapted for dealing with meromorphic functions.)

14.6 Theorem *Suppose $\mathfrak{F} \subset H(\Omega)$ and $\mathfrak{F}$ is uniformly bounded on each compact subset of the region Ω. Then $\mathfrak{F}$ is a normal family.*

PROOF The hypothesis means that to each compact $K \subset \Omega$ there corresponds a number $M(K) < \infty$ such that $|f(z)| \leq M(K)$ for all $f \in \mathfrak{F}$ and all $z \in K$.

Let $\{K_n\}$ be a sequence of compact sets whose union is Ω, such that K_n lies in the interior of K_{n+1}; such a sequence was constructed in Theorem 13.3. Then there exist positive numbers δ_n such that

$$D(z;2\delta_n) \subset K_{n+1} \qquad (z \in K_n). \tag{1}$$

Consider two points z' and z'' in K_n, such that $|z' - z''| < \delta_n$, let γ be the positively oriented circle with center at z' and radius $2\delta_n$, and estimate $|f(z') - f(z'')|$ by the Cauchy formula. Since

$$\frac{1}{\zeta - z'} - \frac{1}{\zeta - z''} = \frac{z' - z''}{(\zeta - z')(\zeta - z'')},$$

we have

$$f(z') - f(z'') = \frac{z' - z''}{2\pi i} \int_\gamma \frac{f(\zeta)}{(\zeta - z')(\zeta - z'')}\, d\zeta, \tag{2}$$

and since $|\zeta - z'| = 2\delta_n$ and $|\zeta - z''| > \delta_n$ for all $\zeta \in \gamma^*$, (2) gives the inequality

$$|f(z') - f(z'')| < \frac{M(K_{n+1})}{\delta_n} |z' - z''|, \tag{3}$$

valid for all $f \in \mathfrak{F}$ and all z' and $z'' \in K_n$, provided that $|z' - z''| < \delta_n$.

This was the crucial step in the proof: We have proved, for each K_n, that the restrictions of the members of $\mathfrak{F}$ to K_n form an *equicontinuous family*. This means, by definition, that to each $\epsilon > 0$ there corresponds a $\delta > 0$ such that $|f(z') - f(z'')| < \epsilon$ for all $f \in \mathfrak{F}$ and all z' and $z'' \in K_n$ for which $|z' - z''| < \delta$. A glance at (3) shows that this requirement is satisfied by

$$\delta = \frac{\epsilon\delta_n}{\epsilon + M(K_{n+1})}. \tag{4}$$

Now let $\{f_m\}$ be a sequence in $\mathfrak{F}$. Choose a countable dense subset $\{z_i\}$ of Ω. Since $\{f_m(z)\}$ is bounded at each $z \in \Omega$, $\{f_m\}$ has a subsequence, say $\{f_{m,1}\}$, which converges at z_1. From $\{f_{m,1}\}$ we can extract a subsequence, say $\{f_{m,2}\}$, which also converges at z_2. Proceed in this manner. We obtain sequences $\{f_{m,i}\}$ which converge at z_i and such that $\{f_{m,i}\}$ is a subsequence of $\{f_{m,i-1}\}$. The "diagonal sequence" $\{f_{m,m}\}$ then converges at every one of our points z_i.

We claim that $\{f_{m,m}\}$ actually converges uniformly on each K_n (and hence on each compact subset K of Ω).

Fix K_n, fix $\epsilon > 0$, and choose δ as in (4). There are points $z_1, \ldots, z_p$ of our set $\{z_i\}$ such that K_n lies in the union of the discs $D(z_i;\delta)$, $i = 1, \ldots, p$, and there is an integer N such that

$$|f_{r,r}(z_i) - f_{s,s}(z_i)| < \epsilon \tag{5}$$

if $r > N$, $s > N$, and $1 \le i \le p$.

To every $z \in K_n$ there corresponds a z_i so that $1 \le i \le p$ and $|z - z_i| < \delta$. Then $|f_{r,r}(z) - f_{s,s}(z)|$ is not larger than

$$|f_{r,r}(z) - f_{r,r}(z_i)| + |f_{r,r}(z_i) - f_{s,s}(z_i)| + |f_{s,s}(z_i) - f_{s,s}(z)|. \tag{6}$$

The first and third differences in (6) are less than ϵ, by our choice of δ; the second term is less than ϵ if $r > N$ and $s > N$. Hence

$$|f_{r,r}(z) - f_{s,s}(z)| < 3\epsilon \tag{7}$$

for every $z \in K_n$, if $r > N$ and $s > N$.

This completes the proof.

The Riemann Mapping Theorem

14.7 Conformal Equivalence We call two regions Ω_1 and Ω_2 *conformally equivalent* if there exists a $\varphi \in H(\Omega_1)$ such that φ is one-to-one in Ω_1 and such that $\varphi(\Omega_1) = \Omega_2$, i.e., if there exists a conformal one-to-one mapping of Ω_1 onto Ω_2. Under these conditions, the inverse of φ is holomorphic in Ω_2 (Theorem 10.34) and hence is a conformal mapping of Ω_2 onto Ω_1.

It follows that conformally equivalent regions are homeomorphic. But there is a much more important relation between conformally equivalent regions: If φ is as above, $f \to f \circ \varphi$ is a one-to-one mapping of $H(\Omega_2)$ onto $H(\Omega_1)$ which preserves sums and products, i.e., which is a ring isomorphism of $H(\Omega_2)$ onto $H(\Omega_1)$. If Ω_1 has a simple structure, problems about $H(\Omega_2)$ can be transferred to problems in $H(\Omega_1)$, and the solutions can be carried back to $H(\Omega_2)$ with the aid of the mapping function φ. The most important case of this is based on the Riemann mapping theorem (where Ω_2 is the unit disc U), which reduces the study of $H(\Omega)$ to the study of $H(U)$, for any simply connected proper subregion of the plane. Of course, for explicit solutions of problems, it may be necessary to have rather precise information about the mapping function.

14.8 Theorem *Every simply connected region Ω in the plane (other than the plane itself) is conformally equivalent to the open unit disc U.*

Note: The case of the plane clearly has to be excluded, by Liouville's theorem. Thus the plane is not conformally equivalent to U, although the two regions are homeomorphic.

The only property of simply connected regions which will be used in the proof is that every holomorphic function which has no zero in such a region has a holomorphic square root there. This will furnish the conclusion "(h) implies (a)" in Theorem 13.18 and will thus complete the proof of that theorem.

PROOF Suppose Ω is a simply connected region in the plane and let w_0 be a complex number, $w_0 \notin \Omega$. Let Σ be the class of all $\psi \in H(\Omega)$ which are one-to-one in Ω and which map Ω into U. We have to prove that some $\psi \in \Sigma$ maps Ω *onto* U.

We first prove that Σ *is not empty.* Since Ω is simply connected, there exists a $\varphi \in H(\Omega)$ so that $\varphi^2(z) = z - w_0$ in Ω. If $\varphi(z_1) = \varphi(z_2)$, then also $\varphi^2(z_1) = \varphi^2(z_2)$, hence $z_1 = z_2$; thus φ is one-to-one. The same argument shows that there are no two points z_1 and z_2 in Ω such that $\varphi(z_1) = -\varphi(z_2)$. Since φ is an open mapping, $\varphi(\Omega)$ contains a disc $D(a;r)$, with $0 < r < |a|$. The disc $D(-a;r)$ therefore fails to intersect $\varphi(\Omega)$, and if we put $\psi = r/(\varphi + a)$, we see that $\psi \in \Sigma$.

The next step consists in showing that *if $\psi \in \Sigma$, if $\psi(\Omega)$ does not cover all of U, and if $z_0 \in \Omega$, then there exists a $\psi_1 \in \Sigma$ with*

$$|\psi_1'(z_0)| > |\psi'(z_0)|.$$

It will be convenient to use the functions φ_α defined by

$$\varphi_\alpha(z) = \frac{z - \alpha}{1 - \bar{\alpha}z}.$$

For $\alpha \in U$, φ_α is a one-to-one mapping of U onto U; its inverse is $\varphi_{-\alpha}$ (Theorem 12.4).

Suppose $\psi \in \Sigma$, $\alpha \in U$, and $\alpha \notin \psi(\Omega)$. Then $\varphi_\alpha \circ \psi \in \Sigma$, and $\varphi_\alpha \circ \psi$ has no zero in Ω; hence there exists a $g \in H(\Omega)$ such that $g^2 = \varphi_\alpha \circ \psi$. We see that g is one-to-one (as in the proof that $\Sigma \neq \emptyset$), hence $g \in \Sigma$; and if $\psi_1 = \varphi_\beta \circ g$, where $\beta = g(z_0)$, it follows that $\psi_1 \in \Sigma$. With the notation $w^2 = s(w)$, we now have

$$\psi = \varphi_{-\alpha} \circ s \circ g = \varphi_{-\alpha} \circ s \circ \varphi_{-\beta} \circ \psi_1.$$

Since $\psi_1(z_0) = 0$, the chain rule gives

$$\psi'(z_0) = F'(0)\psi_1'(z_0),$$

where $F = \varphi_{-\alpha} \circ s \circ \varphi_{-\beta}$. We see that $F(U) \subset U$ and that F is not one-to-one in U. Therefore $|F'(0)| < 1$, by the Schwarz lemma (see Sec. 12.5), so $|\psi'(z_0)| < |\psi_1'(z_0)|$. [Note that $\psi'(z_0) \neq 0$, since ψ is one-to-one in Ω.]

Fix $z_0 \in \Omega$, and put

$$\eta = \sup \{|\psi'(z_0)| : \psi \in \Sigma\}.$$

The foregoing makes it clear that *any* $h \in \Sigma$ *for which* $|h'(z_0)| = \eta$ *will map* Ω *onto* U. Hence the proof will be completed as soon as we prove the existence of such an h.

Since $|\psi(z)| < 1$ for all $\psi \in \Sigma$ and $z \in \Omega$, Theorem 14.6 shows that Σ is a normal family. The definition of η shows that there is a sequence $\{\psi_n\}$ in Σ such that $|\psi_n'(z_0)| \to \eta$, and by the normality of Σ we can extract a subsequence (again denoted by $\{\psi_n\}$, for simplicity) which converges, uniformly on compact subsets of Ω, to a limit $h \in H(\Omega)$. By Theorem 10.27, $|h'(z_0)| = \eta$. Since $\Sigma \neq \varnothing$, $\eta > 0$, so h is not constant. Since $\psi_n(\Omega) \subset U$, for $n = 1, 2, 3, \ldots$, we have $h(\Omega) \subset \bar{U}$, but the open mapping theorem shows that actually $h(\Omega) \subset U$.

So all that remains to be shown is that h is one-to-one. Fix distinct points z_1 and $z_2 \in \Omega$; put $\alpha = h(z_1)$ and $\alpha_n = \psi_n(z_1)$ for $n = 1, 2, 3, \ldots$; and let $\bar{D}$ be a closed circular disc in Ω with center at z_2, such that $z_1 \notin \bar{D}$ and such that $h - \alpha$ has no zero on the boundary of $\bar{D}$. This is possible, since the zeros of $h - \alpha$ have no limit point in Ω. The functions $\psi_n - \alpha_n$ converge to $h - \alpha$, uniformly on $\bar{D}$; they have no zero in D, since they are one-to-one and have a zero at z_1; it now follows from Rouché's theorem that $h - \alpha$ has no zero in D; in particular, $h(z_2) \neq h(z_1)$.

Thus $h \in \Sigma$, and the proof is complete.

A more constructive proof is outlined in Exercise 26.

14.9 Remarks The preceding proof also shows that $h(z_0) = 0$. For if $h(z_0) = \beta \neq 0$, then $\varphi_\beta \circ h \in \Sigma$, and

$$|(\varphi_\beta \circ h)'(z_0)| = |\varphi_\beta'(\beta)h'(z_0)| = \frac{|h'(z_0)|}{1 - |\beta|^2} > |h'(z_0)|.$$

It is interesting to observe that although h was obtained by maximizing $|\psi'(z_0)|$ for $\psi \in \Sigma$, h also maximizes $|f'(z_0)|$ if f is allowed to range over the class consisting of all holomorphic mappings of Ω into U (not necessarily one-to-one). For if f is such a function, then $g = f \circ h^{-1}$ maps U into U, hence $|g'(0)| \leq 1$, with equality holding (by the Schwarz lemma) if and only if g is a rotation, so the chain rule gives the following result:

If $f \in H(\Omega)$, $f(\Omega) \subset U$, *and* $z_0 \in \Omega$, *then* $|f'(z_0)| \leq |h'(z_0)|$. *Equality holds if and only if* $f(z) = \lambda h(z)$, *for some constant* λ *with* $|\lambda| = 1$.

The Class $\mathcal{S}$

14.10 Definition $\mathcal{S}$ is the class of all $f \in H(U)$ which are *one-to-one* in U and which satisfy

(1) $$f(0) = 0, \qquad f'(0) = 1.$$

Thus every $f \in \mathcal{S}$ has a power series expansion

(2) $$f(z) = z + \sum_{n=2}^{\infty} a_n z^n \qquad (z \in U).$$

The class of all F such that $1/F \in \mathcal{S}$ will also be of interest; every such F has a pole of order 1 at $z = 0$, with residue 1, and is holomorphic in $U - \{0\}$. Hence

(3) $$F(z) = \frac{1}{z} + \sum_{n=0}^{\infty} \alpha_n z^n \qquad (z \in U).$$

The class $\mathcal{S}$ is not closed under addition or multiplication, but has many other interesting properties. We shall develop only a few of these in this section. Theorem 14.15 will be used in the proof of Mergelyan's theorem, in Chap. 20.

14.11 Example The function

$$f(z) = \frac{z}{(1-z)^2} = \sum_{n=1}^{\infty} nz^n$$

is a member of $\mathcal{S}$.

For if $f(z) = f(w)$, then $(z - w)(1 + zw) = 0$, and the second factor is not 0 if $|z| < 1$ and $|w| < 1$.

We leave it to the reader to find $f(U)$ for this f.

14.12 Theorem *(a) If* $f \in \mathcal{S}$, $|\alpha| = 1$, *and* $g(z) = \bar{\alpha} f(\alpha z)$, *then* $g \in \mathcal{S}$. *(b) If* $f \in \mathcal{S}$ *there exists a* $g \in \mathcal{S}$ *such that*

(1) $$g^2(z) = f(z^2) \qquad (z \in U).$$

PROOF (*a*) is clear. To prove (*b*), write $f(z) = z\varphi(z)$. Then $\varphi \in H(U)$, $\varphi(0) = 1$, and φ has no zero in U, since f has no zero in $U - \{0\}$. Hence there exists an $h \in H(U)$ with $h(0) = 1$, $h^2(z) = \varphi(z)$. Put

(2) $$g(z) = zh(z^2) \qquad (z \in U).$$

Then $g^2(z) = z^2h^2(z^2) = z^2\varphi(z^2) = f(z^2)$, so that (1) holds. It is clear that $g(0) = 0$ and $g'(0) = 1$. We have to show that g is one-to-one.

Suppose z and $w \in U$ and $g(z) = g(w)$. Since f is one-to-one, (1) implies that $z^2 = w^2$. So either $z = w$ (which is what we want to prove) or $z = -w$. In the latter case, (2) shows that $g(z) = -g(w)$; it follows that $g(z) = g(w) = 0$, and since g has no zero in $U - \{0\}$, we have $z = w = 0$.

14.13 Theorem *If* $1/F \in \mathcal{S}$ *and*

$$F(z) = \frac{1}{z} + \sum_{n=0}^{\infty} \alpha_n z^n \qquad (z \in U), \tag{1}$$

then

$$\sum_{n=1}^{\infty} n|\alpha_n|^2 \leq 1. \tag{2}$$

This is usually called the *area theorem*, for reasons which will become apparent in the proof.

PROOF The choice of α_0 is clearly irrelevant. So assume $\alpha_0 = 0$. Neither the hypothesis nor the conclusion is affected if we replace $F(z)$ by $\lambda F(\lambda z)$ ($|\lambda| = 1$). So we may assume that α_1 is real.

For $0 < r < 1$, put $U_r = \{z\colon |z| < r\}$, $C_r = \{z\colon |z| = r\}$, and $V_r = \{z\colon r < |z| < 1\}$. Then $F(U_r)$ is a neighborhood of ∞ (by the open mapping theorem, applied to $1/F$); and $F(U_r)$, $F(C_r)$, and $F(V_r)$ are disjoint, since F is one-to-one. Write

$$F(z) = \frac{1}{z} + \alpha_1 z + \varphi(z) \qquad (z \in U), \tag{3}$$

$F = u + iv$, and

$$A = \frac{1}{r} + \alpha_1 r, \qquad B = \frac{1}{r} - \alpha_1 r. \tag{4}$$

For $z = re^{i\theta}$, we then obtain

$$u = A\cos\theta + \operatorname{Re}\varphi \qquad \text{and} \qquad v = -B\sin\theta + \operatorname{Im}\varphi. \tag{5}$$

Divide Eqs. (5) by A and B, respectively, square, and add:

$$\frac{u^2}{A^2} + \frac{v^2}{B^2} = 1 + \frac{2\cos\theta}{A}\operatorname{Re}\varphi + \left(\frac{\operatorname{Re}\varphi}{A}\right)^2 - \frac{2\sin\theta}{B}\operatorname{Im}\varphi + \left(\frac{\operatorname{Im}\varphi}{B}\right)^2.$$

By (3), φ has a zero of order at least 2 at the origin; and if we keep account of (4), it follows that there exists an $\eta > 0$ such that, for all sufficiently small r,

$$\frac{u^2}{A^2} + \frac{v^2}{B^2} < 1 + \eta r^3 \qquad (z = re^{i\theta}). \tag{6}$$

This says that $F(C_r)$ is in the interior of the ellipse E_r whose semi-axes are $A\sqrt{1+\eta r^3}$ and $B\sqrt{1+\eta r^3}$, and which therefore bounds an area

$$(7)\quad \pi AB(1+\eta r^3) = \pi\left(\frac{1}{r}+\alpha_1 r\right)\left(\frac{1}{r}-\alpha_1 r\right)(1+\eta r^3) \le \frac{\pi}{r^2}(1+\eta r^3).$$

Since $F(C_r)$ is in the interior of E_r, we have $E_r \subset F(U_r)$; hence $F(V_r)$ is in the interior of E_r, so the area of $F(V_r)$ is no larger than (7). The Cauchy-Riemann equations show that the Jacobian of the mapping $(x,y) \to (u,v)$ is $|F'|^2$. Theorem 8.26 therefore gives the following result:

$$(8)\quad \frac{\pi}{r^2}(1+\eta r^3) \ge \iint_{V_r} |F'|^2$$

$$= \int_r^1 t\,dt \int_0^{2\pi} \left| -t^{-2}e^{-2i\theta} + \sum_1^\infty n\alpha_n t^{n-1}e^{i(n-1)\theta} \right|^2 d\theta$$

$$= 2\pi \int_r^1 \left(t^{-3} + \sum_1^\infty n^2|\alpha_n|^2 t^{2n-1}\right) dt$$

$$= \pi\left\{r^{-2} - 1 + \sum_1^\infty n|\alpha_n|^2(1-r^{2n})\right\}.$$

If we divide (8) by π and then subtract r^{-2} from each side, we obtain

$$(9)\quad \sum_{n=1}^N n|\alpha_n|^2(1-r^{2n}) \le 1 + \eta r$$

for all sufficiently small r and for all positive integers N. Let $r \to 0$ in (9), then let $N \to \infty$. This gives (2).

Corollary *Under the same hypothesis,* $|\alpha_1| \le 1$.

That this is in fact best possible is shown by $F(z) = (1/z) + \alpha z$, $|\alpha| = 1$, which is one-to-one in U.

14.14 Theorem *If $f \in \mathcal{S}$, and*

$$f(z) = z + \sum_{n=2}^\infty a_n z^n,$$

then (a) $|a_2| \le 2$, and (b) $f(U) \supset D(0;\frac{1}{4})$.

The second assertion is that $f(U)$ contains all w with $|w| < \frac{1}{4}$.

PROOF By Theorem 14.12, there exists a $g \in \mathcal{S}$ so that $g^2(z) = f(z^2)$. If $G = 1/g$, then Theorem 14.13 applies to G, and this will give (*a*).

Since $$f(z^2) = z^2(1 + a_2 z^2 + \cdots),$$
we have $$g(z) = z(1 + \tfrac{1}{2}a_2 z^2 + \cdots),$$

and hence $$G(z) = \frac{1}{z}(1 - \tfrac{1}{2}a_2 z^2 + \cdots) = \frac{1}{z} - \frac{a_2}{2} z + \cdots.$$

The Corollary to Theorem 14.13 now shows that $|a_2| \le 2$.

To prove (*b*), suppose $w \notin f(U)$. Define

$$h(z) = \frac{f(z)}{1 - f(z)/w}.$$

Then $h \in H(U)$, h is one-to-one in U, and

$$h(z) = (z + a_2 z^2 + \cdots)\left(1 + \frac{z}{w} + \cdots\right) = z + \left(a_2 + \frac{1}{w}\right) z^2 + \cdots,$$

so that $h \in \mathcal{S}$. Apply (*a*) to h: We have $|a_2 + (1/w)| \le 2$, and since $|a_2| \le 2$, we finally obtain $|1/w| \le 4$. So $|w| \ge \frac{1}{4}$ for every $w \notin f(U)$. This completes the proof.

Example 14.11 shows that both (*a*) and (*b*) are best possible; the point $-\frac{1}{4}$ is not in $f(U)$ for this particular $f \in \mathcal{S}$.

14.15 Theorem *Suppose* $1/F \in \mathcal{S}$, $w_1 \notin F(U)$, *and* $w_2 \notin F(U)$. *Then* $|w_1 - w_2| \le 4$.

PROOF If $f = 1/(F - w_1)$, then $f \in \mathcal{S}$, hence $f(U) \supset D(0;\frac{1}{4})$, so the image of U under $F - w_1$ contains all w with $|w| > 4$. Since $w_2 - w_1$ is not in this image, we have $|w_2 - w_1| \le 4$.

Note that this too is best possible: If $F(z) = z^{-1} + z$, then $F(U)$ does not contain the points 2, -2. In fact, the complement of $F(U)$ is precisely the interval $[-2,2]$ on the real axis.

Continuity at the Boundary

Under certain conditions, every conformal mapping of a simply connected region Ω onto U can be extended to a homeomorphism of its closure $\bar{\Omega}$ onto $\bar{U}$. The nature of the boundary of Ω plays a decisive role here.

14.16 Definition A boundary point β of a simply connected plane region Ω will be called a *simple boundary point of* Ω if β has the following property: To every sequence $\{\alpha_n\}$ in Ω such that $\alpha_n \to \beta$ as $n \to \infty$ there corresponds a curve γ, with parameter interval $[0,1]$, and a sequence $\{t_n\}$, $0 < t_1 < t_2 < \cdots, t_n \to 1$, such that $\gamma(t_n) = \alpha_n$ $(n = 1, 2, 3, \ldots)$ and $\gamma(t) \in \Omega$ for $0 \leq t < 1$.

In other words, there is a curve in Ω which passes through the points α_n and which ends at β.

14.17 Examples Since examples of simple boundary points are obvious, let us look at some that are not simple.

If Ω is $U - \{x: 0 \leq x < 1\}$, then Ω is simply connected; and if $0 < \beta \leq 1$, β is a boundary point of Ω which is not simple.

To get a more complicated example, let Ω_0 be the interior of the square with vertices at the points $0, 1, 1 + i$, and i. Remove the intervals

$$\left[\frac{1}{2n}, \frac{1}{2n} + \frac{n-1}{n} i\right] \quad \text{and} \quad \left[\frac{1}{2n+1} + \frac{i}{n}, \frac{1}{2n+1} + i\right]$$

from Ω_0. The resulting region Ω is simply connected. If $0 \leq y \leq 1$, then iy is a boundary point which is not simple.

14.18 Theorem *Let Ω be a bounded simply connected region in the plane, and let f be a conformal mapping of Ω onto U.*

(a) *If β is a simple boundary point of Ω, then f has a continuous extension to $\Omega \cup \{\beta\}$. If f is so extended, then $|f(\beta)| = 1$.*
(b) *If β_1 and β_2 are distinct simple boundary points of Ω and if f is extended to $\Omega \cup \{\beta_1\} \cup \{\beta_2\}$ as in (a), then $f(\beta_1) \neq f(\beta_2)$.*

PROOF Let g be the inverse of f. Then $g \in H(U)$, by Theorem 10.34, $g(U) = \Omega$, g is one-to-one, and $g \in H^\infty$, since Ω is bounded.

Suppose (a) is false. Then there is a sequence $\{\alpha_n\}$ in Ω such that $\alpha_n \to \beta$, $f(\alpha_{2n}) \to w_1$, $f(\alpha_{2n+1}) \to w_2$, and $w_1 \neq w_2$. Choose γ as in Definition 14.16, and put $\Gamma(t) = f(\gamma(t))$, for $0 \leq t < 1$. Put $K_r = g(\bar{D}(0;r))$, for $0 < r < 1$. Then K_r is a compact subset of Ω. Since $\gamma(t) \to \beta$ as $t \to 1$, there exists a $t^* < 1$ (depending on r) such that $\gamma(t) \notin K_r$ if $t^* < t < 1$. Thus $|\Gamma(t)| > r$ if $t^* < t < 1$. This says that $|\Gamma(t)| \to 1$ as $t \to 1$. Since $\Gamma(t_{2n}) \to w_1$ and $\Gamma(t_{2n+1}) \to w_2$, we also have $|w_1| = |w_2| = 1$.

It now follows that one of the two open arcs J whose union is $T - (\{w_1\} \cup \{w_2\})$ has the property that every radius of U which ends at a point of J intersects the range of Γ in an infinite set. Note that $g(\Gamma(t)) = \gamma(t)$ for $0 \leq t < 1$ and that g has radial limits a.e. on T, since $g \in H^\infty$. Hence

$$(1) \qquad \lim_{r \to 1} g(re^{it}) = \beta \qquad \text{(a.e. on } J),$$

since $g(\Gamma(t)) \to \beta$ as $t \to 1$. By Theorem 11.22, applied to $g - \beta$, (1) shows that g is constant. But g is one-to-one in U, and we have a contradiction. Thus $w_1 = w_2$ and (a) is proved.

Suppose (b) is false. If we multiply f by a suitable constant of absolute value 1, we then have $\beta_1 \neq \beta_2$ but $f(\beta_1) = f(\beta_2) = -1$.

Since β_1 and β_2 are simple boundary points of Ω, there are curves γ_i with parameter interval $[0,1]$ such that $\gamma_i([0,1)) \subset \Omega$ for $i = 1$ and 2 and $\gamma_i(1) = \beta_i$. Put $\Gamma_i(t) = f(\gamma_i(t))$. Then $\Gamma_i([0,1)) \subset U$, and $\Gamma_1(1) = \Gamma_2(1) = -1$. Since $g(\Gamma_i(t)) = \gamma_i(t)$ on $[0,1)$, there exists a $t^* < 1$ such that

$$(2) \qquad |g(\Gamma_1(t)) - g(\Gamma_2(t))| > \tfrac{1}{2}|\beta_1 - \beta_2| \qquad (t^* < t < 1),$$

and there exists a $\delta > 0$ such that $D(-1;\delta)$ intersects neither $\Gamma_1([0;t^*])$ nor $\Gamma_2([0;t^*])$.

Put $A(\delta) = U \cap D(-1;\delta)$. Suppose $0 < r < \delta$; by (2) and the choice of δ there are points w_i on the range of Γ_i such that $|1 + w_i| = r$ and

$$(3) \qquad |g(w_1) - g(w_2)| > \tfrac{1}{2}|\beta_1 - \beta_2|.$$

But $g(w_1) - g(w_2)$ is the integral of g' over the circular arc from w_2 to w_1 in U, with center at -1. Hence

$$(4) \qquad \tfrac{1}{2}|\beta_1 - \beta_2| < \int_{-\eta}^{\eta} |g'(-1 + re^{i\theta})| r\, d\theta \qquad (0 < r < \delta),$$

where $\eta = \eta(r)$ is the largest number such that $-1 + re^{i\theta} \in U$ whenever $|\theta| < \eta$. Then $\eta < \pi/2$, and if we apply the Schwarz inequality to (4) we find

$$(5) \qquad \frac{|\beta_1 - \beta_2|^2}{4\pi r} \leq r \int_{-\eta}^{\eta} |g'(-1 + re^{i\theta})|^2\, d\theta \qquad (0 < r < \delta).$$

Integrate the right side of (5) with respect to r, over $(0,\delta)$. The result is the area of $g(A(\delta))$, which is finite, since $g(A(\delta)) \subset \Omega$ and Ω is bounded. But the integral of the left side of (5) over $(0,\delta)$ is ∞, unless $\beta_1 = \beta_2$.

This completes the proof of (b).

14.19 Theorem *If Ω is a bounded simply connected region in the plane and if every boundary point of Ω is simple, then every conformal mapping of Ω onto U extends to a homeomorphism of $\bar{\Omega}$ onto $\bar{U}$.*

PROOF Suppose $f \in H(\Omega)$, $f(\Omega) = U$, and f is one-to-one. By Theorem 14.18 we can extend f to a mapping of $\bar{\Omega}$ into $\bar{U}$ such that $f(\alpha_n) \to f(z)$ whenever $\{\alpha_n\}$ is a sequence in Ω which converges to z. If $\{z_n\}$ is a sequence in $\bar{\Omega}$ which converges to z, there exist points

$\alpha_n \in \Omega$ such that $|\alpha_n - z_n| < 1/n$ and $|f(\alpha_n) - f(z_n)| < 1/n$. Thus $\alpha_n \to z$, hence $f(\alpha_n) \to f(z)$, and this shows that $f(z_n) \to f(z)$.

We have now proved that our extension of f is continuous on $\bar{\Omega}$. Also, $U \subset f(\bar{\Omega}) \subset \bar{U}$. The compactness of $\bar{\Omega}$ implies that $f(\bar{\Omega})$ is compact. Hence $f(\bar{\Omega}) = \bar{U}$.

Theorem 14.18(*b*) shows that f is one-to-one on $\bar{\Omega}$. Since every continuous one-to-one mapping of a compact set has a continuous inverse ([26], Theorem 4.17), the proof is complete.

14.20 Remarks

(*a*) *The preceding theorem has a purely topological corollary: If every boundary point of a bounded simply connected plane region Ω is simple, then the boundary of Ω is a Jordan curve, and $\bar{\Omega}$ is homeomorphic to $\bar{U}$.*

(A Jordan curve is, by definition, a homeomorphic image of the unit circle.)

The converse is true, but we shall not prove it: If the boundary of Ω is a Jordan curve, then every boundary point of Ω is simple.

(*b*) Suppose f is as in Theorem 14.19, a, b, and c are distinct boundary points of Ω, and A, B, and C are distinct points of T. There is a linear fractional transformation φ which maps the triple $\{f(a), f(b), f(c)\}$ to $\{A,B,C\}$; suppose the orientation of $\{A,B,C\}$ agrees with that of $\{f(a),f(b),f(c)\}$; then $\varphi(U) = U$, and the function $g = \varphi \circ f$ is a homeomorphism of $\bar{\Omega}$ onto $\bar{U}$ which is holomorphic in Ω and which maps $\{a,b,c\}$ to prescribed values $\{A,B,C\}$. It follows from Sec. 14.3 that g is uniquely determined by these requirements.

(*c*) Theorem 14.19, as well as the above remark (*b*), extends without difficulty to simply connected regions Ω in the Riemann sphere S^2, all of whose boundary points are simple, provided that $S^2 - \Omega$ has a nonempty interior, for then a linear fractional transformation brings us back to the case in which Ω is a bounded region in the plane. Likewise, U can be replaced, for instance, by a half plane.

(*d*) More generally, if f_1 and f_2 map Ω_1 and Ω_2 onto U, as in Theorem 14.19, then $f = f_2^{-1} \circ f_1$ is a homeomorphism of $\bar{\Omega}_1$ onto $\bar{\Omega}_2$ which is holomorphic in Ω_1.

Conformal Mapping of an Annulus

14.21 It is a consequence of the Riemann mapping theorem that any two simply connected proper subregions of the plane are conformally equivalent, since each of them is conformally equivalent to the unit disc. This is a very special property of simply connected regions. One may ask whether it extends to the next simplest situation, i.e., whether any two annuli are conformally equivalent. The answer is negative.

For $0 < r < R$, let

$$(1) \qquad A(r,R) = \{z: r < |z| < R\}$$

be the annulus with inner radius r and outer radius R. If $\lambda > 0$, the mapping $z \to \lambda z$ maps $A(r,R)$ onto $A(\lambda r, \lambda R)$. *Hence $A(r,R)$ and $A(r_1,R_1)$ are conformally equivalent if $R/r = R_1/r_1$.* The surprising fact is that this sufficient condition is also necessary; thus among the annuli there is a different conformal type associated with each real number greater than 1.

14.22 Theorem *$A(r_1,R_1)$ and $A(r_2,R_2)$ are conformally equivalent if and only if $R_1/r_1 = R_2/r_2$.*

PROOF Assume $r_1 = r_2 = 1$ without loss of generality, put

$$A_1 = A(1,R_1),$$

$A_2 = A(1,R_2)$, and assume there exists an $f \in H(A_1)$ so that f is one-to-one and $f(A_1) = A_2$. Then either $|f(z)| \to 1$ as $|z| \to 1$ or $|f(z)| \to R_2$ as $|z| \to 1$. In the latter case, replace f by R_2/f. So we can assume that $|f(z)| \to 1$ as $|z| \to 1$, and hence that $|f(z)| \to R_2$ as $|z| \to R_1$. Put

$$\alpha = \frac{\log R_2}{\log R_1}$$

and

$$(1) \qquad u(z) = \log |f(z)| - \alpha \log |z| \qquad (z \in A_1).$$

Since f has no zero in A_1, $\log |f|$ is harmonic in A_1. Our choice of α shows that $u(z) \to 0$ as $|z| \to 1$ and as $|z| \to R_1$. Hence u extends to a continuous function on $\bar{A}_1$, which is 0 on the boundary of A_1. Since nonconstant harmonic functions have no local maxima or minima, we conclude that $u = 0$. Thus

$$(2) \qquad |f(z)| = |z|^\alpha \qquad (z \in A_1).$$

Let D be any disc in A_1. There exists a $g \in H(D)$ such that $f = \exp(g)$ in D. By (2),

$$(3) \qquad \left| \frac{1}{z} \exp \left\{ \frac{g(z)}{\alpha} \right\} \right| = 1 \qquad (z \in D),$$

hence $\exp(g/\alpha) = \lambda z$, where λ is a constant and $|\lambda| = 1$. Differentiation of this last equation gives $g'(z) = \alpha/z$, and hence

$$(4) \qquad \frac{f'(z)}{f(z)} = \frac{\alpha}{z}.$$

Since D was arbitrary, (4) holds for all $z \in A_1$. Divide (4) by $2\pi i$ and integrate over the positively oriented circle with center at 0 and radius $\sqrt{R_1}$. The left side of (4) gives ± 1, since f is a homeomorphism of A_1 onto A_2. The right side gives α. Hence $\alpha = 1$, so $R_2 = R_1$.

Exercises

1 Find necessary and sufficient conditions which the complex numbers a, b, c, and d have to satisfy so that the linear fractional transformation $z \to (az + b)/(cz + d)$ maps the upper half plane onto itself.

2 In Theorem 11.17 the hypotheses were, in simplified form, that $\Omega \subset \Pi^+$, L is on the real axis, and $\operatorname{Im} f(z) \to 0$ as $z \to L$. Use this theorem to establish analogous reflection theorems under the following hypotheses:
(*a*) $\Omega \subset \Pi^+$, L on real axis, $|f(z)| \to 1$ as $z \to L$.
(*b*) $\Omega \subset U$, $L \subset T$, $|f(z)| \to 1$ as $z \to L$.
(*c*) $\Omega \subset U$, $L \subset T$, $\operatorname{Im} f(z) \to 0$ as $z \to L$.
In case (*b*), if f has a zero at $\alpha \in \Omega$, show that its extension has a pole at $1/\bar{\alpha}$. What are the analogues of this in cases (*a*) and (*c*)?

3 Suppose R is a rational function such that $|R(z)| = 1$ if $|z| = 1$. Prove that R is of the form

$$R(z) = cz^m \prod_{n=1}^{k} \frac{z - \alpha_n}{1 - \bar{\alpha}_n z}$$

where c is a constant, m is an integer, and $\alpha_1, \ldots, \alpha_k$ are complex numbers such that $\alpha_n \neq 0$ and $|\alpha_n| \neq 1$. Note that each of the above factors has absolute value 1 if $|z| = 1$.

4 Obtain an analogous description of those rational functions which are positive on T.

Hint: Such a function must have the same number of zeros as poles in U. Consider products of factors of the form

$$\frac{(z - \alpha)(1 - \bar{\alpha}z)}{(z - \beta)(1 - \bar{\beta}z)}$$

where $|\alpha| < 1$ and $|\beta| < 1$.

5 Suppose f is a trigonometric polynomial,

$$f(\theta) = \sum_{k=-n}^{n} a_k e^{ik\theta},$$

and $f(\theta) > 0$ for all real θ. Prove that there is a polynomial $P(z) = c_0 + c_1z + \cdots + c_nz^n$ such that

$$f(\theta) = |P(e^{i\theta})|^2 \qquad (\theta \text{ real}).$$

Hint: Apply Exercise 4 to the rational function $\Sigma a_k z^k$. Is the result still valid if we assume $f(\theta) \geq 0$ instead of $f(\theta) > 0$?

6 Find the fixed points of the mappings φ_α (Definition 12.3). Is there a straight line which φ_α maps to itself?

7 Suppose Ω is a region, $f_n \in H(\Omega)$ for $n = 1, 2, 3, \ldots$, each f_n is one-to-one in Ω, and $f_n \to f$ uniformly on compact subsets of Ω. Prove that f is either constant or one-to-one in Ω. Show that both cases can occur.

8 Find all complex numbers α for which f_α is one-to-one in U, where

$$f_\alpha(z) = \frac{z}{1 + \alpha z^2}.$$

Describe $f_\alpha(U)$ for all these cases.

9 Find a homeomorphism of U onto U which cannot be extended to a continuous function on $\bar{U}$.

10 If $f \in \mathcal{S}$ (Definition 14.10) and n is a positive integer, prove that there exists a $g \in \mathcal{S}$ such that $g^n(z) = f(z^n)$ for all $z \in U$.

11 Suppose Ω is a convex region, $f \in H(\Omega)$, and $\operatorname{Re} f'(z) > 0$ for all $z \in \Omega$. Prove that f is one-to-one in Ω. Is the result changed if the hypothesis is weakened to $\operatorname{Re} f'(z) \geq 0$? (Exclude the trivial case f = constant.) Show by an example that "convex" cannot be replaced by "simply connected."

12 Suppose Ω is a simply connected region, $z_0 \in \Omega$, and f and g are one-to-one conformal mappings of Ω onto U which carry z_0 to 0. What relation exists between f and g? Answer the same question if $f(z_0) = g(z_0) = \alpha$, for some $\alpha \in U$.

13 Suppose $\Omega = \{z: -1 < \operatorname{Re} z < 1\}$. Find an explicit formula for the one-to-one conformal mapping f of Ω onto U for which $f(0) = 0$ and $f'(0) > 0$. Compute $f'(0)$.

14 Note that the inverse of the function constructed in Exercise 13 has its real part bounded in U, whereas its imaginary part is unbounded. Show that this implies the existence of a continuous real function u on $\bar{U}$ which is harmonic in U and whose harmonic conjugate v is unbounded in U. [v is the function which makes $u + iv$ holomorphic in U; we can determine v uniquely by the requirement $v(0) = 0$.]

15 Let $\mathcal{F}$ be the class of all $f \in H(U)$ such that $\operatorname{Re} f > 0$ and $f(0) = 1$. Show that $\mathcal{F}$ is a normal family. Can the condition "$f(0) = 1$" be omitted? Can it be replaced by "$|f(0)| \leq 1$"?

16 Let $\mathfrak{F}$ be the class of all $f \in H(U)$ for which

$$\iint_U |f(z)|^2\, dx\, dy \leq 1.$$

Is this a normal family?

17 Suppose Ω is a bounded region, $a \in \Omega$, $f \in H(\Omega)$, $f(\Omega) \subset \Omega$, and $f(a) = a$.

(*a*) Put $f_1 = f$ and $f_n = f \circ f_{n-1}$, compute $f_n'(a)$, and conclude that $|f'(a)| \leq 1$.

(*b*) If $f'(a) = 1$, prove that $f(z) = z$ for all $z \in \Omega$. *Hint:* If

$$f(z) = z + c_m(z-a)^m + \cdots,$$

compute the coefficient of $(z-a)^m$ in the expansion of $f_n(z)$.

(*c*) What are the possibilities for f if $|f'(a)| = 1$ but $f'(a) \neq 1$? Discuss all cases.

18 Suppose Ω is a region, $f_n \in H(\Omega)$ for $n = 1, 2, 3, \ldots$, $f_n \to f$ uniformly on compact subsets of Ω, and f is one-to-one in Ω. Does it follow that to each compact $K \subset \Omega$ there corresponds an integer $N(K)$ such that f_n is one-to-one on K for all $n > N(K)$? Give proof or counterexample.

19 Suppose f is a one-to-one conformal mapping of U onto a square with center at 0, and $f(0) = 0$. Prove that $f(iz) = if(z)$. If $f(z) = \Sigma c_n z^n$, prove that $c_n = 0$ unless $n - 1$ is a multiple of 4. Generalize this: Replace the square by other simply connected regions with rotational symmetry.

20 Prove the following analogue of Theorem 14.2: If f has a differential at z_0 and if

$$\lim_{z \to z_0} \left| \frac{f(z) - f(z_0)}{z - z_0} \right|$$

exists, then $f'(z_0)$ exists.

21 Suppose $f(z) = z + (1/z)$. Describe the families of ellipses and hyperbolas onto which f maps circles with center at 0 and rays through 0.

22 Let Ω be a bounded region whose boundary consists of two nonintersecting circles. Prove that there is a one-to-one conformal mapping of Ω onto an annulus. (This is true for every region Ω such that $S^2 - \Omega$ has exactly two components, each of which contains more than one point, but this general situation is harder to handle.)

23 Complete the details in the following proof of Theorem 14.22. Suppose $1 < R_2 < R_1$ and f is a one-to-one conformal mapping of $A(1,R_1)$ onto $A(1,R_2)$. Define $f_1 = f$ and $f_n = f \circ f_{n-1}$. Then a subsequence of $\{f_n\}$ converges uniformly on compact subsets of $A(1,R_1)$ to a function g. Show that the range of g cannot contain any nonempty open set (by the three-circle theorem, for instance). On the other hand, show that g cannot be constant on the circle $\{z: |z|^2 = R_1\}$. Hence f cannot exist.

24 Here is yet another proof of Theorem 14.22. If f is as in 14.22, repeated use of the reflection principle extends f to an entire function such that $|f(z)| = 1$ whenever $|z| = 1$. This implies $f(z) = \alpha z^n$, where $|\alpha| = 1$ and n is an integer. Complete the details.

25 Modify the proof of the Riemann mapping theorem so that the role of the square root is taken over by the logarithm.

26 Iteration of Step 2 in the proof of Theorem 14.8 leads to a proof (due to Koebe) of the Riemann mapping theorem which is constructive in the sense that it makes no appeal to the theory of normal families and so does not depend on the existence of some unspecified subsequence. For the final step of the proof it is convenient to assume that Ω has property (g) of Theorem 13.18. Then any region conformally equivalent to Ω will satisfy (g). Recall also that (g) implies (h), trivially.

By Step 1 in Theorem 14.8 we may assume, without loss of generality, that $0 \in \Omega$, $\Omega \subset U$, and $\Omega \neq U$. Put $\Omega = \Omega_0$. The proof consists in the construction of regions $\Omega_1, \Omega_2, \Omega_3, \ldots$ and of functions $f_1, f_2, f_3, \ldots$, so that $f_n(\Omega_{n-1}) = \Omega_n$ and so that the functions $f_n \circ f_{n-1} \circ \cdots \circ f_2 \circ f_1$ converge to a conformal mapping of Ω onto U.

Complete the details in the following outline.

(*a*) Suppose Ω_{n-1} is constructed, let r_n be the largest number such that $D(0;r_n) \subset \Omega_{n-1}$, let α_n be a boundary point of Ω_{n-1} with $|\alpha_n| = r_n$, choose β_n so that $\beta_n{}^2 = -\alpha_n$, and put

$$F_n = \varphi_{-\alpha_n} \circ s \circ \varphi_{-\beta_n}.$$

(The notation is as in the proof of Theorem 14.8.) Show that F_n has a holomorphic inverse G_n in Ω_{n-1}, and put $f_n = \lambda_n G_n$, where $\lambda_n = |c|/c$ and $c = G_n'(0)$. (This f_n is the *Koebe mapping* associated with Ω_{n-1}. Note that f_n is an elementary function. It involves only two linear fractional transformations and a square root.)

(*b*) Compute that $f_n'(0) = (1 + r_n)/2\sqrt{r_n} > 1$.

(*c*) Put $\psi_0(z) = z$ and $\psi_n(z) = f_n(\psi_{n-1}(z))$. Show that ψ_n is a one-to-one mapping of Ω onto a region $\Omega_n \subset U$, that $\{\psi_n'(0)\}$ is bounded, that

$$\psi_n'(0) = \prod_{k=1}^{n} \frac{1 + r_k}{2\sqrt{r_k}},$$

and that therefore $r_n \to 1$ as $n \to \infty$.

(d) Write $\psi_n(z) = zh_n(z)$, for $z \in \Omega$, show that $|h_n| \leq |h_{n+1}|$, apply Harnack's theorem and Exercise 18 of Chap. 11 to $\{\log h_n\}$ to prove that $\{\psi_n\}$ converges uniformly on compact subsets of Ω, and show that $\lim \psi_n$ is a one-to-one mapping of Ω onto U.

27 Prove that $\sum_{n=1}^{\infty} (1 - r_n)^2 < \infty$, where $\{r_n\}$ is the sequence which occurs in Exercise 26. *Hint:*

$$\frac{1 + r}{2\sqrt{r}} = 1 + \frac{(1 - \sqrt{r})^2}{2\sqrt{r}}.$$

28 Suppose that in Exercise 26 we choose $\alpha_n \in U - \Omega_{n-1}$ without insisting that $|\alpha_n| = r_n$. For example, insist only that

$$|\alpha_n| \leq (1 + r_n)/2.$$

Will the resulting sequence $\{\psi_n\}$ still converge to the desired mapping function?

29 Suppose $\Omega = \{x + iy\colon\ -1 < y < 1\}$, $f \in H(\Omega)$, $|f| < 1$, and $f(x) \to 0$ as $x \to \infty$. Prove that

$$\lim_{x \to \infty} f(x + iy) = 0 \qquad (-1 < y < 1)$$

and that the passage to the limit is uniform if y is confined to an interval $[-\alpha,\alpha]$, where $\alpha < 1$. *Hint:* Consider the sequence $\{f_n\}$, where $f_n(z) = z + n$, in the square $|x| < 1$, $|y| < 1$.

What does this theorem tell about the behavior of a function $g \in H^\infty$ near a boundary point of U at which the radial limit of g exists?

30 Let Λ be the set of all linear fractional transformations.

If $\{\alpha,\beta,\gamma,\delta\}$ is an ordered quadruple of distinct complex numbers, its *cross ratio* is defined to be

$$[\alpha,\beta,\gamma,\delta] = \frac{(\alpha - \beta)(\gamma - \delta)}{(\alpha - \delta)(\gamma - \beta)}.$$

If one of these numbers is ∞, the definition is modified in the obvious way, by continuity. The same applies if α coincides with β or γ or δ.

(a) If $\varphi(z) = [z,\alpha,\beta,\gamma]$, show that $\varphi \in \Lambda$ and φ maps $\{\alpha,\beta,\gamma\}$ to $\{0,1,\infty\}$.

(b) Show that the equation $[w,a,b,c] = [z,\alpha,\beta,\gamma]$ can be solved in the form $w = \varphi(z)$; then $\varphi \in \Lambda$ maps $\{\alpha,\beta,\gamma\}$ to $\{a,b,c\}$.

(c) If $\varphi \in \Lambda$, show that

$$[\varphi(\alpha),\varphi(\beta),\varphi(\gamma),\varphi(\delta)] = [\alpha,\beta,\gamma,\delta].$$

(*d*) Show that $[\alpha,\beta,\gamma,\delta]$ is real if and only if the four points lie on the same circle or straight line.

(*e*) Two points z and z^* are said to be *symmetric* with respect to the circle (or straight line) C through α, β, and γ if $[z^*,\alpha,\beta,\gamma]$ is the complex conjugate of $[z,\alpha,\beta,\gamma]$. If C is the unit circle, find a simple geometric relation between z and z^*. Do the same if C is a straight line.

(*f*) Suppose z and z^* are symmetric with respect to C. Show that $\varphi(z)$ and $\varphi(z^*)$ are symmetric with respect to $\varphi(C)$, for every $\varphi \in \Lambda$.

31 (*a*) Show that Λ (see Exercise 30) is a group, with composition as group operation. That is, if $\varphi \in \Lambda$ and $\psi \in \Lambda$, show that $\varphi \circ \psi \in \Lambda$ and that the inverse φ^{-1} of φ is in Λ. Show that Λ is not commutative.

(*b*) Show that each member of Λ (other than the identity mapping) has either one or two fixed points on S^2. [A fixed point of φ is a point α such that $\varphi(\alpha) = \alpha$.]

(*c*) Call two mappings φ and $\varphi_1 \in \Lambda$ *conjugate* if there exists a $\psi \in \Lambda$ such that $\varphi_1 = \psi^{-1} \circ \varphi \circ \psi$. Prove that every $\varphi \in \Lambda$ with a unique fixed point is conjugate to the mapping $z \to z + 1$. Prove that every $\varphi \in \Lambda$ with two distinct fixed points is conjugate to the mapping $z \to \alpha z$, where α is a complex number; to what extent is α determined by φ?

(*d*) Let α be a complex number. Show that to every $\varphi \in \Lambda$ which has α for its unique fixed point there corresponds a β such that

$$\frac{1}{\varphi(z) - \alpha} = \frac{1}{z - \alpha} + \beta.$$

Let G_α be the set of all these φ, plus the identity transformation. Prove that G_α is a subgroup of Λ and that G_α is isomorphic to the additive group of all complex numbers.

(*e*) Let α and β be distinct complex numbers, and let $G_{\alpha,\beta}$ be the set of all $\varphi \in \Lambda$ which have α and β as fixed points. Show that every $\varphi \in G_{\alpha,\beta}$ is given by

$$\frac{\varphi(z) - \alpha}{\varphi(z) - \beta} = \gamma \cdot \frac{z - \alpha}{z - \beta},$$

where γ is a complex number. Show that $G_{\alpha,\beta}$ is a subgroup of Λ which is isomorphic to the multiplicative group of all nonzero complex numbers.

(*f*) If φ is as in (*d*) or (*e*), for which circles C is it true that $\varphi(C) = C$? The answer should be in terms of the parameters α, β, and γ.

15

Zeros of Holomorphic Functions

Infinite Products

15.1 So far we have met only one result concerning the zero set $Z(f)$ of a nonconstant holomorphic function f in a region Ω, namely, $Z(f)$ has no limit point in Ω. We shall see presently that this is all that can be said about $Z(f)$, if no other conditions are imposed on f, because of the theorem of Weierstrass (Theorem 15.11) which asserts that every $A \subset \Omega$ without limit point in Ω is $Z(f)$ for some $f \in H(\Omega)$. If $A = \{\alpha_n\}$, a natural way to construct such an f is to choose functions $f_n \in H(\Omega)$ so that f_n has only one zero, at α_n, and to consider the limit of the products

$$p_n = f_1 f_2 \cdots f_n,$$

as $n \to \infty$. One has to arrange it so that the sequence $\{p_n\}$ converges to some $f \in H(\Omega)$ *and* so that the limit function f is not 0 except at the prescribed points α_n. It is therefore advisable to begin by studying some general properties of infinite products.

15.2 Definition Suppose $\{u_n\}$ is a sequence of complex numbers,

$$p_n = (1 + u_1)(1 + u_2) \cdots (1 + u_n), \tag{1}$$

and $p = \lim_{n \to \infty} p_n$ exists. Then we write

$$p = \prod_{n=1}^{\infty} (1 + u_n). \tag{2}$$

The p_n are the *partial products* of the *infinite product* (2). We shall say that the infinite product (2) converges if the sequence $\{p_n\}$ converges.

In the study of infinite series Σa_n it is of significance whether the a_n approach 0 rapidly. Analogously, in the study of infinite products it is of interest whether the factors are or are not close to 1. This accounts for the above notation: $1 + u_n$ is close to 1 if u_n is close to 0.

15.3 Lemma *If $u_1, \ldots, u_N$ are complex numbers, and if*

(1) $$p_N = \prod_{n=1}^{N} (1 + u_n), \qquad p_N^* = \prod_{n=1}^{N} (1 + |u_n|),$$

then

(2) $$p_N^* \le \exp(|u_1| + \cdots + |u_N|)$$

and

(3) $$|p_N - 1| \le p_N^* - 1.$$

PROOF For $x \ge 0$, the inequality $1 + x \le e^x$ is an immediate consequence of the expansion of e^x in powers of x. Replace x by $|u_1|, \ldots, |u_N|$ and multiply the resulting inequalities. This gives (2). For $N = 1$, (3) is trivial. The general case follows by induction: For $k = 1, \ldots, N - 1$,

$$p_{k+1} - 1 = p_k(1 + u_{k+1}) - 1 = (p_k - 1)(1 + u_{k+1}) + u_{k+1},$$

so that if (3) holds with k in place of N, then also

$$|p_{k+1} - 1| \le (p_k^* - 1)(1 + |u_{k+1}|) + |u_{k+1}| = p_{k+1}^* - 1.$$

15.4 Theorem *Suppose $\{u_n\}$ is a sequence of bounded complex functions on a set S, such that $\Sigma|u_n(s)|$ converges uniformly on S. Then the product*

(1) $$f(s) = \prod_{n=1}^{\infty} (1 + u_n(s))$$

converges uniformly on S, and $f(s_0) = 0$ at some $s_0 \in S$ if and only if $u_n(s_0) = -1$ for some n.

Furthermore, if $\{n_1, n_2, n_3, \ldots\}$ is any permutation of $\{1,2,3, \ldots\}$, then we also have

(2) $$f(s) = \prod_{k=1}^{\infty} (1 + u_{n_k}(s)) \qquad (s \in S).$$

PROOF The hypothesis implies that $\Sigma|u_n(s)|$ is bounded on S, and if p_N denotes the Nth partial product of (1), we conclude from Lemma 15.3 that there is a constant $C < \infty$ such that $|p_N(s)| \le C$ for all N and all s.

Choose ϵ, $0 < \epsilon < \frac{1}{2}$. There exists an N_0 such that

(3) $$\sum_{n=N_0}^{\infty} |u_n(s)| < \epsilon \qquad (s \in S).$$

Let $\{n_1,n_2,n_3, \ldots\}$ be a permutation of $\{1,2,3, \ldots\}$. If $N \geq N_0$, if M is so large that

$$\{1,2, \ldots ,N\} \subset \{n_1,n_2, \ldots ,n_M\}, \tag{4}$$

and if $q_M(s)$ denotes the Mth partial product of (2), then

$$q_M - p_N = p_N \left\{\prod (1+ u_{n_k}) - 1\right\}. \tag{5}$$

The n_k which occur in (5) are all distinct and are larger than N_0. Therefore (3) and Lemma 15.3 show that

$$|q_M - p_N| \leq |p_N|(e^\epsilon - 1) \leq 2|p_N|\epsilon \leq 2C\epsilon. \tag{6}$$

If $n_k = k$ $(k = 1, 2, 3, \ldots)$, then $q_M = p_M$, and (6) shows that $\{p_N\}$ converges uniformly to a limit function f. Also, (6) shows that

$$|p_M - p_{N_0}| \leq 2|p_{N_0}|\epsilon \qquad (M > N_0), \tag{7}$$

so that $|p_M| \geq (1 - 2\epsilon)|p_{N_0}|$. Hence

$$|f(s)| \geq (1 - 2\epsilon)|p_{N_0}(s)| \qquad (s \in S), \tag{8}$$

which shows that $f(s) = 0$ if and only if $p_{N_0}(s) = 0$.

Finally, (6) also shows that $\{q_M\}$ converges to the same limit as $\{p_N\}$.

15.5 Theorem *Suppose* $0 \leq u_n < 1$. *Then*

$$\prod_{n=1}^{\infty} (1 - u_n) > 0 \qquad \textit{if and only if} \qquad \sum_{n=1}^{\infty} u_n < \infty.$$

PROOF If $p_N = (1 - u_1) \cdots (1 - u_N)$, then $p_1 \geq p_2 \geq \cdots , p_N > 0$, so $p = \lim p_N$ exists. If $\Sigma u_n < \infty$, Theorem 15.4 implies $p > 0$. On the other hand,

$$p \leq p_N = \prod_1^N (1 - u_n) \leq \exp \{-u_1 - u_2 - \cdots - u_N\},$$

and the last expression tends to 0 as $N \to \infty$, if $\Sigma u_n = \infty$.

We shall frequently use the following consequence of Theorem 15.4:

15.6 Theorem *Suppose* $f_n \in H(\Omega)$ *for* $n = 1, 2, 3, \ldots$, *no* f_n *is identically 0 in any component of* Ω, *and*

$$\sum_{n=1}^{\infty} |1 - f_n(z)| \tag{1}$$

converges uniformly on compact subsets of Ω. *Then the product*

(2) $$f(z) = \prod_{n=1}^{\infty} f_n(z)$$

converges uniformly on compact subsets of Ω. *Hence* $f \in H(\Omega)$.

Furthermore, we have

(3) $$m(f;z) = \sum_{n=1}^{\infty} m(f_n;z) \qquad (z \in \Omega),$$

where $m(f;z)$ *is defined to be the multiplicity of the zero of* f *at* z. [If $f(z) \neq 0$, then $m(f;z) = 0$.]

PROOF The first part follows immediately from Theorem 15.4. For the second part, observe that each $z \in \Omega$ has a neighborhood V in which at most finitely many of the f_n have a zero, by (1). Take these factors first. The product of the remaining ones has no zero in V, by Theorem 15.4, and this gives (3). Incidentally, we see also that at most finitely many terms in the series (3) can be positive for any given $z \in \Omega$.

The Weierstrass Factorization Theorem

15.7 Definition Put $E_0(z) = 1 - z$, and for $p = 1, 2, 3, \ldots,$

$$E_p(z) = (1 - z) \exp\left\{z + \frac{z^2}{2} + \cdots + \frac{z^p}{p}\right\}.$$

These functions, introduced by Weierstrass, are sometimes called *elementary factors*. Their only zero is at $z = 1$. Their utility depends on the fact that they are close to 1 if $|z| < 1$ and p is large, although $E_p(1) = 0$.

15.8 Lemma *For* $|z| \leq 1$ *and* $p = 0, 1, 2, \ldots,$

$$|1 - E_p(z)| \leq |z|^{p+1}.$$

PROOF For $p = 0$, this is obvious. For $p \geq 1$, direct computation shows that

$$-E_p'(z) = z^p \exp\left\{z + \frac{z^2}{2} + \cdots + \frac{z^p}{p}\right\}.$$

So $-E_p'$ has a zero of order p at $z = 0$, and the expansion of $-E_p'$ in powers of z has nonnegative real coefficients. Since

$$1 - E_p(z) = -\int_{[0,z]} E_p'(w)\, dw,$$

$1 - E_p$ has a zero of order $p + 1$ at $z = 0$, and if

$$\varphi(z) = \frac{1 - E_p(z)}{z^{p+1}},$$

then $\varphi(z) = \Sigma a_n z^n$, with all $a_n \geq 0$. Hence $|\varphi(z)| \leq \varphi(1) = 1$ if $|z| \leq 1$, and this gives the assertion of the lemma.

15.9 Theorem *Let $\{z_n\}$ be a sequence of complex numbers such that $z_n \neq 0$ and $|z_n| \to \infty$ as $n \to \infty$. If $\{p_n\}$ is a sequence of nonnegative integers such that*

$$\sum_{n=1}^{\infty} \left(\frac{r}{r_n}\right)^{1+p_n} < \infty \tag{1}$$

for every positive r (where $r_n = |z_n|$), then the infinite product

$$P(z) = \prod_{n=1}^{\infty} E_{p_n}\left(\frac{z}{z_n}\right) \tag{2}$$

defines an entire function P which has a zero at each point z_n and which has no other zeros in the plane.

More precisely, if α occurs m times in the sequence $\{z_n\}$, then P has a zero of order m at α.

Condition (1) *is always satisfied if $p_n = n - 1$, for instance.*

PROOF For every r, $r_n > 2r$ for all but finitely many n, hence $r/r_n < \frac{1}{2}$ for these n, so (1) holds with $1 + p_n = n$.

Now fix r. If $|z| \leq r$, Lemma 15.8 shows that

$$\left|1 - E_{p_n}\left(\frac{z}{z_n}\right)\right| \leq \left|\frac{z}{z_n}\right|^{1+p_n} \leq \left(\frac{r}{r_n}\right)^{1+p_n}$$

if $r_n \geq r$, which holds for all but finitely many n. It now follows from (1) that the series

$$\sum_{n=1}^{\infty} \left|1 - E_{p_n}\left(\frac{z}{z_n}\right)\right|$$

converges uniformly on compact sets in the plane, and Theorem 15.6 gives the desired conclusion.

Note: For certain sequences $\{r_n\}$, (1) holds for a constant sequence $\{p_n\}$. It is of interest to take this constant as small as possible; the resulting function (2) is then called the *canonical product* corresponding to $\{z_n\}$. For instance, if $\Sigma 1/r_n < \infty$, we can take $p_n = 0$, and the canonical product is simply

$$\prod_{n=1}^{\infty}\left(1-\frac{z}{z_n}\right).$$

If $\Sigma 1/r_n = \infty$ but $\Sigma 1/r_n^2 < \infty$, the canonical product is

$$\prod_{n=1}^{\infty}\left(1-\frac{z}{z_n}\right)e^{z/z_n}.$$

Canonical products are of great interest in the study of entire functions of finite order. (See Exercise 12 for the definition.)

We now state the Weierstrass factorization theorem.

15.10 Theorem *Let f be an entire function, suppose $f(0) \neq 0$, and let $z_1, z_2, z_3, \ldots$ be the zeros of f, listed according to their multiplicities. Then there exist an entire function g and a sequence $\{p_n\}$ of nonnegative integers, such that*

$$f(z) = e^{g(z)} \prod_{n=1}^{\infty} E_{p_n}\left(\frac{z}{z_n}\right). \tag{1}$$

Note: (*a*) If f has a zero of order k at $z = 0$, the preceding applies to $f(z)/z^k$. (*b*) The factorization (1) is not unique; a unique factorization can be associated with those f whose zeros satisfy the condition required for the convergence of a canonical product.

PROOF Let P be the product in Theorem 15.9, formed with the zeros of f. Then f/P has only removable singularities in the plane, hence is (or can be extended to) an entire function. Also, f/P has no zero, and since the plane is simply connected, $f/P = e^g$ for some entire function g.

The proof of Theorem 15.9 is easily adapted to any open set:

15.11 Theorem *Let Ω be an open set in S^2, $\Omega \neq S^2$. Suppose $A \subset \Omega$ and A has no limit point in Ω. With each $\alpha \in A$ associate a positive integer $m(\alpha)$. Then there exists an $f \in H(\Omega)$ all of whose zeros are in A, and such that f has a zero of order $m(\alpha)$ at each $\alpha \in A$.*

PROOF It simplifies the argument, and causes no loss of generality, to assume that $\infty \in \Omega$ but $\infty \notin A$. (If this is not so, a linear fractional transformation will make it so.) Then $S^2 - \Omega$ is a nonempty compact subset of the plane, and ∞ is not a limit point of A.

If A is finite, we can take a rational function for f.

If A is infinite, then A is countable (otherwise there would be a limit point in Ω). Let $\{\alpha_n\}$ be a sequence whose terms are in A and in which each $\alpha \in A$ is listed precisely $m(\alpha)$ times. Associate with each α_n a point $\beta_n \in S^2 - \Omega$ such that $|\beta_n - \alpha_n| \le |\beta - \alpha_n|$ for all $\beta \in S^2 - \Omega$; this is possible since $S^2 - \Omega$ is compact. Then

$$|\beta_n - \alpha_n| \to 0$$

as $n \to \infty$; otherwise A would have a limit point in Ω. We claim that

$$f(z) = \prod_{n=1}^{\infty} E_n\left(\frac{\alpha_n - \beta_n}{z - \beta_n}\right)$$

has the desired properties.

Put $r_n = 2|\alpha_n - \beta_n|$. Let K be a compact subset of Ω. Since $r_n \to 0$, there exists an N such that $|z - \beta_n| > r_n$ for all $z \in K$ and all $n \ge N$. Hence

$$\left|\frac{\alpha_n - \beta_n}{z - \beta_n}\right| \le \frac{1}{2},$$

which implies, by Lemma 15.8, that

$$\left|1 - E_n\left(\frac{\alpha_n - \beta_n}{z - \beta_n}\right)\right| \le \left(\frac{1}{2}\right)^{n+1} \qquad (z \in K,\ n \ge N),$$

and this again completes the proof, by Theorem 15.6.

As a consequence, we can now obtain a characterization of meromorphic functions (see Definition 13.12):

15.12 Theorem *Every meromorphic function in an open set Ω is a quotient of two functions which are holomorphic in Ω.*

The converse is obvious: If $g \in H(\Omega)$, $h \in H(\Omega)$, and h is not identically 0 in any component of Ω, then g/h is meromorphic in Ω.

PROOF Suppose f is meromorphic in Ω; let A be the set of all poles of f in Ω; and for each $\alpha \in A$, let $m(\alpha)$ be the order of the pole of f at α. By Theorem 15.11 there exists an $h \in H(\Omega)$ such that h has a zero of multiplicity $m(\alpha)$ at each $\alpha \in A$, and h has no other zeros. Put $g = fh$. The singularities of g at the points of A are removable, hence we can extend g so that $g \in H(\Omega)$. Clearly, $f = g/h$ in $\Omega - A$.

The Mittag-Leffler Theorem

This theorem does for meromorphic functions what Theorem 15.11 does for holomorphic functions.

15.13 Theorem *Suppose Ω is an open set in the plane, $A \subset \Omega$, A has no limit point in Ω, and to each $\alpha \in A$ there are associated a positive integer*

$m(\alpha)$ and a rational function

$$P_\alpha(z) = \sum_{j=1}^{m(\alpha)} c_{j,\alpha}(z-\alpha)^{-j}.$$

Then there exists a meromorphic function f in Ω, whose principal part at each $\alpha \in A$ is P_α and which has no other poles in Ω.

PROOF We choose a sequence $\{K_n\}$ of compact sets in Ω, as in Theorem 13.3: For $n = 1, 2, 3, \ldots, K_n$ lies in the interior of K_{n+1}, every compact subset of Ω lies in some K_n, and every component of $S^2 - K_n$ contains a component of $S^2 - \Omega$. Put $A_1 = A \cap K_1$, and $A_n = A \cap (K_n - K_{n-1})$ for $n = 2, 3, 4, \ldots$. Since $A_n \subset K_n$ and A has no limit point in Ω (hence none in K_n), each A_n is a finite set. Put

$$(1) \qquad Q_n(z) = \sum_{\alpha \in A_n} P_\alpha(z) \qquad (n = 1, 2, 3, \ldots).$$

Since each A_n is finite, each Q_n is a rational function. The poles of Q_n lie in $K_n - K_{n-1}$, for $n \geq 2$. In particular, Q_n is holomorphic in an open set containing K_{n-1}. It now follows from Runge's theorem that there exist rational functions R_n, all of whose poles are in $S^2 - \Omega$, such that

$$(2) \qquad |R_n(z) - Q_n(z)| < 2^{-n} \qquad (z \in K_{n-1}).$$

We claim that

$$(3) \qquad f(z) = Q_1(z) + \sum_{n=2}^{\infty} (Q_n(z) - R_n(z)) \qquad (z \in \Omega)$$

has the desired properties.

Fix N. On K_N, we have

$$(4) \qquad f = Q_1 + \sum_{n=2}^{N} (Q_n - R_n) + \sum_{N+1}^{\infty} (Q_n - R_n).$$

By (2), each term in the last sum in (4) is less than 2^{-n} on K_N; hence this last series converges uniformly on K_N, to a function which is holomorphic in the interior of K_N. Since the poles of each R_n are outside Ω,

$$f - (Q_1 + \cdots + Q_N)$$

is holomorphic in the interior of K_N. Thus f has precisely the prescribed principal parts in the interior of K_N, and hence in Ω, since N was arbitrary.

15.14 An Interpolation Problem The Mittag-Leffler theorem may be combined with the Weierstrass theorem 15.11 to give a solution of the following problem: Can we take an arbitrary set $A \subset \Omega$, without limit point in Ω, and find a function $f \in H(\Omega)$ which has prescribed values at every point of A? The answer is affirmative. In fact, we can do even better, and also prescribe finitely many derivatives at each point of A:

15.15 Theorem *Suppose Ω is an open set in the plane, $A \subset \Omega$, A has no limit point in Ω, and to each $\alpha \in A$ there are associated a nonnegative integer $m(\alpha)$ and complex numbers $w_{n,\alpha}$, $0 \le n \le m(\alpha)$. Then there exists an $f \in H(\Omega)$ such that*

$$f^{(n)}(\alpha) = n!w_{n,\alpha} \qquad (\alpha \in A,\ 0 \le n \le m(\alpha)). \tag{1}$$

PROOF By Theorem 15.11, there exists a $g \in H(\Omega)$ whose only zeros are in A and such that g has a zero of order $m(\alpha) + 1$ at each $\alpha \in A$. We claim we can associate to each $\alpha \in A$ a function P_α of the form

$$P_\alpha(z) = \sum_{j=1}^{1+m(\alpha)} c_{j,\alpha}(z - \alpha)^{-j} \tag{2}$$

such that gP_α has the power series expansion

$$g(z)P_\alpha(z) = w_{0,\alpha} + w_{1,\alpha}(z - \alpha) + \cdots + w_{m(\alpha),\alpha}(z - \alpha)^{m(\alpha)} + \cdots \tag{3}$$

in some disc with center at α.

To simplify the writing, take $\alpha = 0$ and $m(\alpha) = m$, and omit the subscripts α. For z near 0, we have

$$g(z) = b_1 z^{m+1} + b_2 z^{m+2} + \cdots, \tag{4}$$

where $b_1 \neq 0$. If

$$P(z) = c_1 z^{-1} + \cdots + c_{m+1} z^{-m-1}, \tag{5}$$

then

$$g(z)P(z) = (c_{m+1} + c_m z + \cdots + c_1 z^m)(b_1 + b_2 z + b_3 z^2 + \cdots). \tag{6}$$

The b's are given, and we want to choose the c's so that

$$g(z)P(z) = w_0 + w_1 z + \cdots + w_m z^m + \cdots. \tag{7}$$

If we compare the coefficients of $1, z, \ldots, z^m$ in (6) and (7), we can solve the resulting equations successively for $c_{m+1}, c_m, \ldots, c_1$, since $b_1 \neq 0$.

In this way we obtain the desired P_α's. The Mittag-Leffler theorem now gives us a meromorphic h in Ω whose principal parts are these P_α's, and if we put $f = gh$ we obtain a function with the desired properties.

Jensen's Formula

15.16 As we see from Theorem 15.11, the location of the zeros of a holomorphic function in a region Ω is subject to no restriction except the obvious one concerning the absence of limit points in Ω. The situation is quite different if we replace $H(\Omega)$ by certain subclasses which are defined by certain growth conditions. In those situations the distribution of the zeros has to satisfy certain quantitative conditions. The basis of most of these theorems is Jensen's formula (Theorem 15.18). We shall apply it to certain classes of entire functions and to certain subclasses of $H(U)$.

The following lemma affords an opportunity to apply Cauchy's theorem to the evaluation of a definite integral.

15.17 Lemma $\dfrac{1}{2\pi}\displaystyle\int_0^{2\pi} \log|1 - e^{i\theta}|\,d\theta = 0.$

PROOF Let $\Omega = \{z\colon \operatorname{Re} z < 1\}$. Since $1 - z \neq 0$ in Ω and Ω is simply connected, there exists an $h \in H(\Omega)$ such that

$$\exp\{h(z)\} = 1 - z$$

in Ω, and this h is uniquely determined if we require that $h(0) = 0$. Since $\operatorname{Re}(1 - z) > 0$ in Ω, we then have

$$\text{(1)}\qquad \operatorname{Re} h(z) = \log|1 - z|, \qquad |\operatorname{Im} h(z)| < \frac{\pi}{2} \qquad (z \in \Omega).$$

For small $\delta > 0$, let Γ be the path

$$\text{(2)}\qquad \Gamma(t) = e^{it} \qquad (\delta \le t \le 2\pi - \delta),$$

and let γ be the circular arc whose center is at 1 and which passes from $e^{i\delta}$ to $e^{-i\delta}$ within U. Then

$$\text{(3)}\qquad \frac{1}{2\pi}\int_\delta^{2\pi-\delta} \log|1 - e^{i\theta}|\,d\theta = \operatorname{Re}\left[\frac{1}{2\pi i}\int_\Gamma h(z)\,\frac{dz}{z}\right] = \operatorname{Re}\left[\frac{1}{2\pi i}\int_\gamma h(z)\,\frac{dz}{z}\right].$$

The last equality depended on Cauchy's theorem; note that $h(0) = 0$.

The length of γ is less than $\pi\delta$, so (1) shows that the absolute value of the last integral in (3) is less than $C\delta \log(1/\delta)$, where C is a constant. This gives the result if $\delta \to 0$ in (3).

15.18 Theorem *Suppose* $\Omega = D(0;R)$, $f \in H(\Omega)$, $f(0) \neq 0$, $0 < r < R$, *and* $\alpha_1, \ldots, \alpha_N$ *are the zeros of* f *in* $\bar{D}(0;r)$, *listed according to their multi-*

plicities. Then

$$\text{(1)} \qquad |f(0)| \prod_{n=1}^{N} \frac{r}{|\alpha_n|} = \exp\left\{\frac{1}{2\pi}\int_{-\pi}^{\pi} \log |f(re^{i\theta})|\, d\theta\right\}.$$

This is known as *Jensen's formula*. The hypothesis $f(0) \neq 0$ causes no harm in applications, for if f has a zero of order k at 0, the formula can be applied to $f(z)/z^k$.

PROOF Order the points α_j so that $\alpha_1, \ldots, \alpha_m$ are in $D(0;r)$ and $|\alpha_{m+1}| = \cdots = |\alpha_N| = r$. (Of course, we may have $m = N$ or $m = 0$.) Put

$$\text{(2)} \qquad g(z) = f(z) \prod_{n=1}^{m} \frac{r^2 - \bar{\alpha}_n z}{r(\alpha_n - z)} \prod_{n=m+1}^{N} \frac{\alpha_n}{\alpha_n - z}.$$

Then $g \in H(D)$, where $D = D(0; r + \epsilon)$ for some $\epsilon > 0$, g has no zero in D, hence $\log |g|$ is harmonic in D (Theorem 13.19), and so

$$\text{(3)} \qquad \log |g(0)| = \frac{1}{2\pi}\int_{-\pi}^{\pi} \log |g(re^{i\theta})|\, d\theta.$$

By (2),

$$\text{(4)} \qquad |g(0)| = |f(0)| \prod_{n=1}^{m} \frac{r}{|\alpha_n|}.$$

For $1 \le n \le m$, the factors in (2) have absolute value 1 if $|z| = r$. If $\alpha_n = re^{i\theta_n}$ for $m < n \le N$, it follows that

$$\text{(5)} \qquad \log |g(re^{i\theta})| = \log |f(re^{i\theta})| - \sum_{n=m+1}^{N} \log |1 - e^{i(\theta-\theta_n)}|.$$

Lemma 15.17 therefore shows that the integral in (3) is unchanged if g is replaced by f. Comparison with (4) now gives (1).

Jensen's formula gives rise to an inequality which involves the boundary values of bounded holomorphic functions in U (we recall that the class of these functions has been denoted by H^∞):

15.19 Theorem *If $f \in H^\infty$, and if f^* is the radial limit function of f, as in Theorem 11.21, then*

$$\text{(1)} \qquad \log |f(0)| \le \frac{1}{2\pi}\int_{-\pi}^{\pi} \log |f(re^{i\theta})|\, d\theta \le \frac{1}{2\pi}\int_{-\pi}^{\pi} \log |f^*(e^{i\theta})|\, d\theta$$

for all r between 0 and 1. The central term in (1) is a nondecreasing function of r.

If f is not identically 0, *it follows that the last integral in* (1) *is greater than* $-\infty$ *so that the relation*

$$f^*(e^{i\theta}) \neq 0 \tag{2}$$

holds at almost all points of T.

PROOF The left side of Jensen's formula 15.18(1) evidently does not decrease if r increases. The same is therefore true of the central term in (1). Let us now assume, without loss of generality, that $|f| \leq 1$. Then $\log(1/|f|) \geq 0$, and Fatou's lemma gives

$$\int_{-\pi}^{\pi} \log\left\{\frac{1}{|f^*(e^{i\theta})|}\right\} d\theta \leq \lim_{r\to 1} \int_{-\pi}^{\pi} \log\left\{\frac{1}{|f(re^{i\theta})|}\right\} d\theta. \tag{3}$$

This implies (1). If f is not identically 0 but f has a zero of order m at $z = 0$, put $g(z) = f(z)/z^m$. Then $|g(0)| > 0$, $|f^*| = |g^*|$, and if we apply (1) to g we see that $\int \log|f^*| > -\infty$.

15.20 Zeros of Entire Functions Suppose f is an entire function,

$$M(r) = \sup_{\theta} |f(re^{i\theta})| \qquad (0 < r < \infty), \tag{1}$$

and $n(r)$ is the number of zeros of f in $\bar{D}(0;r)$. Assume $f(0) = 1$, for simplicity. Jensen's formula gives

$$M(2r) \geq \exp\left\{\frac{1}{2\pi}\int_{-\pi}^{\pi} \log|f(2re^{i\theta})|\,d\theta\right\}$$

$$= \prod_{n=1}^{n(2r)} \frac{2r}{|\alpha_n|} \geq \prod_{n=1}^{n(r)} \frac{2r}{|\alpha_n|} \geq 2^{n(r)},$$

if $\{\alpha_n\}$ is the sequence of zeros of f, arranged so that $|\alpha_1| \leq |\alpha_2| \leq \cdots$. Hence

$$n(r)\log 2 \leq \log M(2r). \tag{2}$$

Thus the rapidity with which $n(r)$ can increase (i.e., the density of the zeros of f) is controlled by the rate of growth of $M(r)$. Suppose, to look at a more specific situation, that for large r

$$M(r) < \exp\{Ar^k\} \tag{3}$$

where A and k are given positive numbers. Then (2) leads to

$$\limsup_{r\to\infty} \frac{\log n(r)}{\log r} \leq k. \tag{4}$$

For example, if k is a positive integer and

$$f(z) = 1 - e^{z^k}, \tag{5}$$

then $n(r)$ is about $\pi^{-1}kr^k$, so that

$$\lim_{r\to\infty} \frac{\log n(r)}{\log r} = k. \tag{6}$$

This shows that the estimate (4) cannot be improved.

Blaschke Products

Jensen's formula makes it possible to determine the precise conditions which the zeros of a nonconstant $f \in H^\infty$ must satisfy.

15.21 Theorem *If $\{\alpha_n\}$ is a sequence in U such that $\alpha_n \neq 0$ and*

$$\sum_{n=1}^{\infty} (1 - |\alpha_n|) < \infty, \tag{1}$$

if k is a nonnegative integer, and if

$$B(z) = z^k \prod_{n=1}^{\infty} \frac{\alpha_n - z}{1 - \bar{\alpha}_n z} \frac{|\alpha_n|}{\alpha_n} \qquad (z \in U), \tag{2}$$

then $B \in H^\infty$, and B has no zeros except at the points α_n (and at the origin, if $k > 0$).

We call this function B a *Blaschke product.* Note that some of the α_n may be repeated, in which case B has multiple zeros at those points. Note also that each factor in (2) has absolute value 1 on T.

The term "Blaschke product" will be used also if there are only finitely many factors, and even if there are none, in which case $B(z) = 1$.

PROOF The nth term in the series

$$\sum_{n=1}^{\infty} \left| 1 - \frac{\alpha_n - z}{1 - \bar{\alpha}_n z} \cdot \frac{|\alpha_n|}{\alpha_n} \right|$$

is
$$\left| \frac{\alpha_n + |\alpha_n| z}{(1 - \bar{\alpha}_n z)\alpha_n} \right| (1 - |\alpha_n|) \leq \frac{1 + r}{1 - r} (1 - |\alpha_n|)$$

if $|z| \leq r$. Hence Theorem 15.6 shows that $B \in H(U)$ and that B has only the prescribed zeros. Since each factor in (2) has absolute value less than 1 in U, it follows that $|B(z)| < 1$, and the proof is complete.

15.22 The preceding theorem shows that

$$\sum_{n=1}^{\infty} (1 - |\alpha_n|) < \infty \tag{1}$$

is a *sufficient* condition for the existence of an $f \in H^\infty$ which has only the prescribed zeros $\{\alpha_n\}$. This condition also turns out to be necessary: *If $f \in H^\infty$ and f is not identically zero, the zeros of f must satisfy* (1). This is a special case of Theorem 15.23. It is interesting that (1) is a necessary condition in a much larger class of functions, which we now describe.

For any real number t, define $\log^+ t = \log t$ if $t \geq 1$ and $\log^+ t = 0$ if $t < 1$. We let N (for Nevanlinna) be the class of all $f \in H(U)$ for which

$$\sup_{0<r<1} \frac{1}{2\pi} \int_{-\pi}^{\pi} \log^+ |f(re^{i\theta})| \, d\theta < \infty. \tag{2}$$

It is clear that $H^\infty \subset N$. Note that (2) imposes a restriction on the rate of growth of $|f(z)|$ as $|z| \to 1$, whereas the boundedness of the integrals

$$\frac{1}{2\pi} \int_{-\pi}^{\pi} \log |f(re^{i\theta})| \, d\theta \tag{3}$$

imposes no such restriction. For instance, (3) is independent of r if $f = e^g$ for any $g \in H(U)$. The point is that (3) can stay small because $\log |f|$ assumes large negative values as well as large positive ones, whereas $\log^+ |f| \geq 0$. The class N will be discussed further in Chap. 17.

15.23 Theorem *Suppose $f \in N$, f is not identically 0 in U, and α_1, α_2, α_3, . . . are the zeros of f, listed according to their multiplicities. Then*

$$\sum_{n=1}^{\infty} (1 - |\alpha_n|) < \infty. \tag{1}$$

(We tacitly assume that f has infinitely many zeros in U. If there are only finitely many, the above sum has only finitely many terms, and there is nothing to prove. Also, $|\alpha_n| \leq |\alpha_{n+1}|$.)

PROOF If f has a zero of order m at the origin, and $g(z) = z^{-m}f(z)$, then $g \in N$, and g has the same zeros as f, except at the origin. Hence we may assume, without loss of generality, that $f(0) \neq 0$. Let $n(r)$ be the number of zeros of f in $\bar{D}(0;r)$, fix k, and take $r < 1$ so that $n(r) > k$. Then Jensen's formula

$$|f(0)| \prod_{n=1}^{n(r)} \frac{r}{|\alpha_n|} = \exp \left\{ \frac{1}{2\pi} \int_{-\pi}^{\pi} \log |f(re^{i\theta})| \, d\theta \right\} \tag{2}$$

implies that

$$|f(0)| \prod_{n=1}^{k} \frac{r}{|\alpha_n|} \leq \exp \left\{ \frac{1}{2\pi} \int_{-\pi}^{\pi} \log^+ |f(re^{i\theta})| \, d\theta \right\}. \tag{3}$$

Our assumption that $f \in N$ is equivalent to the existence of a constant $C < \infty$ which exceeds the right side of (3) for all r, $0 < r < 1$.

It follows that

$$(4) \qquad \prod_{n=1}^{k} |\alpha_n| \geq C^{-1} |f(0)| r^k.$$

The inequality persists, for every k, as $r \to 1$. Hence

$$(5) \qquad \prod_{n=1}^{\infty} |\alpha_n| \geq C^{-1} |f(0)| > 0.$$

By Theorem 15.5, (5) implies (1).

Corollary *If $f \in H^\infty$ (or even if $f \in N$), if $\alpha_1, \alpha_2, \alpha_3, \ldots$ are the zeros of f in U, and if $\Sigma(1 - |\alpha_n|) = \infty$, then $f(z) = 0$ for all $z \in U$.*

For instance, no nonconstant bounded holomorphic function in U can have a zero at each of the points $(n-1)/n$ $(n = 1, 2, 3, \ldots)$.

We conclude this section with a theorem which describes the behavior of a Blaschke product near the boundary of U. Recall that as a member of H^∞, B has radial limits $B^*(e^{i\theta})$ at almost all points of T.

15.24 Theorem *If B is a Blaschke product, then $|B^*(e^{i\theta})| = 1$ a.e., and*

$$(1) \qquad \lim_{r \to 1} \frac{1}{2\pi} \int_{-\pi}^{\pi} \log |B(re^{i\theta})| \, d\theta = 0.$$

PROOF The existence of the limit is a consequence of the fact that the integral is a monotonic function of r. Suppose $B(z)$ is as in Theorem 15.21, and put

$$(2) \qquad B_N(z) = \prod_{n=N}^{\infty} \frac{\alpha_n - z}{1 - \bar{\alpha}_n z} \cdot \frac{|\alpha_n|}{\alpha_n}.$$

Since $\log(|B/B_N|)$ is continuous in an open set containing T, the limit (1) is unchanged if B is replaced by B_N. If we apply Theorem 15.19 to B_N we therefore obtain

$$(3) \quad \log |B_N(0)| \leq \lim_{r \to 1} \frac{1}{2\pi} \int_{-\pi}^{\pi} \log |B(re^{i\theta})| \, d\theta \leq \frac{1}{2\pi} \int_{-\pi}^{\pi} \log |B^*(e^{i\theta})| \, d\theta \leq 0.$$

As $N \to \infty$, the first term in (3) tends to 0. This gives (1), and shows that $\int \log |B^*| = 0$. Since $\log |B^*| \leq 0$ a.e., Theorem 1.39(a) now implies that $\log |B^*| = 0$ a.e.

The Müntz-Szasz Theorem

15.25 A classical theorem of Weierstrass ([26], Theorem 7.24) states that the polynomials are dense in $C(I)$, the space of all continuous complex functions on the closed interval $I = [0,1]$, with the supremum norm. In other words, the set of all finite linear combinations of the functions

$$1, t, t^2, t^3, \dots \tag{1}$$

is dense in $C(I)$. This is sometimes expressed by saying that the functions (1) *span* $C(I)$.

This suggests a question: If $0 < \lambda_1 < \lambda_2 < \lambda_3 < \cdots$, under what conditions is it true that the functions

$$1, t^{\lambda_1}, t^{\lambda_2}, t^{\lambda_3}, \dots \tag{2}$$

span $C(I)$?

It turns out that this problem has a very natural connection with the problem of the distribution of the zeros of a bounded holomorphic function in a half plane (or in a disc; the two are conformally equivalent). The surprisingly neat answer is that *the functions* (2) *span* $C(I)$ *if and only if* $\Sigma 1/\lambda_n = \infty$.

Actually, the proof gives an even more precise conclusion:

15.26 Theorem *Suppose* $0 < \lambda_1 < \lambda_2 < \lambda_3 < \cdots$ *and let* X *be the closure in* $C(I)$ *of the set of all finite linear combinations of the functions*

$$1, t^{\lambda_1}, t^{\lambda_2}, t^{\lambda_3}, \dots .$$

(*a*) *If* $\Sigma 1/\lambda_n = \infty$, *then* $X = C(I)$.

(*b*) *If* $\Sigma 1/\lambda_n < \infty$, *and if* $\lambda \notin \{\lambda_n\}$, $\lambda \neq 0$, *then* X *does not contain the function* t^λ.

PROOF It is a consequence of the Hahn-Banach theorem (Theorem 5.19) that $\varphi \in C(I)$ but $\varphi \notin X$ if and only if there is a bounded linear functional on $C(I)$ which does not vanish at φ but which vanishes on all of X. Since every bounded linear functional on $C(I)$ is given by integration with respect to a complex Borel measure on I, (*a*) will be a consequence of the following proposition:

If $\Sigma 1/\lambda_n = \infty$ *and if* μ *is a complex Borel measure on* I *such that*

$$\int_I t^{\lambda_n}\, d\mu(t) = 0 \qquad (n = 1, 2, 3, \dots), \tag{1}$$

then also

$$\int_I t^k\, d\mu(t) = 0 \qquad (k = 1, 2, 3, \dots). \tag{2}$$

For if this is proved, the preceding remark shows that X contains all functions t^k; since $1 \in X$, all polynomials are then in X, and the Weierstrass theorem therefore implies that $X = C(I)$.

So assume that (1) holds. Since the integrands in (1) and (2) vanish at 0, we may as well assume that μ is concentrated on $(0,1]$. We associate with μ the function

$$f(z) = \int_I t^z \, d\mu(t). \tag{3}$$

For $t > 0$, $t^z = \exp(z \log t)$, by definition. We claim that f is holomorphic in the right half plane. The continuity of f is easily checked, and we can then apply Morera's theorem. Furthermore, if $z = x + iy$, $x > 0$, and $0 < t \leq 1$, then $|t^z| = t^x \leq 1$. Thus f is bounded in the right half plane, and (1) says that $f(\lambda_n) = 0$, for $n = 1, 2, 3, \ldots$. Define

$$g(z) = f\left(\frac{1+z}{1-z}\right) \qquad (z \in U). \tag{4}$$

Then $g \in H^\infty$ and $g(\alpha_n) = 0$, where $\alpha_n = (\lambda_n - 1)/(\lambda_n + 1)$. A simple computation shows that $\Sigma(1 - |\alpha_n|) = \infty$ if $\Sigma 1/\lambda_n = \infty$. The Corollary to Theorem 15.23 therefore tells us that $g(z) = 0$ for all $z \in U$. Hence $f = 0$. In particular, $f(k) = 0$ for $k = 1, 2, 3, \ldots$, and this is (2). We have thus proved part (*a*) of the theorem.

To prove (*b*) it will be enough to construct a measure μ on I such that (3) defines a function f which is holomorphic in the half plane $\operatorname{Re} z > -1$ (anything negative would do here), which is 0 at $0, \lambda_1, \lambda_2, \lambda_3, \ldots$ and which has no other zeros in this half plane. For the functional induced by this measure μ will then vanish on X but will not vanish at any function t^λ if $\lambda \neq 0$ and $\lambda \notin \{\lambda_n\}$.

We begin by constructing a function f which has these prescribed zeros, and we shall then show that this f can be represented in the form (3). Define

$$f(z) = \frac{z}{(2+z)^3} \prod_{n=1}^{\infty} \frac{\lambda_n - z}{2 + \lambda_n + z}. \tag{5}$$

Since
$$1 - \frac{\lambda_n - z}{2 + \lambda_n + z} = \frac{2z + 2}{2 + \lambda_n + z},$$

the infinite product in (5) converges uniformly on every compact set which contains none of the points $-\lambda_n - 2$. It follows that f is a meromorphic function in the whole plane, with poles at -2 and $-\lambda_n - 2$, and with zeros at $0, \lambda_1, \lambda_2, \lambda_3, \ldots$. Also, each factor in the infinite product (5) is less than 1 in absolute value if $\operatorname{Re} z > -1$. Thus $|f(z)| \leq 1$ if $\operatorname{Re} z \geq -1$. The factor $(2 + z)^3$ ensures that the restriction of f to the line $\operatorname{Re} z = -1$ is in L^1.

Fix z so that $\operatorname{Re} z > -1$, and consider the Cauchy formula for $f(z)$, where the path of integration consists of the semicircle with center at -1, radius $R > 1 + |z|$, from $-1 - iR$ to $-1 + R$ to $-1 + iR$, followed by the interval from $-1 + iR$ to $-1 - iR$. The integral over the semicircle tends to 0 as $R \to \infty$, so we are left with

$$(6) \quad f(z) = -\frac{1}{2\pi}\int_{-\infty}^{\infty} \frac{f(-1+is)}{-1+is-z}\,ds \qquad (\text{Re } z > -1).$$

But

$$(7) \qquad \frac{1}{1+z-is} = \int_0^1 t^{z-is}\,dt \qquad (\text{Re } z > -1).$$

Hence (6) can be rewritten in the form

$$(8) \qquad f(z) = \int_0^1 t^z \left\{\frac{1}{2\pi}\int_{-\infty}^{\infty} f(-1+is)e^{-is\log t}\,ds\right\} dt.$$

The interchange in the order of integration was legitimate: If the integrand in (8) is replaced by its absolute value, a finite integral results.

Put $g(s) = f(-1 + is)$. Then the inner integral in (8) is $\hat{g}(\log t)$, where $\hat{g}$ is the Fourier transform of g. This is a bounded continuous function on $(0,1]$, and if we set $d\mu(t) = \hat{g}(\log t)\,dt$ we obtain a measure which represents f in the desired form (3).

This completes the proof.

15.27 Remark The theorem implies that whenever $\{1,t^{\lambda_1},t^{\lambda_2}, \ldots\}$ spans $C(I)$, then some infinite subcollection of the t^{λ_i} can be removed without altering the span. In particular, $C(I)$ contains no minimal spanning sets of this type. This is in marked contrast to the behavior of orthonormal sets in a Hilbert space: if any element is removed from an orthonormal set, its span is diminished. Likewise, if $\{1,t^{\lambda_1},t^{\lambda_2}, \ldots\}$ does not span $C(I)$, removal of any of its elements will diminish the span; this follows from Theorem 15.26(*b*).

Exercises

1 Under what conditions on a sequence of real numbers y_n does there exist a bounded holomorphic function in the open right half plane which is not identically zero but which has a zero at each point $1 + iy_n$? In particular, can this happen if (*a*) $y_n = \log n$, (*b*) $y_n = \sqrt{n}$, (c) $y_n = n$, (*d*) $y_n = n^2$?

2 Suppose $0 < |\alpha_n| < 1$, $\Sigma(1 - |\alpha_n|) < \infty$, and B is the Blaschke product with zeros at the points α_n. Let E be the set of all points $1/\bar{\alpha}_n$ and let Ω be the complement of the closure of E. Prove that the product actually converges uniformly on every compact subset of Ω, so that $B \in H(\Omega)$, and that B has a pole at each point of E. (This is of particular interest in those cases in which Ω is connected.)

3 Put $\alpha_n = 1 - n^{-2}$, for $n = 1, 2, 3, \ldots$, let B be the Blaschke product with zeros at these points α, and prove that $\lim_{r \to 1} B(r) = 0$. (It is understood that $0 < r < 1$.)

More precisely, show that the estimate

$$|B(r)| < \prod_{1}^{N-1} \frac{r - \alpha_n}{1 - \alpha_n r} < \prod_{1}^{N-1} \frac{\alpha_N - \alpha_n}{1 - \alpha_n} < e^{-N/3}$$

is valid if $\alpha_{N-1} < r < \alpha_N$.

4 Prove that there is a sequence $\{\alpha_n\}$ with $0 < \alpha_n < 1$, which tends to 1 so rapidly that the Blaschke product with zeros at the points α_n satisfies the condition

$$\limsup_{r \to 1} |B(r)| = 1.$$

Hence this B has no radial limit at $z = 1$.

5 Let φ be a linear fractional transformation which maps U onto U. For any $z \in U$, define the *φ-orbit* of z to be the set $\{\varphi_n(z)\}$, where $\varphi_0(z) = z$, $\varphi_n(z) = \varphi(\varphi_{n-1}(z))$, $n = 1, 2, 3, \ldots$. Ignore the case $\varphi(z) = z$.

(*a*) For which φ is it true that the φ-orbits satisfy the Blaschke condition $\Sigma(1 - |\varphi_n(z)|) < \infty$? [The answer depends in part on the location of the fixed points of φ. There may be one fixed point in U, or one fixed point on T, or two fixed points on T. In the last two cases it is advantageous to transfer the problem to (say) the upper half plane, and to consider transformations on it which either leave only ∞ fixed or leave 0 and ∞ fixed.]

(*b*) For which φ do there exist nonconstant functions $f \in H^\infty$ which are invariant under φ, i.e., which satisfy the relation $f(\varphi(z)) = f(z)$ for all $z \in U$?

6 Find all entire functions f such that $|f(z)| = 1$ whenever $|z| = 1$.

7 Let $Z(f)$ denote the set of all zeros of the function f. Suppose f_1 and f_2 are entire functions and $Z(f_1) \cap Z(f_2) = \varnothing$. Prove that there exist entire functions g_1 and g_2, such that

$$f_1 g_1 + f_2 g_2 = 1.$$

Hint: The Mittag-Leffler theorem shows that there is an entire function g_1 such that $(1 - f_1 g_1)/f_2$ is entire.

Generalize this as follows: If $f_1, \ldots, f_n$ are entire, and if $Z(f_1) \cap \cdots \cap Z(f_n) = \emptyset$, then there exist entire functions $g_1, \ldots, g_n$ such that

$$f_1g_1 + f_2g_2 + \cdots + f_ng_n = 1.$$

Finally, if $f_1, \ldots, f_n$ are entire, can you describe the class of all entire functions h which are representable in the form

$$h = f_1g_1 + \cdots + f_ng_n,$$

where $g_1, \ldots, g_n$ are entire?

[Under discussion here are the finitely generated ideals in the ring of all entire functions. The results apply to any $H(\Omega)$.]

8 Let $\{z_n\}$ be a sequence of distinct complex numbers, $z_n \neq 0$, such that $z_n \to \infty$ as $n \to \infty$, and let $\{m_n\}$ be a sequence of positive integers. Let g be a meromorphic function in the plane, which has simple poles with residue m_n at z_n and which has no other poles. If $z \notin \{z_n\}$, let $\gamma(z)$ be any path from 0 to z which passes through none of the points z_n, and define

$$f(z) = \exp\left\{\int_{\gamma(z)} g(\zeta)\, d\zeta\right\}.$$

Prove that $f(z)$ is independent of the choice of $\gamma(z)$ (although the integral itself is not), that f is holomorphic in the complement of $\{z_n\}$, that f has a removable singularity at each of the points z_n, and that the extension of f has a zero of order m_n at z_n.

Thus the existence theorem contained in Theorem 15.9 can be deduced from the Mittag-Leffler theorem.

9 Suppose $\lambda_1 > \lambda_2 > \cdots$, and $\lambda_n \to 0$ in the Müntz-Szasz theorem. What is the conclusion of the theorem, under these conditions?

10 Prove an analogue of the Müntz-Szasz theorem, with $L^2(I)$ in place of $C(I)$.

11 Put $f_n(t) = t^n e^{-t}$ $(0 \leq t < \infty, n = 0, 1, 2, \ldots)$ and prove that the set of all finite linear combinations of the functions f_n is dense in $L^2(0, \infty)$. *Hint:* If $g \in L^2(0, \infty)$ is orthogonal to each f_n and if

$$F(z) = \int_0^\infty e^{-tz}\overline{g(t)}\, dt \qquad (\text{Re } z > 0),$$

then all derivatives of F are 0 at $z = 1$. Consider $F(1 + iy)$.

12 Suppose f is entire, λ is a positive number, and the inequality

$$|f(z)| < \exp(|z|)^\lambda)$$

holds for all large enough $|z|$. (Such functions f are said to be of *finite order*. The greatest lower bound of all λ for which the above condition holds is the *order* of f.) If $f(z) = \Sigma a_n z^n$, prove that the inequality

$$|a_n| \leq \left(\frac{e\lambda}{n}\right)^{n/\lambda}$$

holds for all large enough n. Consider the functions $\exp(z^k)$, $k = 1, 2, 3, \ldots$, to determine whether the above bound on $|a_n|$ is close to best possible.

13 Find all complex z for which $\exp(\exp(z)) = 1$. Sketch them as points in the plane. Show that there is no entire function of finite order which has a zero at each of these points (except, of course, $f \equiv 0$).

14 Show that the function

$$\pi \cot \pi z = \pi i \frac{e^{\pi i z} + e^{-\pi i z}}{e^{\pi i z} - e^{-\pi i z}}$$

has simple poles with residue 1 at the integers. The same is true of the function

$$f(z) = \frac{1}{z} + \sum_{n=1}^{\infty} \frac{2z}{z^2 - n^2} = \lim_{N\to\infty} \sum_{n=-N}^{N} \frac{1}{z - n}.$$

Show that both functions are periodic $[f(z + 1) = f(z)]$, that their difference is a bounded entire function, hence a constant, and that this constant is actually 0, since

$$\lim_{y\to\infty} f(iy) = -2i \int_0^\infty \frac{dt}{1 + t^2} = -\pi i.$$

This gives the partial fractions decomposition

$$\pi \cot \pi z = \frac{1}{z} + \sum_{1}^{\infty} \frac{2z}{z^2 - n^2}.$$

(Compare with Exercise 16, Chap. 9.) Note that $\pi \cot \pi z$ is $(g'/g)(z)$ if $g(z) = \sin \pi z$. Deduce the product representation

$$\frac{\sin \pi z}{\pi z} = \prod_{n=1}^{\infty} \left(1 - \frac{z^2}{n^2}\right).$$

15 Suppose k is a positive integer, $\{z_n\}$ is a sequence of complex numbers such that $\Sigma |z_n|^{-k-1} < \infty$, and

$$f(z) = \prod_{n=1}^{\infty} E_k\left(\frac{z}{z_n}\right).$$

(See Definition 15.7.) What can you say about the rate of growth of

$$M(r) = \max_{\theta} |f(re^{i\theta})|?$$

16 Suppose f is entire, $f(0) \neq 0$, $|f(z)| < \exp(|z|^{\rho})$ for large $|z|$, and $\{z_n\}$ is the sequence of zeros of f, counted according to their multiplicities. Prove that $\Sigma |z_n|^{-\rho-\epsilon} < \infty$ for every $\epsilon > 0$. (Compare with Sec. 15.20.)

17 Suppose $\{a_n\}$ and $\{b_n\}$ are sequences of complex numbers such that $\Sigma|a_n - b_n| < \infty$. On what sets will the product

$$\prod_{n=1}^{\infty} \frac{z - a_n}{z - b_n}$$

converge uniformly? Where will it define a holomorphic function?

18 Suppose f is an entire function, $f(\sqrt{n}) = 0$ for $n = 1, 2, 3, \ldots,$ and there is a positive constant α such that $|f(z)| < \exp(|z|^{\alpha})$ for all large enough $|z|$. For which α does it follow that $f(z) = 0$ for all z? [Consider $\sin(\pi z^2)$.]

19 Suppose $0 < \alpha < 1$, $0 < \beta < 1$, $f \in H(U)$, $f(U) \subset U$, and $f(0) = \alpha$. How many zeros can f have in the disc $\bar{D}(0;\beta)$? What is the answer if (*a*) $\alpha = \frac{1}{2}$, $\beta = \frac{1}{2}$; (*b*) $\alpha = \frac{1}{4}$, $\beta = \frac{1}{2}$; (*c*) $\alpha = \frac{2}{3}$, $\beta = \frac{1}{3}$; (*d*) $\alpha = 1/1{,}000$, $\beta = 1/10$?

20 Prove the Mittag-Leffler theorem for the case in which Ω is the whole plane, by a direct argument which makes no appeal to Runge's theorem.

21 Suppose $|\alpha_1| \leq |\alpha_2| \leq |\alpha_3| \leq \cdots < 1$, and let $n(r)$ be the number of terms in the sequence $\{\alpha_j\}$ such that $|\alpha_j| \leq r$. Prove that

$$\int_0^1 n(r)\,dr = \sum_{j=1}^{\infty} (1 - |\alpha_j|).$$

22 If $B(z) = \Sigma c_k z^k$ is a Blaschke product with at least one zero off the origin, is it possible to have $c_k \geq 0$ for $k = 0, 1, 2, \ldots$?

23 Suppose B is a Blaschke product all of whose zeros lie on the segment $(0,1)$ and

$$f(z) = (z - 1)^2 B(z).$$

Prove that the derivative of f is bounded in U.

16

Analytic Continuation

In this chapter we shall be concerned with questions which arise because functions which are defined and holomorphic in some region can frequently be extended to holomorphic functions in some larger region. Theorem 10.18 shows that these extensions are uniquely determined by the given functions. The extension process is called *analytic continuation*. It leads in a very natural way to the consideration of functions which are defined on Riemann surfaces rather than in plane regions. This device makes it possible to replace "multiple-valued functions" (such as the square-root function or the logarithm) by functions. A systematic treatment of Riemann surfaces would take us too far afield, however, and we shall restrict the discussion to plane regions.

Regular Points and Singular Points

16.1 Definition Let D be an open circular disc, suppose $f \in H(D)$, and let β be a boundary point of D. We call β a *regular point* of f if there exists a disc D_1 with center at β and a function $g \in H(D_1)$ such that $g(z) = f(z)$ for all $z \in D \cap D_1$. Any boundary point of D which is not a regular point of f is called a *singular point* of f.

It is clear from the definition that the set of all regular points of f is an open (possibly empty) subset of the boundary of D.

In the following theorems we shall take the unit disc U for D, without any loss of generality.

16.2 Theorem *Suppose $f \in H(U)$, and the power series*

(1) $$f(z) = \sum_{n=0}^{\infty} a_n z^n \qquad (z \in U)$$

has radius of convergence 1. Then f has at least one singular point on the unit circle T.

PROOF Suppose, on the contrary, that every point of T is a regular point of f. The compactness of T implies then that there are open discs $D_1, \ldots, D_n$ and functions $g_j \in H(D_j)$ such that the center of each D_j is on T, such that $T \subset D_1 \cup \cdots \cup D_n$, and such that $g_j(z) = f(z)$ in $D_j \cap U$, for $j = 1, \ldots, n$.

If $D_i \cap D_j \neq \emptyset$ and $V_{ij} = D_i \cap D_j \cap U$, then $V_{ij} \neq \emptyset$ (since the centers of the D_j are on T), and we have $g_i = f = g_j$ in V_{ij}. Since $D_i \cap D_j$ is connected, it follows from Theorem 10.18 that $g_i = g_j$ in $D_i \cap D_j$. Hence we may define a function h in $\Omega = U \cup D_1 \cup \cdots \cup D_n$ by

$$(2) \qquad h(z) = \begin{cases} f(z) & (z \in U), \\ g_i(z) & (z \in D_i). \end{cases}$$

Since $\Omega \supset \bar{U}$ and Ω is open, there exists an $\epsilon > 0$ such that $D(0; 1 + \epsilon) \subset \Omega$. But $h \in H(\Omega)$, $h(z)$ is given by (1) in U, and now Theorem 10.16 implies that the radius of convergence of (1) is at least $1 + \epsilon$, contrary to our assumption.

16.3 Definition If $f \in H(U)$ and if every point of T is a singular point of f, then T is said to be the *natural boundary* of f. In this case, f has no holomorphic extension to any region which properly contains U.

16.4 Remark It is very easy to see that there exist $f \in H(U)$ for which T is a natural boundary. In fact, if Ω is *any* region, it is easy to find an $f \in H(\Omega)$ which has no holomorphic extension to any larger region. To see this, let A be any countable set in Ω which has no limit point in Ω but such that every boundary point of Ω is a limit point of A. Apply Theorem 15.11 to get a function $f \in H(\Omega)$ which is 0 at every point of A but is not identically 0. If $g \in H(\Omega_1)$, where Ω_1 is a region which properly contains Ω, and if $g = f$ in Ω, the zeros of g would have a limit point in Ω_1, and we have a contradiction.

A simple explicit example is furnished by

$$(1) \qquad f(z) = \sum_{n=0}^{\infty} z^{2^n} = z + z^2 + z^4 + z^8 + \cdots \qquad (z \in U).$$

This f satisfies the functional equation

$$(2) \qquad f(z^2) = f(z) - z,$$

from which it follows (we leave the details to the reader) that f is unbounded on every radius of U which ends at $\exp \{2\pi ik/2^n\}$, where k and n are positive integers. These points form a dense subset of T; and since the set of all singular points of f is closed, f has T as its natural boundary.

That this example is a power series with large gaps (i.e., with many zero coefficients) is no accident. The example is merely a special case of

Theorem 16.6, due to Hadamard, which we shall derive from the following theorem of Ostrowski:

16.5 Theorem *Suppose λ, p_k, and q_k are positive integers,*

$$p_1 < p_2 < p_3 < \cdots,$$

and

$$\lambda q_k > (\lambda + 1)p_k \qquad (k = 1, 2, 3, \ldots). \tag{1}$$

Suppose

$$f(z) = \sum_{n=0}^{\infty} a_n z^n \tag{2}$$

has radius of convergence 1, and $a_n = 0$ whenever $p_k < n < q_k$ for some k. If $s_p(z)$ is the pth *partial sum of (2), and if β is a regular point of f on T, then the sequence $\{s_{p_k}(z)\}$ converges in some neighborhood of β.*

Note that the full sequence $\{s_p(z)\}$ cannot converge at any point outside $\bar{U}$. The gap condition (1) ensures the existence of a subsequence which converges in a neighborhood of β, hence at some points outside $\bar{U}$. This phenomenon is called *overconvergence.*

PROOF If $g(z) = f(\beta z)$, then g also satisfies the gap condition. Hence we may assume, without loss of generality, that $\beta = 1$. Then f has a holomorphic extension to a region Ω which contains $U \cup \{1\}$. Put

$$\varphi(w) = \tfrac{1}{2}(w^\lambda + w^{\lambda+1}) \tag{3}$$

and define $F(w) = f(\varphi(w))$ for all w such that $\varphi(w) \in \Omega$. If $|w| \le 1$ but $w \ne 1$, then $|\varphi(w)| < 1$, since $|1 + w| < 2$. Also, $\varphi(1) = 1$. It follows that there exists an $\epsilon > 0$ such that $\varphi(D(0; 1 + \epsilon)) \subset \Omega$. Note that the region $\varphi(D(0; 1 + \epsilon))$ contains the point 1. The series

$$F(w) = \sum_{m=0}^{\infty} b_m w^m \tag{4}$$

converges if $|w| < 1 + \epsilon$.

The highest and lowest powers of w in $[\varphi(w)]^n$ have exponents $(\lambda + 1)n$ and λn. Hence the highest exponent in $[\varphi(w)]^{p_k}$ is less than the lowest exponent in $[\varphi(w)]^{q_k}$, by (1). Since

$$F(w) = \sum_{n=0}^{\infty} a_n[\varphi(w)]^n \qquad (|w| < 1), \tag{5}$$

the gap condition satisfied by $\{a_n\}$ now implies that

$$\sum_{n=0}^{p_k} a_n[\varphi(w)]^n = \sum_{m=0}^{(\lambda+1)p_k} b_m w^m \qquad (k = 1, 2, 3, \ldots). \tag{6}$$

The right side of (6) converges, as $k \to \infty$, whenever $|w| < 1 + \epsilon$. Hence $\{s_{p_k}(z)\}$ converges for all $z \in \varphi(D(0; 1 + \epsilon))$. This is the desired conclusion.

Note: Actually, $\{s_{p_k}(z)\}$ converges uniformly in some neighborhood of β. We leave it to the reader to verify this by a more careful examination of the preceding proof.

16.6 Theorem *Suppose λ is a positive integer, $\{p_k\}$ is a sequence of positive integers such that*

$$p_{k+1} > \left(1 + \frac{1}{\lambda}\right) p_k \qquad (k = 1, 2, 3, \ldots), \tag{1}$$

and the power series

$$f(z) = \sum_{k=1}^{\infty} c_k z^{p_k} \tag{2}$$

has radius of convergence 1. *Then f has T as its natural boundary.*

PROOF The subsequence $\{s_{p_k}\}$ of Theorem 16.5 is now the same (except for repetitions) as the full sequence of partial sums of (2). The latter cannot converge at any point outside $\bar{U}$; hence Theorem 16.5 implies that no point of T can be a regular point of f.

16.7 Example Put $a_n = 1$ if n is a power of 2, put $a_n = 0$ otherwise, put $\eta_n = \exp(-\sqrt{n})$, and define

$$f(z) = \sum_{n=0}^{\infty} a_n \eta_n z^n. \tag{1}$$

Since

$$\limsup_{n \to \infty} |a_n \eta_n|^{1/n} = 1, \tag{2}$$

the radius of convergence of (1) is 1. By Hadamard's theorem, f has T as its natural boundary. Nevertheless, the power series of each derivative of f,

$$f^{(k)}(z) = \sum_{n=k}^{\infty} n(n-1) \cdots (n-k+1) a_n \eta_n z^{n-k}, \tag{3}$$

converges uniformly on the closed unit disc. Each $f^{(k)}$ is therefore uniformly continuous on $\bar{U}$, and the restriction of f to T is infinitely differentiable, as a function of θ, in spite of the fact that T is the natural boundary of f.

The example demonstrates rather strikingly that the presence of singularities, in the sense of Definition 16.1, does not imply the presence of discontinuities or (stated less precisely) of any lack of smoothness.

This seems to be the natural place to insert a theorem in which continuity does preclude the existence of singularities:

16.8 Theorem *Suppose Ω is a region, L is a straight line or a circular arc, $\Omega - L$ is the union of two regions Ω_1 and Ω_2, f is continuous in Ω, and f is holomorphic in Ω_1 and in Ω_2. Then f is holomorphic in Ω.*

PROOF The use of linear fractional transformations shows that the general case follows if we prove the theorem for straight lines L. By Morera's theorem, it is enough to show that the integral of f over the boundary $\partial\Delta$ is 0 for every triangle Δ in Ω. The Cauchy theorem implies that the integral of f vanishes over every closed path γ in $\Delta \cap \Omega_1$ or in $\Delta \cap \Omega_2$. The continuity of f shows that this is still true if part of γ is in L, and the integral over $\partial\Delta$ is the sum of at most two terms of this sort.

Continuation along Curves

16.9 Definitions A *function element* is an ordered pair (f,D), where D is an open circular disc and $f \in H(D)$. Two function elements (f_0,D_0) and (f_1,D_1) are *direct continuations* of each other if two conditions hold: $D_0 \cap D_1 \neq \varnothing$, and $f_0(z) = f_1(z)$ for all $z \in D_0 \cap D_1$. In this case we write

$$(1) \qquad (f_0,D_0) \sim (f_1,D_1).$$

A *chain* is a finite sequence $\mathcal{C}$ of discs, say $\mathcal{C} = \{D_0,D_1, \ldots ,D_n\}$, such that $D_{i-1} \cap D_i \neq \varnothing$ for $i = 1, \ldots , n$. If (f_0,D_0) is given and if there exist elements (f_i,D_i) such that $(f_{i-1},D_{i-1}) \sim (f_i,D_i)$ for $i = 1, \ldots , n$, then (f_n,D_n) is said to be the *analytic continuation of* (f_0,D_0) *along* $\mathcal{C}$. Note that f_n is uniquely determined by f_0 and $\mathcal{C}$ (if it exists at all). To see this, suppose (1) holds, and suppose (1) also holds with g_1 in place of f_1. Then $g_1 = f_0 = f_1$ in $D_0 \cap D_1$; and since D_1 is connected, we have $g_1 = f_1$ in D_1. The uniqueness of f_n now follows by induction on the number of terms in $\mathcal{C}$.

If (f_n,D_n) is the continuation of (f_0,D_0) along $\mathcal{C}$, and if $D_n \cap D_0 \neq \varnothing$, it need not be true that $(f_0,D_0) \sim (f_n,D_n)$; in other words, the relation $\sim$ is not transitive. The simplest example of this is furnished by the square-root function: Let D_0, D_1, and D_2 be discs of radius 1, with centers 1, ω, and ω^2, where $\omega^3 = 1$, choose $f_j \in H(D_j)$ so that $f_j^2(z) = z$ and so that $(f_0,D_0) \sim (f_1,D_1)$, $(f_1,D_1) \sim (f_2,D_2)$. In $D_0 \cap D_2$ we have $f_2 = -f_0 \neq f_0$.

A chain $\mathcal{C} = \{D_0, \ldots ,D_n\}$ is said to *cover* a curve γ with parameter interval $[0,1]$ if there are numbers $0 = s_0 < s_1 < \cdots < s_n = 1$ such that $\gamma(0)$ is the center of D_0, $\gamma(1)$ is the center of D_n, and

$$(2) \qquad \gamma([s_i,s_{i+1}]) \subset D_i \qquad (i = 0, \ldots , n-1).$$

If (f_0,D_0) can be continued along this $\mathcal{C}$ to (f_n,D_n) we call (f_n,D_n) an *analytic continuation of* (f_0,D_0) *along* γ (uniqueness will be proved in Theorem 16.11); (f_0,D_0) is then said to *admit* an analytic continuation along γ.

Although the relation (1) is not transitive, a restricted form of transitivity does hold. It supplies the key to the proof of Theorem 16.11.

16.10 Proposition *Suppose* $D_0 \cap D_1 \cap D_2 \neq \varnothing$, $(D_0,f_0) \sim (D_1,f_1)$, *and* $(D_1,f_1) \sim (D_2,f_2)$. *Then* $(D_0,f_0) \sim (D_2,f_2)$.

PROOF By assumption, $f_0 = f_1$ in $D_0 \cap D_1$ and $f_1 = f_2$ in $D_1 \cap D_2$. Hence $f_0 = f_2$ in the nonempty open set $D_0 \cap D_1 \cap D_2$. Since f_0 and f_2 are holomorphic in $D_0 \cap D_2$ and $D_0 \cap D_2$ is connected, it follows that $f_0 = f_2$ in $D_0 \cap D_2$.

16.11 Theorem *If* (f,D) *is a function element and if* γ *is a curve which starts at the center of* D, *then* (f,D) *admits at most one analytic continuation along* γ.

Here is a more explicit statement of what the theorem asserts: If γ is covered by chains $\mathcal{C}_1 = \{A_0,A_1, \ldots ,A_m\}$ and $\mathcal{C}_2 = \{B_0,B_1, \ldots ,B_n\}$, where $A_0 = B_0 = D$, if (f,D) can be analytically continued along $\mathcal{C}_1$ to a function element (g_m,A_m), and if (f,D) can be analytically continued along $\mathcal{C}_2$ to (h_n,B_n), then $g_m = h_n$ in $A_m \cap B_n$.

Since A_m and B_n are, by assumption, discs with the same center $\gamma(1)$, it follows that g_m and h_n have the same expansion in powers of $z - \gamma(1)$, and we may as well replace A_m and B_n by whichever is the larger one of the two. With this agreement, the conclusion is that $g_m = h_n$.

PROOF Let $\mathcal{C}_1$ and $\mathcal{C}_2$ be as above. There are numbers

$$0 = s_0 < s_1 < \cdots < s_m = 1 = s_{m+1}$$

and $0 = \sigma_0 < \sigma_1 < \cdots < \sigma_n = 1 = \sigma_{n+1}$ such that

$$(1) \quad \gamma([s_i,s_{i+1}]) \subset A_i, \qquad \gamma([\sigma_j,\sigma_{j+1}]) \subset B_j \qquad (0 \le i \le m,\ 0 \le j \le n).$$

There are function elements $(g_i,A_i) \sim (g_{i+1},A_{i+1})$ and

$$(h_j,B_j) \sim (h_{j+1},B_{j+1}),$$

for $0 \le i \le m-1$ and $0 \le j \le n-1$. Here $g_0 = h_0 = f$.

We claim that if $0 \le i \le m$ and $0 \le j \le n$, and if $[s_i,s_{i+1}]$ intersects $[\sigma_j,\sigma_{j+1}]$, then $(g_i,A_i) \sim (h_j,B_j)$.

Assume there are pairs (i,j) for which this is wrong. Among them there is one for which $i + j$ is minimal. It is clear that then $i + j > 0$. Suppose $s_i \ge \sigma_j$. Then $i \ge 1$, and since $[s_i,s_{i+1}]$ intersects $[\sigma_j,\sigma_{j+1}]$, we see that

(2) $$\gamma(s_i) \in A_{i-1} \cap A_i \cap B_j.$$

The minimality of $i + j$ shows that $(g_{i-1},A_{i-1}) \sim (h_j,B_j)$; and since $(g_{i-1},A_{i-1}) \sim (g_i,A_i)$, Proposition 16.10 implies that $(g_i,A_i) \sim (h_j,B_j)$. This contradicts our assumption. The possibility $s_i \leq \sigma_j$ is ruled out in the same way.

So our claim is established. In particular, it holds for the pair (m,n), and this is what we had to prove.

16.12 Definition Suppose α and β are points in the plane and φ is a continuous mapping of the unit square $I^2 = I \times I$ (where $I = [0,1]$) into the plane, such that $\varphi(0,t) = \alpha$ and $\varphi(1,t) = \beta$ for all $t \in I$. The curves γ_t defined by

(1) $$\gamma_t(s) = \varphi(s,t) \qquad (s \in I,\ t \in I)$$

are then said to form a *one-parameter family* $\{\gamma_t\}$ *of curves from* α *to* β.

We now come to a very important property of analytic continuation:

16.13 Theorem *Suppose* $\{\gamma_t\}$ $(0 \leq t \leq 1)$ *is a one-parameter family of curves from* α *to* β, D *is a disc with center at* α, *and the function element* (f,D) *admits analytic continuation along each* γ_t, *to an element* (g_t,D_t). *Then* $g_1 = g_0$.

The last equality is to be interpreted as in Theorem 16.11:

$$(g_1,D_1) \sim (g_0,D_0),$$

and D_0 and D_1 are discs with the same center, namely, β.

PROOF Fix $t \in I$. There is a chain $\mathcal{C} = \{A_0, \ldots, A_n\}$ which covers γ_t, with $A_0 = D$. There are numbers $0 = s_0 < \cdots < s_n = 1$ such that

(1) $$E_i = \gamma_t([s_i,s_{i+1}]) \subset A_i \qquad (i = 0, 1, \ldots, n-1).$$

There exists an $\epsilon > 0$ which is less than the distance from any of the compact sets E_i to the complement of the corresponding open disc A_i. The uniform continuity of φ on I^2 (see Definition 16.12) shows that there exists a $\delta > 0$ such that

(2) $$|\gamma_t(s) - \gamma_u(s)| < \epsilon \qquad \text{if } s \in I,\ u \in I,\ |u - t| < \delta.$$

Suppose u satisfies these conditions. Then (2) shows that $\mathcal{C}$ covers γ_u and therefore Theorem 16.11 shows that both g_t and g_u are obtained by continuation of (f,D) along this same chain $\mathcal{C}$. Hence $g_t = g_u$.

Thus each $t \in I$ is covered by a segment J_t such that $g_u = g_t$ for all $u \in I \cap J_t$. Since I is compact, I is covered by finitely many J_t; and since I is connected, we see in a finite number of steps that $g_1 = g_0$.

The Monodromy Theorem

16.14 Definition Let α and β be points in a region Ω, and suppose Γ_0 and Γ_1 are curves in Ω, from α to β. We say that Γ_0 and Γ_1 are Ω-*homotopic* if there is a one-parameter family $\{\gamma_t\}$ of curves from α to β (see Definition 16.12) such that each γ_t is a curve in Ω and such that $\gamma_0 = \Gamma_0$ and $\gamma_1 = \Gamma_1$.

Intuitively, this just means that Γ_0 can be deformed to Γ_1 within Ω, keeping the end points fixed.

16.15 Definition Suppose Ω is a region, (f,D) is a function element, and $D \subset \Omega$. We say that (f,D) admits *unrestricted continuation* in Ω if (f,D) can be analytically continued along every curve in Ω which starts at the center of D.

We can now state the monodromy theorem:

16.16 Theorem *Suppose (f,D) admits unrestricted continuation in a plane region Ω.*

(*a*) *If Γ_0 and Γ_1 are Ω-homotopic curves from α to β, where α is the center of D, then the continuation of (f,D) along Γ_0 coincides with its continuation along Γ_1.*

(*b*) *If, in addition, Ω is simply connected, then there exists a $g \in H(\Omega)$ such that $g(z) = f(z)$ for all $z \in D$.*

PROOF (*a*) is a corollary of Theorem 16.13.

If Ω is simply connected, then there is a homeomorphism h of Ω onto U; and since U is convex, we can define

$$(1)\quad \gamma_t(s) = h^{-1}[(1-t)h(\Gamma_0(s)) + th(\Gamma_1(s))] \qquad (0 \le s \le 1,\ 0 \le t \le 1).$$

The resulting one-parameter family $\{\gamma_t\}$ shows that any two curves Γ_0 and Γ_1 in Ω, from α to β, are Ω-homotopic. It now follows from (*a*) that all continuations of (f,D) to β, along any curve in Ω, lead to the same element (g_β,D_β), where D_β is a disc with center at β. If D_{β_1} intersects D_β, then $(g_{\beta_1},D_{\beta_1})$ can be obtained by first continuing (f,D) to β, then along the straight line from β to β_1. This shows that $g_{\beta_1} = g_\beta$ in $D_{\beta_1} \cap D_\beta$.

The definition

$$(2)\qquad g(z) = g_\beta(z) \qquad (z \in D_\beta)$$

is therefore consistent and gives the desired holomorphic extension of f.

Construction of a Modular Function

16.17 The Modular Group This is the set G of all linear fractional transformations φ of the form

$$(1) \qquad \varphi(z) = \frac{az+b}{cz+d}$$

where a, b, c, and d are integers and $ad - bc = 1$.

Since a, b, c, and d are real, each $\varphi \in G$ maps the real axis onto itself (except for ∞). The imaginary part of $\varphi(i)$ is $(c^2 + d^2)^{-1} > 0$. Hence

$$(2) \qquad \varphi(\Pi^+) = \Pi^+ \qquad (\varphi \in G),$$

where Π^+ is the open upper half plane. If φ is given by (1), then

$$(3) \qquad \varphi^{-1}(w) = \frac{dw - b}{-cw + a}$$

so that $\varphi^{-1} \in G$. Also $\varphi \circ \psi \in G$ if $\varphi \in G$ and $\psi \in G$.

Thus G is a group, with composition as group operation. In view of (2) it is customary to regard G as a group of transformations on Π^+.

The transformations $z \to z + 1$ ($a = b = d = 1$, $c = 0$) and $z \to -1/z$ ($a = d = 0$, $b = -1$, $c = 1$) belong to G. In fact, they generate G (i.e., there is no proper subgroup of G which contains these two transformations). This can be proved by the same method which will be used in Theorem 16.19(c).

A *modular function* is a holomorphic (or meromorphic) function f on Π^+ which is invariant under G or at least under some nontrivial subgroup Γ of G. This means that $f \circ \varphi = f$ for every $\varphi \in \Gamma$.

16.18 A Subgroup We shall take for Γ the group generated by σ and τ, where

$$(1) \qquad \sigma(z) = \frac{z}{2z+1}, \qquad \tau(z) = z + 2.$$

One of our objectives is the construction of a certain function λ which is invariant under Γ and which leads to a quick proof of the Picard theorem. Actually, it is the mapping properties of λ which are important in this proof, not its invariance, and a quicker construction (using just the Riemann mapping theorem and the reflection principle) can be given. But it is instructive to study the action of Γ on Π^+, in geometric terms, and we shall proceed along this route.

Let Q be the set of all z which satisfy the following four conditions, where $z = x + iy$:

$$(2) \qquad y > 0, \qquad -1 \le x < 1, \qquad |2z + 1| \ge 1, \qquad |2z - 1| > 1.$$

Q is bounded by the vertical lines $x = -1$ and $x = 1$ and is bounded below by two semicircles of radius $\frac{1}{2}$, with centers at $-\frac{1}{2}$ and at $\frac{1}{2}$. Q contains those of its boundary points which lie in the left half of Π^+. Q contains no point of the real axis.

We claim that Q is a *fundamental domain* of Γ. This means that statements (*a*) and (*b*) of the following theorem are true.

16.19 Theorem *Let Γ and Q be as above.*

(*a*) *If φ_1 and $\varphi_2 \in \Gamma$ and $\varphi_1 \neq \varphi_2$, then $\varphi_1(Q) \cap \varphi_2(Q) = \varnothing$.*
(*b*) $\bigcup_{\varphi \in \Gamma} \varphi(Q) = \Pi^+$.
(*c*) *Γ contains all transformations $\varphi \in G$ of the form*

$$\varphi(z) = \frac{az + b}{cz + d} \tag{1}$$

for which a and d are odd integers, b and c are even.

PROOF Let Γ_1 be the set of all $\varphi \in G$ described in (*c*). It is easily verified that Γ_1 is a subgroup of G. Since $\sigma \in \Gamma_1$ and $\tau \in \Gamma_1$, it follows that $\Gamma \subset \Gamma_1$. To show that $\Gamma = \Gamma_1$, i.e., to prove (*c*), it is enough to prove that (*a'*) and (*b*) hold, where (*a'*) is the statement obtained from (*a*) by replacing Γ by Γ_1. For if (*a'*) and (*b*) hold, it is clear that Γ cannot be a proper subset of Γ_1.

We shall need the relation

$$\operatorname{Im} \varphi(z) = \frac{\operatorname{Im} z}{|cz + d|^2} \tag{2}$$

which is valid for every $\varphi \in G$ given by (1). The proof of (2) is a matter of straightforward computation, and depends on the relation $ad - bc = 1$.

We now prove (*a'*). Suppose φ_1 and $\varphi_2 \in \Gamma_1$, $\varphi_1 \neq \varphi_2$, and $\varphi = \varphi_1^{-1} \circ \varphi_2$. If $z \in \varphi_1(Q) \cap \varphi_2(Q)$, then $\varphi_1^{-1}(z) \in Q \cap \varphi(Q)$. It is therefore enough to show that

$$Q \cap \varphi(Q) = \varnothing \tag{3}$$

if $\varphi \in \Gamma_1$ and φ is not the identity transformation.

If $c = 0$ in (1), then $ad = 1$, and since a and d are integers, we have $a = d = \pm 1$. Hence $\varphi(z) = z + 2n$ for some integer $n \neq 0$, and the description of Q makes it evident that (3) holds.

If $c \neq 0$, we claim that $|cz + d| > 1$ for every $z \in Q$. Otherwise, the circle with center at $-d/c$ and radius $|1/c|$ would intersect Q. The description of Q shows that if any circle with center on the real axis intersects Q, then at least one of the points $-1, 0, 1$ lies in the interior of this circle. But if w is an integer, then $cw + d$ is an odd integer whose absolute value cannot be less than 1.

So $|cz + d| > 1$, and it now follows from (2) that $\text{Im } \varphi(z) < \text{Im } z$ for every $z \in Q$. If it were true for some $z \in Q$ that $\varphi(z) \in Q$, the same argument would apply to φ^{-1} and would show that

$$\text{(4)} \qquad \text{Im } z = \text{Im } \varphi^{-1}(\varphi(z)) < \text{Im } \varphi(z).$$

This contradiction proves (a').

To prove (b), let Σ be the union of the sets $\varphi(Q)$, for $\varphi \in \Gamma$. It is clear that $\Sigma \subset \Pi^+$. Also, Σ contains the sets $\tau^n(Q)$, for $n = 0, \pm 1, \pm 2, \ldots$, where $\tau^n(z) = z + 2n$. Since σ maps the circle $|2z + 1| = 1$ onto the circle $|2z - 1| = 1$, we see that Σ contains every $z \in \Pi^+$ which satisfies all inequalities

$$\text{(5)} \qquad |2z - (2m + 1)| \geq 1 \qquad (m = 0, \pm 1, \pm 2, \ldots).$$

Fix $w \in \Pi^+$. Since $\text{Im } w > 0$, there are only finitely many pairs of integers c and d such that $|cw + d|$ lies below any given bound, and we can choose $\varphi_0 \in \Gamma$ so that $|cw + d|$ is minimized. By (2), this means that

$$\text{(6)} \qquad \text{Im } \varphi(w) \leq \text{Im } \varphi_0(w) \qquad (\varphi \in \Gamma).$$

Put $z = \varphi_0(w)$. Then (6) becomes

$$\text{(7)} \qquad \text{Im } \varphi(z) \leq \text{Im } z \qquad (\varphi \in \Gamma).$$

Apply (7) to $\varphi = \sigma\tau^{-n}$ and to $\varphi = \sigma^{-1}\tau^{-n}$. Since

$$\text{(8)} \quad (\sigma\tau^{-n})(z) = \frac{z - 2n}{2z - 4n + 1}, \qquad (\sigma^{-1}\tau^{-n})(z) = \frac{z - 2n}{-2z + 4n + 1},$$

it follows from (2) and (7) that

$$\text{(9)} \quad |2z - 4n + 1| \geq 1, \qquad |2z - 4n - 1| \geq 1 \qquad (n = 0, \pm 1, \pm 2, \ldots).$$

Thus z satisfies (5), hence $z \in \Sigma$; and since $w = \varphi_0^{-1}(z)$ and $\varphi_0^{-1} \in \Gamma$, we have $w \in \Sigma$.

This completes the proof.

The following theorem summarizes some of the properties of the modular function λ which was mentioned in Sec. 16.18 and which will be used in Theorem 16.22.

16.20 Theorem *If Γ and Q are as described in Sec.* 16.18, *there exists a function $\lambda \in H(\Pi^+)$ such that*

(a) *$\lambda \circ \varphi = \lambda$ for every $\varphi \in \Gamma$.*
(b) *λ is one-to-one on Q.*

(c) *The range* Ω *of* λ [*which is the same as* $\lambda(Q)$, *by* (a)], *is the region consisting of all complex numbers different from* 0 *and* 1.

(d) λ *has the real axis as its natural boundary.*

PROOF Let Q_0 be the right half of Q. More precisely, Q_0 consists of all $z \in \Pi^+$ such that

$$(1) \qquad 0 < \operatorname{Re} z < 1, \qquad |2z - 1| > 1.$$

By Theorem 14.19 (and Remarks 14.20) there is a continuous function h on $\bar{Q}_0$ which is one-to-one on $\bar{Q}_0$ and holomorphic in Q_0, such that $h(Q_0) = \Pi^+$, $h(0) = 0$, $h(1) = 1$, and $h(\infty) = \infty$. The reflection principle (Theorem 11.17) shows that the formula

$$(2) \qquad h(-x + iy) = \overline{h(x + iy)}$$

extends h to a continuous function on the closure $\bar{Q}$ of Q which is a conformal mapping of the interior of Q onto the complex plane minus the nonnegative real axis. We also see that h is one-to-one on Q, that $h(Q)$ is the region Ω described in (c), that

$$(3) \quad h(-1 + iy) = h(1 + iy) = h(\tau(-1 + iy)) \quad (0 < y < \infty),$$

and that

$$(4) \quad h(-\tfrac{1}{2} + \tfrac{1}{2}e^{i\theta}) = h(\tfrac{1}{2} + \tfrac{1}{2}e^{i(\pi-\theta)}) = h(\sigma(-\tfrac{1}{2} + \tfrac{1}{2}e^{i\theta})) \qquad (0 < \theta < \pi).$$

Since h is real on the boundary of Q, (3) and (4) follow from (2) and the definitions of σ and τ.

We now define the function λ:

$$(5) \qquad \lambda(z) = h(\varphi^{-1}(z)) \qquad (z \in \varphi(Q),\ \varphi \in \Gamma).$$

By Theorem 16.19, each $z \in \Pi^+$ lies in $\varphi(Q)$ for one and only one $\varphi \in \Gamma$. Thus (5) defines $\lambda(z)$ for $z \in \Pi^+$, and we see immediately that λ has properties (a) to (c) and that λ is holomorphic in the interior of each of the sets $\varphi(Q)$.

It follows from (3) and (4) that λ is continuous on $Q \cup \tau^{-1}(Q) \cup \sigma^{-1}(Q)$, hence on an open set V which contains Q. Theorem 16.8 now shows that λ is holomorphic in V. Since Π^+ is covered by the union of the sets $\varphi(V)$, $\varphi \in \Gamma$, and since $\lambda \circ \varphi = \lambda$, we conclude that $\lambda \in H(\Pi^+)$.

Finally, the set of all numbers $\varphi(0) = b/d$ is dense on the real axis. If λ could be analytically continued to a region which properly contains Π^+, the zeros of λ would have a limit point in this region, which is impossible since λ is not constant.

The Picard Theorem

16.21 The so-called "little Picard theorem" asserts that every nonconstant entire function attains each value, with one possible exception. This is the theorem which is proved below. There is a stronger version: *Every entire function which is not a polynomial attains each value infinitely many times, again with one possible exception.* That one exception can occur is shown by $f(z) = e^z$, which omits the value 0. The latter theorem is actually true in a local situation: *If f has an isolated singularity at a point z_0 and if f omits two values in some neighborhood of z_0, then z_0 is a removable singularity or a pole of f.* This so-called "big Picard theorem" is a remarkable strengthening of the theorem of Weierstrass (Theorem 10.21) which merely asserts that the image of every neighborhood of z_0 is dense in the plane if f has an essential singularity at z_0. We shall not prove it here.

16.22 Theorem *If f is an entire function and if there are two distinct complex numbers α and β which are not in the range of f, then f is constant.*

PROOF Without loss of generality we assume that $\alpha = 0$ and $\beta = 1$; if not, replace f by $(f - \alpha)/(\beta - \alpha)$. Then f maps the plane into the region Ω described in Theorem 16.20.

With each disc $D_1 \subset \Omega$ there is associated a region $V_1 \subset \Pi^+$ (in fact, there are infinitely many such V_1, one for each $\varphi \in \Gamma$) such that λ is one-to-one on V_1 and $\lambda(V_1) = D_1$; each such V_1 intersects at most two of the domains $\varphi(Q)$. Corresponding to each choice of V_1 there is a function $\psi_1 \in H(D_1)$ such that $\psi_1(\lambda(z)) = z$ for all $z \in V_1$.

If D_2 is another disc in Ω and if $D_1 \cap D_2 \neq \varnothing$, we can choose a corresponding V_2 so that $V_1 \cap V_2 \neq \varnothing$. The function elements (ψ_1,D_1) and (ψ_2,D_2) will then be direct analytic continuations of each other. Note that $\psi_i(D_i) \subset \Pi^+$.

Since the range of f is in Ω, there is a disc A_0 with center at 0 so that $f(A_0)$ lies in a disc D_0 in Ω. Choose $\psi_0 \in H(D_0)$, as above, put $g(z) = \psi_0(f(z))$ for $z \in A_0$, and let γ be any curve in the plane which starts at 0. The range of $f \circ \gamma$ is a compact subset of Ω. Hence γ can be covered by a chain of discs, $A_0, \ldots, A_n$, so that each A_i lies in a disc D_i in Ω, and we can choose $\psi_i \in D_i$ so that (ψ_i,D_i) is a direct analytic continuation of (ψ_{i-1},D_{i-1}), for $i = 1, \ldots, n$. This gives an analytic continuation of the function element (g,A_0) along the chain $\{A_0, \ldots, A_n\}$; note that $\psi_n \circ f$ has positive imaginary part.

Since (g,A_0) admits unrestricted continuation in the plane and since the plane is simply connected, the monodromy theorem implies that g extends to an entire function. Also, the range of g is in Π^+, hence $(g - i)/(g + i)$ is bounded, hence constant, by Liouville's theorem. This shows that g is constant, and since ψ_0 was one-to-one on $f(A_0)$ and A_0 was a nonempty open set, we conclude that f is constant.

Exercises

1 Suppose $f(z) = \Sigma a_n z^n$, $a_n \geq 0$, and the radius of convergence of the series is 1. Prove that f has a singularity at $z = 1$. *Hint:* Expand f in powers of $z - \frac{1}{2}$. If 1 were a regular point of f, the new series would converge at some $x > 1$. What would this imply about the original series?

2 Suppose (f,D) and (g,D) are function elements, P is a polynomial in two variables, and $P(f,g) = 0$ in D. Suppose f and g can be analytically continued along a curve γ, to f_1 and g_1. Prove that $P(f_1,g_1) = 0$. Extend this to more than two functions. Is there such a theorem for some class of functions P which is larger than the polynomials?

3 Suppose Ω is a simply connected region, and u is a real harmonic function in Ω. Prove that there exists an $f \in H(\Omega)$ such that $u = \operatorname{Re} f$. Show that this fails in every region which is not simply connected.

4 Suppose X is the closed unit square in the plane, f is a continuous complex function on X, and f has no zero in X. Prove that there is a continuous function g on X such that $f = e^g$. For what class of spaces X (other than the above square) is this also true?

5 Prove that the transformations $z \to z + 1$ and $z \to -1/z$ generate the full modular group G. Let R consist of all $z = x + iy$ such that $|x| < \frac{1}{2}$, $y > 0$, and $|z| > 1$, plus those limit points which have $x \leq 0$. Prove that R is a fundamental domain of G.

6 Prove that G is also generated by the transformations φ and ψ, where

$$\varphi(z) = -\frac{1}{z}, \qquad \psi(z) = \frac{z-1}{z}.$$

Show that φ has period 2, ψ has period 3.

7 Find the relation between composition of linear fractional transformations and matrix multiplication. Try to use this to construct an algebraic proof of Theorem 16.19(*c*) or of the first part of Exercise 5.

8 Let E be a compact set on the real axis, of positive Lebesgue measure, let Ω be the complement of E, relative to the plane, and define

$$f(z) = \int_E \frac{dt}{t - z} \qquad (z \in \Omega).$$

Answer the following questions:
(*a*) Is f constant?
(*b*) Can f be extended to an entire function?
(*c*) Does $\lim zf(z)$ exist as $z \to \infty$? If so, what is it?
(*d*) Does f have a holomorphic square root in Ω?
(*e*) Is the real part of f bounded in Ω?
(*f*) Is the imaginary part of f bounded in Ω?
[If "yes" in (*e*) or (*f*), give a bound.]
(*g*) What is $\int_\gamma f(z)\,dz$ if γ is a positively oriented circle which has E in its interior?
(*h*) Does there exist a bounded holomorphic function φ in Ω which is not constant?

9 Check your answers in Exercise 8 against the special case

$$E = [-1,1].$$

10 Call a compact set E in the plane *removable* if there are no nonconstant bounded holomorphic functions in the complement of E.
(*a*) Prove that every countable compact set is removable.
(*b*) If E is a compact subset of the real axis, and $m(E) = 0$, prove that E is removable. *Hint:* E can be surrounded by curves of arbitrarily small total length. Apply Cauchy's formula, as in Exercise 11, Chap. 13.
(*c*) Suppose E is removable, Ω is a region, $E \subset \Omega$, $f \in H(\Omega - E)$, and f is bounded. Prove that f can be extended to a holomorphic function in Ω.
(*d*) Formulate and prove an analogue of part (*b*) for sets E which are not necessarily on the real axis.
(*e*) Prove that no compact connected subset of the plane (with more than one point) is removable.

11 For each positive number α, let Γ_α be the path with parameter interval $(-\infty, \infty)$ defined by

$$\Gamma_\alpha(t) = \begin{cases} -t - \pi i & (-\infty < t \le -\alpha), \\ \alpha + \dfrac{\pi i t}{\alpha} & (-\alpha \le t \le \alpha), \\ t + \pi i & (\alpha \le t < \infty). \end{cases}$$

Let Ω_α be the component of the complement of Γ_α^* which contains the origin, and define

$$f_\alpha(z) = \frac{1}{2\pi i} \int_{\Gamma_\alpha} \frac{\exp(e^w)}{w - z}\, dw \qquad (z \in \Omega_\alpha).$$

Prove that f_β is an analytic continuation of f_α if $\alpha < \beta$. Prove that therefore there is an entire function f whose restriction to Ω_α is f_α. Prove that

$$\lim_{r \to \infty} f(re^{i\theta}) = 0$$

for every $e^{i\theta} \neq 1$. (Here r is positive and θ is real, as usual.) Prove that f is not constant. [*Hint:* Look at $f(r)$.] If

$$g = f \exp(-f)$$

prove that

$$\lim_{r \to \infty} g(re^{i\theta}) = 0$$

for every $e^{i\theta}$.

Show that there exists an entire function h such that

$$\lim_{r \to \infty} h(nz) = \begin{cases} 1 & \text{if } z = 0, \\ 0 & \text{if } z \neq 0. \end{cases}$$

12 Suppose

$$f(z) = \sum_{k=1}^{\infty} \left(\frac{z - z^2}{2}\right)^{3k} = \sum_{n=1}^{\infty} a_n z^n.$$

Find the regions in which the two series converge. Show that this illustrates Theorem 16.5. Find the singular point of f which is nearest to the origin.

13 For real x, define

$$g(x) = \sum_{n=1}^{\infty} \left(\frac{\sin n\pi x}{n\pi}\right)^2.$$

Apply the Poisson summation formula to $y^{-2} \sin^2 y$ (see Exercise 1, Chap. 9) to get another expression for $g(x)$. Your computation should produce entire functions G_m (one for each integer m) such that $G_m(x) = g(x)$ if $m \le x \le m + 1$, although the series defining $g(x)$ diverges for every x which is not real. To check your computation, verify that $g((\frac{1}{2}) = \frac{1}{8}$ and $g(\frac{1}{3}) = \frac{1}{9}$.

17

H^p-spaces

This chapter is devoted to the study of certain subspaces of $H(U)$ which are defined by certain growth conditions; in fact, they are all contained in the class N defined in Chap. 15. These so-called H^p-spaces (named for G. H. Hardy) have a large number of interesting properties concerning factorizations, boundary values, and Cauchy-type representations in terms of measures on the boundary of U. We shall merely give some of the highlights, such as the theorem of F. and M. Riesz on measures μ whose Fourier coefficients $\hat{\mu}(n)$ are 0 for all $n < 0$, Beurling's classification of the invariant subspaces of H^2, and M. Riesz's theorem on conjugate functions.

A convenient approach to the subject is via subharmonic functions, and we begin with a brief outline of their properties.

Subharmonic Functions

17.1 Definition A function u defined in an open set Ω in the plane is said to be *subharmonic* if

(*a*) $-\infty \leq u(z) < \infty$ for all $z \in \Omega$.
(*b*) u is upper semicontinuous in Ω.
(*c*) Whenever $\bar{D}(a;r) \subset \Omega$, then

$$u(a) \leq \frac{1}{2\pi} \int_{-\pi}^{\pi} u(a + re^{i\theta})\, d\theta.$$

(*d*) None of the integrals in (*c*) is $-\infty$.

Note that the integrals in (*c*) always exist and are not $+\infty$, since (*a*) and (*b*) imply that u is bounded above on every compact $K \subset \Omega$. [Proof: If K_n is the set of all $z \in K$ at which $u(z) \geq n$, then $K \supset K_1 \supset K_2 \cdots$, so either $K_n = \varnothing$ for some n, or $\bigcap K_n \neq \varnothing$, in which case $u(z) = \infty$ for some $z \in K$.] Hence (*d*) says that the integrands in (*c*) belong to $L^1(T)$.

Every real harmonic function is obviously subharmonic.

17.2 Theorem *If u is subharmonic in Ω, and if φ is a monotonically increasing convex function on R^1, then $\varphi \circ u$ is subharmonic.*

[To have $\varphi \circ u$ defined at all points of Ω, we put $\varphi(-\infty) = \lim \varphi(x)$ as $x \to -\infty$.]

PROOF First, $\varphi \circ u$ is upper semicontinuous, since φ is increasing and continuous. Next, if $\bar{D}(a;r) \subset \Omega$, we have

$$\varphi(u(a)) \leq \varphi\left(\frac{1}{2\pi}\int_{-\pi}^{\pi} u(a + re^{i\theta})\, d\theta\right) \leq \frac{1}{2\pi}\int_{-\pi}^{\pi} \varphi(u(a + re^{i\theta}))\, d\theta.$$

The first of these inequalities holds since φ is increasing and u is subharmonic; the second follows from the convexity of φ, by Theorem 3.3.

17.3 Theorem *If Ω is a region, $f \in H(\Omega)$, and f is not identically 0, then* $\log|f|$ *is subharmonic in Ω, and so are* $\log^+|f|$ *and* $|f|^p$ $(0 < p < \infty)$.

PROOF It is understood that $\log|f(z)| = -\infty$ if $f(z) = 0$. Then $\log|f|$ is upper semicontinuous in Ω, and Theorem 15.19 implies that $\log|f|$ is subharmonic.

The other assertions follow if we apply Theorem 17.2 to $\log|f|$ in place of u, with

$$\varphi(t) = \max(0,t) \qquad \text{and} \qquad \varphi(t) = e^{pt}.$$

17.4 Theorem *Suppose u is a continuous subharmonic function in Ω, K is a compact subset of Ω, h is a continuous real function on K which is harmonic in the interior V of K, and $u(z) \leq h(z)$ at all boundary points of K. Then $u(z) \leq h(z)$ for all $z \in K$.*

This theorem accounts for the term "subharmonic." Continuity of u is not necessary here, but we shall not need the general case and leave it as an exercise.

PROOF Put $u_1 = u - h$, and assume, to get a contradiction, that $u_1(z) > 0$ for some $z \in V$. Since u_1 is continuous on K, u_1 attains its maximum m on K; and since $u_1 \leq 0$ on the boundary of K, the set $E = \{z \in K\colon u_1(z) = m\}$ is a nonempty compact subset of V. Let z_0 be a boundary point of E. Then for some $r > 0$ we have $\bar{D}(z_0;r) \subset V$, but some subarc of the boundary of $\bar{D}(z_0;r)$ lies in the complement of E. Hence

$$u_1(z_0) = m > \frac{1}{2\pi} \int_{-\pi}^{\pi} u_1(z_0 + re^{i\theta})\, d\theta,$$

and this means that u_1 is not subharmonic in V. But if u is subharmonic, so is $u - h$, by the mean value property of harmonic functions, and we have our contradiction.

17.5 Theorem *Suppose u is a continuous subharmonic function in U, and*

(1) $$m(r) = \frac{1}{2\pi} \int_{-\pi}^{\pi} u(re^{i\theta})\, d\theta \qquad (0 \le r < 1).$$

If $r_1 < r_2$, then $m(r_1) \le m(r_2)$.

PROOF Let h be the continuous function on $\bar{D}(0;r_2)$ which coincides with u on the boundary of $\bar{D}(0;r_2)$ and which is harmonic in $D(0;r_2)$. By Theorem 17.4, $u \le h$ in $D(0;r_2)$. Hence

$$m(r_1) \le \frac{1}{2\pi} \int_{-\pi}^{\pi} h(r_1e^{i\theta})\, d\theta = h(0) = \frac{1}{2\pi} \int_{-\pi}^{\pi} h(r_2e^{i\theta})\, d\theta = m(r_2).$$

The Spaces H^p and N

17.6 Theorem *If $f \in H(U)$, and if*

$$M_0(f;r) = \exp\left\{\frac{1}{2\pi} \int_{-\pi}^{\pi} \log^+ |f(re^{i\theta})|\, d\theta\right\},$$

$$M_p(f;r) = \left\{\frac{1}{2\pi} \int_{-\pi}^{\pi} |f(re^{i\theta})|^p\, d\theta\right\}^{1/p} \qquad (0 < p < \infty),$$

$$M_\infty(f;r) = \sup_\theta |f(re^{i\theta})|,$$

then M_0, M_p, and M_∞ are monotonically increasing functions of r in $[0,1)$.

PROOF For M_0 and M_p this is an immediate consequence of Theorems 17.3 and 17.5. For M_∞ it follows from the maximum modulus theorem.

This suggests the following definition:

17.7 Definition For any $f \in H(U)$ and for $0 \le p \le \infty$, we put

$$\|f\|_p = \lim_{r \to 1} M_p(f;r),$$

where $M_p(f;r)$ is as in Theorem 17.6.

For $0 < p \le \infty$, the class H^p is defined to consist of all $f \in H(U)$ for which $\|f\|_p < \infty$. Note that this coincides with our previously introduced terminology in the case $p = \infty$.

The class N consists of all $f \in H(U)$ for which $\|f\|_0 < \infty$.

It is clear that $H^\infty \subset H^p \subset H^s \subset N$ if $0 < s < p < \infty$.

17.8 Remarks For $1 \le p \le \infty$, $\|f\|_p$ satisfies the triangle inequality, so that H^p is a normed linear space. To see this, apply the Minkowski inequality to $M_p(f;r)$:

$$(1) \qquad M_p(f + g; r) \le M_p(f;r) + M_p(g;r) \qquad (0 \le r < 1).$$

As $r \to 1$, we obtain

$$(2) \qquad \|f + g\|_p \le \|f\|_p + \|g\|_p.$$

Actually, *H^p is a Banach space,* if $1 \le p \le \infty$: To prove the completeness, suppose $\{f_n\}$ is a Cauchy sequence in H^p, $|z| \le r < R < 1$, and apply the Cauchy formula to $f_n - f_m$, integrating around the circle of radius R. This leads to the inequalities

$$(R - r)|f_n(z) - f_m(z)| \le M_1(f_n - f_m; R) \le M_p(f_n - f_m; R) \le \|f_n - f_m\|_p,$$

and we conclude that $\{f_n\}$ converges uniformly on compact subsets of U to a function of $f \in H(U)$. Given $\epsilon > 0$, there exists an m such that $\|f_n - f_m\|_p < \epsilon$ for all $n > m$, and then, for every $r < 1$,

$$M_p(f - f_m; r) = \lim_{n \to \infty} M_p(f_n - f_m; r) \le \epsilon.$$

This gives $\|f - f_m\|_p \to 0$ as $m \to \infty$.

For $p < 1$, H^p is still a vector space, but the triangle inequality is no longer satisfied by $\|f\|_p$.

We saw in Theorem 15.23 that the zeros of any $f \in N$ satisfy the Blaschke condition $\Sigma(1 - |\alpha_n|) < \infty$. Hence the same is true in every H^p. It is interesting that the zeros of any $f \in H^p$ can be divided out without increasing the norm:

17.9 Theorem *Suppose $f \in N$, $f \not\equiv 0$, and B is the Blaschke product formed with the zeros of f. Put $g = f/B$. Then $g \in N$ and $\|g\|_0 = \|f\|_0$. Moreover, if $f \in H^p$, then $g \in H^p$ and $\|g\|_p = \|f\|_p$ $(0 < p \le \infty)$.*

PROOF Note first that

$$(1) \qquad |g(z)| \ge |f(z)| \qquad (z \in U).$$

In fact, strict inequality holds for every $z \in U$, unless f has no zeros in U, in which case $B = 1$ and $g = f$.

If s and t are nonnegative real numbers, the inequality

$$(2) \qquad \log^+ (st) \le \log^+ s + \log^+ t$$

holds since the left side is 0 if $st < 1$ and is $\log s + \log t$ if $st \geq 1$. Since $|g| = |f|/|B|$, (2) gives

$$\text{(3)} \qquad \log^+ |g| \leq \log^+ |f| + \log \frac{1}{|B|}.$$

By Theorem 15.24, (3) implies that $\|g\|_0 \leq \|f\|_0$, and since (1) holds, we actually have $\|g\|_0 = \|f\|_0$.

Now suppose $f \in H^p$ for some $p > 0$. Let B_n be the finite Blaschke product formed with the first n zeros of f (we arrange these zeros in some sequence, taking multiplicities into account). Put $g_n = f/B_n$. For each n, $|B_n(re^{i\theta})| \to 1$ uniformly, as $r \to 1$. Hence $\|g_n\|_p = \|f\|_p$. As $n \to \infty$, $|g_n|$ increases to $|g|$, so that

$$\text{(4)} \qquad M_p(g;r) = \lim_{n\to\infty} M_p(g_n;r) \qquad (0 < r < 1),$$

by the monotone convergence theorem. The right side of (4) is at most $\|f\|_p$, for all $r < 1$; and if we let $r \to 1$, we obtain $\|g\|_p \leq \|f\|_p$. Equality now follows from (1), as before.

The Space H^2

The particular importance of H^2 is due to the fact that it is a Hilbert space and that it can be very easily identified with a certain subspace of $L^2(T)$, where T is the unit circle. We recall that the norm of any $g \in L^2(T)$ is

$$\|g\|_2 = \left\{\frac{1}{2\pi}\int_{-\pi}^{\pi} |g(e^{i\theta})|^2\, d\theta\right\}^{\frac{1}{2}}$$

and that each $g \in L^2(T)$ has Fourier coefficients

$$\hat{g}(n) = \frac{1}{2\pi}\int_{-\pi}^{\pi} g(e^{i\theta})e^{-in\theta}\, d\theta \qquad (n = 0, \pm 1, \pm 2, \ldots).$$

The basic properties of H^2 are summarized in the following theorem

17.10 Theorem

(*a*) *A function $f \in H(U)$, of the form*

$$\text{(1)} \qquad f(z) = \sum_0^\infty a_n z^n \qquad (z \in U),$$

is in H^2 if and only if $\Sigma |a_n|^2 < \infty$; in that case,

$$\text{(2)} \qquad \|f\|_2 = \left\{\sum_0^\infty |a_n|^2\right\}^{\frac{1}{2}}.$$

(b) *If $f \in H^2$, then f has radial limits $f^*(e^{i\theta})$ at almost all points of T; $f^* \in L^2(T)$; the nth Fourier coefficient of f^* is a_n if $n \geq 0$ and 0 if $n < 0$; the L^2-approximation*

$$\lim_{r\to 1} \frac{1}{2\pi} \int_{-\pi}^{\pi} |f^*(e^{i\theta}) - f(re^{i\theta})|^2 \, d\theta = 0 \tag{3}$$

holds; and f is the Poisson integral as well as the Cauchy integral of f^*: If $z = re^{i\theta}$, then

$$f(z) = \frac{1}{2\pi} \int_{-\pi}^{\pi} P_r(\theta - t) f^*(e^{it}) \, dt \tag{4}$$

and

$$f(z) = \frac{1}{2\pi i} \int_{\Gamma} \frac{f^*(\zeta)}{\zeta - z} \, d\zeta, \tag{5}$$

where Γ is the positively oriented unit circle.

(c) *The mapping $f \to f^*$ is an isometry of H^2 onto the subspace of $L^2(T)$ which consists of those $g \in L^2(T)$ which have $\hat{g}(n) = 0$ for all $n < 0$.*

PROOF Direct computation (Parseval's theorem) shows that

$$M_2(f;r) = \left\{\sum_0^\infty |a_n|^2 r^{2n}\right\}^{\frac{1}{2}} \qquad (0 \leq r < 1). \tag{6}$$

This proves (a).

Now suppose $f \in H^2$. For $0 < s < 1$, define functions f_s on T by

$$f_s(e^{i\theta}) = f(se^{i\theta}) = \sum_0^\infty a_n s^n e^{in\theta}. \tag{7}$$

Since $\Sigma |a_n|^2 < \infty$, the Riesz-Fischer theorem ensures the existence of a function $g \in L^2(T)$ such that $\hat{g}(n) = a_n$ for $n \geq 0$ and $\hat{g}(n) = 0$ for $n < 0$. The Fourier coefficients of $g - f_s$ are $(1 - s^n)a_n$ if $n \geq 0$. Another application of Parseval's theorem therefore shows that

$$\|g - f_s\|_2^2 = \sum_1^\infty (1 - s^n)^2 |a_n|^2. \tag{8}$$

As $s \to 1$, the right side of (8) tends to 0, and we conclude that

$$\lim_{s\to 1} \|g - f_s\|_2 = 0. \tag{9}$$

For any fixed $s \in (0,1)$, $f(sz)$ is holomorphic in $D(0;1/s)$. Hence if $z \in U$ and $z = re^{i\theta}$, we have

$$f(sz) = \frac{1}{2\pi} \int_{-\pi}^{\pi} P_r(\theta - t) f_s(e^{it}) \, dt \tag{10}$$

and

$$f(sz) = \frac{1}{2\pi i}\int_\Gamma \frac{f_s(\zeta)}{\zeta - z}\,d\zeta. \tag{11}$$

Consider the differences between these integrals and the corresponding ones with g in place of f_s. The Schwarz inequality, combined with (9), then gives (4) and (5), with g in place of f^*. So f is the Poisson integral of g; and since $g \in L^1(T)$, the Corollary to Theorem 11.10 shows that the radial limits of f exist and are equal to g a.e. on T. This proves (*b*).

That $\|f^*\|_2 = \|f\|_2$ follows from (3). The proof of (*b*) shows that all Fourier coefficients of f^* are 0 for $n < 0$. To complete the proof of (*c*), suppose $g \in L^2(T)$ and $\hat{g}(n) = 0$ for all $n < 0$, and put

$$f(z) = \sum_0^\infty \hat{g}(n)z^n. \tag{12}$$

Then $f \in H^2$ by (*a*), and the proof of (*b*) shows that $f^* = g$.

17.11 Remark Suppose $f \in H^p$ for some $p > 0$, B is the Blaschke product formed with the zeros of f, and $g = f/B$. Theorem 17.9 shows that $g \in H^p$, and even that $\|g\|_p = \|f\|_p$. Since g has no zero in U and U is simply connected, there exists $\varphi \in H(U)$ such that $\exp(\varphi) = g$ (Theorem 13.18). Put $h = \exp(p\varphi/2)$. Then $h \in H(U)$, and $|h|^2 = |g|^p$, hence $h \in H^2$. In fact, $\|h\|_2^2 = \|g\|_p^p$.

Thus f has a factorization of the form

$$f = B \cdot h^{2/p} \tag{1}$$

where $h \in H^2$ and h has no zero in U. This makes it possible, in many cases, to apply H^2-results to functions in any H^p. The proof which follows uses this technique.

17.12 Theorem *If $f \in H^1$, then*

$$f^*(e^{i\theta}) = \lim_{r\to 1} f(re^{i\theta}) \tag{1}$$

exists at almost all points of T, and

$$\lim_{r\to 1} \frac{1}{2\pi}\int_{-\pi}^{\pi} |f^*(e^{i\theta}) - f(re^{i\theta})|\,d\theta = 0. \tag{2}$$

PROOF That the limit (1) exists a.e. follows from the Corollary to Theorem 11.19. If B is the Blaschke product formed with the zeros of f, the preceding remark shows that there exists an $h \in H^2$ such that $h^2 = f/B$ and $\|h\|_2^2 = \|f\|_1$. Put $g = Bh$. Then $g \in H^2$, $\|g\|_2 = \|h\|_2$, and $f = gh$. We have factored f into a product of two functions belonging to H^2.

Define f_r on T by $f_r(e^{i\theta}) = f(re^{i\theta})$, and define g_r and h_r in the same manner. Since $f^* = g^*h^*$ a.e., we have

$$f^* - f_r = g^*(h^* - h_r) + h_r(g^* - g_r). \tag{3}$$

By Theorem 17.10, $\|h^* - h_r\|_2 \to 0$ and $\|g^* - g_r\|_2 \to 0$ as $r \to 1$. Also,

$$\|g^*\|_2^2 = \|g\|_2^2 = \|f\|_1 \tag{4}$$

and

$$\|h_r\|_2^2 \leq \|h\|_2^2 = \|f\|_1. \tag{5}$$

If we apply the Schwarz inequality to each of the two products on the right of (3), we therefore conclude that $\|f^* - f_r\|_1 \to 0$ as $r \to 1$.

Corollary *If $f \in H^1$, then f is the Poisson integral and the Cauchy integral of f^*.*

PROOF If $R < 1$ and $g(z) = f(Rz)$, then $g \in H(D)$, where

$$D = D(0;1/R).$$

Hence, for $z \in U$,

$$f(Rz) = \frac{1}{2\pi i}\int_\Gamma \frac{f(R\zeta)}{\zeta - z}\,d\zeta = \frac{1}{2\pi}\int_{-\pi}^{\pi} \frac{f(Re^{it})}{e^{it} - z}\,e^{it}\,dt.$$

Now fix $z \in U$, let $R \to 1$, and use (2). This gives the Cauchy representation. The Poisson representation is obtained in the same manner.

The Theorem of F. and M. Riesz

17.13 Theorem *If μ is a complex Borel measure on the unit circle T and if*

$$\int_T e^{-int}\,d\mu(t) = 0 \qquad (n = -1, -2, -3, \ldots), \tag{1}$$

then μ is absolutely continuous with respect to Lebesgue measure.

PROOF For $z \in U$, define

$$f(z) = \int_T \frac{d\mu(t)}{1 - ze^{-it}}. \tag{2}$$

If $z = re^{i\theta}$, then

$$(1 - ze^{-it})^{-1} = \sum_{n=0}^{\infty} r^n e^{in(\theta - t)}. \tag{3}$$

and since

$$P_r(\theta - t) = \sum_{-\infty}^{\infty} r^{|n|} e^{in(\theta - t)}, \tag{4}$$

(1) shows that f is also given by the Poisson integral

$$f(z) = \int_T P_r(\theta - t)\, d\mu(t). \tag{5}$$

Hence

$$M_1(f;r) \leq \int_T d|\mu|(t) \frac{1}{2\pi} \int_{-\pi}^{\pi} P_r(\theta - t)\, d\theta = \|\mu\|, \tag{6}$$

so that $f \in H^1$. But then it follows from Theorem 17.12 that

$$f(z) = \frac{1}{2\pi} \int_{-\pi}^{\pi} P_r(\theta - t) f^*(e^{it})\, dt, \tag{7}$$

where $f^* \in L^1(T)$. Comparison of (5) and (7) yields

$$d\mu(t) = \frac{1}{2\pi} f^*(e^{it})\, dt, \tag{8}$$

by Theorem 11.19. This gives the desired conclusion.

The remarkable feature of this theorem is that it derives the absolute continuity of a measure from an apparently unrelated condition, namely, the vanishing of one-half of its Fourier coefficients. In recent years the theorem has been extended to various other situations.

Factorization Theorems

We already know from Theorem 17.9 that every $f \in H^p$ (except $f = 0$) can be factored into a Blaschke product and a function $g \in H^p$ which has no zeros in U. There is also a factorization of g which is of a more subtle nature. It concerns, roughly speaking, the rapidity with which g tends to 0 along certain radii.

17.14 Definition An *inner function* is a function $M \in H^\infty$ for which $|M^*| = 1$ a.e. on T. (As usual, M^* denotes the radial limits of M.)

If φ is a positive measurable function on T such that $\log \varphi \in L^1(T)$, and if

$$Q(z) = c \exp\left\{\frac{1}{2\pi} \int_{-\pi}^{\pi} \frac{e^{it} + z}{e^{it} - z} \log \varphi(e^{it})\, dt\right\} \tag{1}$$

for $z \in U$, then Q is called an *outer function*. Here c is a constant, $|c| = 1$.

Theorem 15.24 shows that every Blaschke product is an inner function, but there are others. They can be described as follows.

17.15 Theorem *Suppose c is a constant, $|c| = 1$, B is a Blaschke product, μ is a finite positive Borel measure on T which is singular with respect to Lebesgue measure, and*

$$(1) \qquad M(z) = cB(z) \exp\left\{-\int_{-\pi}^{\pi} \frac{e^{it}+z}{e^{it}-z}\, d\mu(t)\right\} \qquad (z \in U).$$

Then M is an inner function, and every inner function is of this form.

PROOF If (1) holds and $g = M/B$, then $\log |g|$ is the Poisson integral of $-d\mu$, hence $\log |g| \le 0$, so that $g \in H^\infty$, and the same is true of M. Also, $D\mu = 0$ a.e., since μ is singular (Theorem 8.6), and therefore the radial limits of $\log |g|$ are 0 a.e. (Theorem 11.10). Since $|B^*| = 1$ a.e., we see that M is an inner function.

Conversely, let B be the Blaschke product formed with the zeros of a given inner function M and put $g = M/B$. Then $\log |g|$ is harmonic in U. Theorems 15.24 and 17.9 show that $|g| \le 1$ in U and that $|g^*| = 1$ a.e. on T. Thus $\log |g| \le 0$. We conclude from Theorem 11.19 that $\log |g|$ is the Poisson integral of $-d\mu$, for some positive measure μ on T. Since $\log |g^*| = 0$ a.e. on T, we have $D\mu = 0$ a.e. on T, so μ is singular. Finally, $\log |g|$ is the real part of

$$h(z) = -\int_{-\pi}^{\pi} \frac{e^{it}+z}{e^{it}-z}\, d\mu(t),$$

and this implies that $g = c \exp(h)$ for some constant c with $|c| = 1$. Thus M is of the form (1).

This completes the proof.

The simplest example of an inner function which is not a Blaschke product is the following: Take $c = 1$ and $B = 1$, and let μ be the unit mass at $t = 0$. Then

$$M(z) = \exp\left\{\frac{z+1}{z-1}\right\},$$

which tends to 0 very rapidly along the radius which ends at $z = 1$.

17.16 Theorem *Suppose Q is the outer function related to φ as in Definition 17.14. Then*

(*a*) $\log |Q|$ *is the Poisson integral of* $\log \varphi$.
(*b*) $\lim_{r \to 1} |Q(re^{i\theta})| = \varphi(e^{i\theta})$ *a.e. on T.*
(*c*) $Q \in H^p$ *if and only if* $\varphi \in L^p(T)$. *In this case,* $\|Q\|_p = \|\varphi\|_p$.

PROOF (*a*) is clear by inspection, and (*a*) implies that the radial limits of $\log |Q|$ are equal to $\log \varphi$ a.e. on T, which proves (*b*). If

$Q \in H^p$, Fatou's lemma implies that $\|Q^*\|_p \le \|Q\|_p$, so $\|\varphi\|_p \le \|Q\|_p$, by (*b*). Conversely, if $\varphi \in L^p(T)$, then

$$|Q(re^{i\theta})|^p = \exp\left\{\frac{1}{2\pi}\int_{-\pi}^{\pi} P_r(\theta - t)\log \varphi^p(e^{it})\,dt\right\}$$

$$\le \frac{1}{2\pi}\int_{-\pi}^{\pi} P_r(\theta - t)\varphi^p(e^{it})\,dt,$$

by the inequality between the geometric and arithmetic means (Theorem 3.3), and if we integrate the last inequality with respect to θ we find that $\|Q\|_p \le \|\varphi\|_p$ if $p < \infty$. The case $p = \infty$ is trivial.

17.17 Theorem *Suppose* $0 < p \le \infty$, $f \in H^p$, *and* f *is not identically* 0. *Then* $\log|f^*| \in L^1(T)$, *the outer function*

$$Q_f(z) = \exp\left\{\frac{1}{2\pi}\int_{-\pi}^{\pi}\frac{e^{it}+z}{e^{it}-z}\log|f^*(e^{it})|\,dt\right\} \tag{1}$$

is in H^p, *and there is an inner function* M_f *such that*

$$f = M_f Q_f. \tag{2}$$

Furthermore,

$$\log|f(0)| \le \frac{1}{2\pi}\int_{-\pi}^{\pi}\log|f^*(e^{it})|\,dt. \tag{3}$$

Equality holds in (3) *if and only if* M_f *is constant.*

The functions M_f and Q_f are called the *inner* and *outer factors* of f, respectively; Q_f depends only on the boundary values of $|f|$.

PROOF We assume first that $f \in H^1$. If B is the Blaschke product formed with the zeros of f and if $g = f/B$, Theorem 17.9 shows that $g \in H^1$; and since $|g^*| = |f^*|$ a.e. on T, it suffices to prove the theorem with g in place of f.

So let us assume that f has no zero in U and that $f(0) = 1$. Then $\log|f|$ is harmonic in U, $\log|f(0)| = 0$, and since $\log = \log^+ - \log^-$, the mean value property of harmonic functions implies that

$$\frac{1}{2\pi}\int_{-\pi}^{\pi}\log^-|f(re^{i\theta})|\,d\theta = \frac{1}{2\pi}\int_{-\pi}^{\pi}\log^+|f(re^{i\theta})|\,d\theta \le \|f\|_0 \le \|f\|_1 \tag{4}$$

for $0 < r < 1$. It now follows from Fatou's lemma that both $\log^+|f^*|$ and $\log^-|f^*|$ are in $L^1(T)$, hence so is $\log|f^*|$.

This shows that the definition (1) makes sense. By Theorem 17.16, $Q_f \in H^1$. Also, $|Q_f^*| = |f^*| \ne 0$ a.e., since $\log|f^*| \in L^1(T)$. If we can prove that

$$(5) \qquad |f(z)| \le |Q_f(z)| \qquad (z \in U),$$

then f/Q_f will be an inner function, and we obtain the factorization (2).

Since $\log |Q_f|$ is the Poisson integral of $\log |f^*|$, (5) is equivalent to the inequality

$$(6) \qquad \log |f| \le P[\log |f^*|],$$

which we shall now prove. Our notation is as in Chap. 11: $P[h]$ is the Poisson integral of the function $h \in L^1(T)$.

For $|z| \le 1$ and $0 < R < 1$, put $f_R(z) = f(Rz)$. Fix $z \in U$. Then

$$(7) \qquad \log |f_R(z)| = P[\log^+ |f_R|](z) - P[\log^- |f_R|](z).$$

Since $|\log^+ u - \log^+ v| \le |u - v|$ for all real numbers u and v, and since $\|f_R - f^*\|_1 \to 0$ as $R \to 1$ (Theorem 17.12), the first Poisson integral in (7) converges to $P[\log^+ |f^*|]$, as $R \to 1$. Hence Fatou's lemma gives

$$(8) \qquad P[\log^- |f^*|] \le \liminf_{R\to 1} P[\log^- |f_R|] = P[\log^+ |f^*|] - \log |f|,$$

which is the same as (6).

We have now established the factorization (2). If we put $z = 0$ in (5) we obtain (3); equality holds in (3) if and only if $|f(0)| = |Q_f(0)|$, i.e., if and only if $|M_f(0)| = 1$; and since $\|M_f\|_\infty = 1$, this happens only when M_f is a constant.

This completes the proof for the case $p = 1$.

If $1 < p \le \infty$, then $H^p \subset H^1$, hence all that remains to be proved is that $Q_f \in H^p$. But if $f \in H^p$, then $|f^*| \in L^p(T)$, by Fatou's lemma; hence $Q_f \in H^p$, by Theorem 17.16(*c*).

If $p < 1$, we can use the technique described in Sec. 17.11. We leave the details as an exercise.

The fact that $\log |f^*| \in L^1(T)$ has a consequence which we have already used in the proof but which is important enough to be stated separately:

17.18 Theorem *If* $0 < p \le \infty$, $f \in H^p$, *and* f *is not identically* 0, *then at almost all points of* T *we have* $f^*(e^{i\theta}) \ne 0$.

PROOF If $f^* = 0$ then $\log |f^*| = -\infty$, and if this happens on a set of positive measure, then

$$\int_{-\pi}^{\pi} \log |f^*(e^{it})| \, dt = -\infty.$$

Observe that Theorem 17.18 imposes a quantitative restriction on the location of the zeros of the radial limits of an $f \in H^p$. Inside U the zeros are also quantitatively restricted, by the Blaschke condition.

As usual, we can rephrase the above result about zeros as a uniqueness theorem:

If $f \in H^p$, $g \in H^p$, and $f^*(e^{i\theta}) = g^*(e^{i\theta})$ on some subset of T whose Lebesgue measure is positive, then $f(z) = g(z)$ for all $z \in U$.

17.19 Let us take a quick look at the class N, with the purpose of determining how much of Theorems 17.17 and 17.18 is true here. If $f \in N$ and $f \not\equiv 0$, we can divide by a Blaschke product and get a quotient g which has no zero in U and which is in N (Theorem 17.9). Then $\log |g|$ is harmonic, and since

$$(1) \qquad |\log |g|\,| = 2 \log^+ |g| - \log |g|$$

and

$$(2) \qquad \frac{1}{2\pi} \int_{-\pi}^{\pi} \log |g(re^{i\theta})|\, d\theta = \log |g(0)|,$$

we see that $\log |g|$ satisfies the hypotheses of Theorem 11.19 and is therefore the Poisson integral of a real measure μ. Thus

$$(3) \qquad f(z) = cB(z) \exp \left\{ \int_T \frac{e^{it} + z}{e^{it} - z}\, d\mu(t) \right\},$$

where c is a constant, $|c| = 1$, and B is a Blaschke product.

Observe how the assumption that the integrals of $\log^+ |g|$ are bounded (which is a quantitative formulation of the statement that $|g|$ does not get too close to ∞) implies the boundedness of the integrals of $\log^- |g|$ (which says that $|g|$ does not get too close to 0 at too many places).

If μ is a negative measure, the exponential factor in (3) is in H^∞. Apply the Jordan decomposition to μ. This shows:

To every $f \in N$ there correspond two functions b_1 and $b_2 \in H^\infty$ such that b_2 has no zero in U and $f = b_1/b_2$.

Since $b_2^* \neq 0$ a.e., it follows that f has finite radial limits a.e. Also, $f^* \neq 0$ a.e.

Is $\log |f^*| \in L^1(T)$? Yes, and the proof is identical to the one given in Theorem 17.17.

However, the inequality (3) of Theorem 17.17 need no longer hold. For example, if

$$(4) \qquad f(z) = \exp \left\{ \frac{1 + z}{1 - z} \right\},$$

then $\|f\|_0 = e$, $|f^*| = 1$ a.e., and

(5) $$\log |f(0)| = 1 > 0 = \frac{1}{2\pi} \int_{-\pi}^{\pi} \log |f^*(e^{it})| \, dt.$$

The Shift Operator

17.20 Invariant Subspaces Consider a bounded linear operator S on a Banach space X; that is to say, S is a bounded linear transformation of X into X. If a closed subspace Y of X has the property that $S(Y) \subset Y$, we call Y an *S-invariant subspace*. Thus the S-invariant subspaces of X are exactly those which are mapped into themselves by S.

The knowledge of the invariant subspaces of an operator S helps us to visualize its action. (This is a very general—and hence rather vague—principle: in studying any transformation of any kind, it helps to know what the transformation leaves fixed.) For instance, if S is a linear operator on an n-dimensional vector space X and if S has n linearly independent characteristic vectors $x_1, \ldots, x_n$, the one-dimensional spaces spanned by any of these x_i are S-invariant, and we obtain a very simple description of S if we take $\{x_1, \ldots, x_n\}$ as a basis of X.

We shall describe the invariant subspaces of the so-called "shift operator" S on ℓ^2. Here ℓ^2 is the space of all complex sequences

(1) $$x = \{\xi_0, \xi_1, \xi_2, \xi_3, \ldots\}$$

for which

(2) $$\|x\| = \left\{ \sum_{n=0}^{\infty} |\xi_n|^2 \right\}^{\frac{1}{2}} < \infty,$$

and S takes the element $x \in \ell^2$ given by (1) to

(3) $$Sx = \{0, \xi_0, \xi_1, \xi_2, \ldots\}.$$

It is clear that S is a bounded linear operator on ℓ^2 and that $\|S\| = 1$.

A few S-invariant subspaces are immediately apparent: If Y_k is the set of all $x \in \ell^2$ whose first k coordinates are 0, then Y_k is S-invariant.

To find others we make use of a Hilbert space isomorphism between ℓ^2 and H^2 which converts the shift operator S to a multiplication operator on H^2. The point is that this multiplication operator is easier to analyze (because of the richer structure of H^2 as a space of holomorphic functions) than is the case in the original setting of the sequence space ℓ^2.

We associate with each $x \in \ell^2$, given by (1), the function

(4) $$f(z) = \sum_{n=0}^{\infty} \xi_n z^n \qquad (z \in U).$$

By Theorem 17.10, this defines a linear one-to-one mapping of ℓ^2 onto H^2. If

(5) $$y = \{\eta_n\}, \qquad g(z) = \sum_{n=0}^{\infty} \eta_n z^n$$

and if the inner product in H^2 is defined by

(6) $$(f,g) = \frac{1}{2\pi}\int_{-\pi}^{\pi} f^*(e^{i\theta})\overline{g^*(e^{i\theta})}\,d\theta,$$

the Parseval theorem shows that $(f,g) = (x,y)$. Thus we have a Hilbert space isomorphism of ℓ^2 onto H^2, and the shift operator S has turned into a multiplication operator (which we still denote by S) on H^2:

(7) $$(Sf)(z) = zf(z) \qquad (f \in H^2,\ z \in U).$$

The previously mentioned invariant subspaces Y_k are now seen to consist of all $f \in H^2$ which have a zero of order at least k at the origin. This gives a clue: For any finite set $\{\alpha_1, \ldots, \alpha_k\} \subset U$, the space Y of all $f \in H^2$ such that $f(\alpha_1) = \cdots = f(\alpha_k) = 0$ is S-invariant. If B is the finite Blaschke product with zeros at $\alpha_1, \ldots, \alpha_k$, then $f \in Y$ if and only if $f/B \in H^2$. Thus $Y = BH^2$.

This suggests that *infinite* Blaschke products may also give rise to S-invariant subspaces and, more generally, that Blaschke products might be replaced by arbitrary inner functions φ. It is not hard to see that each φH^2 is a closed S-invariant subspace of H^2, but that *every* closed S-invariant subspace of H^2 is of this form is a deeper result.

17.21 Beurling's Theorem

(*a*) *For each inner function* φ *the space*

$$\varphi H^2 = \{\varphi f : f \in H^2\}$$

is a closed S*-invariant subspace of* H^2.

(*b*) *If* φ_1 *and* φ_2 *are inner functions and if* $\varphi_1 H^2 = \varphi_2 H^2$, *then* φ_1/φ_2 *is constant.*

(*c*) *Every closed* S*-invariant subspace* Y *of* H^2, *other than* $\{0\}$, *contains an inner function* φ *such that* $Y = \varphi H^2$.

PROOF H^2 is a Hilbert space, relative to the norm

(2) $$\|f\|_2 = \left\{\frac{1}{2\pi}\int_{-\pi}^{\pi} |f^*(e^{i\theta})|^2\,d\theta\right\}^{\frac{1}{2}}.$$

If φ is an inner function, then $|\varphi^*| = 1$ a.e. The mapping $f \to \varphi f$ is therefore an isometry of H^2 into H^2; being an isometry, its range φH^2 is a closed subspace of H^2. [Proof: If $\varphi f_n \to g$ in H^2, then $\{\varphi f_n\}$

is a Cauchy sequence, hence so is $\{f_n\}$, hence $f_n \to f \in H^2$, so $g = \varphi f \in \varphi H^2$.] The S-invariance of φH^2 is also trivial, since $z \cdot \varphi f = \varphi \cdot zf$. Hence (a) holds.

If $\varphi_1 H^2 = \varphi_2 H^2$, then $\varphi_1 = \varphi_2 f$ for some $f \in H^2$, hence $\varphi_1/\varphi_2 \in H^2$. Similarly, $\varphi_2/\varphi_1 \in H^2$. Put $\varphi = \varphi_1/\varphi_2$ and $h = \varphi + (1/\varphi)$. Then $h \in H^2$, and since $|\varphi^*| = 1$ a.e. on T, h^* is real a.e. on T. Since h is the Poisson integral of h^* it follows that h is real in U, hence h is constant. Then φ must be constant, and (b) is proved.

The proof of (c) will use a method originated by Helson and Lowdenslager. Suppose Y is a closed S-invariant subspace of H^2 which does not consist of 0 alone. Then there is a smallest integer k such that Y contains a function f of the form

$$f(z) = \sum_{n=k}^{\infty} c_n z^n, \qquad c_k = 1. \tag{3}$$

Then $f \notin zY$, where we write zY for the set of all g of the form $g(z) = zf(z)$, $f \in Y$. It follows that zY is a *proper* closed subspace of Y [closed by the argument used in the proof of (a)], so Y contains a nonzero vector which is orthogonal to zY (Theorem 4.11).

So there exists a $\varphi \in Y$ such that $\|\varphi\|_2 = 1$ and $\varphi \perp zY$. Then $\varphi \perp z^n\varphi$, for $n = 1, 2, 3, \ldots$. By the definition of the inner product in H^2 [see 17.20(6)] this means that

$$\frac{1}{2\pi}\int_{-\pi}^{\pi} |\varphi^*(e^{i\theta})|^2 e^{-in\theta}\, d\theta = 0 \qquad (n = 1, 2, 3, \ldots). \tag{4}$$

These equations are preserved if we replace the left sides by their complex conjugates, i.e., if we replace n by $-n$. Thus all Fourier coefficients of the function $|\varphi^*|^2 \in L^1(T)$ are 0, except the one corresponding to $n = 0$, which is 1. Since L^1-functions are determined by their Fourier coefficients (Theorem 5.15), it follows that $|\varphi^*| = 1$ a.e. on T. But $\varphi \in H^2$, so φ is the Poisson integral of φ^*, and hence $|\varphi| \le 1$. We conclude that φ is an inner function.

Since $\varphi \in Y$ and Y is S-invariant, we have $\varphi z^n \in Y$ for

$$n = 0, 1, 2, \ldots,$$

hence $\varphi P \in Y$ for every polynomial P. The polynomials are dense in H^2 (the partial sums of the power series of any $f \in H^2$ converge to f in the H^2-norm, by Parseval's theorem), and since Y is closed and $|\varphi| \le 1$ it follows that $\varphi H^2 \subset Y$. We have to prove that this inclusion is *not* proper. Since φH^2 is closed, it is enough to show that the assumptions $h \in Y$ and $h \perp \varphi H^2$ imply $h = 0$.

If $h \perp \varphi H^2$, then $h \perp \varphi z^n$ for $n = 0, 1\ 2, \ldots$, or

$$(5)\quad \frac{1}{2\pi}\int_{-\pi}^{\pi} h^*(e^{i\theta})\overline{\varphi^*(e^{i\theta})e^{-in\theta}}\,d\theta = 0 \qquad (n = 0, 1, 2, \ldots).$$

If $h \in Y$, then $z^n h \in zY$ if $n = 1, 2, 3, \ldots$, and our choice of φ shows that $z^n h \perp \varphi$, or

$$(6)\quad \frac{1}{2\pi}\int_{-\pi}^{\pi} h^*(e^{i\theta})\overline{\varphi^*(e^{i\theta})}e^{-in\theta}\,d\theta = 0 \qquad (n = -1, -2, -3, \ldots).$$

Thus all Fourier coefficients of $h^*\overline{\varphi^*}$ are 0, hence $h^*\overline{\varphi^*} = 0$ a.e. on T; and since $|\varphi^*| = 1$ a.e., we have $h^* = 0$ a.e. Therefore $h = 0$, and the proof is complete.

17.22 Remark If we combine Theorems 17.15 and 17.21 we see that the S-invariant subspaces of H^2 are characterized by the following data: a sequence of complex numbers $\{\alpha_n\}$ (possibly finite, or even empty) such that $|\alpha_n| < 1$ and $\Sigma(1 - |\alpha_n|) < \infty$, and a positive Borel measure μ on T, singular with respect to Lebesgue measure (so $D\mu = 0$ a.e.). It is easy (we leave this as an exercise) to find conditions, in terms of $\{\alpha_n\}$ and μ, which ensure that one S-invariant subspace of H^2 contains another. The partially ordered set of all S-invariant subspaces is thus seen to have an extremely complicated structure, much more complicated than one might have expected from the simple definition of the shift operator on ℓ^2.

We conclude the section with an easy consequence of Theorem 17.21 which depends on the factorization described in Theorem 17.17.

17.23 Theorem *Suppose M_f is the inner factor of a function $f \in H^2$, and Y is the smallest closed S-invariant subspace of H^2 which contains f. Then*

$$(1)\qquad Y = M_f H^2.$$

In particular, $Y = H^2$ if and only if f is an outer function.

PROOF Let $f = M_f Q_f$ be the factorization of f into its inner and outer factors. It is clear that $f \in M_f H^2$; and since $M_f H^2$ is closed and S-invariant, we have $Y \subset M_f H^2$.

On the other hand, Theorem 17.21 shows that there is an inner function φ such that $Y = \varphi H^2$. Since $f \in Y$, there exists an $h = M_h Q_h \in H^2$ such that

$$(2)\qquad M_f Q_f = \varphi M_h Q_h.$$

Since inner functions have absolute value 1 a.e. on T, (2) implies that $Q_f = Q_h$, hence $M_f = \varphi M_h \in Y$, and therefore Y must contain the smallest S-invariant closed subspace which contains M_f. Thus $M_f H^2 \subset Y$, and the proof is complete.

It may be of interest to summarize these results in terms of two questions to which they furnish answers.

If $f \in H^2$, which functions $g \in H^2$ can be approximated in the H^2-norm by functions of the form fP, where P runs through the polynomials? *Answer:* Precisely those g for which $g/M_f \in H^2$.

For which $f \in H^2$ is it true that the set $\{fP\}$ is dense in H^2? *Answer:* Precisely for those f for which

$$\log |f(0)| = \frac{1}{2\pi} \int_{-\pi}^{\pi} \log |f^*(e^{it})| \, dt.$$

Conjugate Functions

17.24 Formulation of the Problem Every real harmonic function u in the unit disc U is the real part of one and only one $f \in H(U)$ such that $f(0) = u(0)$. If $f = u + iv$, the last requirement can also be stated in the form $v(0) = 0$. The function v is called the *harmonic conjugate* of u, or the *conjugate function* of u.

Define $M_p(u;r)$ as in Theorem 17.6 (with u in place of f). Since $|u|$ is subharmonic, Theorem 17.6 applies to $M_p(u;r)$. Hence, if $p \geq 1$,

$$\lim_{r \to 1} M_p(u;r) = \sup_{0<r<1} M_p(u;r). \tag{1}$$

We shall denote this common value by $\|u\|_p$.

The following question now arises: *Does the finiteness of $\|u\|_p$ imply the finiteness of $\|v\|_p$?*

The question is equivalent to the following: *Must $f \in H^p$ if $\|u\|_p < \infty$?*

Yet another formulation of the question is contained in Exercise 17.

The answer (given by M. Riesz) is affirmative if $1 < p < \infty$. (For $p = 1$ and $p = \infty$ it is negative; see Exercise 16.) The precise statement is given in Theorem 17.26.

17.25 Lemma *Suppose $1 < p \leq 2$. There exists a positive constant B, depending only on p, such that*

$$(1 + B)(B \cos \beta)^p - B \cos p\beta \geq 1 \qquad \left(-\frac{\pi}{2} \leq \beta \leq \frac{\pi}{2}\right). \tag{1}$$

PROOF Put $B = (\cos \delta)^{-1}$, where δ is chosen so that $(1 + p)\delta = \pi$. Then $\delta < \pi/2$, so that $B > 0$, and $\cos p\delta = -\cos \delta$.

If $0 \leq |\beta| \leq \delta$, then $B \cos \beta \geq B \cos \delta = 1$, so that the left side of (1) is at least $(1 + B) - B = 1$.

If $\delta < |\beta| \leq \pi/2$, then $p\delta < p|\beta| \leq p\pi/2 \leq \pi$, so that

$$\cos p\beta < \cos p\delta = -1/B.$$

Hence $-B \cos p\beta > 1$, and (1) holds again.

17.26 Theorem *To each p such that $1 < p < \infty$ there corresponds a constant A_p such that the inequality*

$$(1) \qquad \|v\|_p \le A_p \|u\|_p$$

holds for every real harmonic function u in U if v is the harmonic conjugate of u.

PROOF We first assume $1 < p \le 2$, and put $f = u + iv$.

The lemma settles the case in which $u > 0$ in U. For then f has no zero in U; and since U is simply connected there exists a $g \in H(U)$ such that $f = e^g$, $g = \alpha + i\beta$ (so that α and β are harmonic), and $\beta(0) = 0$. Since $u > 0$, we have $|\beta| < \pi/2$ in U. Since

$$(2) \qquad u = e^\alpha \cos \beta = |f| \cos \beta,$$

Lemma 17.25 shows that

$$(3) \qquad |f|^p \le (1 + B)B^p u^p - B|f|^p \cos p\beta.$$

Observe that $|f|^p \cos p\beta$ is the real part of $\exp(pg)$ and is therefore harmonic, so that

$$(4) \qquad \frac{1}{2\pi} \int_{-\pi}^{\pi} |f(re^{i\theta})|^p \cos [p\beta(re^{i\theta})]\, d\theta = |f(0)|^p > 0 \qquad (0 < r < 1).$$

Hence integration of (3) leads to

$$(5) \qquad \|f\|_p \le C\|u\|_p$$

where $C = (1 + B)^{1/p}B$.

This is the crux of the proof. The rest is a matter of routine and can be handled in various ways.

If $u > 0$ in U and u is continuous on $\bar{U}$, then (5) can be written in the form

$$(6) \qquad \|f\|_p \le C \left\{ \frac{1}{2\pi} \int_{-\pi}^{\pi} u(e^{it})^p\, dt \right\}^{1/p}.$$

Now suppose u is continuous on $\bar{U}$, real and harmonic in U, and define

$$(7) \qquad f_1(z) = \frac{1}{2\pi} \int_{-\pi}^{\pi} \frac{e^{it} + z}{e^{it} - z}\, u^+(e^{it})\, dt = u_1(z) + iv_1(z),$$

for $z \in U$; define $f_2 = u_2 + iv_2$ in the same way, with u^- in place of u^+. Then (6) applies to the pairs f_1, u_1 and f_2, u_2 in place of f, u. On T we have $u_1 = u^+ \le |u|$. On $\bar{U}$, $u = u_1 - u_2$. In $U, f = f_1 - f_2$. It follows that the pair f, u satisfies (6) with $2C$ in place of C. Hence (1) holds with $A_p = 2C$, provided u is continuous on $\bar{U}$.

In the general case, choose $R < 1$, and put $f_R(z) = f(Rz)$, for $z \in U$. The preceding case applies to f_R. Since $\|u_R\|_p \leq \|u\|_p$, we obtain

$$(8) \qquad \|f_R\|_p \leq A_p\|u_R\|_p \leq A_p\|u\|_p$$

for every $R < 1$, and this gives (1), since $|v| \leq |f|$.

We have now proved the theorem for $1 < p \leq 2$.

To complete the proof, suppose $2 \leq q < \infty$ and let p be the exponent conjugate to q.

Let u and v be as in the statement of the theorem, put $f = u + iv$, and let $g(z) = \alpha(z) + i\beta(z)$ be a polynomial, with $g(0)$ real. We claim that

$$(9) \qquad \frac{1}{2\pi}\int_{-\pi}^{\pi} u(re^{i\theta})\beta(e^{i\theta})\, d\theta = -\frac{1}{2\pi}\int_{-\pi}^{\pi} v(re^{i\theta})\alpha(e^{i\theta})\, d\theta$$

for $0 < r < 1$. To see this, note that $u\beta + v\alpha$ is harmonic, being the imaginary part of fg. Hence

$$(10) \quad \frac{1}{2\pi}\int_{-\pi}^{\pi} [u(re^{i\theta})\beta(e^{i\theta}) + v(re^{i\theta})\alpha(e^{i\theta})]\, d\theta = u(0)\beta(0) + v(0)\alpha(0),$$

and since $\beta(0) = 0$ and $v(0) = 0$, we obtain (9). The Hölder inequality now gives

$$(11) \quad \left|\frac{1}{2\pi}\int_{-\pi}^{\pi} v(re^{i\theta})\alpha(e^{i\theta})\, d\theta\right| \leq \|u\|_q\|\beta\|_p \leq \|u\|_q A_p\|\alpha\|_p.$$

Since the real trigonometric polynomials α are dense in the space of all real L^p-functions on T, (11) and Theorem 6.16 show that

$$\|v\|_q \leq A_p\|u\|_q.$$

We have now proved the theorem for $2 \leq q < \infty$, and we see that $A_q \leq A_p$. If we take the smallest admissible values for A_p and A_q, the last computation can be reversed, and we find that $A_p = A_q$.

Exercises

1 Suppose $f \in H(U)$ and $f(U)$ is not dense in the plane. Prove that f has finite radial limits at almost all points of T.

2 Prove that $f \in N$ if and only if $f = g/h$, where g and $h \in H^\infty$ and h has no zero in U.

3 If $f \in H^1$ and $f^* \in L^p(T)$, prove that $f \in H^p$.

4 Fix $\alpha \in U$. Prove that the mapping $f \to f(\alpha)$ is a bounded linear functional on H^2. Since H^2 is a Hilbert space, this functional can be represented as an inner product with some $g \in H^2$. Find this g.

5 Fix $\alpha \in U$. How large can $|f'(\alpha)|$ be if $\|f\|_2 \leq 1$? Find the extremal functions. Do the same for $f^{(n)}(\alpha)$.

6 Suppose $0 < p \leq \infty$ and $f \in H(U)$. Prove that $f \in H^p$ if and only if there is a harmonic function u in U such that $|f(z)|^p \leq u(z)$ for all $z \in U$. Prove that if there is one such *harmonic majorant* u of $|f|^p$, then there is a least one, say u_f. (Explicitly, $|f|^p \leq u_f$ and u_f is harmonic; and if $|f|^p \leq u$ and u is harmonic, then $u_f \leq u$.) Prove that $\|f\|_p = u_f(0)^{1/p}$. *Hint:* Consider the harmonic functions in $D(0;R)$, $R < 1$, with boundary values $|f|^p$, and let $R \to 1$.

7 Prove likewise that $f \in N$ if and only if $\log^+ |f|$ has a harmonic majorant in U.

8 Suppose $f \in H^p$, $\varphi \in H(U)$, and $\varphi(U) \subset U$. Does it follow that $f \circ \varphi \in H^p$? Answer the same question with N in place of H^p.

9 If $0 < r < s \leq \infty$, show that H^s is a *proper* subclass of H^r.

10 Show that H^∞ is a *proper* subclass of the intersection of all H^p with $p < \infty$.

11 Prove Theorems 17.4 and 17.5 for upper semicontinuous subharmonic functions.

12 Suppose $p \geq 1$, $f \in H^p$, and f^* is real a.e. on T. Prove that f is then constant. Show that this result is false for every $p < 1$.

13 Complete the proof of Theorem 17.17 for the case $0 < p < 1$.

14 Let φ be a nonconstant inner function with no zero in U.

(*a*) Prove that $1/\varphi \notin H^p$ if $p > 0$.

(*b*) Prove that there is at least one $e^{i\theta} \in T$ such that $\lim_{r \to 1} \varphi(re^{i\theta}) = 0$.

Hint: $\log|\varphi|$ is a negative harmonic function.

15 Suppose φ is a nonconstant inner function, $|\alpha| < 1$, and $\alpha \notin \varphi(U)$. Prove that $\lim_{r \to 1} \varphi(re^{i\theta}) = \alpha$ for at least one $e^{i\theta} \in T$.

16 The conformal mapping of U onto a vertical strip shows that M. Riesz's theorem on conjugate functions cannot be extended to $p = \infty$. Deduce that it cannot be extended to $p = 1$ either.

17 Suppose $1 < p < \infty$, and associate with each $f \in L^p(T)$ its Fourier coefficients

$$\hat{f}(n) = \frac{1}{2\pi} \int_{-\pi}^{\pi} f(e^{it}) e^{-int}\, dt \qquad (n = 0, \pm 1, \pm 2, \ldots).$$

Deduce the following statements from Theorem 17.26:

(*a*) To each $f \in L^p(T)$ there corresponds a function $g \in L^p(T)$ such that $\hat{g}(n) = \hat{f}(n)$ for $n \geq 0$ but $\hat{g}(n) = 0$ for all $n < 0$. In fact, there is a constant C, depending only on p, such that

$$\|g\|_p \leq C\|f\|_p.$$

The mapping $f \rightarrow g$ is thus a bounded linear projection of $L^p(T)$ into $L^p(T)$. The Fourier series of g is obtained from that of f by deleting the terms with $n < 0$.

(*b*) Show that the same is true if we delete the terms with $n < k$, where k is any given integer.

(*c*) Deduce from (*b*) that the partial sums s_n of the Fourier series of any $f \in L^p(T)$ form a bounded sequence in $L^p(T)$. Conclude further that we actually have

$$\lim_{n \rightarrow \infty} \|f - s_n\|_p = 0.$$

(*d*) If $f \in L^p(T)$ and if

$$F(z) = \sum_{n=0}^{\infty} \hat{f}(n)z^n,$$

then $F \in H^p$, and every $F \in H^p$ is so obtained. Thus the projection mentioned in (*a*) may be regarded as a mapping of $L^p(T)$ onto H^p.

18 Show that there is a much simpler proof of Theorem 17.26 if $p = 2$, and find the best value of A_2.

19 Suppose $f \in H^1$ and $1/f \in H^1$. Prove that f is then an outer function.

20 Suppose $f \in H^1$ and $\text{Re}\,[f(z)] > 0$ for all $z \in U$. Prove that f is an outer function.

21 Suppose $f \in H(U)$, and suppose there exists an $M < \infty$ such that f maps every circle of radius $r < 1$ and center 0 onto a curve γ_r whose length is at most M. Prove that f has continuous extension to $\bar{U}$ and that the restriction of f to T is absolutely continuous.

22 Suppose μ is a complex Borel measure on T such that

$$\int_T e^{int}\, d\mu(t) = 0 \qquad (n = 1, 2, 3, \ldots).$$

Prove that then either $\mu = 0$ or the support of μ is all of T.

23 Suppose K is a *proper* compact subset of the unit circle T. Prove that every continuous function on K can be uniformly approximated on K by polynomials. *Hint:* Use Exercise 22.

24 Prove that the following statements are correct if $\{n_k\}$ is a sequence of positive integers which tends to ∞ sufficiently rapidly. If

$$f(z) = \sum_{k=1}^{\infty} \frac{z^{n_k}}{k}$$

then $|f'(z)| > n_k/(10k)$ for all z such that

$$1 - \frac{1}{n_k} < |z| < 1 - \frac{1}{2n_k}.$$

Hence
$$\int_0^1 |f'(re^{i\theta})|\, dr = \infty$$

for every θ, although

$$\lim_{R\to 1} \int_0^R f'(re^{i\theta})\, dr$$

exists (and is finite) for almost all θ. Interpret this geometrically, in terms of the lengths of the images under f of the radii in U.

25 Suppose $f(z) = \sum_0^\infty a_n z^n$ in U and $\Sigma|a_n| < \infty$. Prove that

$$\int_0^1 |f'(re^{i\theta})|\, dr < \infty$$

for all θ.

26 Find the conditions mentioned in Sec. 17.22.

27 Prove the following converse of Theorem 15.24:

If $f \in H(U)$ and if

(*)
$$\lim_{r\to 1} \int_{-\pi}^{\pi} |\log |f(re^{i\theta})||\, d\theta = 0,$$

then f is a Blaschke product. *Hint:* (*) implies

$$\lim_{r\to 1} \int_{-\pi}^{\pi} \log^+ |f(re^{i\theta})|\, d\theta = 0.$$

Since $\log^+ |f| \geq 0$, it follows from Theorems 17.3 and 17.5 that $\log^+ |f| = 0$, so $|f| \leq 1$. Now $f = Bg$, g has no zeros, $|g| \leq 1$, and (*) holds with $1/g$ in place of f. By the first argument, $|1/g| \leq 1$. Hence $g = 1$.

18

Elementary Theory of Banach Algebras

Introduction

18.1 Definitions A *complex algebra* is a vector space A over the complex field in which an associative and distributive multiplication is defined, i.e.,

(1) $x(yz) = (xy)z, \qquad (x + y)z = xz + yz, \qquad x(y + z) = xy + xz$

for x, y, and $z \in A$, and which is related to scalar multiplication so that

(2) $$\alpha(xy) = x(\alpha y) = (\alpha x)y$$

for x and $y \in A$, α a scalar.

If there is a norm defined in A which makes A into a normed linear space and which satisfies the multiplicative inequality

(3) $$\|xy\| \leq \|x\| \, \|y\| \qquad (x \text{ and } y \in A),$$

then A is a *normed complex algebra*. If, in addition, A is a complete metric space relative to this norm, i.e., if A is a Banach space, then we call A a *Banach algebra*.

The inequality (3) makes multiplication a continuous operation. This means that if $x_n \to x$ and $y_n \to y$, then $x_n y_n \to xy$, which follows from (3) and the identity

(4) $$x_n y_n - xy = (x_n - x)y_n + x(y_n - y).$$

Note that we have not required that A be commutative, i.e., that $xy = yx$ for all x and $y \in A$, and we shall not do so except when explicitly stated.

However, we *shall* assume that A has a *unit.* This is an element e such that

(5) $$xe = ex = x \qquad (x \in A).$$

It is easily seen that there is at most one such e ($e' = e'e = e$) and that $\|e\| \geq 1$, by (3). We shall make the additional assumption that

$$\|e\| = 1. \tag{6}$$

An element $x \in A$ will be called *invertible* if x has an *inverse* in A, i.e., if there exists an element $x^{-1} \in A$ such that

$$x^{-1}x = xx^{-1} = e. \tag{7}$$

Again, it is easily seen that no $x \in A$ has more than one inverse.

If x and y are invertible in A, so are x^{-1} and xy, since $(xy)^{-1} = y^{-1}x^{-1}$. The invertible elements therefore form a group with respect to multiplication.

The *spectrum* of an element $x \in A$ is the set of all complex numbers λ such that $x - \lambda e$ is *not* invertible. We shall denote the spectrum of x by $\sigma(x)$.

18.2 The theory of Banach algebras contains a great deal of interplay between algebraic properties on the one hand and topological ones on the other. We already saw an example of this in Theorem 9.21, and shall see others. There are also close relations between Banach algebras and holomorphic functions: The easiest proof of the fundamental fact that $\sigma(x)$ is never empty depends on Liouville's theorem concerning entire functions, and the spectral radius formula follows naturally from theorems about power series. This is one reason for restricting our attention to *complex* Banach algebras. The theory of real Banach algebras (we omit the definition, which should be obvious) is not so satisfactory.

The Invertible Elements

In this section, A will be a complex Banach algebra with unit e, and G will be the set of all invertible elements of A.

18.3 Theorem *If $x \in A$ and $\|x\| < 1$, then $e + x \in G$,*

$$(e + x)^{-1} = \sum_{n=0}^{\infty} (-1)^n x^n, \tag{1}$$

and

$$\|(e + x)^{-1} - e + x\| \leq \frac{\|x\|^2}{1 - \|x\|}. \tag{2}$$

PROOF The multiplicative inequality satisfied by the norm shows that $\|x^n\| \leq \|x\|^n$. If

$$s_N = e - x + x^2 - \cdots + (-1)^N x^N, \tag{3}$$

it follows that $\{s_N\}$ is a Cauchy sequence in A, hence the series in (1) converges (with respect to the norm of A) to an element $y \in A$. Since multiplication is continuous and

$$(4) \qquad (e + x)s_N = e + (-1)^N x^{N+1} = s_N(e + x),$$

we see that $(e + x)y = e = y(e + x)$. This gives (1), and (2) follows from

$$(5) \quad \left\| \sum_{n=2}^{\infty} (-1)^n x^n \right\| \le \sum_{n=2}^{\infty} \|x^n\| \le \sum_{n=2}^{\infty} \|x\|^n = \frac{\|x\|^2}{1 - \|x\|}.$$

18.4 Theorem *Suppose $x \in G$, $\|x^{-1}\| = 1/\alpha$, $h \in A$, and $\|h\| = \beta < \alpha$. Then $x + h \in G$, and*

$$(1) \qquad \|(x + h)^{-1} - x^{-1} + x^{-1}hx^{-1}\| \le \frac{\beta^2}{\alpha^2(\alpha - \beta)}.$$

PROOF $\|x^{-1}h\| \le \beta/\alpha < 1$, hence $e + x^{-1}h \in G$, by Theorem 18.3; and since $x + h = x(e + x^{-1}h)$, we have $x + h \in G$ and

$$(2) \qquad (x + h)^{-1} = (e + x^{-1}h)^{-1}x^{-1}.$$

Thus

$$(3) \quad (x + h)^{-1} - x^{-1} + x^{-1}hx^{-1} = [(e + x^{-1}h)^{-1} - e + x^{-1}h]x^{-1},$$

and the inequality (1) follows from Theorem 18.3, with $x^{-1}h$ in place of x.

Corollary 1 *G is an open set, and the mapping $x \to x^{-1}$ is a homeomorphism of G onto G.*

For if $x \in G$ and $\|h\| \to 0$, (1) implies that $\|(x + h)^{-1} - x^{-1}\| \to 0$. Thus $x \to x^{-1}$ is continuous; it clearly maps G onto G, and since it is its own inverse, it is a homeomorphism.

Corollary 2 *The mapping $x \to x^{-1}$ is differentiable. Its differential at any $x \in G$ is the linear operator which takes $h \in A$ to $-x^{-1}hx^{-1}$.*

This can also be read off from (1). Note that the notion of the differential of a transformation makes sense in any normed linear space, not just in R^k, as in Definition 8.22. If A is commutative, the above differential takes h to $-x^{-2}h$, which agrees with the fact that the derivative of the holomorphic function z^{-1} is $-z^{-2}$.

Corollary 3 *For every $x \in A$, $\sigma(x)$ is compact, and $|\lambda| \le \|x\|$ if $\lambda \in \sigma(x)$.*

For if $|\lambda| > \|x\|$, then $e - \lambda^{-1}x \in G$, by Theorem 18.3, and the same is true of $x - \lambda e = -\lambda(e - \lambda^{-1}x)$; hence $\lambda \notin \sigma(x)$. To prove that $\sigma(x)$

is closed, observe (*a*) $\lambda \in \sigma(x)$ if and only if $x - \lambda e \notin G$; (*b*) the complement of G is a closed subset of A, by Corollary 1; and (*c*) the mapping $\lambda \to x - \lambda e$ is a continuous mapping of the complex plane into A.

18.5 Theorem *Let Φ be a bounded linear functional on A, fix $x \in A$, and define*

$$f(\lambda) = \Phi[(x - \lambda e)^{-1}] \qquad (\lambda \notin \sigma(x)). \tag{1}$$

Then f is holomorphic in the complement of $\sigma(x)$, and $f(\lambda) \to 0$ as $\lambda \to \infty$.

PROOF Fix $\lambda \notin \sigma(x)$ and apply Theorem 18.4 with $x - \lambda e$ in place of x and with $(\lambda - \mu)e$ in place of h. We see that there is a constant C, depending on x and λ, such that

$$\|(x - \mu e)^{-1} - (x - \lambda e)^{-1} + (\lambda - \mu)(x - \lambda e)^{-2}\| \le C|\mu - \lambda|^2 \tag{2}$$

for all μ which are close enough to λ. Thus

$$\frac{(x - \mu e)^{-1} - (x - \lambda e)^{-1}}{\mu - \lambda} \to (x - \lambda e)^{-2} \tag{3}$$

as $\mu \to \lambda$, and if we apply Φ to both sides of (3), the continuity and linearity of Φ show that

$$\frac{f(\mu) - f(\lambda)}{\mu - \lambda} \to \Phi[(x - \lambda e)^{-2}]. \tag{4}$$

So f is differentiable and hence holomorphic outside $\sigma(x)$. Finally, as $\lambda \to \infty$ we have

$$\lambda f(\lambda) = \Phi[\lambda(x - \lambda e)^{-1}] = \Phi\left[\left(\frac{x}{\lambda} - e\right)^{-1}\right] \to \Phi(-e), \tag{5}$$

by the continuity of the inversion mapping in G.

18.6 Theorem *For every $x \in A$, $\sigma(x)$ is compact and not empty.*

PROOF We already know that $\sigma(x)$ is compact. Fix $x \in A$, and fix $\lambda_0 \notin \sigma(x)$. Then $(x - \lambda_0 e)^{-1} \neq 0$, and the Hahn-Banach theorem implies the existence of a bounded linear functional Φ on A such that $f(\lambda_0) \neq 0$, where f is defined as in Theorem 18.5. If $\sigma(x)$ were empty, Theorem 18.5 would imply that f is an entire function which tends to 0 at ∞, hence $f(\lambda) = 0$ for every λ, by Liouville's theorem, and this contradicts $f(\lambda_0) \neq 0$. So $\sigma(x)$ is not empty.

18.7 Theorem (Gelfand-Mazur) *If A is a complex Banach algebra with unit in which each nonzero element is invertible, then A is (isometrically isomorphic to) the complex field.*

An algebra in which each nonzero element is invertible is called a *division algebra*. Note that the commutativity of A is not part of the hypothesis; it is part of the conclusion.

PROOF If $x \in A$ and $\lambda_1 \neq \lambda_2$, at least one of the elements $x - \lambda_1 e$ and $x - \lambda_2 e$ must be invertible, since they cannot both be 0. It now follows from Theorem 18.6 that $\sigma(x)$ consists of exactly one point, say $\lambda(x)$, for each $x \in A$. Since $x - \lambda(x)e$ is not invertible, it must be 0, hence $x = \lambda(x)e$. The mapping $x \to \lambda(x)$ is therefore an isomorphism of A onto the complex field, which is also an isometry, since $|\lambda(x)| = \|\lambda(x)e\| = \|x\|$ for all $x \in A$.

18.8 Definition For any $x \in A$, the *spectral radius* $\rho(x)$ of x is the radius of the smallest closed disc with center at the origin which contains $\sigma(x)$ (sometimes this is also called the *spectral norm* of x; see Exercise 14):

$$\rho(x) = \sup \{|\lambda| : \lambda \in \sigma(x)\}.$$

18.9 Theorem (Spectral Radius Formula) *For every $x \in A$,*

(1) $$\lim_{n \to \infty} \|x^n\|^{1/n} = \rho(x).$$

(The existence of the limit is part of the conclusion.)

PROOF Fix $x \in A$, let n be a positive integer, λ a complex number, and assume $\lambda^n \notin \sigma(x^n)$. We have

(2) $$(x^n - \lambda^n e) = (x - \lambda e)(x^{n-1} + \lambda x^{n-2} + \cdots + \lambda^{n-1} e).$$

Multiply both sides of (2) by $(x^n - \lambda^n e)^{-1}$. This shows that $x - \lambda e$ is invertible, hence $\lambda \notin \sigma(x)$.

So if $\lambda \in \sigma(x)$, then $\lambda^n \in \sigma(x^n)$ for $n = 1, 2, 3, \ldots$, Corollary 3 to Theorem 18.4 shows that $|\lambda^n| \leq \|x^n\|$, and therefore $|\lambda| \leq \|x^n\|^{1/n}$. This gives

(3) $$\rho(x) \leq \liminf_{n \to \infty} \|x^n\|^{1/n}.$$

Now if $|\lambda| > \|x\|$, it is easy to verify that

(4) $$(\lambda e - x) \sum_{n=0}^{\infty} \lambda^{-n-1} x^n = e.$$

The above series is therefore $-(x - \lambda e)^{-1}$. Let Φ be a bounded linear functional on A and define f as in Theorem 18.5. By (4), the expansion

(5) $$f(\lambda) = -\sum_{n=0}^{\infty} \Phi(x^n)\lambda^{-n-1}$$

is valid for all λ such that $|\lambda| > \|x\|$. By Theorem 18.5, f is holomorphic outside $\sigma(x)$, hence in the set $\{\lambda: |\lambda| > \rho(x)\}$. It follows that the power series (5) converges if $|\lambda| > \rho(x)$. In particular,

$$\sup_n |\Phi(\lambda^{-n}x^n)| < \infty \qquad (|\lambda| > \rho(x)) \tag{6}$$

for every bounded linear functional Φ on A.

It is a consequence of the Hahn-Banach theorem (Sec. 5.21) that the norm of any element of A is the same as its norm as a linear functional on the dual space of A. Since (6) holds for every Φ, we can now apply the Banach-Steinhaus theorem and conclude that to each λ with $|\lambda| > \rho(x)$ there corresponds a real number $C(\lambda)$ such that

$$\|\lambda^{-n}x^n\| \leq C(\lambda) \qquad (n = 1, 2, 3, \ldots). \tag{7}$$

Multiply (7) by $|\lambda|^n$ and take nth roots. This gives

$$\|x^n\|^{1/n} \leq |\lambda|[C(\lambda)]^{1/n} \qquad (n = 1, 2, 3, \ldots) \tag{8}$$

if $|\lambda| > \rho(x)$, and hence

$$\limsup_{n\to\infty} \|x^n\|^{1/n} \leq \rho(x). \tag{9}$$

The theorem follows from (3) and (9).

18.10 Remarks

(*a*) Whether an element of A is or is not invertible in A is a purely algebraic property. Thus the spectrum of x, and likewise the spectral radius $\rho(x)$, are defined in terms of the algebraic structure of A, regardless of any metric (or topological) considerations. The limit in the statement of Theorem 18.9, on the other hand, depends on metric properties of A. This is one of the remarkable features of the theorem: It asserts the equality of two quantities which arise in entirely different ways.

(*b*) Our algebra may be a subalgebra of a larger Banach algebra B (an example follows), and then it may very well happen that some $x \in A$ is not invertible in A but is invertible in B. The spectrum of x therefore depends on the algebra; using the obvious notation, we have $\sigma_A(x) \supset \sigma_B(x)$, and the inclusion may be proper. The *spectral radius* of x, however, is unaffected by this, since Theorem 18.9 shows that it can be expressed in terms of metric properties of powers of x, and these are independent of anything that happens outside A.

18.11 Example Let $C(T)$ be the algebra of all continuous complex functions on the unit circle T (with pointwise addition and multiplication and the supremum norm), and let A be the set of all $f \in C(T)$ which can be extended to a continuous function F on the closure of the unit disc U, such that F is holomorphic in U. It is easily seen that A is a subalgebra of $C(T)$. If $f_n \in A$ and $\{f_n\}$ converges uniformly on T, the maximum modulus theorem forces the associated sequence $\{F_n\}$ to converge uniformly on the closure of U. This shows that A is a *closed* subalgebra of $C(T)$, and so A is itself a Banach algebra.

Define the function f_0 by $f_0(e^{i\theta}) = e^{i\theta}$. Then $F_0(z) = z$. The spectrum of f_0 as an element of A consists of the closed unit disc; with respect to $C(T)$, the spectrum of f_0 consists only of the unit circle. In accordance with Theorem 18.9, the two spectral radii coincide.

Ideals and Homomorphisms

From now on we shall deal only with *commutative* algebras.

18.12 Definition A subset I of a commutative complex algebra A is said to be an *ideal* if (a) I is a subspace of A (in the vector space sense) and (b) $xy \in I$ whenever $x \in A$ and $y \in I$. If $I \neq A$, I is a *proper* ideal. *Maximal ideals* are proper ideals which are not contained in any larger proper ideals. Note that no proper ideal contains an invertible element.

If B is another complex algebra, a mapping φ of A into B is called a *homomorphism* if φ is a linear mapping which also preserves multiplication: $\varphi(x)\varphi(y) = \varphi(xy)$ for all x and $y \in A$. The *kernel* (or null space) of φ is the set of all $x \in A$ such that $\varphi(x) = 0$. It is trivial to verify that the kernel of a homomorphism is an ideal. For the converse, see Sec. 18.14.

18.13 Theorem *If A is a commutative complex algebra with unit, every proper ideal of A is contained in a maximal ideal. If, in addition, A is a Banach algebra, every maximal ideal of A is closed.*

PROOF The first part is an almost immediate consequence of the Hausdorff maximality principle (and holds in any commutative ring with unit). Let I be a proper ideal of A. Partially order the collection $\mathcal{P}$ of all proper ideals of A which contain I (by set inclusion), and let M be the union of the ideals in some maximal linearly ordered subcollection $\mathcal{Q}$ of $\mathcal{P}$. Then M is an ideal (being the union of a *linearly* ordered collection of ideals), $I \subset M$, and $M \neq A$, since no member of $\mathcal{P}$ contains the unit of A. The maximality of $\mathcal{Q}$ implies that M is a maximal ideal of A.

If A is a Banach algebra, the closure $\bar{M}$ of M is also an ideal (we leave the details of the proof of this statement to the reader). Since M contains no invertible element of A and since the set of all invertible elements is open, we have $\bar{M} \neq A$, and the maximality of M therefore shows that $\bar{M} = M$.

18.14 Quotient Spaces and Quotient Algebras Suppose J is a subspace of a vector space A, and associate with each $x \in A$ the coset

$$(1) \qquad \varphi(x) = x + J = \{x + y : y \in J\}.$$

If $x_1 - x_2 \in J$, then $\varphi(x_1) = \varphi(x_2)$. If $x_1 - x_2 \notin J$, $\varphi(x_1) \cap \varphi(x_2) = \varnothing$. The set of all cosets of J is denoted by A/J; it is a vector space if we define

$$(2) \qquad \varphi(x) + \varphi(y) = \varphi(x + y), \qquad \lambda\varphi(x) = \varphi(\lambda x)$$

for x and $y \in A$ and scalars λ. Since J is a vector space, the operations (2) are well defined; this means that if $\varphi(x) = \varphi(x')$ and $\varphi(y) = \varphi(y')$, then

$$(3) \qquad \varphi(x) + \varphi(y) = \varphi(x') + \varphi(y'), \qquad \lambda\varphi(x) = \lambda\varphi(x').$$

Also, φ is clearly a linear mapping of A onto A/J; the zero element of A/J is $\varphi(0) = J$.

Suppose next that A is not merely a vector space but a commutative algebra and that J is a proper ideal of A. If $x' - x \in J$ and $y' - y \in J$, the identity

$$(4) \qquad x'y' - xy = (x' - x)y' + x(y' - y)$$

shows that $x'y' - xy \in J$. Therefore multiplication can be defined in A/J in a consistent manner:

$$(5) \qquad \varphi(x)\varphi(y) = \varphi(xy) \qquad (x \text{ and } y \in A).$$

It is then easily verified that A/J is an algebra, and φ is a homomorphism of A onto A/J whose kernel is J.

If A has a unit element e, then $\varphi(e)$ is the unit of A/J, and *A/J is a field if and only if J is a maximal ideal.*

To see this, suppose $x \in A$ and $x \notin J$, and put

$$(6) \qquad I = \{ax + y : a \in A,\ y \in J\}.$$

Then I is an ideal in A which contains J properly, since $x \in I$. If J is maximal, $I = A$, hence $ax + y = e$ for some $a \in A$ and $y \in J$, hence $\varphi(a)\varphi(x) = \varphi(e)$; and this says that every nonzero element of A/J is invertible, so that A/J is a field. If J is not maximal, we can choose x as above so that $I \neq A$, hence $e \notin I$, and then $\varphi(x)$ is not invertible in A/J.

18.15 Quotient Norms Suppose A is a normed linear space, J is a *closed* subspace of A, and $\varphi(x) = x + J$, as above. Define

$$(1) \qquad \|\varphi(x)\| = \inf \{\|x + y\| : y \in J\}.$$

Note that $\|\varphi(x)\|$ is the greatest lower bound of the norms of those elements which lie in the coset $\varphi(x)$; this is the same as the distance from

PROOF Since sums, products, and uniform limits of holomorphic functions are holomorphic, $A(U)$ is a Banach algebra, with the supremum norm. The set J of all functions $\Sigma f_i g_i$, where the g_i are arbitrary members of $A(U)$, is an ideal of $A(U)$. We have to prove that J contains the unit element 1 of $A(U)$. By Theorem 18.13 this happens if and only if J lies in no maximal ideal of $A(U)$. By Theorem 18.17(*a*) it is therefore enough to prove that there is no homomorphism h of $A(U)$ onto the complex field such that $h(f_i) = 0$ for every i $(1 \leq i \leq n)$.

Before we determine these homomorphisms, let us note that the polynomials form a dense subset of $A(U)$. To see this, suppose $f \in A(U)$ and $\epsilon > 0$; since f is uniformly continuous on $\bar{U}$, there exists an $r < 1$ such that $|f(z) - f(rz)| < \epsilon$ for all $z \in \bar{U}$; the expansion of $f(rz)$ in powers of z converges if $|rz| < 1$, hence converges to $f(rz)$ uniformly for $z \in \bar{U}$, and this gives the desired approximation.

Now let h be a complex homomorphism of $A(U)$. Put $f_0(z) = z$. Then $f_0 \in A(U)$. It is obvious that $\sigma(f_0) = \bar{U}$. By Theorem 18.17(*d*) there exists an $\alpha \in \bar{U}$ such that $h(f_0) = \alpha$. Hence $h(f_0^n) = \alpha^n = f_0^n(\alpha)$, for $n = 1, 2, 3, \ldots$, so $h(P) = P(\alpha)$ for every polynomial P. Since h is continuous and since the polynomials are dense in $A(U)$, it follows that $h(f) = f(\alpha)$ for every $f \in A(U)$.

Our hypothesis (1) implies that $|f_i(\alpha)| > 0$ for at least one index i, $1 \leq i \leq n$. Thus $h(f_i) \neq 0$.

We have proved that to each $h \in \Delta$ there corresponds at least one of the given functions f_i such that $h(f_i) \neq 0$, and this, as we noted above, is enough to prove the theorem.

Note: We have also determined all maximal ideals of $A(U)$, in the course of the preceding proof, since each is the kernel of some $h \in \Delta$: *If $\alpha \in \bar{U}$ and if M_α is the set of all $f \in A(U)$ such that $f(\alpha) = 0$, then M_α is a maximal ideal of $A(U)$, and all maximal ideals of $A(U)$ are obtained in this way.*

18.19 The restrictions of the members of $A(U)$ to the unit circle T form a closed subalgebra of $C(T)$. This is the algebra A discussed in Example 18.11. In fact, A is a *maximal* subalgebra of $C(T)$. More explicitly, *if $A \subset B \subset C(T)$ and B is a closed (relative to the supremum norm) subalgebra of $C(T)$, then either $B = A$ or $B = C(T)$.*

It follows from Theorem 11.21 that A consists precisely of those $f \in C(T)$ for which

$$(1) \quad \hat{f}(n) = \frac{1}{2\pi} \int_{-\pi}^{\pi} f(e^{i\theta}) e^{-in\theta}\, d\theta = 0 \qquad (n = -1, -2, -3, \ldots).$$

Hence the above-mentioned maximality theorem can be stated as an approximation theorem:

18.20 Theorem *Suppose $g \in C(T)$ and $\hat{g}(n) \neq 0$ for some $n < 0$. Then to every $f \in C(T)$ and to every $\epsilon > 0$ there correspond polynomials*

$$P_n(e^{i\theta}) = \sum_{k=0}^{m(n)} a_{n,k}e^{ik\theta} \qquad (n = 0, \ldots, N) \tag{1}$$

such that

$$\left| f(e^{i\theta}) - \sum_{n=0}^{N} P_n(e^{i\theta})g^n(e^{i\theta}) \right| < \epsilon \qquad (e^{i\theta} \in T). \tag{2}$$

PROOF Let B be the closure in $C = C(T)$ of the set of all functions of the form

$$\sum_{n=0}^{N} P_n g^n. \tag{3}$$

The theorem asserts that $B = C$. Let us assume $B \neq C$.

The set of all functions (3) (note that N is not fixed) is a complex algebra. Its closure B is a Banach algebra which contains the function f_0, where $f_0(e^{i\theta}) = e^{i\theta}$. Our assumption that $B \neq C$ implies that $1/f_0 \notin B$, for otherwise B would contain f_0^n for all integers n, hence all trigonometric polynomials would be in B; and since the trigonometric polynomials are dense in C (Theorem 4.25) we should have $B = C$.

So f_0 is not invertible in B. By Theorem 18.17 there is a complex homomorphism h of B such that $h(f_0) = 0$. Every homomorphism onto the complex field satisfies $h(1) = 1$; and since $h(f_0) = 0$, we also have

$$h(f_0^n) = [h(f_0)]^n = 0 \qquad (n = 1, 2, 3, \ldots). \tag{4}$$

We know that h is a linear functional on B, of norm at most 1. The Hahn-Banach theorem extends h to a linear functional on C (still denoted by h) of the same norm. Since $h(1) = 1$ and $\|h\| \leq 1$, the argument used in Sec. 5.22 shows that h is a *positive* linear functional on C. In particular, $h(f)$ is real for real f; hence $h(\bar{f}) = \overline{h(f)}$. Since f_0^{-n} is the complex conjugate of f_0^n, it follows that (4) also holds for $n = -1, -2, -3, \ldots$. Thus

$$h(f_0^n) = \begin{cases} 1 & \text{if } n = 0, \\ 0 & \text{if } n \neq 0. \end{cases} \tag{5}$$

Since the trigonometric polynomials are dense in C, there is only one bounded linear functional on C which satisfies (5). Hence h is given by the formula

$$h(f) = \frac{1}{2\pi}\int_{-\pi}^{\pi} f(e^{i\theta})\, d\theta \qquad (f \in C). \tag{6}$$

Now if n is a positive integer, $gf_0^n \in B$; and since h is multiplicative on B, (6) gives

$$(7)\quad \hat{g}(-n) = \frac{1}{2\pi}\int_{-\pi}^{\pi} g(e^{i\theta})e^{in\theta}\,d\theta = h(gf_0^n) = h(g)h(f_0^n) = 0,$$

by (5). This contradicts the hypothesis of the theorem.

We conclude with a theorem due to Wiener.

18.21 Theorem *Suppose*

$$(1)\qquad f(e^{i\theta}) = \sum_{-\infty}^{\infty} c_n e^{in\theta}, \qquad \sum_{-\infty}^{\infty} |c_n| < \infty,$$

and $f(e^{i\theta}) \neq 0$ *for every real* θ. *Then*

$$(2)\qquad \frac{1}{f(e^{i\theta})} = \sum_{-\infty}^{\infty} \gamma_n e^{in\theta} \qquad \textit{with} \qquad \sum_{-\infty}^{\infty} |\gamma_n| < \infty.$$

PROOF We let A be the space of all complex functions f on the unit circle which satisfy (1), with the norm

$$(3)\qquad \|f\| = \sum_{-\infty}^{\infty} |c_n|.$$

It is clear that A is a Banach space. In fact, A is isometrically isomorphic to ℓ^1, the space of all complex functions on the integers which are integrable with respect to the counting measure. But A is also a commutative Banach algebra, under pointwise multiplication. For if $g \in A$ and $g(e^{i\theta}) = \Sigma b_n e^{in\theta}$, then

$$(4)\qquad f(e^{i\theta})g(e^{i\theta}) = \sum_n \Big(\sum_k c_{n-k}b_k\Big) e^{in\theta}$$

and hence

$$(5)\qquad \|fg\| = \sum_n \Big|\sum_k c_{n-k}b_k\Big| \le \sum_k |b_k| \sum_n |c_{n-k}| = \|f\|\cdot\|g\|.$$

Also, the function 1 is the unit of A, and $\|1\| = 1$.

Put $f_0(e^{i\theta}) = e^{i\theta}$, as before. Then $f_0 \in A$, $1/f_0 \in A$, and $\|f_0^n\| = 1$ for $n = 0, \pm 1, \pm 2, \ldots$. If h is any complex homomorphism of A and $h(f_0) = \lambda$, the fact that $\|h\| \le 1$ implies that

$$(6)\quad |\lambda^n| = |h(f_0^n)| \le \|f_0^n\| = 1 \qquad (n = 0, \pm 1, \pm 2, \ldots).$$

Hence $|\lambda| = 1$. In other words, to each h there corresponds a point $e^{i\alpha} \in T$ such that $h(f_0) = e^{i\alpha}$, so

$$(7)\qquad h(f_0^n) = e^{in\alpha} = f_0^n(e^{i\alpha}) \qquad (n = 0, \pm 1, \pm 2, \ldots).$$

If f is given by (1), then $f = \Sigma c_n f_0^n$. This series converges in A; and since h is a continuous linear functional on A, we conclude from (7) that

$$h(f) = f(e^{i\alpha}) \qquad (f \in A). \tag{8}$$

Our hypothesis that f vanishes at no point of T therefore says that f is not in the kernel of any complex homomorphism of A, and now Theorem 18.17 implies that f is invertible in A. But this is precisely what the theorem asserts.

Exercises

1 Suppose $B(X)$ is the algebra of all bounded linear operators on the Banach space X, with

$$(A_1 + A_2)(x) = A_1x + A_2x, \quad (A_1A_2)(x) = A_1(A_2x), \quad \|A\| = \sup \frac{\|Ax\|}{\|x\|},$$

if A, A_1, and $A_2 \in B(X)$. Prove that $B(X)$ is a Banach algebra.

2 Let n be a positive integer, let X be the space of all complex n-tuples (normed in any way, as long as the axioms for a normed linear space are satisfied), and let $B(X)$ be as in Exercise 1. Prove that the spectrum of each member of $B(X)$ consists of at most n complex numbers. What are they?

3 Take $X = L^2(-\infty, \infty)$, suppose $\varphi \in L^\infty(-\infty, \infty)$, and let M be the multiplication operator which takes $f \in L^2$ to φf. Show that M is a bounded linear operator on L^2 and that the spectrum of M is equal to the essential range of φ (Chap. 3, Exercise 19).

4 What is the spectrum of the shift operator on ℓ^2? (See Theorem 17.20 for the definition.)

5 Prove that the closure of an ideal in a Banach algebra is an ideal.

6 If X is a compact Hausdorff space, find all maximal ideals in $C(X)$.

7 Suppose A is a commutative Banach algebra with unit, which is generated by a single element x. This means that the polynomials in x are dense in A. Prove that the complement of $\sigma(x)$ is a connected subset of the plane. *Hint:* If $\lambda \notin \sigma(x)$, there are polynomials P_n such that $P_n(x) \to (x - \lambda e)^{-1}$ in A. Prove that $P_n(z) \to (z - \lambda)^{-1}$ uniformly for $z \in \sigma(x)$.

8 Suppose $\sum_0^\infty |c_n| < \infty$, $f(z) = \sum_0^\infty c_n z^n$, $|f(z)| > 0$ for every $z \in \bar{U}$, and $1/f(z) = \sum_0^\infty a_n z^n$. Prove that $\sum_0^\infty |a_n| < \infty$.

9 Prove that a closed linear subspace of the Banach algebra $L^1(R^1)$ (see Sec. 9.19) is translation invariant if and only if it is an ideal.

10 Show that $L^1(T)$ is a commutative Banach algebra (without unit) if multiplication is defined by

$$(f * g)(t) = \frac{1}{2\pi} \int_{-\pi}^{\pi} f(t - s)g(s)\, ds.$$

Find all complex homomorphisms of $L^1(T)$, as in Theorem 9.23. If E is a set of integers and if I_E is the set of all $f \in L^1(T)$ such that $\hat{f}(n) = 0$ for all $n \in E$, prove that I_E is a closed ideal in $L^1(T)$, and prove that every closed ideal in $L^1(T)$ is obtained in this manner.

11 The *resolvent* $R(\lambda,x)$ of an element x in a Banach algebra with unit is defined as

$$R(\lambda,x) = (\lambda e - x)^{-1}$$

for all complex λ for which this inverse exists. Prove the identity

$$R(\lambda,x) - R(\mu,x) = (\mu - \lambda)R(\lambda)R(\mu)$$

and use it to give an alternative proof of Theorem 18.5.

12 Let A be a commutative Banach algebra with unit. The *radical* of A is defined to be the intersection of all maximal ideals of A. Prove that the following three statements about an element $x \in A$ are equivalent:

(*a*) x is in the radical of A.

(*b*) $\lim_{n \to \infty} \|x^n\|^{1/n} = 0$.

(*c*) $h(x) = 0$ for every complex homomorphism of A.

13 Find an element x in a Banach algebra A (for instance, a bounded linear operator on a Hilbert space) such that $x^n \neq 0$ for all $n > 0$, but $\lim_{n \to \infty} \|x^n\|^{1/n} = 0$.

14 Suppose A is a commutative Banach algebra with unit, and let Δ be the set of all complex homomorphisms of A, as in Sec. 18.16. Associate with each $x \in A$ a function $\hat{x}$ on Δ by the formula

$$\hat{x}(h) = h(x) \qquad (h \in \Delta).$$

$\hat{x}$ is called the Gelfand transform of x.

Prove that the mapping $x \to \hat{x}$ is a homomorphism of A onto an algebra $\hat{A}$ of complex functions on Δ, with pointwise multiplication. Under what condition on A is this homomorphism an isomorphism? (See Exercise 12.)

Prove that the spectral radius $\rho(x)$ is equal to

$$\|\hat{x}\|_\infty = \sup \{|\hat{x}(h)| : h \in \Delta\}.$$

Prove that the range of the function $\hat{x}$ is exactly the spectrum $\sigma(x)$.

15 If A is a commutative Banach algebra *without* unit, let A_1 be the algebra of all ordered pairs (x,λ), with $x \in A$ and λ a complex number; addition and multiplication are defined in the "obvious" way, and $\|(x,\lambda)\| = \|x\| + |\lambda|$. Prove that A_1 is a commutative Banach algebra with unit and that the mapping $x \to (x,0)$ is an isometric isomorphism of A onto a maximal ideal of A_1. This is a standard embedding of an algebra without unit in one with unit.

16 Show that H^∞ is a commutative Banach algebra with unit, relative to the supremum norm and pointwise addition and multiplication. The mapping $f \to f(\alpha)$ is a complex homomorphism of H^∞, whenever $|\alpha| < 1$. Prove that there must be others.

17 Show that the set of all functions $(z - 1)^2 f$, where $f \in H^\infty$, is an ideal in H^∞ which is not closed. *Hint:*

$$|(1 - z)^2(1 + \epsilon - z)^{-1} - (1 - z)| < \epsilon \qquad \text{if } |z| < 1, \epsilon > 0.$$

18 Suppose φ is an inner function. Prove that $\{\varphi f : f \in H^\infty\}$ is a closed ideal in H^∞. In other words, prove that if $\{f_n\}$ is a sequence in H^∞ such that $\varphi f_n \to g$ uniformly in U, then $g/\varphi \in H^\infty$.

19

Holomorphic Fourier Transforms

Introduction

19.1 In Chap. 9 the Fourier transform of a function f on R^1 was defined to be a function $\hat{f}$ on R^1. Frequently $\hat{f}$ can be extended to a function which is holomorphic in a certain region of the plane. For instance, if $f(t) = e^{-|t|}$, then $\hat{f}(x) = (1 + x^2)^{-1}$, a rational function. This should not be too surprising. For each real t, the kernel e^{itz} is an entire function of z, so one should expect that there are conditions on f under which $\hat{f}$ will be holomorphic in certain regions.

We shall describe two classes of holomorphic functions which arise in this manner.

For the first one, let F be any function in $L^2(-\infty, \infty)$ which vanishes on $(-\infty, 0)$ [i.e., take $F \in L^2(0, \infty)$] and define

$$f(z) = \int_0^\infty F(t)e^{itz}\, dt \qquad (z \in \Pi^+), \tag{1}$$

where Π^+ is the set of all $z = x + iy$ with $y > 0$. If $z \in \Pi^+$ then $|e^{itz}| = e^{-ty}$, which shows that the integral in (1) exists as a Lebesgue integral. The continuity of f in Π^+ is easily verified; and if γ is any closed path in Π^+ we can apply the theorems of Fubini and Morera to conclude that $f \in H(\Pi^+)$.

Let us rewrite (1) in the form

$$f(x + iy) = \int_0^\infty F(t)e^{-ty}e^{itx}\, dt, \tag{2}$$

regard y as fixed, and apply Plancherel's theorem. We obtain

$$\frac{1}{2\pi}\int_{-\infty}^{\infty} |f(x + iy)|^2\, dx = \int_0^\infty |F(t)|^2 e^{-2ty}\, dt \le \int_0^\infty |F(t)|^2\, dt \tag{3}$$

for every $y > 0$. [Note that our notation now differs from that in Chap. 9. There the underlying measure was Lebesgue measure divided by $\sqrt{2\pi}$. Here we just use Lebesgue measure. This accounts for the factor $1/(2\pi)$ in (3).] This shows:

(*a*) *If f is of the form* (1), *then f is holomorphic in Π^+ and its restrictions to horizontal lines in Π^+ form a bounded set in $L^2(-\infty, \infty)$.*

Our second class consists of all f of the form

$$f(z) = \int_{-A}^{A} F(t)e^{itz}\,dt \tag{4}$$

where $0 < A < \infty$ and $F \in L^2(-A,A)$. These functions f are entire (the proof is the same as above), and they satisfy a growth condition:

$$|f(z)| \le \int_{-A}^{A} |F(t)|e^{-ty}\,dt \le e^{A|y|} \int_{-A}^{A} |F(t)|\,dt. \tag{5}$$

If C is this last integral, then $C < \infty$, and (5) implies that

$$|f(z)| \le Ce^{A|z|}. \tag{6}$$

[Entire functions which satisfy (6) are said to be of *exponential type.*] Thus:

(*b*) *Every f of the form* (4) *is an entire function which satisfies* (6) *and whose restriction to the real axis lies in L^2* (by the Plancherel theorem).

It is a remarkable fact that the converses of (*a*) and (*b*) are true. This is the content of Theorems 19.2 and 19.3.

Two Theorems of Paley and Wiener

19.2 Theorem *Suppose $f \in H(\Pi^+)$ and*

$$\sup_{0<y<\infty} \frac{1}{2\pi} \int_{-\infty}^{\infty} |f(x + iy)|^2\,dx = C < \infty. \tag{1}$$

Then there exists an $F \in L^2(0, \infty)$ such that

$$f(z) = \int_{0}^{\infty} F(t)e^{itz}\,dt \qquad (z \in \Pi^+) \tag{2}$$

and

$$\int_{0}^{\infty} |F(t)|^2\,dt = C. \tag{3}$$

Note: The function F we are looking for is to have the property that $f(x + iy)$ is the Fourier transform of $F(t)e^{-yt}$ (we regard y as a positive constant). Let us apply the inversion formula (whether or not this is correct does not matter; we are trying to motivate the proof that follows): The desired F should be of the form

$$(4)\qquad F(t) = e^{ty} \cdot \frac{1}{2\pi} \int_{-\infty}^{\infty} f(x + iy)e^{-itx}\, dx = \frac{1}{2\pi} \int f(z)e^{-itz}\, dz.$$

The last integral is over a horizontal line in Π^+, and if this argument is correct at all, the integral will not depend on the particular line we happen to choose. This suggests that the Cauchy theorem should be invoked.

PROOF Fix y, $0 < y < \infty$. For each $\alpha > 0$ let Γ_α be the rectangular path with vertices at $\pm\alpha + i$ and $\pm\alpha + iy$. By Cauchy's theorem

$$(5)\qquad \int_{\Gamma_\alpha} f(z)e^{-itz}\, dz = 0.$$

We consider only real values of t. Let $\Phi(\beta)$ be the integral of $f(z)e^{-itz}$ over the straight line interval from $\beta + i$ to $\beta + iy$ (β real). Put $I = [y,1]$ if $y < 1$, $I = [1,y]$ if $1 < y$. Then

$$(6)\qquad |\Phi(\beta)|^2 = \left| \int_I f(\beta + iu)e^{-it(\beta+iu)}\, du \right|^2 \leq \int_I |f(\beta + iu)|^2\, du \int_I e^{2tu}\, du.$$

Put

$$(7)\qquad \Lambda(\beta) = \int_I |f(\beta + iu)|^2\, du.$$

Then (1) shows, by Fubini's theorem, that

$$(8)\qquad \frac{1}{2\pi} \int_{-\infty}^{\infty} \Lambda(\beta)\, d\beta \leq Cm(I).$$

Hence there is a sequence $\{\alpha_j\}$ such that $\alpha_j \to \infty$ and

$$(9)\qquad \Lambda(\alpha_j) + \Lambda(-\alpha_j) \to 0 \qquad (j \to \infty).$$

By (6), this implies that

$$(10)\qquad \Phi(\alpha_j) \to 0, \qquad \Phi(-\alpha_j) \to 0 \qquad \text{as } j \to \infty.$$

Note that this holds for every t and that the sequence $\{\alpha_j\}$ does not depend on t.

Let us define

$$(11)\qquad g_j(y,t) = \frac{1}{2\pi} \int_{-\alpha_j}^{\alpha_j} f(x + iy)e^{-itx}\, dx.$$

Then we deduce from (5) and (10) that

$$(12)\qquad \lim_{j\to\infty} [e^{ty}g_j(y,t) - e^{t}g_j(1,t)] = 0 \qquad (-\infty < t < \infty).$$

Write $f_y(x)$ for $f(x+iy)$. Then $f_y \in L^2(-\infty,\infty)$, by hypothesis, and the Plancherel theorem asserts that

$$(13) \qquad \lim_{j\to\infty} \int_{-\infty}^{\infty} |\hat{f}_y(t) - g_j(y,t)|^2\,dt = 0,$$

where $\hat{f}_y$ is the Fourier transform of f_y. A subsequence of $\{g_j(y,t)\}$ therefore converges pointwise to $\hat{f}_y(t)$, for almost all t (Theorem 3.12). If we define

$$(14) \qquad F(t) = e^t \hat{f}_1(t)$$

it now follows from (12) that

$$(15) \qquad F(t) = e^{ty}\hat{f}_y(t).$$

Note that (14) does not involve y and that (15) holds for every $y \in (0,\infty)$. Plancherel's theorem can be applied to (15):

$$(16) \quad \int_{-\infty}^{\infty} e^{-2ty}|F(t)|^2\,dt = \int_{-\infty}^{\infty} |\hat{f}_y(t)|^2\,dt = \frac{1}{2\pi}\int_{-\infty}^{\infty} |f_y(x)|^2\,dx \le C.$$

If we let $y \to \infty$, (16) shows that $F(t) = 0$ a.e. in $(-\infty,0)$. If we let $y \to 0$, (16) shows that

$$(17) \qquad \int_0^{\infty} |F(t)|^2\,dt \le C.$$

It now follows from (15) that $\hat{f}_y \in L^1$ if $y > 0$. Hence Theorem 9.14 gives

$$(18) \qquad f_y(x) = \int_{-\infty}^{\infty} \hat{f}_y(t)e^{itx}\,dt$$

or

$$(19) \quad f(z) = \int_0^{\infty} F(t)e^{-yt}e^{itx}\,dt = \int_0^{\infty} F(t)e^{itz}\,dt \qquad (z \in \Pi^+).$$

This is (2), and now (3) follows from (17) and formula 19.1(3).

19.3 Theorem *Suppose A and C are positive constants and f is an entire function such that*

$$(1) \qquad |f(z)| \le Ce^{A|z|}$$

for all z, and

$$(2) \qquad \int_{-\infty}^{\infty} |f(x)|^2\,dx < \infty.$$

Then there exists an $F \in L^2(-A,A)$ such that

$$(3) \qquad f(z) = \int_{-A}^{A} F(t)e^{itz}\,dt.$$

PROOF Put $f_\epsilon(x) = f(x)e^{-\epsilon|x|}$, for $\epsilon > 0$ and x real. We shall show that

$$(4) \qquad \lim_{\epsilon\to 0} \int_{-\infty}^{\infty} f_\epsilon(x)e^{-itx}\,dx = 0 \qquad (t \text{ real}, |t| > A).$$

Since $\|f_\epsilon - f\|_2 \to 0$ as $\epsilon \to 0$, the Plancherel theorem implies that the Fourier transforms of f_ϵ converge in L^2 to the Fourier transform F of f (more precisely, of the restriction of f to the real axis). Hence (4) will imply that F vanishes outside $[-A,A]$, and then Theorem 9.14 shows that (3) holds for almost every real z. Since each side of (3) is an entire function, it follows that (3) holds for every complex z. Thus (4) implies the theorem.

For each real α, let Γ_α be the path defined by

$$(5) \qquad \Gamma_\alpha(s) = se^{i\alpha}, \qquad 0 \le s < \infty,$$

put

$$(6) \qquad \Pi_\alpha = \{w\colon \text{Re}\,(we^{i\alpha}) > A\},$$

and if $w \in \Pi_\alpha$, define

$$(7) \quad \Phi_\alpha(w) = \int_{\Gamma_\alpha} f(z)e^{-wz}\,dz = e^{i\alpha}\int_0^\infty f(se^{i\alpha})\exp\,(-wse^{i\alpha})\,ds.$$

By (1) and (5), the absolute value of the integrand is at most

$$C\exp\,\{-[\text{Re}\,(we^{i\alpha}) - A]s\},$$

and it follows (as in Sec. 19.1) that Φ_α is holomorphic in the half plane Π_α.

However, more is true if $\alpha = 0$ and if $\alpha = \pi$: We have

$$(8) \qquad \Phi_0(w) = \int_0^\infty f(x)e^{-wx}\,dx \qquad (\text{Re}\,w > 0),$$

$$(9) \qquad \Phi_\pi(w) = -\int_{-\infty}^0 f(x)e^{-wx}\,dx \qquad (\text{Re}\,w < 0).$$

Φ_0 and Φ_π are holomorphic in the indicated half planes because of (2).

The significance of the functions Φ_α to (4) lies in the easily verified relation

$$(10) \quad \int_{-\infty}^{\infty} f_\epsilon(x)e^{-itx}\,dx = \Phi_0(\epsilon + it) - \Phi_\pi(-\epsilon + it) \qquad (t \text{ real}).$$

Hence we have to prove that the right side of (10) tends to 0 as $\epsilon \to 0$, if $t > A$ and if $t < -A$.

We shall do this by showing that any two of our functions Φ_α agree in the intersection of their domains of definition, i.e., that they are analytic continuations of each other. Once this is done, we can replace Φ_0 and Φ_π by $\Phi_{\pi/2}$ in (10) if $t < -A$, and by $\Phi_{-\pi/2}$ if $t > A$, and it is then obvious that the difference tends to 0 as $\epsilon \to 0$.

So suppose $0 < \beta - \alpha < \pi$. Put

$$\gamma = \frac{\alpha + \beta}{2}, \qquad \eta = \cos \frac{\beta - \alpha}{2} > 0. \tag{11}$$

If $w = |w|e^{-i\gamma}$, then

$$\text{Re}\,(we^{i\alpha}) = \eta|w| = \text{Re}\,(we^{i\beta}) \tag{12}$$

so that $w \in \Pi_\alpha \cap \Pi_\beta$ as soon as $|w| > A/\eta$. Consider the integral

$$\int_\Gamma f(z)e^{-wz}\,dz \tag{13}$$

over the circular arc Γ given by $\Gamma(t) = re^{it}$, $\alpha \le t \le \beta$. Since

$$\text{Re}\,(-wz) = -|w|r\cos(t - \gamma) \le -|w|r\eta, \tag{14}$$

the absolute value of the integrand in (13) does not exceed

$$C \exp\{(A - |w|\eta)r\}.$$

If $|w| > A/\eta$ it follows that (13) tends to 0 as $r \to \infty$.

We now apply the Cauchy theorem. The integral of $f(z)e^{-wz}$ over the interval $[0,re^{i\beta}]$ is equal to the sum of (13) and the integral over $[0,re^{i\alpha}]$. Since (13) tends to 0 as $r \to \infty$, we conclude that $\Phi_\alpha(w) = \Phi_\beta(w)$ if $w = |w|e^{-i\gamma}$ and $|w| > A/\eta$, and then Theorem 10.18 shows that Φ_α and Φ_β coincide in the intersection of the half planes in which they were originally defined.

This completes the proof.

19.4 Remarks Each of the two preceding proofs depended on a typical application of Cauchy's theorem. In Theorem 19.2 we replaced integration over one horizontal line by integration over another to show that 19.2(15) was independent of y. In Theorem 19.3, replacement of one ray by another was used to construct analytic continuations; the result actually was that the functions Φ_α are restrictions of one function Φ which is holomorphic in the complement of the interval $[-Ai,Ai]$.

The class of functions described in Theorem 19.2 is the half plane analogue of the class H^2 discussed in Chap. 17. Theorem 19.3 will be used in the proof of the Denjoy-Carleman theorem (Theorem 19.11).

Quasi-analytic Classes

19.5 If Ω is a region and if $z_0 \in \Omega$, every $f \in H(\Omega)$ is uniquely determined by the numbers $f(z_0), f'(z_0), f''(z_0), \ldots$ On the other hand, there exist infinitely differentiable functions on R^1 which are not identically 0 but which vanish on some interval. Thus we have here a uniqueness property which holomorphic functions possess but which does not hold in C^∞ (the class of all infinitely differentiable complex functions on R^1).

If $f \in H(\Omega)$, the growth of the sequence $\{|f^{(n)}(z_0)|\}$ is restricted by Theorem 10.25. It is therefore reasonable to ask whether the above uniqueness property holds in suitable subclasses of C^∞ in which the growth of the derivatives is subject to some restrictions. This motivates the following definitions; the answer to our question is given by Theorem 19.11.

19.6 The Classes $C\{M_n\}$ If $M_0, M_1, M_2, \ldots$ are positive numbers, we let $C\{M_n\}$ be the class of all $f \in C^\infty$ which satisfy inequalities of the form

$$\|D^n f\|_\infty \le \beta_f B_f^n M_n \qquad (n = 0, 1, 2, \ldots). \tag{1}$$

Here $D^0 f = f$, $D^n f$ is the nth derivative of f if $n \ge 1$, the norm is the supremum norm over R^1, and β_f and B_f are positive constants (depending on f, but not on n).

If f satisfies (1), then

$$\limsup_{n\to\infty} \left\{\frac{\|D^n f\|_\infty}{M_n}\right\}^{1/n} \le B_f. \tag{2}$$

This shows that B_f is a more significant quantity than β_f. However, if β_f were omitted in (1), the case $n = 0$ would imply $\|f\|_\infty \le M_0$, an undesirable restriction. The inclusion of β_f makes $C\{M_n\}$ into a vector space.

Each $C\{M_n\}$ is invariant under affine transformations. More explicitly, suppose $f \in C\{M_n\}$ and $g(x) = f(ax + b)$. Then g satisfies (1), with $\beta_g = \beta_f$ and $B_g = aB_f$.

We shall make two standing assumptions on the sequences $\{M_n\}$ under consideration:

$$M_0 = 1. \tag{3}$$

$$M_n^2 \le M_{n-1}M_{n+1} \qquad (n = 1, 2, 3, \ldots). \tag{4}$$

Assumption (4) can be expressed in the form: *$\{\log M_n\}$ is a convex sequence.*

These assumptions will simplify some of our work, and they involve no loss of generality. [One can prove, although we shall not do so, that every class $C\{M_n\}$ is equal to a class $C\{\bar{M}_n\}$, where $\{\bar{M}_n\}$ satisfies (3) and (4).]

The following result illustrates the utility of (3) and (4):

19.7 Theorem *Each $C\{M_n\}$ is an algebra, with respect to pointwise multiplication.*

PROOF Suppose f and $g \in C\{M_n\}$, and β_f, B_f, β_g, and B_g are the corresponding constants. The product rule for differentiation shows that

$$(1) \qquad D^n(fg) = \sum_{j=0}^{n} \binom{n}{j} (D^j f) \cdot (D^{n-j} g).$$

Hence

$$(2) \qquad |D^n(fg)| \le \beta_f \beta_g \sum_{j=0}^{n} \binom{n}{j} B_f^j B_g^{n-j} M_j M_{n-j}.$$

The convexity of $\{\log M_n\}$, combined with $M_0 = 1$, shows that $M_j M_{n-j} \le M_n$ for $0 \le j \le n$. Hence the binomial theorem leads from (2) to

$$(3) \quad \|D^n(fg)\|_\infty \le \beta_f \beta_g (B_f + B_g)^n M_n \qquad (n = 0, 1, 2, \ldots),$$

so that $fg \in C\{M_n\}$.

19.8 Definition A class $C\{M_n\}$ is said to be *quasi-analytic* if the conditions

$$(1) \qquad f \in C\{M_n\}, \qquad (D^n f)(0) = 0 \qquad \text{for } n = 0, 1, 2, \ldots$$

imply that $f(x) = 0$ for all $x \in R^1$.

The content of the definition is of course unchanged if $(D^n f)(0)$ is replaced by $(D^n f)(x_0)$, where x_0 is any given point.

The quasi-analytic classes are thus the ones which have the uniqueness property we mentioned in Sec. 19.5. One of these classes is very intimately related to holomorphic functions:

19.9 Theorem *The class $C\{n!\}$ consists of all f to which there corresponds a $\delta > 0$ such that f can be extended to a bounded holomorphic function in the strip defined by $|\mathrm{Im}\,(z)| < \delta$.*

Consequently $C\{n!\}$ is a quasi-analytic class.

PROOF Suppose $f \in H(\Omega)$ and $|f(z)| < \beta$ for all $z \in \Omega$, where Ω consists of all $z = x + iy$ with $|y| < \delta$. It follows from Theorem 10.25 that

$$(1) \qquad |(D^n f)(x)| \le \beta \delta^{-n} n! \qquad (n = 0, 1, 2, \ldots)$$

for all real x. The restriction of f to the real axis therefore belongs to $C\{n!\}$.

Conversely, suppose f is defined on the real axis and $f \in C\{n!\}$. In other words,

$$(2) \qquad \|D^n f\|_\infty \le \beta B^n n! \qquad (n = 0, 1, 2, \ldots).$$

We claim that the representation

$$f(x) = \sum_{n=0}^{\infty} \frac{(D^n f)(a)}{n!} (x - a)^n \tag{3}$$

is valid for all $a \in R^1$ if $a - B^{-1} < x < a + B^{-1}$. This follows from Taylor's formula

$$f(x) = \sum_{j=0}^{n-1} \frac{(D^j f)(a)}{j!} (x - a)^j + \frac{1}{(n-1)!} \int_a^x (x - t)^{n-1} (D^n f)(t)\, dt, \tag{4}$$

which one obtains by repeated integrations by part. By (2) the last term in (4) (the "remainder") is dominated by

$$n\beta B^n \left| \int_a^x (x - t)^{n-1}\, dt \right| = \beta |B(x - a)|^n. \tag{5}$$

If $|B(x - a)| < 1$, this tends to 0 as $n \to \infty$, and (3) follows.

We can now replace x in (3) by any complex number z such that $|z - a| < 1/B$. This defines a holomorphic function F_a in the disc with center at a and radius $1/B$, and $F_a(x) = f(x)$ if x is real and $|x - a| < 1/B$. The various functions F_a are therefore analytic continuations of each other; they form a holomorphic extension F of f in the strip $|y| < 1/B$.

If $0 < \delta < 1/B$ and $z = a + iy$, $|y| < \delta$, then

$$|F(z)| = |F_a(z)| = \left| \sum_{n=0}^{\infty} \frac{(D^n f)(a)}{n!} (iy)^n \right| \leq \beta \sum_{n=0}^{\infty} (B\delta)^n = \frac{\beta}{1 - B\delta}.$$

This shows that F is bounded in the strip $|y| < \delta$, and the proof is complete.

19.10 Theorem *The class $C\{M_n\}$ is quasi-analytic if and only if $C\{M_n\}$ contains no nontrivial function with compact support.*

PROOF If $C\{M_n\}$ is quasi-analytic, if $f \in C\{M_n\}$, and if f has compact support, then evidently f and all its derivatives vanish at some point, hence $f(x) = 0$ for all x.

Suppose $C\{M_n\}$ is not quasi-analytic. Then there exists an $f \in C\{M_n\}$ such that $(D^n f)(0) = 0$ for $n = 0, 1, 2, \ldots$, but $f(x_0) \neq 0$ for some x_0. We may assume $x_0 > 0$. If $g(x) = f(x)$ for $x \geq 0$ and $g(x) = 0$ for $x < 0$, then $g \in C\{M_n\}$. Put $h(x) = g(x)g(2x_0 - x)$. By Theorem 19.7, $h \in C\{M_n\}$. Also, $h(x) = 0$ if $x < 0$ and if $x > 2x_0$. But $h(x_0) = f^2(x_0) \neq 0$. Thus h is a nontrivial member of $C\{M_n\}$ with compact support.

We are now ready for the fundamental theorem about quasi-analytic classes.

The Denjoy-Carleman Theorem

19.11 Theorem *Suppose* $M_0 = 1$, $M_n^2 \leq M_{n-1}M_{n+1}$ *for* $n = 1, 2, 3, \ldots,$ *and*

$$Q(x) = \sum_{n=0}^{\infty} \frac{x^n}{M_n}, \qquad q(x) = \sup_{n \geq 0} \frac{x^n}{M_n},$$

for $x > 0$. *Then each of the following five conditions implies the other four:*

(*a*) $C\{M_n\}$ *is not quasi-analytic.*

(*b*) $\displaystyle\int_0^\infty \log Q(x) \frac{dx}{1 + x^2} < \infty.$

(*c*) $\displaystyle\int_0^\infty \log q(x) \frac{dx}{1 + x^2} < \infty.$

(*d*) $\displaystyle\sum_{n=1}^{\infty} \left(\frac{1}{M_n}\right)^{1/n} < \infty.$

(*e*) $\displaystyle\sum_{n=1}^{\infty} \frac{M_{n-1}}{M_n} < \infty.$

Note: If $M_n \to \infty$ very rapidly as $n \to \infty$, then $Q(x)$ tends to infinity slowly as $x \to \infty$. Thus each of the five conditions says, in its own way, that $M_n \to \infty$ rapidly. Note also that $Q(x) \geq 1$ and $q(x) \geq 1$. The integrals in (*b*) and (*c*) are thus always defined. It may happen that $Q(x) = \infty$ for some $x < \infty$. In that case, the integral (*b*) is $+\infty$, and the theorem asserts that $C\{M_n\}$ is quasi-analytic.

If $M_n = n!$, then $M_{n-1}/M_n = 1/n$, hence (*e*) is violated, and the theorem asserts that $C\{n!\}$ is quasi-analytic, in accordance with Theorem 19.9.

PROOF THAT (*a*) IMPLIES (*b*) Assume that $C\{M_n\}$ is not quasi-analytic. Then $C\{M_n\}$ contains a nontrivial function with compact support (Theorem 19.10). An affine change of variable gives a function $F \in C\{M_n\}$, with support in some interval $[0,A]$, such that

$$\|D^nF\|_\infty \leq 2^{-n}M_n \qquad (n = 0, 1, 2, \ldots) \tag{1}$$

and such that F is not identically zero. Define

$$f(z) = \int_0^A F(t)e^{itz}\, dt \tag{2}$$

and

$$(3) \qquad g(w) = f\left(\frac{i - iw}{1 + w}\right).$$

Then f is entire. If $\text{Im } z > 0$, the absolute value of the integrand in (2) is at most $|F(t)|$. Hence f is bounded in the upper half plane, therefore g is bounded in U. Also, g is continuous on $\bar{U}$, except at the point $w = -1$. Since f is not identically 0 (by the uniqueness theorem for Fourier transforms) the same is true of g, and now Theorem 15.19 shows that

$$(4) \qquad \frac{1}{2\pi} \int_{-\pi}^{\pi} \log |g(e^{i\theta})| \, d\theta > -\infty.$$

If $x = i(1 - e^{i\theta})/(1 + e^{i\theta}) = 2 \tan (\theta/2)$, then $d\theta = 2(1 + x^2)^{-1} \, dx$, so (4) is the same as

$$(5) \qquad \frac{1}{\pi} \int_{-\infty}^{\infty} \log |f(x)| \frac{dx}{1 + x^2} > -\infty.$$

On the other hand, partial integration of (2) gives

$$(6) \qquad f(z) = (iz)^{-n} \int_0^A (D^nF)(t) e^{itz} \, dt \qquad (z \neq 0)$$

since F and all its derivatives vanish at 0 and at A. It now follows from (1) and (6) that

$$(7) \qquad |x^n f(x)| \leq 2^{-n} A M_n \qquad (x \text{ real}, n = 0, 1, 2, \ldots).$$

Hence

$$(8) \qquad Q(x)|f(x)| = \sum_{n=0}^{\infty} \frac{x^n |f(x)|}{M_n} \leq 2A \qquad (x \geq 0),$$

and (5) and (8) imply that (*b*) holds.

PROOF THAT (*b*) IMPLIES (*c*) $\quad q(x) \leq Q(x)$.

PROOF THAT (*c*) IMPLIES (*d*) $\quad$ Put $a_n = M_n^{1/n}$. Since $M_0 = 1$ and $M_n^2 \leq M_{n-1} M_{n+1}$ it is easily verified that $a_n \leq a_{n+1}$, for $n > 0$. If $x \geq e a_n$, then $x^n/M_n \geq e^n$, so

$$(9) \qquad \log q(x) \geq \log \frac{x^n}{M_n} \geq \log e^n = n.$$

Hence

$$(10)\quad e\int_{ea_1}^{\infty} \log q(x)\cdot\frac{dx}{x^2} \geq e\sum_{n=1}^{N} n\int_{ea_n}^{ea_{n+1}} x^{-2}\,dx + e\int_{ea_{N+1}}^{\infty} (N+1)x^{-2}\,dx$$

$$= \sum_{n=1}^{N} n\left(\frac{1}{a_n} - \frac{1}{a_{n+1}}\right) + \frac{N+1}{a_{N+1}} = \sum_{n=1}^{N+1} \frac{1}{a_n}$$

for every N. This shows that (*c*) implies (*d*).

PROOF THAT (*d*) IMPLIES (*e*) Put

$$(11)\qquad \lambda_n = \frac{M_{n-1}}{M_n} \qquad (n = 1, 2, 3, \ldots).$$

Then $\lambda_1 \geq \lambda_2 \geq \lambda_3 \geq \cdots$, and if $a_n = M_n^{1/n}$, as above, we have

$$(12)\qquad (a_n\lambda_n)^n \leq M_n\cdot\lambda_1\lambda_2\cdots\lambda_n = 1.$$

Thus $\lambda_n \leq 1/a_n$, and the convergence of $\Sigma(1/a_n)$ implies that of $\Sigma\lambda_n$.

PROOF THAT (*e*) IMPLIES (*a*) The assumption now is that $\Sigma\lambda_n < \infty$, where λ_n is given by (11). We claim that the function

$$(13)\qquad f(z) = \left(\frac{\sin z}{z}\right)^2 \prod_{n=1}^{\infty} \frac{\sin\lambda_n z}{\lambda_n z}$$

is an entire function of exponential type, not identically zero, which satisfies the inequalities

$$(14)\quad |x^k f(x)| \leq M_k\left(\frac{\sin x}{x}\right)^2 \qquad (x \text{ real}, k = 0, 1, 2, \ldots).$$

Note first that $1 - z^{-1}\sin z$ has a zero at the origin. Hence there is a constant B such that

$$(15)\qquad \left|1 - \frac{\sin z}{z}\right| \leq B|z| \qquad (|z| \leq 1).$$

It follows that

$$(16)\qquad \left|1 - \frac{\sin\lambda_n z}{\lambda_n z}\right| \leq B\lambda_n|z| \qquad \left(|z| \leq \frac{1}{\lambda_n}\right),$$

so that the series

$$(17)\qquad \sum_{n=1}^{\infty}\left|1 - \frac{\sin\lambda_n z}{\lambda_n z}\right|$$

converges uniformly on compact sets. (Note that $1/\lambda_n \to \infty$ as $n \to \infty$, since $\Sigma\lambda_n < \infty$.) The infinite product (13) therefore defines an entire function f which is not identically zero.

Next, the identity

$$\text{(18)} \qquad \frac{\sin z}{z} = \frac{1}{2}\int_{-1}^{1} e^{itz}\,dt$$

shows that $|z^{-1}\sin z| \le e^{|y|}$ if $z = x + iy$. Hence

$$\text{(19)} \qquad |f(z)| \le e^{A|z|}, \qquad \text{with } A = 2 + \sum_{n=1}^{\infty} \lambda_n.$$

For real x, we have $|\sin x| \le |x|$ and $|\sin x| \le 1$. Hence

$$\text{(20)} \qquad |x^k f(x)| \le |x^k| \left(\frac{\sin x}{x}\right)^2 \prod_{n=1}^{k} \left|\frac{\sin \lambda_n x}{\lambda_n x}\right|$$
$$\le \left(\frac{\sin x}{x}\right)^2 (\lambda_1 \cdots \lambda_k)^{-1} = M_k \left(\frac{\sin x}{x}\right)^2.$$

This gives (14), and if we integrate (14) we obtain

$$\text{(21)} \qquad \frac{1}{\pi}\int_{-\infty}^{\infty} |x^k f(x)|\,dx \le M_k \qquad (k = 0, 1, 2, \ldots).$$

We have proved that f satisfies the hypotheses of Theorem 19.3. The Fourier transform of f,

$$\text{(22)} \qquad F(t) = \frac{1}{2\pi}\int_{-\infty}^{\infty} f(x)e^{-itx}\,dx \qquad (t \text{ real})$$

is therefore a function with compact support, not identically zero, and (21) shows that $F \in C^\infty$ and that

$$\text{(23)} \qquad (D^k F)(t) = \frac{1}{2\pi}\int_{-\infty}^{\infty} (-ix)^k f(x)e^{-itx}\,dx,$$

by repeated application of Theorem 9.2(f). Hence $\|D^k F\|_\infty \le M_k$, by (21), which shows that $F \in C\{M_n\}$.

Hence $C\{M_n\}$ is not quasi-analytic, and the proof is complete.

Exercises

1 Suppose f is an entire function of exponential type and

$$\varphi(y) = \int_{-\infty}^{\infty} |f(x + iy)|^2\,dx.$$

Prove that either $\varphi(y) = \infty$ for all real y or $\varphi(y) < \infty$ for all real y. Prove that $f = 0$ if φ is a bounded function.

2 Suppose f is an entire function of exponential type such that the restriction of f to two nonparallel lines belongs to L^2. Prove that $f = 0$.

3 Suppose f is an entire function of exponential type whose restriction to two nonparallel lines is bounded. Prove that f is constant. (Apply Exercise 6 of Chap. 12.)

4 Suppose f is entire, $|f(z)| < C \exp(A|z|)$, and $f(z) = \Sigma a_n z^n$. Put

$$\Phi(w) = \sum_{n=0}^{\infty} \frac{n! a_n}{w^{n+1}}.$$

Prove that the series converges if $|w| > A$, that

$$f(z) = \frac{1}{2\pi i} \int_\Gamma \Phi(w) e^{wz}\, dw$$

if $\Gamma(t) = (A + \epsilon)e^{it}$, $0 \le t \le 2\pi$, and that Φ is the function which occurred in the proof of Theorem 19.3. (See also Sec. 19.4.)

5 Suppose f satisfies the hypothesis of Theorem 19.2. Prove that the Cauchy formula

$$(*) \qquad f(z) = \frac{1}{2\pi i} \int_{-\infty}^{\infty} \frac{f(\xi + i\epsilon)}{\xi + i\epsilon - z}\, d\xi \qquad (0 < \epsilon < y)$$

holds; here $z = x + iy$. Prove that

$$f^*(x) = \lim_{y \to 0} f(x + iy)$$

exists for almost all x. What is the relation between f^* and the function F which occurs in Theorem 19.2? Is $(*)$ true with $\epsilon = 0$ and with f^* in place of f in the integrand?

6 Suppose $\varphi \in L^2(-\infty, \infty)$ and $\varphi > 0$. Prove that there exists an f with $|f| = \varphi$ such that the Fourier transform of f vanishes on a half line if and only if

$$\int_{-\infty}^{\infty} \log \varphi(x) \frac{dx}{1 + x^2} > -\infty.$$

Suggestion: Consider f^*, as in Exercise 5, where $f = \exp(u + iv)$ and

$$u(z) = \frac{1}{\pi} \int_{-\infty}^{\infty} \frac{y}{(x - t)^2 + y^2} \log \varphi(t)\, dt.$$

7 Let f be a complex function on a closed set E in the plane. Prove that the following two conditions on f are equivalent:

(*a*) There is an open set $\Omega \supset E$ and a function $F \in H(\Omega)$ such that $F(z) = f(z)$ for $z \in E$.

(b) To each $\alpha \in E$ there corresponds a neighborhood V_α of α and a function $F_\alpha \in H(V_\alpha)$ such that $F_\alpha(z) = f(z)$ in $V_\alpha \cap E$.

(A special case of this was proved in Theorem 19.9.)

8 Prove that $C\{n!\} = C\{n^n\}$.

9 Prove that there are quasi-analytic classes which are larger than $C\{n!\}$.

10 Put $\lambda_n = M_{n-1}/M_n$, as in the proof of Theorem 19.11. Pick $g_0 \in C_c(R^1)$, and define

$$g_n(x) = (2\lambda_n)^{-1} \int_{-\lambda_n}^{\lambda_n} g_{n-1}(x - t)\, dt \qquad (n = 1, 2, 3, \ldots).$$

Prove directly (without using Fourier transforms or holomorphic functions) that $g = \lim g_n$ is a function which demonstrates that (e) implies (a) in Theorem 19.11. (You may choose any g_0 that is convenient.)

11 Find an explicit formula for a function $\varphi \in C^\infty$, with support in $[-2,2]$, such that $\varphi(x) = 1$ if $-1 \le x \le 1$.

12 Prove that to every sequence $\{\alpha_n\}$ of complex numbers there corresponds a function $f \in C^\infty$ such that $(D^n f)(0) = \alpha_n$ for $n = 0, 1, 2, \ldots$. *Suggestion:* If φ is as in Exercise 11, if $\beta_n = \alpha_n/n!$, if $g_n(x) = \beta_n x^n \varphi(x)$, and if

$$f_n(x) = \lambda_n^{-n} g_n(\lambda_n x) = \beta_n x^n \varphi(\lambda_n x),$$

then $\|D^k f_n\|_\infty < 2^{-n}$ for $k = 0, \ldots, n - 1$, provided that λ_n is large enough. Take $f = \Sigma f_n$.

13 Construct a function $f \in C^\infty$ such that the power series

$$\sum_{n=0}^{\infty} \frac{(D^n f)(a)}{n!} (x - a)^n$$

has radius of convergence 0 for every $a \in R^1$. *Suggestion:* Put

$$f(x) = \sum_{k=1}^{\infty} c_k e^{i\lambda_k x},$$

where $\{c_k\}$ and $\{\lambda_k\}$ are sequences of positive numbers, chosen so that $\Sigma c_k \lambda_k^n < \infty$ for $n = 0, 1, 2, \ldots$ and so that $c_n \lambda_n^n$ increases very rapidly and is much larger than the sum of all the other terms in the series $\Sigma c_k \lambda_k^n$.

For instance, put $c_k = \lambda_k^{1-k}$, and choose $\{\lambda_k\}$ so that

$$\lambda_k > 2 \sum_{j=1}^{k-1} c_j \lambda_j^k \qquad \text{and} \qquad \lambda_k > k^{2k}.$$

14 Suppose $C\{M_n\}$ is quasi-analytic, $f \in C\{M_n\}$, and $f(x) = 0$ for infinitely many $x \in [0,1]$. What follows?

20

Uniform Approximation by Polynomials

Introduction

20.1 Let K^0 be the interior of a compact set K in the complex plane. (By definition, K^0 is the union of all open discs which are subsets of K; of course, K^0 may be empty although K is not.) Let $P(K)$ denote the set of all functions on K which are uniform limits of polynomials in z.

Which functions belong to $P(K)$?

Two necessary conditions come to mind immediately: If $f \in P(K)$, then $f \in C(K)$ and $f \in H(K^0)$.

The question arises whether these necessary conditions are also sufficient. The answer is negative whenever K separates the plane (i.e., when the complement of K is not connected). We saw this in Sec. 13.8. On the other hand, if K is an interval on the real axis (in which case $K^0 = \emptyset$), the Weierstrass approximation theorem asserts that

$$P(K) = C(K).$$

So the answer is positive if K is an interval. Runge's theorem also points in this direction, since it states, for compact sets K which do not separate the plane, that $P(K)$ contains at least all those $f \in C(K)$ which have holomorphic extensions to some open set $\Omega \supset K$.

In this chapter we shall prove the theorem of Mergelyan which states, without any superfluous hypotheses, that the above-mentioned necessary conditions are also sufficient if K does not separate the plane.

The principal ingredients of the proof are: Tietze's extension theorem, a smoothing process involving convolutions, Runge's theorem, and Lemma 20.2, whose proof depends on properties of the class $\mathcal{S}$ which was introduced in Chap. 14.

Some Lemmas

20.2 Lemma *Suppose D is an open disc of radius $r > 0$, $E \subset D$, E is compact and connected, $\Omega = S^2 - E$ is connected, and the diameter of E is at least r. Then there is a function $g \in H(\Omega)$ and a constant b, with the following property: If*

$$Q(\zeta,z) = g(z) + (\zeta - b)g^2(z), \tag{1}$$

the inequalities

$$|Q(\zeta,z)| < \frac{100}{r} \tag{2}$$

$$\left| Q(\zeta,z) - \frac{1}{z-\zeta} \right| < \frac{1{,}000r^2}{|z-\zeta|^3} \tag{3}$$

hold for all $z \in \Omega$ and for all $\zeta \in D$.

We recall that S^2 is the Riemann sphere and that the diameter of E is the supremum of the numbers $|z_1 - z_2|$, where $z_1 \in E$ and $z_2 \in E$.

PROOF We assume, without loss of generality, that the center of D is at the origin. So $D = D(0;r)$.

The implication (c) $\rightarrow$ (b) of Theorem 13.18 shows that Ω is simply connected. (Note that $\infty \in \Omega$.) By the Riemann mapping theorem there is therefore a conformal mapping F of U onto Ω such that $F(0) = \infty$. F has an expansion of the form

$$F(w) = \frac{a}{w} + \sum_{n=0}^{\infty} c_n w^n \qquad (w \in U). \tag{4}$$

We define

$$g(z) = \frac{1}{a} F^{-1}(z) \qquad (z \in \Omega), \tag{5}$$

where F^{-1} is the mapping of Ω onto U which inverts F, and we put

$$b = \frac{1}{2\pi i} \int_\Gamma zg(z)\,dz, \tag{6}$$

where Γ is the positively oriented circle with center 0 and radius r.

Choose $c \in E$. Then $F - c$ has no zero in U. By (4), $a/(F - c) \in \mathcal{S}$ (see Definition 14.10), so Theorem 14.15 asserts that the diameter of the complement of $(F/a)(U)$ is at most 4. So diam $E \le 4\,|a|$. Since diam $E \ge r$, it follows that

$$|a| \ge \frac{r}{4}. \tag{7}$$

Since g is a conformal mapping of Ω onto $D(0;1/|a|)$, (7) shows that

(8) $$|g(z)| < \frac{4}{r} \qquad (z \in \Omega)$$

and since Γ is a path in Ω, of length $2\pi r$, (6) gives

(9) $$|b| < 4r.$$

If $\zeta \in D$, then $|\zeta| < r$, so (1), (8), and (9) imply

(10) $$|Q| \le \frac{4}{r} + 5r\left(\frac{16}{r^2}\right) < \frac{100}{r}.$$

This proves (2).

Fix $\zeta \in D$.

If $z = F(w)$, then $zg(z) = wF(w)/a$; and since $wF(w) \to a$ as $w \to 0$, we have $zg(z) \to 1$ as $z \to \infty$. Hence g has an expansion of the form

(11) $$g(z) = \frac{1}{z-\zeta} + \frac{\lambda_2(\zeta)}{(z-\zeta)^2} + \frac{\lambda_3(\zeta)}{(z-\zeta)^3} + \cdots \qquad (|z-\zeta| > 2r).$$

Let Γ_0 be a large circle with center at 0; (11) gives (by Cauchy's theorem) that

(12) $$\lambda_2(\zeta) = \frac{1}{2\pi i}\int_{\Gamma_0} (z-\zeta)g(z)\,dz = b - \zeta.$$

Substitute this value of $\lambda_2(\zeta)$ into (11). Then (1) shows that the function

(13) $$\varphi(z) = \left[Q(\zeta,z) - \frac{1}{z-\zeta}\right](z-\zeta)^3$$

is bounded as $z \to \infty$. Hence φ has a removable singularity at ∞. If $z \in \Omega \cap D$, then $|z-\zeta| < 2r$, so (2) and (13) give

(14) $$|\varphi(z)| < 8r^3|Q(\zeta,z)| + 4r^2 < 1{,}000r^2.$$

By the maximum modulus theorem, (14) holds for all $z \in \Omega$. This proves (3).

20.3 Lemma *Suppose $f \in C_c'(R^2)$, the space of all continuously differentiable functions in the plane, with compact support. Put*

(1) $$\bar\partial = \frac{1}{2}\left(\frac{\partial}{\partial x} + i\frac{\partial}{\partial y}\right).$$

Then the following "Cauchy formula" holds:

(2) $$f(z) = -\frac{1}{\pi}\iint_{R^2} \frac{(\bar\partial f)(\zeta)}{\zeta - z}\,d\xi\,d\eta \qquad (\zeta = \xi + i\eta).$$

PROOF This may be deduced from Green's theorem. However, here is a simple direct proof:

Put $\varphi(r,\theta) = f(z + re^{i\theta})$, $r > 0$, θ real. If $\zeta = z + re^{i\theta}$, the chain rule gives

$$(3)\qquad (\bar\partial f)(\zeta) = \frac{1}{2} e^{i\theta}\left[\frac{\partial}{\partial r} + \frac{i}{r}\frac{\partial}{\partial\theta}\right]\varphi(r,\theta).$$

The right side of (2) is therefore equal to the limit, as $\epsilon \to 0$, of

$$(4)\qquad -\frac{1}{2\pi}\int_\epsilon^\infty \int_0^{2\pi}\left(\frac{\partial\varphi}{\partial r} + \frac{i}{r}\frac{\partial\varphi}{\partial\theta}\right)d\theta\, dr.$$

For each $r > 0$, φ is periodic in θ, with period 2π. The integral of $\partial\varphi/\partial\theta$ is therefore 0, and (4) becomes

$$(5)\qquad -\frac{1}{2\pi}\int_0^{2\pi} d\theta \int_\epsilon^\infty \frac{\partial\varphi}{\partial r}\, dr = \frac{1}{2\pi}\int_0^{2\pi}\varphi(\epsilon,\theta)\, d\theta.$$

As $\epsilon \to 0$, $\varphi(\epsilon,\theta) \to f(z)$ uniformly. This gives (2).

We shall establish Tietze's extension theorem in the same setting in which we proved Urysohn's lemma, since it is a fairly direct consequence of that lemma.

20.4 Tietze's Extension Theorem *Suppose K is a compact subset of a locally compact Hausdorff space X and $f \in C(K)$. Then there exists an $F \in C_c(X)$ such that $F(x) = f(x)$ for all $x \in K$.*

(As in the proof of Lusin's theorem, we can also arrange it so that $\|F\|_X = \|f\|_K$.)

PROOF Assume f is real, $-1 \le f \le 1$. Let W be an open set with compact closure so that $K \subset W$. Put

$$(1)\qquad K^+ = \{x \in K : f(x) \ge \tfrac{1}{3}\},\qquad K^- = \{x \in K : f(x) \le -\tfrac{1}{3}\}.$$

Then K^+ and K^- are disjoint compact subsets of W. As a consequence of Urysohn's lemma there is a function $f_1 \in C_c(X)$ such that $f_1(x) = \frac{1}{3}$ on K^+, $f_1(x) = -\frac{1}{3}$ on K^-, $-\frac{1}{3} \le f(x) \le \frac{1}{3}$ for all $x \in X$, and the support of f_1 lies in W. Thus

$$(2)\qquad |f - f_1| \le \tfrac{2}{3} \text{ on } K,\qquad |f_1| \le \tfrac{1}{3} \text{ on } X.$$

Repeat this construction with $f - f_1$ in place of f: There exists an $f_2 \in C_c(X)$, with support in W, so that

$$(3)\qquad |f - f_1 - f_2| \le (\tfrac{2}{3})^2 \text{ on } K,\qquad |f_2| \le \tfrac{1}{3}\cdot\tfrac{2}{3} \text{ on } X.$$

In this way we obtain functions $f_n \in C_c(X)$, with support in W, such that

$$(4)\qquad |f - f_1 - \cdots - f_n| \le (\tfrac{2}{3})^n \text{ on } K,\qquad |f_n| \le \tfrac{1}{3}\cdot(\tfrac{2}{3})^{n-1} \text{ on } X.$$

Put $F = f_1 + f_2 + f_3 + \cdots$. By (4), the series converges to f on K, and it converges uniformly on X. Hence F is continuous. Also, the support of F lies in $\bar{W}$.

Mergelyan's Theorem

20.5 Theorem *If K is a compact set in the plane whose complement is connected, if f is a continuous complex function on K which is holomorphic in the interior of K, and if $\epsilon > 0$, then there exists a polynomial P such that $|f(z) - P(z)| < \epsilon$ for all $z \in K$.*

If the interior of K is empty, then part of the hypothesis is vacuously satisfied, and the conclusion holds for every $f \in C(K)$. Note that K need not be connected.

PROOF By Tietze's theorem, f can be extended to a continuous function in the plane, with compact support. We fix one such extension, and denote it again by f.

For any $\delta > 0$, let $\omega(\delta)$ be the supremum of the numbers

$$|f(z_2) - f(z_1)|$$

where z_1 and z_2 are subject to the condition $|z_2 - z_1| \leq \delta$. Since f is uniformly continuous, we have

$$\lim_{\delta \to 0} \omega(\delta) = 0. \tag{1}$$

From now on, δ will be fixed. We shall prove that there is a polynomial P such that

$$|f(z) - P(z)| < 10{,}000\, \omega(\delta) \qquad (z \in K). \tag{2}$$

By (1), this proves the theorem.

Our first objective is the construction of a function $\Phi \in C_c'(R^2)$, such that for all z

$$|f(z) - \Phi(z)| \leq \omega(\delta), \tag{3}$$

$$|(\bar{\partial}\Phi)(z)| < \frac{2\omega(\delta)}{\delta}, \tag{4}$$

and

$$\Phi(z) = -\frac{1}{\pi} \iint_X \frac{(\bar{\partial}\Phi)(\zeta)}{\zeta - z}\, d\xi\, d\eta \qquad (\zeta = \xi + i\eta), \tag{5}$$

where X is the set of all points in the support of Φ whose distance from the complement of K does not exceed δ. (Thus X contains no point which is "far within" K.)

We construct Φ as the convolution of f with a smoothing function A. Put $a(r) = 0$ if $r > \delta$, put

$$a(r) = \frac{3}{\pi\delta^2}\left(1 - \frac{r^2}{\delta^2}\right)^2 \qquad (0 \le r \le \delta), \tag{6}$$

and define

$$A(z) = a(|z|) \tag{7}$$

for all complex z. It is clear that $A \in C_c'(R^2)$. We claim that

$$\iint_{R^2} A = 1, \tag{8}$$

$$\iint_{R^2} \bar{\partial} A = 0, \tag{9}$$

$$\iint_{R^2} |\bar{\partial} A| = \frac{24}{15\delta} < \frac{2}{\delta}. \tag{10}$$

The constants are so adjusted in (6) that (8) holds. (Compute the integral in polar coordinates.) (9) holds simply because A has compact support. To compute (10), express $\bar{\partial}A$ in polar coordinates, as in the proof of Lemma 20.3, and note that $\partial A/\partial\theta = 0$,

$$|\partial A/\partial r| = -a'(r).$$

Now define

$$\Phi(z) = \iint_{R^2} f(z - \zeta)A(\zeta)\, d\xi\, d\eta = \iint_{R^2} A(z - \zeta)f(\zeta)\, d\xi\, d\eta. \tag{11}$$

Since f and A have compact support, so does Φ. Since

$$\Phi(z) - f(z) = \iint_{R^2} [f(z - \zeta) - f(z)]A(\zeta)\, d\xi\, d\eta \tag{12}$$

and $A(\zeta) = 0$ if $|\zeta| > \delta$, (3) follows from (8). The difference quotients of A converge boundedly to the corresponding partial derivatives, since $A \in C_c'(R^2)$. Hence the last expression in (11) may be differentiated under the integral sign, and we obtain

$$\begin{aligned}(\bar{\partial}\Phi)(z) &= \iint_{R^2} (\bar{\partial}A)(z - \zeta)f(\zeta)\, d\xi\, d\eta \\ &= \iint_{R^2} f(z - \zeta)(\bar{\partial}A)(\zeta)\, d\xi\, d\eta \\ &= \iint_{R^2} [f(z - \zeta) - f(z)](\bar{\partial}A)(\zeta)\, d\xi\, d\eta.\end{aligned} \tag{13}$$

The last equality depends on (9). Now (10) and (13) give (4). If we write (13) with Φ_x and Φ_y in place of $\bar\partial\Phi$, we see that Φ has continuous partial derivatives. Hence Lemma 20.3 applies to Φ, and (5) will follow if we can show that $\bar\partial\Phi = 0$ in G, where G is the set of all $z \in K$ whose distance from the complement of K exceeds δ. We shall do this by showing that

$$\Phi(z) = f(z) \qquad (z \in G); \tag{14}$$

note that $\bar\partial f = 0$ in G, since f is holomorphic there. (We recall that $\bar\partial$ is the Cauchy-Riemann operator defined in Sec. 11.1.) Now if $z \in G$, then $z - \zeta$ is in the interior of K for all ζ with $|\zeta| < \delta$. The mean value property for harmonic functions therefore gives, by the first equation in (11),

$$\begin{aligned} \Phi(z) &= \int_0^\delta a(r) r\,dr \int_0^{2\pi} f(z - re^{i\theta})\,d\theta \\ &= 2\pi f(z) \int_0^\delta a(r) r\,dr = f(z) \iint_{R^2} A = f(z) \end{aligned} \tag{15}$$

for all $z \in G$.

We have now proved (3), (4), and (5).

The definition of X shows that X is compact and that X can be covered by finitely many open discs $D_1, \ldots, D_n$, of radius 2δ, whose centers are *not* in K. Since $S^2 - K$ is connected, the center of each D_j can be joined to ∞ by a polygonal path in $S^2 - K$. It follows that each D_j contains a compact connected set E_j, of diameter at least 2δ, so that $S^2 - E_j$ is connected and so that $K \cap E_j = \varnothing$.

We now apply Lemma 20.2, with $r = 2\delta$. There are functions $g_j \in H(S^2 - E_j)$ and constants b_j so that the inequalities

$$|Q_j(\zeta,z)| < \frac{50}{\delta}, \tag{16}$$

$$\left| Q_j(\zeta,z) - \frac{1}{z - \zeta} \right| < \frac{4{,}000\,\delta^2}{|z - \zeta|^3} \tag{17}$$

hold for $z \notin E_j$ and $\zeta \in D_j$, if

$$Q_j(\zeta,z) = g_j(z) + (\zeta - b_j) g_j^2(z). \tag{18}$$

Let Ω be the complement of $E_1 \cup \cdots \cup E_n$. Then Ω is an open set which contains K.

Put $X_1 = X \cap D_1$ and $X_j = (X \cap D_j) - (X_1 \cup \cdots \cup X_{j-1})$, for $2 \le j \le n$. Define

$$R(\zeta,z) = Q_j(\zeta,z) \qquad (\zeta \in X_j,\ z \in \Omega) \tag{19}$$

and

$$(20) \qquad F(z) = \frac{1}{\pi} \iint\limits_X (\bar\partial\Phi)(\zeta)R(\zeta,z)\, d\xi\, d\eta \qquad (z \in \Omega).$$

Since

$$(21) \qquad F(z) = \sum_{j=1}^{n} \frac{1}{\pi} \iint\limits_{X_j} (\bar\partial\Phi)(\zeta)Q_j(\zeta,z)\, d\xi\, d\eta,$$

(18) shows that F is a finite linear combination of the functions g_j and g_j^2. Hence $F \in H(\Omega)$.

By (20), (4), and (5) we have

$$(22) \quad |F(z) - \Phi(z)| < \frac{2\omega(\delta)}{\pi\delta} \iint\limits_X \left| R(\zeta,z) - \frac{1}{z-\zeta} \right| d\xi\, d\eta \qquad (z \in \Omega).$$

Observe that the inequalities (16) and (17) are valid with R in place of Q_j if $\zeta \in X$ and $z \in \Omega$. For if $\zeta \in X$ then $\zeta \in X_j$ for some j, and then $R(\zeta,z) = Q_j(\zeta,z)$ for all $z \in \Omega$.

Now fix $z \in \Omega$, put $\zeta = z + \rho e^{i\theta}$, and estimate the integrand in (22) by (16) if $\rho < 4\delta$, by (17) if $4\delta \le \rho$. The integral in (22) is then seen to be less than the sum of

$$(23) \qquad 2\pi \int_0^{4\delta} \left(\frac{50}{\delta} + \frac{1}{\rho}\right) \rho\, d\rho = 808\pi\delta$$

and

$$(24) \qquad 2\pi \int_{4\delta}^{\infty} \frac{4{,}000\delta^2}{\rho^3}\, \rho\, d\rho = 2{,}000\pi\delta.$$

Hence (22) yields

$$(25) \qquad |F(z) - \Phi(z)| < 6{,}000\ \omega(\delta) \qquad (z \in \Omega).$$

Since $F \in H(\Omega)$, $K \subset \Omega$, and $S^2 - K$ is connected, Runge's theorem shows that F can be uniformly approximated on K by polynomials. Hence (3) and (25) show that (2) can be satisfied.

This completes the proof.

One unusual feature of this proof should be pointed out. We had to prove that the given function f is in the closed subspace $P(K)$ of $C(K)$. (We use the terminology of Sec. 20.1.) Our first step consisted in approximating f by Φ. But this step took us outside $P(K)$, since Φ was so constructed that in general Φ will not be holomorphic in the whole interior of K. Hence Φ is at some positive distance from $P(K)$. However, (25) shows that this distance is less than a constant multiple of $\omega(\delta)$. [In fact, having proved the theorem, we know that this distance is at most $\omega(\delta)$, by (3), rather than 6,000 $\omega(\delta)$.] The proof of (25) depends on the inequality (4) and on the fact that $\bar{\partial}\Phi = 0$ in G. Since holomorphic functions φ are characterized by $\bar{\partial}\varphi = 0$, (4) may be regarded as saying that Φ is not too far from being holomorphic, and this interpretation is confirmed by (25).

Exercises

1 Extend Mergelyan's theorem to the case in which $S^2 - K$ has finitely many components: Prove that then every $f \in C(K)$ which is holomorphic in the interior of K can be uniformly approximated on K by rational functions.

2 Show that the result of Exercise 1 does not extend to arbitrary compact sets K in the plane, by verifying the details of the following example. For $n = 1, 2, 3, \ldots$, let $D_n = D(\alpha_n; r_n)$ be disjoint open discs in U whose union V is dense in U, such that $\Sigma r_n < \infty$. Put $K = \bar{U} - V$. Let Γ and γ_n be the paths $\Gamma(t) = e^{it}$,

$$\gamma_n(t) = \alpha_n + r_n e^{it},$$

$0 \leq t \leq 2\pi$, and define

$$L(f) = \int_\Gamma f(z)\,dz - \sum_{n=1}^{\infty} \int_{\gamma_n} f(z)\,dz \qquad (f \in C(K)).$$

Prove that L is a bounded linear functional on $C(K)$, prove that $L(R) = 0$ for every rational function R whose poles are outside K, and prove that there exists an $f \in C(K)$ for which $L(f) \neq 0$.

3 Show that the function g constructed in the proof of Lemma 20.2 has the smallest supremum norm among all $f \in H(\Omega)$ such that $zf(z) \to 1$ as $z \to \infty$. (This motivates the proof of the lemma.)

Show also that $b = c_0$ in that proof and that the inequality $|b| < 4r$ can therefore be replaced by $|b| < r$. In fact, b lies in the convex hull of the set E.

Appendix

Hausdorff's Maximality Theorem

We shall first prove a lemma which, when combined with the axiom of choice, leads to an almost instantaneous proof of Theorem 4.21.

If $\mathfrak{F}$ is a collection of sets and $\Phi \subset \mathfrak{F}$, we call Φ a *subchain* of $\mathfrak{F}$ provided that Φ is totally ordered by set inclusion. Explicitly, this means that if $A \in \Phi$ and $B \in \Phi$, then either $A \subset B$ or $B \subset A$. The union of all members of Φ will simply be referred to as the *union of* Φ.

Lemma *Suppose $\mathfrak{F}$ is a nonempty collection of subsets of a set X such that the union of every subchain of $\mathfrak{F}$ belongs to $\mathfrak{F}$. Suppose g is a function which associates to each $A \in \mathfrak{F}$ a set $g(A) \in \mathfrak{F}$ such that $A \subset g(A)$ and $g(A) - A$ consists of at most one element. Then there exists an $A \in \mathfrak{F}$ for which $g(A) = A$.*

PROOF Fix $A_0 \in \mathfrak{F}$. Call a subcollection $\mathfrak{F}'$ of $\mathfrak{F}$ a *tower* if $\mathfrak{F}'$ has the following three properties:

(*a*) $A_0 \in \mathfrak{F}'$.
(*b*) The union of every subchain of $\mathfrak{F}'$ belongs to $\mathfrak{F}'$.
(*c*) If $A \in \mathfrak{F}'$, then also $g(A) \in \mathfrak{F}'$.

The family of all towers is nonempty. For if $\mathfrak{F}_1$ is the collection of all $A \in \mathfrak{F}$ such that $A_0 \subset A$, then $\mathfrak{F}_1$ is a tower. Let $\mathfrak{F}_0$ be the intersection of all towers. Then $\mathfrak{F}_0$ is a tower (the verification is trivial), but no proper subcollection of $\mathfrak{F}_0$ is a tower. Also, $A_0 \subset A$ if $A \in \mathfrak{F}_0$. The idea of the proof is to show that $\mathfrak{F}_0$ is a subchain of $\mathfrak{F}$.

Let Γ be the collection of all $C \in \mathfrak{F}_0$ such that every $A \in \mathfrak{F}_0$ satisfies either $A \subset C$ or $C \subset A$.

For each $C \in \Gamma$, let $\Phi(C)$ be the collection of all $A \in \mathfrak{F}_0$ such that either $A \subset C$ or $g(C) \subset A$.

Properties (a) and (b) are clearly satisfied by Γ and by each $\Phi(C)$. Fix $C \in \Gamma$, and suppose $A \in \Phi(C)$. We want to prove that $g(A) \in \Phi(C)$. If $A \in \Phi(C)$, there are three possibilities: Either $A \subset C$ and $A \neq C$, or $A = C$, or $g(C) \subset A$. If A is a proper subset of C, then C cannot be a proper subset of $g(A)$, otherwise $g(A) - A$ would contain at least two elements; since $C \in \Gamma$, it follows that $g(A) \subset C$. If $A = C$, then $g(A) = g(C)$. If $g(C) \subset A$, then also $g(C) \subset g(A)$, since $A \subset g(A)$. Thus $g(A) \in \Phi(C)$, and we have proved that $\Phi(C)$ is a tower. The minimality of $\mathfrak{F}_0$ now implies that $\Phi(C) = \mathfrak{F}_0$, for every $C \in \Gamma$.

In other words, if $A \in \mathfrak{F}_0$ and $C \in \Gamma$, then either $A \subset C$ or $g(C) \subset A$. But this says that $g(C) \in \Gamma$. Hence Γ is a tower, and the minimality of $\mathfrak{F}_0$ shows that $\Gamma = \mathfrak{F}_0$. It now follows from the definition of Γ that $\mathfrak{F}_0$ is totally ordered.

Let A be the union of $\mathfrak{F}_0$. Since $\mathfrak{F}_0$ satisfies (b), $A \in \mathfrak{F}_0$. By (c), $g(A) \in \mathfrak{F}_0$. Since A is the largest member of $\mathfrak{F}_0$ and since $A \subset g(A)$, it follows that $A = g(A)$.

Definition A *choice function* for a set X is a function f which associates to each nonempty subset E of X an element of E: $f(E) \in E$.

In more informal terminology, f "chooses" an element out of each nonempty subset of X.

The Axiom of Choice *For every set there is a choice function.*

Hausdorff's Maximality Theorem *Every nonempty partially ordered set P contains a maximal totally ordered subset.*

PROOF Let $\mathfrak{F}$ be the collection of all totally ordered subsets of P. Since every subset of P which consists of a single element is totally ordered, $\mathfrak{F}$ is not empty. Note that the union of any chain of totally ordered sets is totally ordered.

Let f be a choice function for P. If $A \in \mathfrak{F}$, let A^* be the set of all x in the complement of A such that $A \cup \{x\} \in \mathfrak{F}$. If $A^* \neq \emptyset$, put $g(A) = A \cup \{f(A^*)\}$. If $A^* = \emptyset$, put $g(A) = A$.

By the lemma, $A^* = \emptyset$ for at least one $A \in \mathfrak{F}$, and any such A is a maximal element of $\mathfrak{F}$.

Notes and Comments

Chapter 1

The first book on the modern theory of integration and differentiation is Lebesgue's "Leçons sur l'intégration," published in 1904.

The approach to abstract integration presented in the text is inspired by Saks [28].† Greater generality can be attained if σ-algebras are replaced by σ-rings (Axioms: $\bigcup A_i \in \mathfrak{R}$ and $A_1 - A_2 \in \mathfrak{R}$ if $A_i \in \mathfrak{R}$ for $i = 1, 2, 3, \ldots$; it is not required that $X \in \mathfrak{R}$), but at the expense of a necessarily fussier definition of measurability. See sec. 18 of [7]. In all classical applications the measurability of X is more or less automatic. This is the reason for our choice of the somewhat simpler theory based on σ-algebras.

Sec. 1.11. This definition of $\mathfrak{B}$ is as in [12]. In [7] the Borel sets are defined as the σ-ring generated by the compact sets. In spaces which are not σ-compact, this is a smaller family than ours.

Chapter 2

Sec. 2.12. The usual statement of Urysohn's lemma is: If K_0 and K_1 are disjoint closed sets in a *normal* Hausdorff space X, then there is a continuous function on X which is 0 on K_0 and 1 on K_1. The proof is exactly as in the text.

Sec. 2.14. The original form of this theorem, with $X = [0,1]$, is due to F. Riesz (1909). See [5], pp. 373, 380–381, and [12], pp. 134–135 for its further history. The theorem is here presented in the same generality as in [12]. The set function μ which is defined for all subsets of X in the proof of Theorem 2.14 is called an *outer measure* because of its countable subadditivity (Step I). For systematic exploitations (originated by Carathéodory) of this notion, see [25] and [28].

† Numbers in brackets refer to the Bibliography.

Sec. 2.20 For direct constructions of Lebesgue measure, along more classical lines, see [31], [35], and [26].

Sec. 2.22. A very instructive paper on the subject of nonmeasurable sets in relation to measures invariant under a group is: J. von Neumann, Zur allgemeinen Theorie des Masses, *Fundamenta Math.*, vol. 13, pp. 73–116, 1929. See also Halmos's article in the special (May, 1958) issue of *Bull. Am. Math. Soc.* devoted to von Neumann's work.

Sec. 2.23. [28], p. 72.

Sec. 2.24. [28], p. 75. There is another approach to the Lebesgue theory of integration, due to Daniell (*Ann. Math.*, vol. 19, pp. 279–294, 1917–1918) based on extensions of positive linear functionals. When applied to $C_c(X)$ it leads to a construction which virtually turns the Vitali-Carathéodory theorem into the definition of measurability. See [17] and, for the full treatment, [18].

Exercise 16. This example appears in A Theory of Radon Measures on Locally Compact Spaces, by R. E. Edwards, *Acta Math.*, vol. 89, p. 160, 1953. Its existence was unfortunately overlooked in [27].

Exercise 17. [7], p. 231; originally due to Dieudonné.

Chapter 3

The best general reference is [9]. See also chap. 1 of [36].

Exercise 3. Volume 1 (1920) of *Fundamenta Math.* contains three papers relevant to the parenthetical remark.

Exercise 16. [28], p. 18.

Exercise 18. Convergence in measure is a natural concept in probability theory. See [7], chap. IX.

Chapter 4

There are many books dealing with Hilbert space theory. We cite [6] and [24] as main references. See also [5], [17], and [19].

The standard work on Fourier series is [36]. For simpler introductions, see [10] and [31].

Chapter 5

The classical work here is [2]. More recent treatises are [5], [14], and [24]. See also [17] and [19].

Sec. 5.22. For a deeper discussion of representing measures see Arens and Singer, *Proc. Am. Math. Soc.*, vol. 5, pp. 735–745, 1954.

Chapter 6

Sec. 6.9. von Neumann's proof is in a section on measure theory in his paper: On Rings of Operators, III, *Ann. Math.*, vol. 41, pp. 94–161, 1940. See pp. 124–130.

Sec. 6.15. The phenomenon $L^\infty \neq (L^1)^*$ is discussed by J. T. Schwartz in *Proc. Am. Math. Soc.*, vol. 2, pp. 270–275, 1951, and by H. W. Ellis and D. O.

Snow in *Can. Math. Bull.*, vol. 6, pp. 211–229, 1963. See also [7], p. 131, and [28], p. 36.

Sec. 6.19. The references to Theorem 2.14 apply here as well.

Exercise 6. See [17], p. 43.

Exercise 10. See [36], vol. I, p. 167.

Chapter 7

Fubini's theorem is developed here as in [7] and [28]. For a different approach, see [25].

Sec. 7.9(*c*) is in *Fundamenta Math.*, vol. 1, p. 145, 1920.

Exercise 2. Corresponding to the idea that an integral is an area under a curve, the theory of the Lebesgue integral can be developed in terms of measures of ordinate sets. This is done in [16].

Exercise 8. Part (*b*), in even more precise form, was proved by Lebesgue in *J. Mathématiques*, ser. 6, vol. 1, p. 201, 1905, and seems to have been forgotten. It is quite remarkable in view of another example of Sierpinski (*Fundamenta Math.*, vol. 1, p. 114, 1920): There is a plane set E which is not Lebesgue measurable and which has at most two points on each straight line. If $f = \chi_E$, then f is not Lebesgue measurable, although all of the sections f_x and f^y are upper semicontinuous; in fact, each has at most two points of discontinuity. (This example depends on the axiom of choice, but not on the continuum hypothesis.)

Chapter 8

Usually (see [28]) $(D\mu)(x)$ is defined as a limit of quotients $\mu(E)/m(E)$, where E ranges over a suitable family of *closed* sets containing x. In most applications the sets E are nice sets like balls or cubes, and the utility of the differentiation theorems does not depend on whether these are open or closed. The use of open sets permits the exploitation of the finiteness property of open covers of compact sets. The rather difficult covering theorem of Vitali ([28], p. 109) can be replaced by the almost trivial Theorem 8.5 in the proof of the basic Theorem 8.6. This approach seems to have been originated by W. Hurewicz, in a course given at M.I.T. in 1950 (or earlier).

Sec. 8.19. For an elementary proof that every monotone function (hence every $f \in BV$) is differentiable a.e., see [24], pp. 5–9. In that work, this theorem is made the starting point of the Lebesgue theory. Even simpler is the recent proof by D. Austin in *Proc. Am. Math. Soc.*, vol. 16, pp. 220–221, 1965.

Sec. 8.21. See [16], Theorems 260–264, for situations in which the same conclusion is obtained from somewhat weaker hypotheses. Note that the proof of Theorem 8.21 uses the existence and integrability of only the *right-hand* derivative of f, plus the continuity of f.

Chapter 9

For another brief introduction, see [36], chap. XVI. A different proof of Plancherel's theorem is in [33]. Group-theoretic aspects and connections with Banach algebras are discussed in [17], [19], and [27]. For more on invariant subspaces (Sec. 9.16) see [11]; the present status of the corresponding problem in L^1 is described in [27], chap. 7.

Chapter 10

General references: [1], [4], [13], [20], [29], and [31].

Sec. 10.8. Integration can also be defined over arbitrary rectifiable curves. See [13], vol. I, Appendix C.

Sec. 10.10. The topological concept of index is applied in [29] and is fully utilized in [1]. The computational proof of Theorem 10.10 is as in [1], p. 93.

Sec. 10.13. Cauchy published his theorem in 1825, under the additional assumption that f' is continuous. Goursat showed that this assumption is redundant, and stated the theorem in its present form. See [13], p. 163, for further historical remarks.

Sec. 10.16. The standard proofs of the power series representation and of the fact that $f \in H(\Omega)$ implies $f' \in H(\Omega)$ proceed via the Cauchy integral formula, as here. Recently proofs have been constructed which use the winding number but make no appeal to integration. For details see [34].

Sec. 10.32. The open mapping theorem and the discreteness of $Z(f)$ are topological properties of the class of all nonconstant holomorphic functions which characterize this class up to homeomorphisms. This is Stoilov's theorem. See [34].

Sec. 10.37. A very elementary proof of the algebraic completeness of the complex field is in [26], p. 170.

Chapter 11

General references: [1], chap. 5; [20], chap. 1.

Sec. 11.10. Actually, "nontangential" limits exist a.e. on the circle. See [15], pp. 34–37, and [36], vol. I, pp. 96–106, especially Theorem (7.6).

Sec. 11.17. The reflection principle was used by H. A. Schwarz to solve problems concerning conformal mappings of polygonal regions. See sec. 17.6 of [13]. Further results along these lines were obtained by Carathéodory; see [4], vol. II, pp. 88–92, and *Commentarii Mathematici Helvetici*, vol. 19, pp. 263–278, 1946–1947.

Sec. 11.19. This is due to Herglotz, *Leipziger Berichte*, vol. 63, pp. 501–511, 1911.

Sec. 11.21. See Fatou's thesis, Séries trigonométriques et séries de Taylor, *Acta Math.*, vol. 30, pp. 335–400, 1906.

Chapter 12

Sec. 12.7. For further examples, see [31], pp. 176–186.

Sec. 12.11. This theorem was first proved for trigonometric series by W. H. Young (1912;, $q = 2, 4, 6, \ldots$) and F. Hausdorff (1923; $2 \leq q \leq \infty$). F. Riesz (1923) extended it to uniformly bounded orthonormal sets, M. Riesz (1926) derived this extension from a general interpolation theorem, and G. O. Thorin (1939) discovered the complex-variable proof of M. Riesz's theorem. The proof of the text is the Calderón-Zygmund adaptation (1950) of Thorin's idea. Full references and discussions of other interpolation theorems are in chap. XII of [36].

Sec. 12.12. In slightly different form, this is in *Duke Math. J.*, vol. 20, pp. 449–458, 1953.

Chapter 13

Sec. 13.9. Runge's theorem was published in *Acta Math.*, vol. 6, 1885. (Incidentally, this is the same year in which the Weierstrass theorem on uniform approximation by polynomials on an interval was published; see *Mathematische Werke*, vol. 3, pp. 1–37.) See [29], pp. 171–177, for a proof which is close to the original one. The functional analysis proof of the text is known to many analysts and has probably been independently discovered several times in recent years. It was communicated to me by L. A. Rubel. In [13], vol. II, pp. 299–308, attention is paid to the closeness of the approximation if the degree of the polynomial is fixed.

Sec. 13.11. Cauchy's theorem in simply connected regions is derived from Runge's theorem in [29], p. 177. The general formulation of Cauchy's theorem in terms of homology is in [1], p. 118. It is proved there via theorems about exact differentials, with no appeal to approximation theorems.

Exercises 7, 8. For yet another method, see D. G. Cantor, *Proc. Am. Math. Soc.*, vol. 15, pp. 335–336, 1964.

Chapter 14

General reference: [20]. Many special mapping functions are described there in great detail.

Sec. 14.3. More details on linear fractional transformations may be found in [1], pp. 22–35; in [13], pp. 46–57; in [4]; and especially in Chap. 1 of L. R. Ford's book "Automorphic Functions," McGraw-Hill Book Company, New York, 1929.

Sec. 14.5. Normal families were introduced by Montel. See chap. 15 of [13].

Sec. 14.8. The history of Riemann's theorem is discussed in [13], pp. 320–321, and in [29], p. 230. Koebe's proof (Exercise 26) is in *J. für Math.*, vol. 145, pp. 177–223, 1915; doubly connected regions are also considered there.

Sec. 14.10. The as yet unproved conjecture of Bieberbach is that $|a_n| \leq n$ for all n if $f \in \mathfrak{S}$. See [13], pp. 346–358.

Sec. 14.18(b). This argument occurs in [20], p. 179.

Sec. 14.19. The boundary behavior of conformal mappings was investigated by Carathéodory in *Math. Ann.*, vol. 73, pp. 323–370, 1913. Theorem 14.19 was proved there for regions bounded by Jordan curves, and the notion of prime ends was introduced. See also [4], vol. II, pp. 88–107.

Exercise 23. This proof is due to Y. N. Moschovakis.

Chapter 15

Sec. 15.9. The relation between canonical products and entire functions of finite order is discussed in chap. 2 of [3], chap. VII of [29], and chap. VIII of [31].

Sec. 15.25. See Szasz, *Math. Ann.*, vol. 77, pp. 482–496, 1916, for further results in this direction. Also chap. II of [21].

Exercise 7. See Kakutani's article in "Lectures on Functions of a Complex Variable" (W. Kaplan, ed.), The University of Michigan Press, Ann Arbor, 1955.

Chapter 16

The classical work on Riemann surfaces is [32]. (The first edition appeared in 1913.) Other references: Chapter VI of [1], chap. 10 of [13], chap. VI of [29], and [30].

Sec. 16.5. Ostrowski's theorem is in *J. London Math. Soc.*, vol. 1, pp. 251–263, 1926. See J. P. Kahane, Lacunary Taylor and Fourier Series, *Bull. Am. Math. Soc.*, vol. 70, pp. 199–213, 1964, for a recent account of gap series.

Sec. 16.17. Chapter 13 of [13], chap. VIII of [29], and part 7 of [4].

Sec. 16.21. Picard's big theorem is proved with the aid of modular functions in part 7 of [4]. "Elementary" proofs may be found in [31], pp. 277–284, and in chap. VII of [29].

Exercise 10. Various classes of removable sets are discussed by Ahlfors and Beurling in Conformal Invariants and Function-theoretic Null-Sets, *Acta Math.*, vol. 83, pp. 101–129, 1950.

Chapter 17

The best general reference here is [15]. See also [36], chap. VII. Although [15] deals mainly with the unit disc, most proofs are so constructed that they apply to more general situations which are described there. Some of these generalizations are presented in chap. 8 of [27].

Sec. 17.1. See [22] for a thorough treatment of subharmonic functions.

Sec. 17.13. For a different proof, see [15], or the paper by Helson and Lowdenslager in *Acta Math.*, vol. 99, pp. 165–202, 1958.

Sec. 17.14. The terms "inner function" and "outer function" were coined by Beurling in the paper in which Theorem 17.21 was proved: On Two Problems Concerning Linear Transformations in Hilbert Space, *Acta Math.*, vol. 81, pp. 239–255, 1949. For further developments, see [11].

Secs. 17.25, 17.26. This proof of M. Riesz's theorem is due to A. P. Calderón. See *Proc. Am. Math. Soc.*, vol. 1, pp. 533–535, 1950. See also [36], vol. I, pp. 252–262.

Exercise 6. This forms the basis of a definition of H^p-spaces in other regions. See *Trans. Am. Math. Soc.*, vol. 78, pp. 46–66, 1955.

Chapter 18

General references: [17], [19], and [23]; also [14]. The theory was originated by Gelfand in 1941.

Sec. 18.18. This was proved in elementary fashion by P. J. Cohen in *Proc. Am. Math. Soc.*, vol. 12, pp. 159–163, 1961.

Sec. 18.20. This theorem is Wermer's, *Proc. Am. Math. Soc.*, vol. 4, pp. 866–869, 1953. The proof of the text is due to Hoffman and Singer. See [15], pp. 93–94, where an extremely short proof by P. J. Cohen is also given. (See the reference to Sec. 18.18.)

Sec. 18.21. This was one of the major steps in Wiener's original proof of his Tauberian theorem. See [33], p. 91. The painless proof given in the text was the first spectacular success of the Gelfand theory.

Exercise 14. The set Δ can be given a compact Hausdorff topology with respect to which the functions $\hat{x}$ are continuous. Thus $x \to \hat{x}$ is a homomorphism of A into $C(\Delta)$. This representation of A as an algebra of continuous functions is a most important tool in the study of commutative Banach algebras.

Chapter 19

Secs. 19.2, 19.3: [21], pp. 1–13. See also [3], where functions of exponential type are the main subject.

Sec. 19.5. For a more detailed introduction to the classes $C\{M_n\}$, see S. Mandelbrojt, "Séries de Fourier et classes quasi-analytiques," Gauthier-Villars, Paris, 1935.

Sec. 19.11. In [21], the proof of this theorem is based on Theorem 19.2 rather than on 19.3.

Exercise 4. The function Φ is called the Borel transform of f. See [3], chap. 5.

Exercise 12. The suggested proof is due to H. Mirkil, *Proc. Am. Math. Soc.*, vol. 7, pp. 650–652, 1956. The theorem was proved by Borel in 1895.

Chapter 20

See S. N. Mergelyan, Uniform Approximations to Functions of a Complex Variable, *Usephi Mat. Nauk* (N.S.) 7, no. 2 (48), 31–122, 1952; Amer. Math. Soc. Translation No. 101, 1954. Our Theorem 20.5 is Theorem 1.4 in Mergelyan's paper.

A functional analysis proof, based on measure-theoretic considerations, has recently been published by L. Carleson in *Math. Scandinavica*, vol. 15, pp. 167–175, 1964.

Appendix

The maximality theorem was first stated by Hausdorff on p. 140 of his book "Grundzüge der Mengenlehre," 1914. The proof of the text is patterned after section 16 of Halmos's book [8]. The idea to choose g so that $g(A) - A$ has at most one element appears there, as does the term "tower." The proof is similar to one of Zermelo's proofs of the well-ordering theorem; see *Math. Ann.*, vol. 65, pp. 107–128, 1908.

Bibliography

1. *L. V. Ahlfors:* "Complex Analysis," 2d ed., McGraw-Hill Book Company, York, 1966.
2. *S. Banach:* Théorie des Opérations linéaires, "Monografje Matematyczne," vol. 1, Warsaw, 1932.
3. *R. P. Boas:* "Entire Functions," Academic Press Inc., New York, 1954.
4. *C. Carathéodory:* "Theory of Functions of a Complex Variable," Chelsea Publishing Company, New York, 1954.
5. *N. Dunford and J. T. Schwartz:* "Linear Operators," Interscience Publishers, Inc., New York, 1958.
6. *P. R. Halmos:* "Introduction to Hilbert Space and the Theory of Spectral Multiplicity," Chelsea Publishing Company, New York, 1951.
7. *P. R. Halmos:* "Measure Theory," D. Van Nostrand Company, Inc., Princeton, N.J., 1950.
8. *P. R. Halmos:* "Naive Set Theory," D. Van Nostrand Company, Inc., Princeton, N.J., 1960.
9. *G. H. Hardy, J. E. Littlewood, and G. Pólya:* "Inequalities," Cambridge University Press, New York, 1934.
10. *G. H. Hardy and W. W. Rogosinski:* "Fourier Series," Cambridge Tracts no. 38, Cambridge, London, and New York, 1950.
11. *H. Helson:* "Lectures on Invariant Subspaces," Academic Press Inc., New York, 1964.
12. *E. Hewitt and K. A. Ross:* Abstract Harmonic Analysis," Springer-Verlag OHG, Berlin, 1963.
13. *E. Hille:* "Analytic Function Theory," Ginn and Company, Boston, vol. I, 1959; vol. II, 1962.
14. *E. Hille and R. S. Phillips:* "Functional Analysis and Semigroups," Amer. Math. Soc. Colloquium Publ. 31, Providence, 1957.
15. *K. Hoffman:* "Banach Spaces of Analytic Functions," Prentice-Hall, Inc., Englewood Cliffs, N.J., 1962.
16. *H. Kestelman:* "Modern Theories of Integration," Oxford University Press, New York, 1937.
17. *L. H. Loomis:* "An Introduction to Abstract Harmonic Analysis," D. Van Nostrand Company, Inc., Princeton, N.J., 1953.

18. *E. J. McShane:* "Integration," Princeton University Press, Princeton, N.J., 1944.
19. *M. A. Naimark:* "Normed Rings," Erven P. Noordhoff, NV, Groningen, Netherlands, 1959.
20. *Z. Nehari:* "Conformal Mapping," McGraw-Hill Book Company, New York, 1952.
21. *R. E. A. C. Paley and N. Wiener:* "Fourier Transforms in the Complex Domain," Amer. Math. Soc. Colloquium Publ. 19, New York, 1934.
22. *T. Rado:* Subharmonic Functions, *Ergeb. Math.*, vol. 5, no. 1, Berlin, 1937.
23. *C. E. Rickart:* "General Theory of Banach Algebras," D. Van Nostrand Company, Inc., Princeton, N.J., 1960.
24. *F. Riesz and B. Sz.-Nagy:* "Leçons d'Analyse Fonctionnelle," Akadémiai Kiadó, Budapest, 1952.
25. *H. L. Royden:* "Real Anaysis," The Macmillan Company, New York, 1963.
26. *W. Rudin:* "Principles of Mathematical Analysis," 2d ed., McGraw-Hill Book Company, New York, 1964.
27. *W. Rudin:* "Fourier Analysis on Groups," Interscience Publishers, Inc., New York, 1962.
28. *S. Saks:* "Theory of the Integral," 2d ed., "Monografje Matematyczne," vol. 7, Warsaw, 1937. Reprinted by Hafner Publishing Company, Inc., New York.
29. *S. Saks and A. Zygmund:* "Analytic Functions," "Monografje Matematyczne," vol. 28, Warsaw, 1952.
30. *G. Springer:* "Introduction to Riemann Surfaces," Addison-Wesley Publishing Company, Inc., Reading, Mass., 1957.
31. *E. C. Titchmarsh:* "The Theory of Functions," 2d ed., Oxford University Press, Fair Lawn, N.J., 1939.
32. *H. Weyl:* "The Concept of a Riemann Surface," 3d ed., Addison-Wesley Publishing Company, Inc., Reading, Mass., 1964.
33. *N. Wiener:* "The Fourier Integral and Certain of Its Applications," Cambridge University Press, New York, 1933. Reprinted by Dover Publications, Inc., New York.
34. *G. T. Whyburn:* "Topological Analysis," 2d ed., Princeton University Press, Princeton, N.J., 1964.
35. *J. H. Williamson:* "Lebesgue Integration," Holt, Rinehart and Winston, Inc., New York, 1962.
36. *A. Zygmund:* "Trigonometric Series," 2d ed., Cambridge University Press, New York, 1959.

List of Special Symbols and Abbreviations†

† The standard set-theoretic symbols are described on pages 6 and 7 and are not listed here.

Index